GAS CHROMATOGRAPHY
Principles, Techniques, and Applications

Second Edition

Gas Chromatography

Principles, Techniques, and Applications

Second Edition

A. B. LITTLEWOOD

School of Chemistry
The University
Newcastle upon Tyne
England

1970

ACADEMIC PRESS · *New York and London*

ACADEMIC PRESS, INC.
111 Fifth Avenue, New York, New York 10003

United Kingdom Edition published by
ACADEMIC PRESS, INC. (LONDON) LTD.
Berkeley Square House, London W1X 6BA

LIBRARY OF CONGRESS CATALOG CARD NUMBER: 70-86369

PRINTED IN THE UNITED STATES OF AMERICA

Contents

Chapter 1
Definitions and Technical Terms

Chapter 2
Retention Volume and Column Variables

Chapter 3
Retention Volume and Thermodynamic Variables

Chapter 4

Adsorbent Stationary Phases

Chapter 5

Column Performance—Fundamentals

Chapter 6

Column Performance—Mechanisms

Chapter 7

The Preparation and Use of Columns

Chapter 8

The Use of Detectors for Quantitative Analysis

Chapter 9

Ionisation Detectors

Chapter 10

Thermal Conductivity Detectors

Preface

My aim in this book has been to produce a general textbook on gas chromatography suitable for users of the technique and for research workers. It does not presuppose any knowledge of the subject, which is introduced in the first chapter.

The text has been largely rewritten for the second edition. At the time of the first edition in 1962, gas chromatography was still developing as a technique; its technology was only just becoming well defined, and its range of application was still growing rapidly. Since then, however, it has become fully established and is no longer a novelty. Thus, in this edition, I have tended to emphasise what has now become the standard theory, and what have now become standard items of equipment used in the great majority of commercial instruments. The book is now addressed rather to the routine user than to those engaged in developing the technique.

The first half of the book is primarily concerned with the ability of gas chromatography to perform separations. The theory of the operation and design of gas chromatographic columns, both packed and open-tube, is described in detail, and it is shown how columns may be designed so as to secure any desired separation. The factors influencing separations are numerous, and I have tried to plan my presentation so that each of the many factors is described independently. Thus, the discussion of the thermo-dynamics of solution (Chapter 5) is completely separate from the section on the kinetics of chromatography (Chapter 6), and, within the latter, I have tried where possible to separate each kinetic mechanism by discussing independently the contribution of each to peak variance.

The third quarter of the book deals with detectors, which are the means of obtaining quantitative analyses by gas chromatography. It also contains, in Chapter 11, a description of the union of gas chromatography with other techniques, and some indication of the use of the more sophisticated methods of handling gas-chromatographic data, which will, in my opinion, be used increasingly in analysis in the next few years.

The last quarter of the book is a single chapter in a series of sections, each dealing with the chromatography of a particular class of chemical compound. It is impossible in a textbook to deal comprehensively with all of the enormous number of applications of gas chromatography published to date. However, I have tried to choose my sections so as to cover those applications which are most commonly encountered, and to be able to show how these illustrate and use the general principles described in the rest of the book.

Acknowledgments

The author would like to acknowledge the kindness of the following organisations, journals, and individuals in allowing him to reproduce copyright material.

The American Chemical Society (Journal, Journal of Physical Chemistry, Analytical Chemistry)

The Biochemical Society (The Biochemical Journal)

The British Council (British Medical Bulletin)

The Chemical Society, London (Journal)

The Institute of Petroleum (Journal)

The Institute of Physics and the Physical Society (Journal of Scientific Instruments)

The National Research Council of Canada (Canadian Journal of Chemistry)

The New York Academy of Sciences (Annals)

The Society of Chemical Industry (Chemistry and Industry)

Academic Press Inc., New York (Proceedings of International Symposia organised by the Instrument Society of America)

Butterworths & Co., London (Proceedings of International Symposia organised by the Institute of Petroleum and others)

Elsevier Publishing Company, Amsterdam (Journal of Chromatography, Anal. Chim. Acta)

The Macmillan Company, New York (Nature)

Pergamon Press Inc., New York (Chemical Engineering Science)

Reinhold Publishing Corporation, New York ("Gas Chromatography" by A. I. M. Keulemans)

Dr. Robert L. Bowman, Mr. Nathaniel Brenner, Dr. J. E. Caller, Mr. E. W. Ciepelinski, Dr. F. van der Craats, Mr. D. H. Desty; Mr. R. D. Eanes, Dr. L. S. Ettre, Dr. A. Goldup, Prof. I. Halasz, Dr. E. Heine, Dr. A. T. James, Dr. J. E. Lovelock, Dr. I. G. McWilliam, Dr. L. Ongkiehong, Mr. C. S. G. Phillips, Professor V. Pretorius, Mr. G. R. Primavesi, Dr. J. H. Purnell, Dr. G. Schomburg, Dr. F. C. Snowden, Dr. G. A. P. Tuey, Dr. J. J. Walraven.

GAS CHROMATOGRAPHY
Principles, Techniques, and Applications

Second Edition

Chapter 1

Definitions and Technical Terms

1.1. GAS CHROMATOGRAPHY

Gas chromatography is a method for separating components of mixtures of volatile compounds. In most applications, the separations are made to identify and determine the quantity of each component of a sample of the mixture, and analytical gas chromatographic apparatus includes additional devices for this purpose. In some applications, separations are made for preparative purposes, but the scale is not generally greater than that required for quantities of the order of 100 g. The technology and applications of gas chromatography overlap comparatively little with other chromatographic techniques (*1–3*), to which little reference will be made.

The central item in the apparatus for gas chromatography is the chromatographic *Column*, a long tube packed permeably with some adsorbent (in the general, rather than the specifically chemical, sense). In the commonest technique of gas chromatography, the *Elution* technique, a stream of inert gas, the *Carrier* gas, passes continuously through the column, and the mixture to be separated is introduced instantaneously at the beginning of the column (Fig. 1.1) as a sample either of a gas or a volatile liquid. Let us suppose that the sample consists of one pure component. After introduction, it is swept by the carrier gas on to the column, first evaporating to form a *Vapour* if it is introduced as a liquid. When it reaches the column, it is largely adsorbed, but an equilibrium is set up between the column and the gas in the interstices of the column so that a proportion of the sample always remains in the gas phase. This portion moves a little further along the column in the carrier gas stream, where it again equilibrates with the column. At the same time, material already adsorbed in the column re-enters the gas phase so as to restore equilibrium with the clean carrier gas which follows up the zone of vapour. This process

1

is shown by the arrows in Fig. 1.1b, which is an idealisation of the column in which the carrier gas is assumed to flow down the left-hand half and the adsorbent is contained in the right-hand half. The interface between the phases is used as a length abscissa along the column, and positive ordinates in each phase represent the concentrations of vapour therein. The process in which carrier gas containing the vapour is stripped by the adsorbent in front of the zone while the vapour enters the carrier gas at the rear goes on continuously, with the result that the zone of vapour moves along the column more or less compactly.

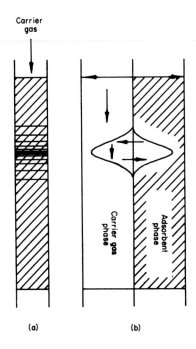

FIG. 1.1. Diagram of a permeably packed column and its idealisation, in which gas and adsorbed phases are represented separately.

    The speed at which the zone moves depends mainly on two factors, the rate of flow of the carrier gas and the extent to which the vapour is adsorbed. The faster the flow of carrier gas, the faster the zone moves; and the more strongly the vapour is adsorbed on the column, the more slowly the zone moves. The quantitative relations describing this are given in Chapter 2. When two or more components are present in the sample, each usually behaves independently of the others, so that for a given carrier gas flow rate, the speed of the zone of each component will depend on the extent to which it is adsorbed. Since different substances differ in their adsorption, they may therefore be separated by making use of their different speeds of progress through the column. If they are eluted to the far end of the column, they will appear one after the other in the gas stream, the fastest first and the slowest last.

It remains to specify the nature of the adsorbent. We have used this word in a general sense, rather than in the strict chemical sense of a substrate which will retain a vapour on its surface. In a few cases, some of which are important, adsorbents in the chemical sense, such as carbon, alumina, or silica gel, are used as the packing material for columns, but in more than 90% of applications, the column material is a liquid held in place on the column by being *absorbed* on an inert solid support. Gas chromatography with this kind of column is called *Gas Liquid Chromatography* (G.L.C.). This method is a direct extension of liquid-liquid partition chromatography used for separating solutes from mixed solutions, since the vapour in the carrier gas is exactly analogous to the solute in the eluting liquid. The distribution of solute between eluting liquid and stationary liquid in partition chromatography is described by the same law as the distribution of vapour between eluting gas and stationary liquid in gas-liquid chromatography, so that G.L.C. has often been called "Gas Partition Chromatography," though international convention no longer favours this name. In the case of G.L.C., the solution of a vapour in a liquid is described by Henry's law, which is:

$$q = \beta c, \tag{1.1}$$

where q is the concentration of vapour in the stationary phase, c is the concentration of vapour in the gas phase, and β is a constant. The constant β is a measure of the adsorption of a vapour in the adsorbent, and therefore determines the speed of the zone of vapour through the column. Though it should strictly be called the "Henry's Law Constant," it is conventionally called the *Partition Coefficient* by virtue of the analogy with liquid-liquid chromatography. The illogicality of refusing to use the word "Partition" in the name of the technique, but using it in the name of the principal quantitative measure in the technique is too well established to change.

Though the elution technique is the most common, there are two other techniques by which gas chromatography can be used, *Displacement* and *Frontal* analysis. Both techniques apply only when chemical adsorbents are used for the columns, and chemical adsorbents are more suitable for use with these techniques than with elution. Displacement and frontal techniques will be described briefly in part of Chapter 7. The rest of the book is concerned solely with elution chromatography.

1.2. Basic Apparatus of Gas Chromatography

The instrumentation of gas chromatography is remarkably simple compared to many other recent analytical techniques. Figure 1.2 shows a block schematic diagram of a typical gas-liquid chromatography apparatus, such as might be used for analysis.

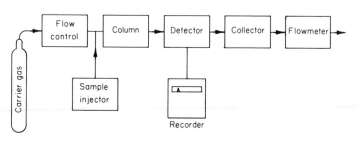

Fig. 1.2. Block schematic diagram of apparatus for analytical gas chromatography.

Carrier gas from the tank of compressed gas first passes to a controller, the usual purpose of which is to maintain a constant flow of gas. The gas then passes to the beginning of the column, at the inlet to which is a *Sample Injector* through which the sample to be analysed can be introduced. The carrier gas then elutes the components of the mixture through the column. At the far end is a device, the *Detector*, the purpose of which is to detect the separate components of the mixture as they emerge one by one. The detector uses some physical or chemical property of the vapours by which they can be indicated and, if possible, measured. A further piece of apparatus not always incorporated is a *Flowmeter* to measure the rate of flow of gas.

The details of the design of the apparatus for chromatography will be considered in later chapters. For the moment it is sufficient to outline the operation of the various sections of the apparatus simply to indicate how the technique works and to introduce technical terms.

(1) Any gas which is easily distinguishable in the detector from any components of the mixture can be chosen as the carrier gas. In most cases a permanent gas such as helium, argon, nitrogen, or hydrogen is used.

(2) Flow controls can either be true flow controls, which allow a definite rate of flow of gas, or they can be pressure controls which control the input pressure to the column. Since the column generally acts as a constant choke, a constant input pressure will itself ensure a constant flow. Pressure controls are simpler than flow controls and are used more commonly.

(3) For analytical purposes, reasonable dimensions for a permeably packed column might be 6 feet long by $\frac{1}{4}$ inch diameter. In G.L.C. the actual dissolving agent is a liquid which must remain stationary in the column without draining. It is therefore absorbed or otherwise held upon an inert solid support of some porous material which will allow the passage of gas. Kieselguhr, which can absorb up to 40% by weight of a liquid without becoming unduly moist, is commonly used. The application of this property in making dynamite is, of course, well known. More recently other supporting materials have been used, such as ground firebrick, glass beads, etc., and these will be discussed in detail in Chapter 7. A further necessary property of the supporting material is that it should not itself adsorb any of the components of the mixture, and therefore must be inert. The supporting material is often simply called the *Support*. The liquid solvent is called the *Stationary Liquid*. The two together are called the *Stationary Phase*, though this phrase is often used for the stationary liquid alone.

Another kind of column consists of a long fine tube of which the inner surface is coated with stationary liquid. Such columns, called *Capillary Columns*, are particularly useful in the analysis of microscopic samples. A monograph on their use has been written by Ettre (4).

The stationary liquid must be of such a nature as to dissolve all the components of the mixture (with the possible exception of one) and furthermore it must be completely involatile relative to any of them. For relatively involatile mixtures, columns are operated at elevated temperatures. The best temperature at which to run the column for a given mixture depends upon the design of the column and upon the mixture; the temperature of the column may be anything between 100°C above and 100°C below the boiling points of components in the mixture. Stationary liquids must have boiling points which are high in comparison with the boiling points of the components of the mixture. Almost any high-boiling liquid may be used, for example, silicone oils, high-boiling esters such as phthalates, high-boiling paraffins, and liquid polymers. Factors affecting the choice of stationary liquids and other column conditions are discussed in Chapter 3.

(4) One of the properties most commonly used for detecting vapours is the electrical conductivity of a hydrogen flame in which the vapour is burned. In the detector, the carrier gas (if not hydrogen already) is mixed with a constant flow of hydrogen, and the mixed gases are burned at a small metal jet, above which is positioned an electrode. A potential of about 300 V is set between the electrode and the jet, and the current passing is measured by suitable electronic equipment. In the absence of organic vapour, the current is extremely small ($\approx 10^{-14}$ amp), but organic vapour causes a large increase

in conductivity. The conductivity is recorded continuously on a strip-chart recorder, or other such device. The recorder produces a straight line while no vapour is being eluted, and zones of vapour emerging from the column will show as deflections from the line. The straight line corresponding to pure carrier gas is called the *Base Line*, and the deflections due to the vapours are called *Peaks*. The whole plot is called the *Chromatogram*. Flame ionisation detectors are considered in Chapter 9.

The *Catharometer*, or thermal conductivity cell, is familiar and commonly used in GC, its lack of sensitivity being compensated by its simplicity and remarkable ruggedness. Catharometers are considered in Chapter 10.

Many other kinds of detector are used, and these can be classified in many different ways. One important classification gives two classes (Fig. 1.3):

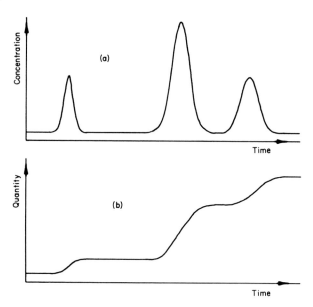

Fɪɢ. 1.3. (a) Peaks given by a differentiating detector. (b) Steps given by an integrating detector.

(i) *Differentiating detectors*, which record concentrations $(\partial w/\partial V)$ or rate of flow of mass of vapour $(\partial w/\partial t)$ rather than actual masses (w). The chromatogram given by these consists of peaks (Fig. 1.3a). If the deflection of the meter is proportional to the concentration of vapour, then the total amount of vapour present in the zone corresponding to a peak is proportional to the area of the peak. Differentiating detectors are used in the great majority of applications, and in all discussion the chromatogram should be assumed to be of the differential class unless it is specified otherwise.

(ii) *Integrating detectors*, in which the deflection is proportional to the total quantity rather than to the concentration. When no vapour is passing through, the recorder gives a straight line. As a zone of vapour passes through, the recorder moves across the strip-chart by a distance proportional to the quantity of vapour that has appeared. When another vapour appears, the recorder moves further across the chart, and so on (Fig. 1.3b). The chromatogram of an integrating detector consists of a series of steps, the sloping part of each step corresponding to the appearance of a peak in a differential detector. It is clear from Fig. 1.3 that the upper chromatogram is the plot of the differential coefficient of the lower one. For general convenience, and accurate work, differential detectors are more satisfactory than the integrating class, though there are a few useful applications of the latter.

(5) In the larger analytical installations, gas chromatographic data may be handled with varying degrees of automation, varying from simple analog integration of peak areas to systems in which gas chromatographs are controlled by, and their outputs analysed by, digital computers. Such systems are described in Section 11.7.

(6) In many analytical applications, all the information required can be obtained from the chromatogram, as described below. In many other cases, particularly in complex analyses, the separate components are required for further analysis, e.g., by mass-spectrometry or by infra-red spectrophotometry. The coupling of GC and other analytical techniques is described in Chapter 11.

(7) There remain other items of auxiliary apparatus, e.g., sample collectors, flowmeters, together with apparatus for temperature control of the column and other apparatus. Most of these are familiar items of scientific hardware and are not discussed.

1.3. THE CHROMATOGRAM

Analytically useful information obtainable from the chromatogram is of three kinds.

The simplest thing a chromatogram can show is whether or not a given sample is pure. If the chromatogram contains more than one peak, the sample contains more than one component. Very often this technique is used as a test of purity of substances. When one is looking for possible trace impurities in a sample of nearly pure substance, the detector must be sufficiently sensitive to be able to detect possible traces. This application is considered in more detail in Chapter 8.

The second use of the chromatogram is to enable one to identify the individual components of a mixture qualitatively. This information is sometimes obtainable directly by measuring the distance on the strip-chart from the point corresponding to the beginning of a run to the centre of the peak, which, for given conditions of operation, is characteristic of the component. As mentioned above, the speed of movement of a zone through the column is governed, amongst other things, by the ease of adsorption of the vapour, which in the case of G.L.C. is measured by the partition coefficient. The speed of movement of the zone through the column determines the total time it takes to move from one end of the column to the other, and it is this time that is registered by the above distance measured on the strip-chart. Thus, the distance on the strip-chart is determined by the partition coefficient of the vapour in the column, which is a characteristic of the vapour. The time taken by a zone to traverse the column is called the *Retention Time*.

The retention time of a component is itself a function of the many variables of column operation which are discussed in Chapter 2. Among the more important of these is the flow rate of the carrier gas. The greater the flow rate, the smaller the retention time, and to a first approximation, the retention time and the flow rate are inversely proportional so long as the pressure drop across the column is small. The constant product of the flow rate and the retention time is equal to the total volume of gas required to move a component from one end of the column to the other. This volume can also be used as a characteristic of the component in a given column, and has the advantage that it is independent of at least one operating variable, the flow rate; it is called the *Retention Volume*.

Retention volumes are themselves functions of many other column operating variables, which in routine analytical work are not generally measured. In order that retention data may still be used without measuring all these variables, use can be made of the fact that change in many of the operating variables affects all retention volumes by a similar factor, so that retention volumes stand in the same ratios one to another whatever the conditions. Hence, in many cases one substance, of which the retention volume is set arbitrarily at unity, is chosen from a mixture, and the retention volumes of all other components are quoted relative to this. Such a reference substance is called an *Internal Standard* for *Relative Retention Volumes.* If the internal standard is not a component of a mixture of interest, it is added to the mixture before chromatographing.

Gas chromatography provides only one number as a characteristic of each vapour. This is insufficient to characterise any particular one from the totality of volatile substances, since retention volumes can only be measured with an accuracy of about 0.1 to 1%, and many vapours have virtually identical retention volumes on a given column. The scope of retention data for qualitative identification can be somewhat enlarged by comparing chromatograms of a mixture obtained on two different columns (Section 3.9), but even with this, gas chromatography should not be regarded as an absolute means of qualitative analysis. Its use in this field is generally in conjunction with some other source of information. In this connection, the separative power of the technique is relevant, for a vapour giving an unknown peak can be condensed separately from the gas stream and submitted to more unambiguous analysis, for example, chemical analysis, infrared spectrophotometry, or mass spectrometry. Many such applications can be found in the literature.

The third kind of information obtainable from the chromatogram is a quantitative analysis of the mixture, which is provided by the detector rather than the column. With most detectors, the deflection of the meter is proportional to the concentration of vapour, and so, if the flow rate is constant, the area of the peak will give the total amount of vapour. This may be made the basis for an exact quantitative analysis. Gas chromatography is mainly used for quantitative analysis, for the method is particularly suitable for the routine analysis of industrial samples, the interpretation of the data is simple, and the apparatus does not require skilled personnel.

It has been assumed hitherto that the components of a mixture are completely separated on their appearance at the far end of the column. There remains another factor to consider; the ability of the column to perform its separations. In the case of two components of which the partition coefficients are not very different, the retention times also will not be very different, and the two zones may be incompletely separated. The chromatogram resulting from such a case is shown in Fig. 1.4a. The overlap of the two peaks is produced by two causes: (1) the closeness of the peaks and (2) the width of the peaks. These two causes are largely independent. The overlap could be reduced either by arranging the peaks to lie further apart (Fig. 1.4b) or by making each peak narrower (Fig. 1.4c). The first is due to the closeness of the partition coefficients, which is a function of the chemical natures of the components concerned and the nature of the stationary liquid, and separations can often be improved by judicious choice of stationary liquid. The second is a function of the column design and the manner of operation; attention to these can often make the peaks narrower. The closeness and width of peaks are each described by numerical quantities. The closeness is measured by the *Relative Retention*, which is the ratio of the retention volumes of the two components (subject to the qualifications

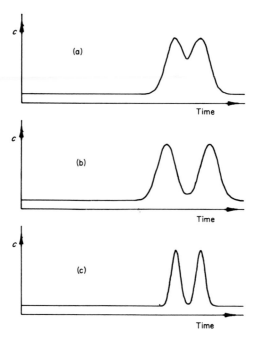

FIG. 1.4. (a) Incompletely resolved peaks. (b) The same resolved by increasing the relative retention. (c) The same resolved by increasing the column performance.

given in Chapter 2). The peak width is measured by the *Column Performance*, which is related to the ratio of the standard deviation of the peak to its retention volume, σ/V. The separation as a whole is improved by increasing the relative retention and improving the column performance. A number describing the separation as a whole is called the *Peak Resolution*. A more precise measure is the *Impurity Fraction* of the contents of one peak in another. Relative retentions are discussed in Chapter 3. Column performance, peak resolution, and impurity fraction are discussed in Chapters 5 and 6.

1.4. Peak Shape

The shape of a peak is largely a function of the operation of the column, though it is also related to the way in which the vapour is introduced. The usual effect of the column is to broaden out any given input distribution so as to make the peak shape progressively wider and shallower; it is this broadening that is described by the column performance. Broadening factors can be specified, and for theoretical purposes it is also possible to specify a column in which broadening factors are absent, though no such column can be made in practice. Such a column is called an *Ideal* column.

A further important factor which affects the shape of peaks is the way in which the vapour giving the peak interacts with the stationary phase. For every vapour and every stationary phase there is a relation between the concentration of vapour in the gas phase and its concentration in the stationary phase when there is equilibrium between the two. This can be expressed by an equation which is called the *Isotherm* of interaction between the phases; the use of the word isotherm implies that the temperature must be specified for the equation to hold.

The simplest isotherm that can hold is the *Linear* isotherm, in which the concentration in the gas phase (c) and the concentration in the stationary phase (q) are connected by Eq. (1.1). In the case of ideal chromatography with a linear isotherm, it can be shown (Chapter 2) that whatever the input distribution of a particular component, the output distribution will have exactly the same shape. Figure 1.5a illustrates the output distribution for a sharp input distribution, and Fig. 1.5b illustrates the output distribution for a non-sharp input distribution. For good separations, the input distribution should be as narrow as possible, so that the output distribution can be similarly narrow, and, in practice, sample injectors are designed with this end in view.

In the case of non-ideal chromatography with a linear isotherm, such as is found in practical gas-liquid chromatography, the broadening factors operate upon the input distribution, and it can be shown (5) that they do this in such a way that any input distribution tends to be broadened out into a distribution that is very close to the distribution of the normal curve of error, or "Gaussian Distribution." In the case of a sharp input distribution, the output distribution is virtually an exact Gaussian distribution (see, however, Section 6.6). This is illustrated in Fig. 1.5c. In the case where the input distribution is not sharp, the output distribution is more or less a Gaussian distribution convoluted with the input distribution, as is shown in Fig. 1.5d.

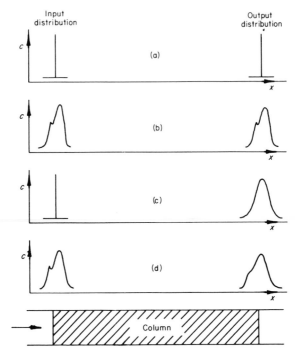

FIG. 1.5. Effect of input distribution and column ideality on peak shape. (a) Linear ideal chromatography, sharp input. (b) Linear ideal chromatography, non-sharp input. (c) Linear non-ideal chromatography, sharp input. (d) Linear non-ideal chromatography, non-sharp input.

When the isotherm of interaction of the vapour with the phases is not linear, the shapes of the peaks produced are more complex. We shall consider only the shapes resulting from a sharp input distribution. Non-linear isotherms generally fall into two categories:

(1) The case when the concentration in the stationary phase (q) lags behind that corresponding to simple proportionality as the concentration in the gas phase (c) rises (Fig. 1.6a), which commonly happens when the vapour is adsorbed on rather than dissolved in the stationary phase. As sites for adsorption become filled, it becomes increasingly difficult for any further vapour to enter. The effect of this in the chromatography of the vapour is as if the partition coefficient were lower at higher concentrations of vapour. The lower the partition coefficient, the more rapidly the chromatographic zone moves, and since the concentration is highest in the middle of the zone, the middle of the zone tends to move faster than the edges. This results in the zone becoming skewed towards the outlet of the column,

so that the peak shape shows a sharp front profile and a diffuse rear profile (Fig. 1.6b). The extent of this skewing depends on the degree of curvature of the isotherm; the greater the curvature, the greater the skewing.

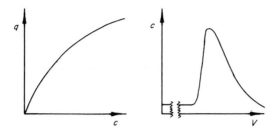

Fig. 1.6. Peak shape for isotherms concave towards the pressure axis.

(2) The opposite case also occurs sometimes; here the isotherm is such that the concentration in the stationary phase exceeds that of simple proportionality at higher concentrations (Fig. 1.7a). The partition coefficient is effectively higher at the higher concentrations, with the result that the centre of the peak tends to lag, and the chromatogram shows a peak with a diffuse front profile and a sharp rear profile (Fig. 1.7b).

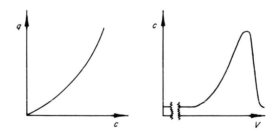

Fig. 1.7. Peak shape for isotherms convex towards the pressure axis.

The most common case of the first kind of non-linearity occurs when the vapours are adsorbed according to the Langmuir adsorption isotherm:

$$q = \frac{ac}{1 + bc},\qquad(1.2)$$

where a and b are constants. The equation gives a virtually linear relation between q and c when c is small compared with $1/b$, but this ceases to be so when c becomes appreciable compared with $1/b$. When c is large, so that it is large compared with $1/b$, then q becomes virtually independent of c; this corresponds to saturation of the adsorbent. The asymmetry of peaks from columns of adsorbents was formerly a serious drawback to their use by the elution technique, so that in the first couple of years of elution gas chromatography, adsorbents were almost totally neglected. However, more recently, the sensitivity of methods of detection of vapours has increased so much that adsorbent columns can be effectively used with samples of vapour so small that the concentration is always small compared with $1/b$. In these circumstances, the part of the isotherm that is used is nearly linear, and the asymmetry produced is small. Such adsorbent columns are regularly used for the analysis of permanent gases and other substances of very low boiling point, and can be used for less volatile compounds if required.

Non-linearity of the second kind described is rarer than adsorption non-linearity. There is no case reported where it is useful, and when it appears, its removal is desirable. This kind of isotherm arises when the vapour has ˄ greater affinity for itself than for the stationary phase. At first the stationary phase adsorbs or dissolves a small quantity of the vapour, and after that the quantity already adsorbed or dissolved attracts more of itself. This isotherm, therefore, tends to arise with strongly polar vapours having strong mutual attraction, for instance, with water upon charcoal. Further cases often arise in partition chromatography when the vapour is polar but the stationary phase is not. These cases are treated in Section 3.6.

1.5. APPLICATIONS OF GAS CHROMATOGRAPHY

The application of the technique is widespread. It can be used for the analysis of mixtures of volatile or vaporisable compounds boiling at any temperature between absolute zero and about 450°C, and for any substance which can be heated sufficiently without decomposing to give a vapour pressure of a few millimetres of mercury. Applications to a large range of specific classes of compound are considered in Chapter 12.

The size of sample used in gas chromatography may vary over a wide range. Analyses may be easily performed on quantities of the order of micrograms, and with a little care on quantities of the order of millimicrograms. There is no theoretical upper limit to the size of sample that may be handled if the chromatographic apparatus is built to accomodate it, but in gas chromatography, the ratio of price to throughput is so great that commercial considerations are limiting. Preparative apparatuses dealing with up to hundreds of grams of sample are available.

In addition to analytical and preparative applications, gas chromatographic methods have also been used in pure scientific studies, e.g., for the determination of partition coefficients, heats of solution, etc. Such applications are implicit in Chapter 3.

1.6. History

Several reports of techniques similar to gas chromatography appeared in the 1930's, but the first publications recognising it as a separate technique were those of Claesson et al. (6), who used columns of chemical adsorbents, and somewhat insensitive catharometers as detectors. As previously explained, these were not very suitable for use with elution chromatography, and Claesson used displacement and frontal techniques.

The development of gas chromatography was enormously accelerated by the introduction in 1952 of gas-liquid chromatography by James and Martin (7), following an earlier suggestion made by Martin and Synge (8). Since then, the subject has expanded rapidly in a manner resembling logarithmic growth. After James and Martin's papers, a few workers developed the subject, until in the middle of 1956 there were some tens of papers on gas-liquid chromatography, which contained most of the basic principles of the subject. Between 1956 and 1962 most of the present-day instrumentation was established. Since 1962, most attention has been on instrumental refinements and application of the technique to an ever-increasing range of analytical problems.

References

1. Heftman, E., ed., "Chromatography," 2nd ed. Reinhold, New York, 1967.
2. Kirchner, J. C., "Thin Layer Chromatography," Vol. XII of "Technique of Organic Chemistry" (A. Weissburger, ed.). Wiley (Interscience), New York, 1967.
3. Lederer, M., ed., "Chromatographic Reviews: Progress in Chromatography, Electrophoresis, and Related Methods." Elsevier, Amsterdam, 1959 (pub. annually).
4. Ettre, L. S., "Open Tubular Columns in Gas Chromatography." Plenum Press, New York, 1965.
5. Klinkenberg, A., and Sjenitzer, F., *Chem. Eng. Sci.* **5**, 258 (1956).
6. Claesson, S., *Arkiv. Kemi.* **23A**, 1 (1946).
7. James, A. T., and Martin, A. J. P., *Biochem. J.* **50**, 679 (1952).
8. Martin, A. J. P., and Synge, R. L. M., *Biochem. J.* **35**, 1358 (1941).

Chapter 2

Retention Volume and Column Variables

2.1. Introduction

The retention volume, retention time, flow rate, partition coefficient, and other quantities defined in the last chapter can be inter-related. In a chromatographic experiment, the quantity which is actually observed is the retention time of a peak. This time is a function of the partition coefficient of the vapour producing the peak, and therefore of the chemical nature of the vapour, but it is also a function of the several operating variables of the column. It is useful to separate the variables affecting retention time into two classes; first, those due to the way in which the column is operated and made, and second, those defined by the thermodynamics of the interaction of the vapour between the phases. These two classes of variable may be listed:

(*1*) *Column variables*

    (i) Dead volume
    (ii) Pressure drop across the column
    (iii) Temperature of the carrier gas as it affects the flow rate
    (iv) Weight of stationary phase or stationary liquid

(*2*) *Thermodynamic variables*

    (i) Chemical nature of the vapour
    (ii) Chemical nature of the stationary phase
    (iii) Temperature of the column as it affects the equilibrium of the vapour
    (iv) Chemical nature of carrier gas (of minor practical importance)

Specification of a set of values for the thermodynamic variables produces a quantity, the partition coefficient, which is in practice virtually independent of the column variables. We consider the way in which the thermodynamic variables determine partition coefficients in Chapter 3; in the present chapter, we consider the way in which the column variables, together with the partition coefficient, determine retention times.

The basic relation between retention time and the partition of a vapour between the phases can be appreciated as follows: let there be a column with carrier gas flowing, and let the stationary phase be such that, for a given vapour,

$$k = \frac{\text{weight of vapour dissolved in unit column length of stationary phase}}{\text{weight dissolved in unit column length of mobile phase}}.$$

This ratio is normally called the *partition ratio*.* If the vapour did not dissolve at all in the stationary phase, i.e., if $k = 0$, its retention time, t_R, would merely be the time taken for the gas to traverse the gas volume of the column; let this time be t_M. In the case of $k \neq 0$, for every unit of time that an average molecule of vapour spends in the gas phase, it spends k units of time in the stationary phase, from the definition of k. The average molecule must necessarily spend t_M in the gas phase in order to traverse the column. Thus, the total time t_R required for it to traverse the column is given by:

$$t_R = t_M(1 + k), \tag{2.1}$$

so that a fraction of its time $1/(1 + k)$ is spent in the mobile phase, while a fraction $k/(1 + k)$ is spent in the stationary phase.

It is possible to continue the discussion of retention in terms such as the above, in which one specifies precisely what is meant by an "average" molecule, etc. A stochastic approach of this kind to the formation and development of chromatographic peaks has been given by Giddings and Eyring (*1*), Giddings (*2, 3*), and by Beynon *et al.* (*4*). In any discussion of processes which, like chromatography, are determined by migration of molecules, there is a choice between a stochastic approach of a statistical nature, and a "continuous" approach, using differential equations to define the gradients and flows. In this book, we choose the latter approach, which seems capable of treating the more complex aspects of chromatography more concisely.

---

* The term "retardation ratio," used previously, and in the first edition of this book, is less satisfactory.

2.2. The First Order Conservation Equation

The quantitative theory may be explained simply and concisely through a first order partial differential conservation equation with the concentrations of the vapour in the gas and the liquid phases as dependent variables, and the volume of gas passed and the distance along the column as independent variables. An oversimplified form of the equation was first given by Wilson (5) and this was modified by DeVault (6) to give the equation that appears as Eq. (2.5).

Let V = volume of gas passed through the column (cc),
   x = distance from inlet end of the column (cm),
   q = concentration of the vapour in the stationary phase (mole/g),
   c = concentration of the vapour in the gas phase (mole/cc),
   m = mass of stationary phase per unit length of column (g/cm),
   a = volume of gas phase per unit length of column (cm²).

Consider a small cross section of infinitesimal thickness dx chosen so as to be in a zone of vapour in the chromatographic column (Fig. 2.1). At

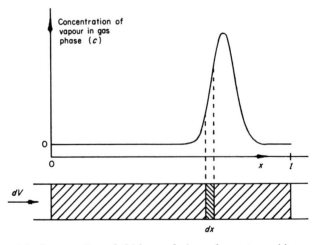

Fig. 2.1. Cross section of thickness dx in a chromatographic zone.

any instant, the cross section will contain a certain amount of vapour, some in each phase. The change in this amount when a volume of eluting gas dV is passed will be considered from two points of view: (1) that of an observer outside the cross section, and (2) that of an observer inside the cross section. Since mass is conserved, the observations made from each point of view must be equal.

(1) The concentration difference of vapour in the gas phase across the cross section is:

$$\frac{\partial c}{\partial x} \cdot dx.$$

Hence, the decrease in the total mass of vapour in the zone as a result of passing dV of eluting gas is:

$$\frac{\partial c}{\partial x} \cdot dx \, dV. \tag{2.2}$$

(2) From the point of view of an observer inside the cross section, the vapour is distributed between two phases. The decrease in the total amount of vapour due to change in the amount in the gas phase is:

$$-a \, dx \cdot \frac{\partial c}{\partial V} \cdot dV. \tag{2.3}$$

Similarly, the decrease in the total amount of vapour due to the change in the amount in the stationary phase is:

$$-m \, dx \cdot \frac{\partial q}{\partial V} \cdot dV. \tag{2.4}$$

However, the amount of solute removed from the cross section must be the same whether regarded from inside or outside, since vapour is not lost inside the cross section. Hence, the sum of expressions (2.3) and (2.4) must be equal to expression (2.2):

$$\frac{\partial c}{\partial x} \cdot dx \, dV = -a \, dx \cdot \frac{\partial c}{\partial V} \, dV - m \, dx \cdot \frac{\partial q}{\partial V} \, dV,$$

or, cancelling the $dx \, dV$,

$$\frac{\partial c}{\partial x} + a \frac{\partial c}{\partial V} + m \frac{\partial q}{\partial V} = 0. \tag{2.5}$$

This equation of DeVault may be called the "First Order Conservation Equation" of chromatography. When an isotherm between c and q is specified, and boundary conditions are given, this equation may be solved for c or q. When diffusion occurs in the column, the time, t, is also a significant variable; the use of the equation in these circumstances is considered in Chapter 6. In the present chapter, diffusion in the column is to be neglected.

In any isotherm observed in practice, $\partial c/\partial q$ is always positive, so that $\partial c/\partial V$ always has the same sign as $\partial q/\partial V$, and, since a and m are both positive, it necessarily follows from Eq. (2.5) that these and $\partial c/\partial x$ have opposite signs. This fact and its importance are illustrated in Fig. 2.2. If the chromatogram, regarded as a function of c against x, has a given shape

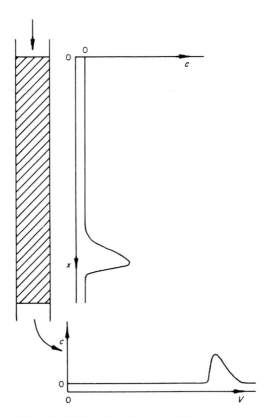

FIG. 2.2. Distinction between $c(V)$ and $c(x)$.

while it is in the column, its shape when it is regarded as a function of c against V at the far end of the column will be the mirror image. In the figure, while the asymmetric peak is in the column, its sharp profile is further along the column than its diffuse profile, and consequently at the end of the column the sharp profile appears first, with the diffuse profile coming later at a greater value of V. This is not significant in the case of symmetrical peaks such as are usually found in partition chromatography, but it should be remembered in the discussion of asymmetrical peaks such as appear by elution from adsorbents or in partition chromatography in conditions where symmetrical peaks are not obtained.

2.3. The Conservation Equation for Linear Isotherms

When the isotherm of interaction of a vapour between the phases is linear as in the case of partition chromatography, the relation between q and c is simply:

$$q = \beta c, \tag{1.1}$$

where β is the partition coefficient. If this is substituted in the conservation equation, the result is:

$$\frac{\partial c}{\partial x} + (a + m\beta) \frac{\partial c}{\partial V} = 0, \tag{2.6}$$

which has the general solution:

$$c = \phi\{V - x(a + m\beta)\}, \tag{2.7}$$

where ϕ is an arbitrary function. The form of ϕ is determined by the initial conditions, that is, by the way in which the vapour is introduced into the beginning of the column. In partition chromatography using the elution technique, the ideal method of introduction is that of an infinitely thin band of vapour instantaneously introduced, which minimises overlap between successive bands of different vapours at the end of the column. Such an input distribution may be expressed by the "Delta Function," defined by:

$$\delta(y) = 0 \qquad (y \neq 0),$$
$$\int_{-\infty}^{+\infty} \delta(y) = 1. \tag{2.8}$$

Using this, Eq. (2.7) becomes:

$$c = \delta\{V - x(a + m\beta)\} \tag{2.9}$$

which has a non-zero value only when

$$V = x(a + m\beta). \tag{2.10}$$

When the distance x is defined to be the length of the column, l, V becomes the volume of gas required to move the delta-function plug of vapour from one end of the column to the other. By definition, this is the retention volume (see, however, Section 2.4), for which the recommended symbol is V_R^0. Hence,

$$V_R^0 = l(a + m\beta). \qquad (2.11)$$

Equation (2.11) is basic to gas chromatography, for it relates the retention volume of a vapour to its partition coefficient; that is, it relates the most important chromatographic characteristic of the vapour to a purely thermodynamic characteristic which is independent of the actual column used. Normally, a, m, and l are all easily measurable quantities, so that Eq. (2.11) enables the chromatographic behaviour of the vapour to be predicted from its partition coefficient. The direct use of Eq. (2.11) as it stands, however, is complicated by the fact that the gas is compressible, as discussed in the next section.

Two assumptions are made in the derivation of Eq. (2.11). The first is that the input distribution is that of a delta function. Such a distribution is never possible in practice, for a finite weight of pure vapour occupies a finite volume. However, the width of the input distribution measured in volume units is small compared to the retention volume, so that the effect of the input distribution on the retention volume is usually only a minor one (Section 2.8). The second assumption is that there is no broadening in the column as the zone of vapour moves along. In fact, this is not so; the zone broadens, largely because of diffusion occurring in the column. It is shown in Sections 6.3 and 6.4, however, that if the vapour has a linear isotherm and the volume V_R^0 is the retention volume of the maximum of the broadened peak, Eq. (2.11) still holds in most circumstances.

In Eq. (2.11), the product al is the total gas hold-up, or dead volume, of the column, and the product ml is the total weight of stationary phase in the column. If these are given the symbols V_M^0 and W, respectively, the equation becomes:

$$V_R^0 = V_M^0 + W\beta \qquad (2.12)$$

Substances which are separated by the column necessarily have nonzero values of β, and thus their retention volumes are greater than V_M^0. As a general rule, most practical separations involve retention volumes from 3 times to about 200 times the gas hold-up with packed columns, and from 1.2 to about 20 times with capillary columns.

The retention time, which, as was pointed out in Section 2.1, is the observed quantity, is related to the retention volume $V_R{}^0$ by:

$$V_R{}^0 = \dot{V} t_R,$$

(2.13)

where $\dot{V}$ is the volume flow rate of carrier gas in units, for example, of milliliters per second or cubic centimeters per minute. When there is an appreciable pressure drop across the column, $\dot{V}$ is not constant, and Eq. (2.13) must be given a more general form [Eq. (2.29)]. By dividing Eq. (2.12) by $\dot{V}$ and substituting Eq. (2.13), an equation for retention time is obtained:

$$t_R = \frac{V_M{}^0}{\dot{V}} + \frac{W\beta}{\dot{V}}.$$

(2.14)

The two terms of this equation are equivalent to those of Eq. (2.1). The first term is simply the gas hold-up time, t_M, defined in Section 2.1, while the second gives the delay imposed on the vapour by the solvent action of the stationary phase, different delays being provided by different values of β.

The partition ratio k defined in Section 2.1 is, from its definition, given by qm/ca; for the case of a linear isotherm, this becomes $m\beta/a$. If m and a are assumed to be uniform through the column, this becomes $W\beta/V_M{}^0$. Thus, there are the following basic relations for k:

$$k = \frac{qm}{ca} = \frac{m\beta}{a} = \frac{W\beta}{V_M{}^0}.$$

(2.15)

Practical values of k are usually between about 2 and 200 for packed columns and between about 0.2 and 20 for capillary columns. Substitution of the last form of writing of Eq. (2.15) into Eq. (2.14) gives:

$$t_R = \frac{V_M{}^0}{\dot{V}}(1+k) = t_M(1+k),$$

(2.16)

which is Eq. (2.1), now proved in a systematic manner from the conservation equation.

The quantity usually employed in liquid-liquid partition chromatography as a characteristic of the retention of a vapour is the retardation factor, R_F, defined as the ratio of the speed of the zone of solute to the speed of the eluting solvent. The common gas chromatographic equivalents of R_F are related to it by any of the equations:

$$R_F = \frac{1}{1+k} = \frac{V_M{}^0}{V_M{}^0 + W\beta} = \frac{t_M}{t_M + (W\beta/\dot{V})}.$$

(2.17)

Though the flow rate as measured by the flowmeter is a volume flow rate, it is often more convenient to express flow rates as the average linear gas velocity in the column. If this is denoted by u, its connection with $\dot{V}$ is easily seen to be:

$$\dot{V} = au. \tag{2.18}$$

In terms of the measurable quantities $V_M{}^0$ and l, this becomes:

$$\dot{V} = \frac{V_M{}^0}{l} \cdot u. \tag{2.19}$$

In analytical columns, u is generally of the order of 1 to 10 cm/sec.

2.4. Effect of Pressure Gradient

In a gas chromatographic column, the gas flows in the narrow interstices between the particles of packing, which offer resistance to flow, and thus, because of the finite viscosity of the gas, there is a pressure gradient along the length of the column. Such a pressure gradient would have no effect upon retention volumes and retention times were it not for the fact that the gas is compressible. Because of this, the existence of a higher pressure at the inlet than at the outlet means that the density of the gas is greater at the inlet than at the outlet, and since the number of molecules per second flowing past a given point at the inlet must be the same as that flowing past a point at the outlet, it follows that the volume flow rate is greater at the outlet than at the inlet. Thus, a velocity gradient is an inevitable consequence of the pressure gradient in the column. These two gradients have several consequences in gas chromatography, one of which is an effect on the measurement of retention volumes. See also Section 6.18.

Normally, the flow rate is measured at the outlet from the column, so that the measured flow rate is greater than the flow rate at any other point in the column. Hence, a measured retention volume obtained by multiplying the observed retention time by the outlet flow rate is greater than the true retention volume. In order to correct for this, the form of the velocity gradient in the column must be known, and this in turn depends on the form of the pressure gradient. Following the original work of James and Martin (7) the forms of these gradients will be calculated, and then a correction factor to convert the retention volume measured as above into the true retention volume will be produced [Eq. (2.34)].

(a) *The Pressure Gradient*

The pressure gradient, dP/dx, and the linear velocity, u, in a column are connected by the equation:

$$\frac{dP}{dx} = -\frac{\eta}{K}u, \tag{2.20}$$

where η is the gas viscosity and K is the "Column Permeability," which measures the conductance of the column to gas. It is more convenient to use volume flow rate than linear flow rate, so that, substituting Eq. (2.18), this becomes:

$$\frac{dP}{dx} = -\frac{\eta}{Ka}\dot{V}. \tag{2.21}$$

In this equation, $\dot{V}$ is a function of x. By a simple extension of Boyle's law, $\dot{V}(x)$ can be substituted by $P(x)$, since

$$P_o\dot{V}_o = P\dot{V}, \tag{2.22}$$

where P_o and $\dot{V}_o$ are the values at the outlet. Substitution of Eq. (2.22) into Eq. (2.21) gives:

$$\frac{dP}{dx} = -\left[\frac{\eta P_o\dot{V}_o}{Ka}\right]\frac{1}{P}. \tag{2.23}$$

The solution of this equation is simplified by the fact that the gas viscosity is independent of pressure, so that all the quantities in the square bracket can be regarded as constant. If the contents of the square bracket are denoted by $-K'$, the solution to Eq. (2.23) is simply:

$$x = \frac{P^2}{2K'} + K'', \tag{2.24}$$

where K'' is another constant. The two constants can be obtained from the initial and final conditions, for, if the inlet pressure is P_i and the outlet pressure P_o,

$$\begin{aligned} P &= P_i, \quad\text{when}\quad x = 0, \\ P &= P_o, \quad\text{when}\quad x = l. \end{aligned} \tag{2.25}$$

Substituting these in Eq. (2.24) gives:

$$K' = \frac{P_o{}^2 - P_i{}^2}{2l}, \quad K'' = -\frac{P_i{}^2}{2K'}. \tag{2.26}$$

When these are substituted back in Eq. (2.24), the result is an equation for the pressure at any point in the column,

$$\frac{x}{l} = \frac{P_i^2 - P^2}{P_i^2 - P_o^2}.$$ (2.27)

The other quantities in the equation, P_o, P_i, and l, are all easily measurable. Figure 2.3 shows a plot of P/P_o as a function of x/l for various values of the pressure ratio across the column, P_i/P_o. The fact that the lines are curved is a result of the compressibility of the gas in conjunction with the fact that the viscosity is independent of pressure. Were the moving phase not compressible, as in liquid-liquid chromatography, the plot would be linear. Note that the curves steepen towards the outlet end of the column,

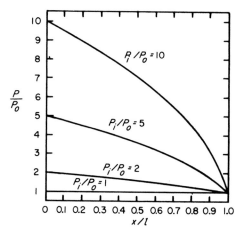

FIG. 2.3. Plots of P/P_0 against x/l with P_i/P_0 as parameter.

particularly at high pressure ratios, since in the later regions of the column, the gas velocity is greater and thus the pressure gradient must be greater in order to maintain that velocity.

(b) The Velocity Gradient

This is obtained from Eqs. (2.27) and (2.22). The result is:

$$\frac{x}{l} = \frac{(P_i/P_o)^2 - (\dot{V}_o/\dot{V})^2}{(P_i/P_o)^2 - 1}.$$ (2.28)

In Fig. 2.4, $V/\dot{V}_o$ is plotted as a function of x/l for various values of the

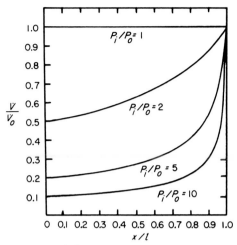

FIG. 2.4. Plots of $\dot{V}/\dot{V}_0$ against x/l with P_i/P_0 as parameter.

pressure ratio. Note that when the pressure ratio is large, the great majority of the change in velocity takes place at the end of the column, almost as if the end of the column were acting as a choke. This observation is significant for the choice of flow rate for the best column performance (Section 6.18).

(c) Retention Volume

Equation (2.13), connecting retention time and retention volume, holds in any small region of the column, and over the whole column when the flow rate is the same throughout, but when the flow rate is a function of distance down the column, a more generalised form must be used. Regarding volume rather than distance as the independent variable, the general relation is easily seen to be:

$$t_R = \int_0^{V_R{}^0} \frac{dV}{\dot{V}}. \tag{2.29}$$

Using Eq. (2.22), this becomes:

$$t_R = \int_0^{V_R{}^0} \frac{P\, dV}{\dot{V}_0 P_0}. \tag{2.30}$$

Changing the variable of integration by means of Eq. (2.10),

$$t_R = (a + m\beta) \int_0^l \frac{P\, dx}{\dot{V}_0 P_0}, \tag{2.31}$$

and again by means of Eq. (2.23), the result is:

$$t_R = (a + m\beta) \int_{P_i}^{P_o} \frac{P^2 \, dP}{K' \dot{V}_o P_o}. \tag{2.32}$$

Substituting the value of K' from Eq. (2.26), integrating, and rearranging,

$$t_R \dot{V}_o = l(a + m\beta) \times \left[\frac{2}{3} \cdot \frac{(P_i/P_o)^3 - 1}{(P_i/P_o)^2 - 1} \right]. \tag{2.33}$$

In this equation, the L.H.S., i.e., the product of the outlet flow rate and the measured retention time, is the measured retention volume. The first term of the product on the R.H.S. is seen by reference to Eq. (2.11) to be the true retention volume. Thus, the expression in square brackets is the correction factor required to correct the measured retention volume for the effect of the pressure drop across the column. The equation can be rewritten

$$V_R{}^0 = V_R \times \frac{3}{2} \cdot \frac{(P_i/P_o)^2 - 1}{(P_i/P_o)^3 - 1} = j V_R, \tag{2.34}$$

where V_R is the measured retention volume. The symbols V_R, $V_R{}^0$, and

$$j = \frac{3}{2} \cdot \frac{(P_i/P_o)^2 - 1}{(P_i/P_o)^3 - 1} \tag{2.35}$$

are internationally accepted. The measured quantity V_R is called the "Retention Volume" without any qualification. The quantity $V_R{}^0$ is called *Corrected Retention Volume*, thus modifying the definition given in Section 2.3. If V_M (uncorrected for pressure drop) is subtracted from V_R, the difference is called the *Adjusted Retention Volume*, $V_R{}'$. If j is applied to the adjusted retention volume, $V_R{}'$, rather than to V_R, the result is the *Net Retention Volume*, V_N. It will be appreciated that the gas hold-up considered hitherto is a corrected quantity.

A plot of the correction factor as a function of the pressure ratio is given in Fig. 2.5. When the pressure ratio is less than 1.5, the correction factor is given by:

$$\frac{1}{j} = \frac{1}{2} + \frac{1}{2} \cdot \frac{P_i}{P_o} \tag{2.36}$$

within $\frac{1}{2}\%$. When the pressure ratio is large compared with unity, the correction factor approximates to $j = 3P_o/2P_i$. The correction factor has the value of unity when $P_i = P_o$, and is less than unity when $P_i > P_o$. Table 2.1 gives values of j for pressure ratios in the range where it is most likely to be used.

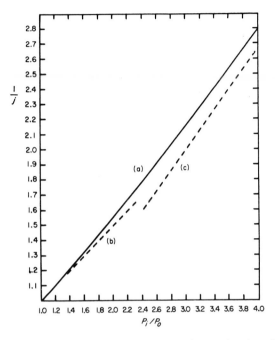

FIG. 2.5. Plot of the inverse correction factor, $1/j$. (a) As given by Eq. (2.34). (b) As given by approximation Eq. (2.36). (c) As given by the approximation $j = 3P_o/2P_i$.

The above calculation has been made on the assumption that the flow-meter is on the outlet side of the column, so that the measured retention volume involves $\dot{V}_o$. A similar calculation can be made in which the measured retention volume is assumed to be the product of the inlet flow rate and the retention time. In this case, the equivalent of Eqs. (2.33) and (2.36) is:

$$V_R = V_R{}^0 \left[\frac{2}{3} \left(1 + \frac{P_o/P_i}{1 + P_i/P_o} \right) \right] \simeq V_R{}^0 \left(\frac{1}{2} + \frac{1}{2} \frac{P_o}{P_i} \right). \qquad (2.37)$$

It is interesting to note that in this case measured retention volumes are smaller than the true retention volumes, and also that the size of the correction is smaller than in the previous case. This corresponds with the fact that most of the velocity gradient is at the outlet end of the column.

TABLE 2.1

THE PRESSURE CORRECTION FUNCTION j

p_i/p_o ^{a} ⟶	0	2	4	6	8
↓					
1.0	1.0000	0.9901	0.9803	0.9706	0.9611
1.1	0.9517	0.9424	0.9332	0.9242	0.9154
1.2	0.9066	0.8980	0.8895	0.8811	0.8728
1.3	0.8647	0.8566	0.8487	0.8409	0.8333
1.4	0.8257	0.8182	0.8109	0.8036	0.7965
1.5	0.7895	0.7825	0.7757	0.7690	0.7624
1.6	0.7558	0.7494	0.7430	0.7368	0.7306
1.7	0.7245	0.7185	0.7126	0.7068	0.7010
1.8	0.6954	0.6898	0.6843	0.6788	0.6735
1.9	0.6682	0.6630	0.6579	0.6528	0.6478
2.0	0.6429	0.6380	0.6332	0.6285	0.6238
2.1	0.6192	0.6146	0.6101	0.6057	0.6013
2.2	0.5970	0.5928	0.5885	0.5844	0.5803
2.3	0.5763	0.5723	0.5683	0.5644	0.5606
2.4	0.5568	0.5530	0.5493	0.5456	0.5420
2.5	0.5385	0.5349	0.5314	0.5280	0.5246
2.6	0.5212	0.5179	0.5146	0.5114	0.5082
2.7	0.5050	0.5019	0.4988	0.4957	0.4927
2.8	0.4897	0.4867	0.4838	0.4809	0.4781
2.9	0.4752	0.4724	0.4697	0.4669	0.4642

^{a} Vertical column headings are for hundredths values of p_i/p_o.

2.5. THE CALCULATION AND USE OF RETENTION VOLUMES

As pointed out in Section 2.1, the partition coefficient, β, is invariant and independent of the column operating variables. It is convenient, therefore, to quote and to tabulate retention data in terms of partition coefficients or some closely related quantity, so that this invariant quantity is applicable to any chromatograph whatever its operating circumstances. In this section we summarise the practical use of the standard equations given earlier relating to retention times and partition coefficients.

In a practical GC experiment, the retention time, t_R, is related with the partition coefficient via the variable column parameters, which are the outlet flow rate, $\dot{V}_o$, the inlet and outlet pressures, P_i and P_o, and the column temperature, T (°K). In addition, the dead volume $V_M{}^0$ and the weight of stationary liquid, W, are parameters built into the column. All these quantities are related by the following equation, derived from Eqs. (2.14) and (2.33):

$$t_R = \frac{1}{j\dot{V}_o} (V_M{}^0 + W\beta), \tag{2.38}$$

where j is given by Eq. (2.35). For the less common case that $\dot{V}_i$ is measured, j takes on the form given in Eq. (2.37).

The flow rate of a column is normally measured by a flowmeter which operates at or near room temperature, while the column itself may be at any temperature either hotter or cooler. During its passage through the column, the gas acquires the temperature of the column, and thus, by a simple extension of Charles' law, if the flowmeter is calibrated at $T_f°K$, and the column is at $T_c°K$,

$$\dot{V}_{T_c} = \dot{V}_{T_f} \times \frac{T_c}{T_f}. \tag{2.39}$$

In Eq. (2.38), the quantity $\dot{V}_o$ pertains to column temperature, and therefore must be calculated from the flow rate measured by a flowmeter calibrated at T_f by Eq. (2.39). Note in this connection that T_f is the temperature of the gas by which the flowmeter is calibrated, and not necessarily the temperature of the flowmeter.

The determination of the inlet and outlet pressures to the column and hence j is usually straightforward, and requires no comment.

The gas hold-up column is most easily determined by observing the retention of an unadsorbed substance, in which case it is given from Eq. (2.38) with $\beta = 0$, i.e.

$$V_M{}^0 = j\dot{V}_o/t_M . \tag{2.40}$$

When certain kinds of detectors are used (e.g., ionisation detectors, Chapter 9), no undissolved substance can be found which produces a peak from which retention times can be measured. In such a case, it may be possible to calculate the gas hold-up from the dimensions of the column, especially in the case of capillary columns. In capillary columns, however, where values of the retardation ratio, k, are generally small, a particularly accurate knowledge of the gas hold-up is required, not only because a small error in the gas hold-up produces a relatively large error in the relative retention volumes, but also because accurate values of relative retention volumes are significant on account of the high column performance. One method for finding the gas hold-up makes use of the fact (Section 3.6) that a plot of log V_R' against carbon number is accurately linear for any homologous series, so that the retention times of successive homologs are in geometrical progression, as illustrated in Fig. 2.6. With higher members of homologous series, it is apparent that as the homolog number declines, peaks converge rapidly as the retention becomes negligible, and the limiting point gives the retention of an unabsorbed component. In practice, if a few

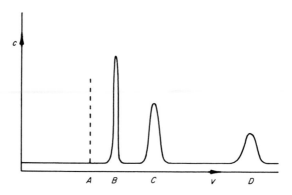

Fɪɢ. 2.6. A chromatogram in which retention times measured from a given point for successive homologues are in geometrical progression. A is point corresponding to V_M^0; $AC/AB = AD/AC$.

successive homologs are incorporated in a mixture (if not already present), a point is easily found by trial and error such that successive relative retention volumes measured from it are constant. A more systematic procedure has been defined by Peterson and Hirsch (8). Include three homologs the carbon numbers of which satisfy the relation $n_2 - n_1 = n_3 - n_2$, and measure the distances to their peaks from an arbitrary point (y_1, y_2, y_3). Then the distance δ of the arbitrary point from the point corresponding to the gas hold-up time is given by:

$$\delta = \frac{y_2{}^2 - y_3 y_1}{y_3 + y_1 - 2y_2}. \tag{2.41}$$

If the gas hold-up is measured in any way involving the retention of a real or extrapolated non-adsorbed substance, it will also include the volume between the sample injector cavity and the column, and between the column and the detector. In normal practice, these volumes are small compared to the gas hold-up of the column itself and very small compared to practical retention volumes (see Section 2.7).

Though β can be calculated easily from measurements of t_R in given experimental conditions using Eq. (2.38), absolute (as opposed to relative; see next section) retentions are more commonly expressed in a derived unit, the *Specific Retention Volume*, V_g (9, 10), which is related with β by the equation:

$$V_g = \frac{273.16}{T_c} \cdot \beta. \tag{2.42}$$

The convenience of this quantity is seen from the following equations, obtained by substitution of Eqs. (2.39), (2.41), and (2.42) into Eq. (2.38):

$$t_R - t_M = \frac{W}{j\dot{V}_{o(T_c)}} \cdot \beta = \frac{W}{j\dot{V}_{o(273.16)}} \cdot V_g. \tag{2.43}$$

Whereas the relation between β and the retention times involves the flow rate at the column temperature, the relation between V_g and the retention times involves the flow rate as measured by a flow meter calibrated at 0°C. Thus, the calculation of specific retention volumes requires no correction for column temperature. This distinction between β and V_g is of long standing in physical chemistry. Both are coefficients in Henry's law; V_g is identical with Bunsen's "Absorption Coefficient" of 1857, while β is Ostwald's "Coefficient of Solubility" of 1888.

The calculation of V_g and β from experimental data is illustrated below by an example, which also gives an idea of the sort of conditions which would pertain to a simple packed chromatographic column of 1 or 2 m length.

Example. In a chromatogram run at 55°C, the retention time of a component was 15.6 min. The retention time of an air peak in similar conditions was 1.1 min. The outlet flow rate, as measured on a flowmeter calibrated at 0°C, was 25.7 ml/min; outlet pressure was atmospheric at 75 Torr; inlet pressure was 25 cm above atmospheric. The weight of stationary liquid in the column was 2.80 g.

Here, $t_R = 15.6$, $t_M = 1.1$. $P_i = 100$ Torr and $P_o = 75$ Torr, so that $P_i/P_o = 1.33$. With these values, the approximation to j given by Eq. (2.36) can be used, so that:

$$j = (\tfrac{1}{2} + \tfrac{1}{2} \times 1.33)^{-1} = 0.855$$

Finally, $W = 2.80$ g and $V_o = 25.7$ ml/min. Substituting all these values into the second form of writing of Eq. (2.43),

$$V_g = \frac{25.7 \times 0.855 \times (15.6 - 1.1)}{2.80} = 144 \quad \text{ml/g.}$$

Using Eq. (2.42),

$$\beta = 114 \times \frac{(273 + 55)}{273} = 137 \quad \text{ml/g.}$$

2.6. The Presentation of Relative Retentions

The presentation of specific retention volumes described in the last section requires calculation and also requires measurements of column variables to be at least as accurate as the retention times. An alternative to the use of specific retention volumes is the use of *relative retentions*. One particular solute is chosen as a standard, and the relative retention of a solute may be defined as the ratio of the value of V_g for that solute divided by the value of V_g for the standard. The relative retention is thus a dimensionless pure number.

In order to use and to determine values of relative retentions, the standard substance is incorporated with a mixture of a substance of interest, and the positions of the peaks of the substance of interest are compared with that of the standard. In a normal chromatographic run, conditions such as flow rate, temperature, and pressure drop are constant throughout the run, so that $\dot{V}$, j, W, and T are the same for the substances of interest as for the sample. Hence, the relative retention defined by the ratio of specific retention volumes is equally well defined by the ratio of any quantity which is related proportionally with V_g through $\dot{V}$, j, W, and T. Survey of the earlier equations of this chapter, shows, therefore, that, if the relative retention of any two vapours, 2 and 3, is r_{23}, then:

$$r_{23} = \frac{V_{g2}}{V_{g3}} = \frac{\beta_2}{\beta_3} = \frac{V_{N2}}{V_{N3}} = \frac{V'_{R2}}{V'_{R3}}. \tag{2.44}$$

It will be noted that the ratio of any two quantities which include the gas hold-up or the gas hold-up time is *not* equal to the relative retention, since the gas hold-up always contributes as an *additive* term. In practice, relative retentions are most easily obtained by measurements along the chart paper of the chromatogram. If the retention length measured from the start of a run is L, then the length corresponding to the gas hold-up time, L_M, must first be subtracted before forming the ratio. Thus:

$$r_{23} = \frac{t_{R2} - t_M}{t_{R3} - t_M} = \frac{L_2 - L_M}{L_3 - L_M}. \tag{2.45}$$

The use of relative retentions rather than specific retentions for defining retention has the great practical advantage that it is not necessary to measure the column conditions, except perhaps temperature, with accuracy, and it is only necessary that they remain constant. This advantage in practice outweighs the slightly more detailed information which is conveyed by quotation of a specific retention volume, with the result that the use of specific retention volumes tends to be restricted to applications of a physicochemical nature, in which the absolute values of partition coefficients are significant.

In general, it is best to use for standards substances of the same general chemical nature as that of the samples of interest. In the case of hydrocarbon analyses, it is universally accepted, therefore, that any of the series of n-alkanes are suitable. For fatty acid esters, the series of methyl esters of the saturated n-acids are used. For most other classes of compound, there is less agreement.

Other more complex ways of expressing and presenting retention depend on thermodynamic relations involving retentions, and hence are discussed in the next chapter (Section 3.6f).

2.7. EFFECT OF INPUT DISTRIBUTION ON RETENTION VOLUME

In practice, the delta-function input distribution which has been assumed throughout is unattainable, since both the vapour and the sample injector cavity occupy a finite volume. As previously mentioned, the effect of these on the retention volume is small, but in accurate work it is necessary to consider it. Two extreme kinds of possible input distribution have been recognised by Porter et al. (11) who have considered the effect of these on retention volumes. In the first extreme, it is assumed that the vapour goes onto the column as a compact plug of finite volume within which there is a uniform vapour concentration. This would happen if the sample were completely evaporated in the sample injector cavity, and then swept out by the carrier gas without any mixing. The effect of non-ideal linear chromatography upon such an input distribution is to superimpose a Gaussian distribution upon the plug of vapour as described in Section 1.4. The resulting output distribution is illustrated in Fig. 2.7a, which is merely a specific form of Fig. 1.5d. The output distribution is symmetrical, and its maximum corresponds to the mid-point of the plug in the input distribution. Thus, if the retention time is measured from the instant that the front of the plug enters the column, as is usual practice, the retention volume measured to the maximum of the output distribution will be greater than the retention volume corresponding to a delta-function input distribution

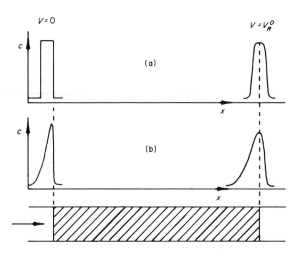

Fig. 2.7. Effect of (a) plug type input distribution, (b) Poisson-type input distribution on the chromatogram.

by half the width of the plug measured in volume units. If the measured retention volume is V_R^0, the true retention volume corresponding to Eq. (2.11) is V_r^0, and the volume of the plug is V_i,

$$V_R^0 = V_r^0 + \tfrac{1}{2}V_i. \tag{2.46}$$

In practice, the volumes both of the sample vapour and of the sample injector cavity should be less than about $1/100$ of a retention volume, so that the error involved in neglecting the above correction is almost certainly less than 1%.

The other extreme considered by Porter *et al.* is that in which complete mixing occurs in the sample injector cavity, so that the input distribution is of the Poisson type (Fig. 2.7b). In this also, the measured retention volume is slightly greater than the true retention volume if the time zero is the instant the front of the distribution reaches the column. There is, however, no simple formula corresponding to Eq. (2.46). Porter *et al.* show that in experiments using specific sample injectors of their design, the behaviour lies between the two extreme cases of plug flow and complete mixing.

2.8. EFFECT OF SAMPLE SIZE ON RETENTION VOLUME

Sample size has a definite and complex effect on retention volumes which is usually small, but often significant. Increase in sample size can cause either an increase or a decrease in retention volume according to circumstances, and no complete quantitative discussion is possible. One can distinguish five factors by which sample size can influence retention:

(1) *Non-sharp input distribution*

(2) *Finite vapour concentration in the column*

(3) *Viscosity of the peak*

(4) *Inexact linearity of the isotherm*

(5) *Adsorption effects*

(1) *Non-sharp Input Distribution.* The best possible practical input distribution for a finite sample is one in which a plug of pure sample vapour undiluted with carrier gas enters the column. If the sample weighs w mg, and its molecular weight is M, the volume of its vapour at NTP is 24 w/M ml, and its volume at any other temperature and pressure is easily calculable. For example, a sample consisting of 10 mg of n-hexane ($M = 86$) cannot have an input distribution narrower than about 3 ml (see Section 6.20). In the introduction of liquid samples at temperatures below their boiling point, the vapour is necessarily diluted with carrier gas, and moreover, there may be a period during which the sample is evaporating. For both of these reasons, therefore, the input distribution occupies a considerably larger volume than that of pure vapour, particularly for the less volatile components of a mixture. The width of this input distribution can be described by a volume, V_i, as discussed in the previous section, and its effect is to make retention volumes increase with the quantity of sample. This is illustrated in Fig. 2.8, which shows retention volume plotted against sample size (author's results). It is noteworthy that the least volatile component shows the largest effect.

(2) *Finite Vapour Concentration.* The retention of vapours in a chromatographic column in the case that the vapour concentration is not assumed to be infinitely small has been studied in detail by Conder and Purnell

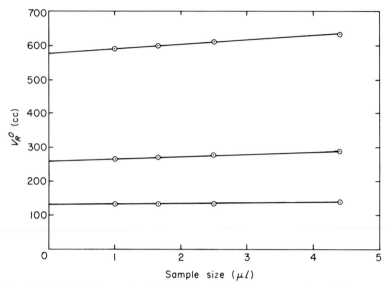

FIG. 2.8. Effect of sample size on retention volume; case in which retention volumes increase with increase in sample.

(*12, 13*), following earlier work particularly by Bosanquet and Morgan (*14, 15*), and Haarhoff and van der Linde (*16*).

The effect of a finite vapour concentration in the column is to cause retention volumes to decrease with increase in sample size. The total pressure inside a zone in the column is not different from the total pressure elsewhere in the column (neglecting the over-all pressure gradient). Hence since there is a finite vapour pressure of sample, the partial pressure of carrier must be correspondingly reduced. Since the mass flow rate of carrier gas in the column must remain constant along its length, it follows that the carrier velocity is greater inside the zone than elsewhere, particularly in those parts of the zone where the concentration is high. The effect of this is to move the centre of the zone through the column more rapidly than the other parts, so that it becomes skewed towards the end of the column, and so that a slight asymmetry is imposed upon the peaks, making their front profiles sharper than their rear profiles.

The augmented flow rate inside a zone of vapour can be calculated using considerations of conservation similar in kind to those of Section 2.2. The result is that, if the mole fraction of vapour in the gas phase is c', and the flow rate is regarded as a function of this, then (*12, 16, 17*):

$$\frac{\dot{V}(c')}{\dot{V}_{(c'=0)}} = \frac{1 + k}{1 + k(1 - c')}. \tag{2.47}$$

The effect of this acceleration on retentions is calculated in detail by Conder and Purnell; an approximate but simple estimate of its practical effect can be made as follows. Let c'_{max} be the mole fraction of vapour in the gas phase at the peak maximum. It can be proved that (Section 5.3):

$$c'^2_{max} \propto \frac{1}{x},\qquad(2.48)$$

where x is, as usual, length along the column. If c'_{Rmax} is the value of c'_{max} as the peak emerges from the column,

$$c'_{max} = c'_{Rmax}\left(\frac{l}{x}\right)^{1/2}.\qquad(2.49)$$

In the case that $\dot{V}$ as it pertains to a peak is a function of its position in the column, the retention time, $t_R{}^*$, is given by (cf. Eq. 2.29):

$$t_R{}^* = (a + m\beta)\int_0^l \frac{1}{\dot{V}(x)}\,dx,\qquad(2.50)$$

where, here, $\dot{V}$ has been written as a function of x. Substituting Eq. (2.49) into Eq. (2.47), and substituting the result into Eq. (2.50),

$$
\begin{aligned}
t_R{}^* &= \frac{(a + m\beta)}{\dot{V}_{(c'=0)}}\int_0^l \frac{1 + k[1 - c'_{Rmax}(l/x)^{1/2}]}{1 + k}\,dx \\
&= \frac{l(a + m\beta)}{\dot{V}_{(c'=0)}}\left(1 - 2c'_{Rmax}\frac{k}{1 + k}\right).
\end{aligned}\qquad(2.51)
$$

If t_R is the retention time for the case of limitingly small vapour concentration, then:

$$t_R{}^* = t_R\left(1 - 2c'_{Rmax}\frac{k}{1 + k}\right).\qquad(2.52)$$

Usually, c'_{Rmax} is small, but there may be cases where it is great as 0.01 or 0.02 mole fraction. Also, the term in k is usually close to unity. It is thus possible for this effect to produce definite errors in retentions of several percent. In the case of a mixture with components in very unequal proportions, it is clear that the effect can also influence relative retentions. Figure 2.9 shows a set of peaks of different samples of chloroform chromatographed in dinonyl phthalate (18), and illustrates a case in which retention decreases with sample size. In this case, the variation in retention is in rough accord with Eq. (2.52).

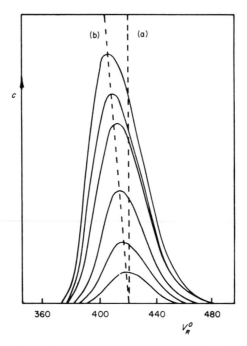

FIG. 2.9. Effect of sample size on retention volume; case in which retention volumes decrease with increase in sample [after Pollard and Hardy (*18*)]. (a) Retention volume of small sample. (b) Line of decreasing retention volumes with increasing sample.

(3) *Viscosity of the Peak.* In the equations relating the pressure drop across a column to the flow through it, the viscosity was considered to be a constant. However, if there is a finite vapour concentration within a peak or peaks inside a column, the viscosity of the mixture composed of the vapour plus carrier gas differs from that of the pure carrier gas. In practice, therefore, curves such as are shown in Fig. 2.4 contain perturbations at the points in the column where there are zones of vapour. The effect of these on the column pressure has been studied by Haarhoff and van der Linde (*16*), and their effect on the overall column resistance by Dyson and Little-wood (*19*). In the common case that the flow through the column is controlled by maintaining a constant pressure differential, the viscosity of peaks perturbs the flow rate through the column in proportion to the sample size by an amount which may in practice amount to several percent. The effect can also perturb quantitative analysis, and is discussed further in Section 8.1d.

(4) *Inexact Linearity of Isotherms.* It is apparent from the discussion

of the next chapter that if the mole fraction of the vapour in the stationary phase rises above a certain figure, then the ratio between q and c can begin to deviate. This is particularly true in the case of a polar substance dissolving in a non-polar solvent, where the presence of the polar substance in solution promotes further solution, and in such cases, the mole fraction of vapour in the stationary phase at which non-linearity becomes sufficient to perturb measurement of retentions is very small indeed.

(5) *Adsorption Effects.* Very frequently, the solid support for the stationary material is adsorptive and will adsorb a vapour very strongly. The retention of a small sample of vapour, therefore, is the result both of solution in the stationary liquid and of adsorption on the support. If, however, a larger sample of vapour is used, a small fraction of the vapour goes to saturate the support, which thereafter has no influence on the retention, and the retention of the bulk of the vapour is determined by partition alone. In cases (1) and (4) above, any perturbations to retentions have been the result of using samples that were too large. This is the only effect in which retentions become perturbed though using a sample which is *small*. With samples of polar vapours on the more adsorptive supports (see Section 7.1), the effect can render meaningless the retentions of microgram samples.

2.9. Retention Volumes in Non-Linear Chromatography

Whereas in linear chromatography the effect of the sample size on the retention volume is small, in non-linear chromatography, where the speed of a zone depends on the concentrations inside it, the effect is so large that retention volumes often cease to be useful. In the case of Langmuir isotherms, where the speed of the zone increases as the concentrations increase, the larger the sample, the smaller the retention volume measured to the maximum of the peak. In the case of its anti-Langmuir type isotherm, the opposite applies, and the larger the sample, the larger the retention volume (Fig. 2.10).

In normal practice, there is no way of calculating the change in retention volume as a function of the sample size. There is, however, one part of the peak produced in chromatography on a non-linear isotherm that changes but little with change in sample size: when the concentration is very small, the isotherm is virtually linear, and a small change in concentration will not affect the speed, so that a part of the peak in which the concentration is always small will move at a speed more or less independent of the total sample size. In the Langmuir case, this part is the bottom of the rear profile, with the result that as sample sizes are increased, though retention volumes measured to the peak maximum decrease, retention volumes measured to the very end of the peak are very nearly constant. This is illustrated in Fig. 2.10a, where chromatograms from a number of sample sizes are superimposed. With anti-Langmuir type isotherms, it is the beginning of the front profile that is nearly constant, as in Fig. 2.10b. This observation has been made the basis of an empirical method for correcting retention volumes for asymmetry in anti-Langmuir type peaks (9).

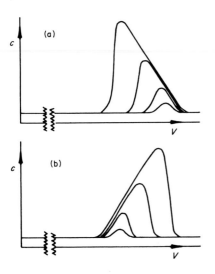

FIG. 2.10. Peak shapes and retention volumes for various sample sizes in non-linear chromatography. (a) Langmuir isotherms. (b) Anti-Langmuir isotherms.

The conclusion from the above observations is that retention volumes from columns and vapours with non-linear isotherms have meaning only when the whole peak is formed at a very low concentration, so that the non-linearity is small and has little effect. This means that such retention volumes are significant only for very small samples.

REFERENCES

1. Giddings, J. C., and Eyring, H., *J. Phys. Chem.* **39**, 416 (1955).
2. Giddings, J. C., *J. Chem. Phys.* **26**, 169 (1957).
3. Giddings, J. C., *J. Chromatog.* **2**, 44 (1959).
4. Beynon, J. H., Clough, S., Crookes, D. A., and Lester, G. R., *Trans. Faraday Soc.* **54**, 705 (1958).
5. Wilson, J. N., *J. Am. Chem. Soc.* **62**, 1583 (1940).
6. DeVault, D., *J. Am. Chem. Soc.* **65**, 532 (1943).
7. James, A. T., and Martin, A. J. P., *Biochem. J.* **50**, 679 (1952).

8. Peterson, M. L., and Hirsch, J., *J. Lipid Res.* **1**, 132 (1959).

9. Littlewood, A. B., Phillips, C. S. G., and Price, D. T., *J. Chem. Soc.* 1480 (1955).

10. Ambrose, D., Keulemans, A. I. M., and Purnell, J. H., *Anal. Chem.* **30**, 1582 (1958).

11. Porter, P. E., Deal, C. H., and Stross, F. H., *J. Am. Chem. Soc.*, **78**, 2999 (1956).

12. Conder, J. R. and Purnell, J. H., *Trans. Faraday Soc.* **64**, 1505, (1968).

13. Conder, J. R., and Purnell, J. H., *Trans. Faraday Soc.* **65**, 824 (1969).

14. Bosanquet, C. H., and Morgan, G. O., *in* "Vapour Phase Chromatography," Proceedings of the First Symposium, London, May, 1956 (D. H. Desty ed.), p. 35. Academic Press, New York, 1957.

15. Bosanquet, C. H., in "Gas Chromatography 1958," Proceedings of the Second Symposium, Amsterdam, May, 1958 (D. H. Desty, ed.), p. 107. Academic Press, New York, 1958.

16. Haarhoff, P. C. and van der Linde, H. J., *Anal. Chem.* **37**, 1742 (1965).

17. Golay, M. J. E., *Nature* **202**, 489 (1964).

18. Pollard, F. H., and Hardy, C. H., in "Vapour Phase Chromatography," Proceedings of the First Symposium, London, May, 1956 (D. H. Desty, ed.), p. 115. Academic Press, New York, 1957.

19. Dyson, N., and Littlewood, A. B., *Anal. Chem.* **39**, 638 (1967).

Chapter 3

Retention Volume and Thermodynamic Variables

3.1. Introduction

The preceding chapter describes how the measured retention volume is related to the partition coefficient and the column variables. In any particular chromatographic run, the column variables are the same for each vapour (see, however, Section 8.2), so the separation depends on the values of the partition coefficients; if these are sufficiently different, there will be adequate separation; if not, there will not be. The difference between two partition coefficients is normally expressed by their ratio, the relative retention (Sections 1.3, 2.6). In this chapter, therefore, the factors determining partition coefficients are discussed in detail, and it is shown how a knowledge of these factors may be applied to predict the relative retention of a given pair of solutes in a given stationary phase, so that the stationary phase may be chosen to provide the most satisfactory relative retention. These factors are best discussed in terms of thermodynamic functions governing the equilibrium of the vapour between the gas and the stationary phase. In the discussion, vapours are generally called *solutes*, and stationary liquids are called *solvents*.

There are two main approaches to finding a relation between the chemical nature of a solute and its retention in a given solvent. One approach is to consider the classical thermodynamics of a dilute solution of the solute in the solvent. The thermodynamic equations thus obtained make use of Henry's law, and the eventual equation obtained [Eq. (3.14)] relates the partition coefficient with the vapour pressure of the pure liquid solute. This approach was the first to be developed and is described in Sections 3.2 and 3.3. The other approach is more mechanical; when a solute dissolves in a solvent, the partition coefficient is determined by the changes in intermolecular interactions in the solution caused by entry of solute molecules. These intermolecular interactions can in favourable cases be

44

specified, and, in particular, the differences in the intermolecular interactions of two solutes with a given solvent can enable one to deduce whether or not the solutes will have sufficiently different partition coefficients. This approach is considered in Sections 3.4–3.6.

Neither of the above approaches is complete. The thermodynamic approach is incontrovertible, but can only be applied in practice if the relevant thermodynamic parameters for solutes and solvents of interest are known, e.g., vapour pressures, heats of solution, activity coefficients, thermodynamic excess functions, etc. In the majority of practical instances, these parameters are not known. The mechanical approach employs specific models for the process of solution, and as in all cases where mechanical models are employed to explain molecular phenomena, they are oversimplified and imperfect. Nevertheless, the use of mechanical models and the use of simplifying assumptions derived from them enable a great body of experimental evidence on gas-chromatographic retention to be codified and, to an increasing extent, predicted.

Concentrations can be expressed in several kinds of units, and therefore the partition coefficient can be expressed in several different forms. It is convenient to use either of the forms described below, which should be clearly distinguished. The most fundamental form is:

$$\alpha = \frac{\text{weight of solute per cc of stationary phase}}{\text{weight of solute per cc of gas at column temperature}}.$$

This is a dimensionless quantity, but its use in practice is restricted because the volume of the stationary phase is not easily known. For this and other reasons, we define:

$$\beta = \frac{\text{weight of solute per gram of stationary phase}}{\text{weight of solute per cc of gas at column temperature}}.$$

In practice it is more convenient to use β than α, for the total weight of stationary phase on the column is an easy quantity to measure, and the theory is discussed in terms of β rather than α. The form β has already been used in Chapter 2 in discussing the relation of retention volume to column variables. The forms α and β are related by:

$$\alpha = \beta\varrho, \tag{3.1}$$

where ϱ is the density of the stationary phase at the temperature at which α and β are measured. The relations between the two forms of the partition coefficient and the specific retention volume can be obtained from Eqs. (2.42) and (3.1):

$$V_g = \frac{273.16}{T_c} \cdot \beta = \frac{273.16}{\varrho T_c} \cdot \alpha. \tag{3.2}$$

Also, it is clear that the relative retention of two solutes can be expressed as the ratio of two α's as well as the ratio of two β's as in Eq. (2.44).

3.2. THERMODYNAMIC EQUATIONS FOR PARTITION COEFFICIENT AND VAPOUR PRESSURE

The system which is defined by the partition coefficient consists of the vapour of the solute in equilibrium with its solution in the solvent. This system has been extensively studied in thermodynamics (1–3), and the thermodynamic treatment enables relations to be derived between partition coefficients and measurable properties of solute and solvent. In general, let the solvent be designated species 1, let the solute be species 2, and let a second solute be species 3 in cases where relative retentions are to be considered.

Mixtures, such as that of solute and solvent, can be classified into *perfect*, *ideal*, and *non-ideal*, of which the first two are relevant in normal GC. We consider first the case of a perfect mixture, elaborating it later for the ideal mixture.

(a) *Properties of the Perfect Solution*

The equilibrium of the vapour with the solution is most conveniently considered in terms of the chemical potentials, since at equilibrium the chemical potentials of the solute in each phase are equal. The chemical potential, $\mu_2{}^l$, of solute in a perfect solution is given, by definition of a perfect solution (e.g., 2):

$$\mu_2{}^l = \mu_2{}^0 + RT \ln x_2, \tag{3.3}$$

where x_2 is the mole fraction of solute and $\mu_2{}^0$ is a constant, and pertains to pure liquid solute, i.e., $x_2 = 1$. We shall assume in this treatment that the solute vapour in the gas phase behaves perfectly (see, however, Section 3.2d), so that:

$$\mu_2{}^g = \mu_2{}^+ + RT \ln p_2, \tag{3.4}$$

where p_2 is the vapour pressure of solute, and $\mu_2{}^\dagger$ is another constant which pertains to a standard pressure of vapour, $p_2 = 1$. Its numerical value depends on the units of p (e.g., atm or Torr). At equilibrium, $\mu_2{}^l = \mu_2{}^g$, so that:

$$\ln \frac{x_2}{p_2} = \frac{\mu_2{}^\dagger - \mu_2{}^0}{RT}.$$

(3.5)

Thus, x_2/p_2 is a constant at a given temperature; this equation holds over the whole range of values of x_2, in particular for the case that $x_2 = 1$. In this special case, $p_2 = p_2{}^0$, the vapour pressure of pure liquid solute. Thus, in general, for a perfect solution:

$$p_2 = x_2 p_2{}^0.$$

(3.6)

This relation is Raoult's law.

(b) Properties of the Ideal Solution

In practice, solutions of a volatile solute in a non-volatile solvent are usually not even approximately perfect. Instead of a plot of p_2 against x_2 being linear as would be line FC in Fig. 3.1, the plot is more often like either curve I or curve II, in which the vapour pressure is either greater or smaller than given by Raoult's law. Different systems differ in the degree of "bowing" away from the perfect line, but, unless there is some kind of

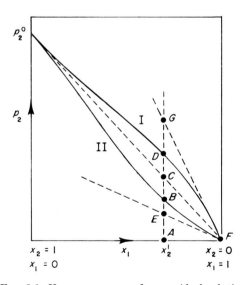

FIG. 3.1. Vapour pressure of a non-ideal solution.

compound formation at intermediate values of x_2, the shape is consistently as shown.

If the proportion of non-volatile component is small, the vapour pressure curve generally follows the perfect line, so that the classical method of determining molecular weights from Raoult's law can still be used even though the solution is not perfect. However, at the other end of the line, where the proportion of volatile component is small, there is a real difference between the slope of the actual vapour pressure curve and the slope of the perfect line. This difference persists even as $x_2 \rightarrow 0$.

When x_2 is small, the curvature of the vapour pressure curve is small, so that there is a substantially linear relation between p_2 and x_2, even though the constant of proportionality is not $p_2{}^0$. Such a linear relation is the characteristic of a system obeying Henry's law, and can be used to characterise the *Ideal Solution*. The departure from perfection of a particular solution is expressed quantitatively as the ratio of the vapour pressure actually exerted above the solution to the vapour pressure it would have if it were perfect. This ratio is called the *Activity Coefficient*, γ, of the solute. In Fig. 3.1, the activity coefficient at a mole fraction $x_2{}'$ is given by the ratio of the distance AB/AC for curve II and AD/AC for curve I. We also define the *activity coefficient at infinite dilution* as the ratio of the slope of the line FG to the slope of the perfect line, FC, in the case of curve I, and by the ratio of the slopes of FE and FC in the case of curve II. In gas chromatography, where x_2 is always small, the relevant activity coefficient is that defined for the case of infinite dilution. From its definition, the vapour pressure above an ideal but non-perfect solution is given at small x_2 by:

$$p_2 = \gamma x_2 p_2{}^0. \qquad (3.7)$$

The activity coefficient γ is defined here in terms of departures from Raoult's law. It is also possible to define an activity coefficient in terms of departures from Henry's law. Thus, in Fig. 3.1, the activity coefficient could also be defined by the ratios AE/AB or AG/AD, in which an infinitely dilute solution is taken as the standard. These cases have been clearly distinguished, for example, by Guggenheim (*1*). In gas chromatography, the activity coefficient is always relative to a perfect solution defined by Eq. (3.6) and not relative to an infinitely dilute solution.

(c) Equation for the Partition Coefficient in an Ideal Solution

In Eq. (3.7), x_2 is a measure of the concentration of the solute in the stationary phase, and p_2 is a measure of the concentration of the solute in the gas phase. Thus, p_2 and x_2 are measures of the denominators and numerators of the partition coefficients described in the previous section. By converting the units of x_2 and p_2 into those contained in the definitions of the partition coefficients, expressions for the latter may be obtained. Let

$$\beta = \frac{\mathscr{W}_2'}{\mathscr{W}_2''}, \tag{3.8}$$

where $\mathscr{W}_2'$ and $\mathscr{W}_2''$ are the values of the numerator and the denominator of the definition of β. We derive expressions for $\mathscr{W}_2'$ and $\mathscr{W}_2''$ in the next two paragraphs.

If n_1 and n_2 are the number of moles of solvent and solute in an arbitrary weight of solution, then

$$x_2 = \frac{n_2}{n_1 + n_2},$$

from the definition of mole fraction. We assume that the solute concentration is always small enough than $n_1 \gg n_2$, so that n_2 may be neglected in comparison with n_1 on the denominator of the above. Also, the number of moles, n, may now be converted into weight units, w, by the relations:

$$w_1 = M_1 n_1, \qquad w_2 = M_2 n_2, \tag{3.9}$$

where M_1 and M_2 are the molecular weights of the solvent and solute, respectively. Hence,

$$x_2 \approx \frac{M_1 w_2}{M_2 w_1} = \frac{M_1 \mathscr{W}_2'}{M_2}. \tag{3.10}$$

Except where the approximation is discussed specifically, this is regarded as an equation.

The general form of the gas law may be written:

$$PV = RT, \tag{3.11}$$

where R has the same value for one mole of any vapour. Hence, for a weight w_2 of vapour, the gas law is:

$$PV = RT \frac{w_2}{M_2},$$

using Eq. (3.9). If the volume of gas, V, is 1 cc, then w_2 becomes $\mathscr{W}_2''$, the denominator of β. Thus, for vapour of pressure p_2,

$$p_2 = RT \frac{\mathscr{W}_2''}{M_2}. \tag{3.12}$$

We may now substitute Eqs. (3.12) and (3.10) into Eq. (3.7), to give:

$$RT \frac{\mathscr{W}_2''}{M_2} = \gamma p_2^0 \frac{M_1 \mathscr{W}_2'}{M_2},$$

which, after substitution in Eq. (3.8) and rearrangement, gives:

$$\beta = \frac{RT}{\gamma M_1 p_2^0}. \tag{3.13}$$

If p_2^0 is measured in Torr and T in °K, the units of R are cc (Torr)/(mole °K), and its value is 62,370. Substitution of Eq. (3.2) into this equation gives a similar, but more convenient form:

$$V_g = \frac{273R}{M_1 \gamma p_2^0} = \frac{1.7027 \times 10^7}{M_1 \gamma p_2^0}. \tag{3.14}$$

In the case that the chromatography is linear, the partition coefficient must be constant, and thus the concentration of solute must be sufficiently small that the activity coefficient is constant and equal to the activity coefficient at infinite dilution. In subsequent discussion of activity coefficients, they are assumed to be those at infinite dilution except in specific discussions of activity coefficients at large values of x_2.

Equations (3.13) and (3.14) are of great importance, for they connect specific retention volumes or partition coefficients with four quantities [three in the case of Eq. (3.14)] which can be either determined or estimated with some degree of accuracy. The temperature of the column can be measured directly, and M_1 can easily be determined: the separation of different solutes on a given column depends upon the vapour pressure of the pure liquid solute and the activity coefficient. Both of these vary in a more or less regular manner with chemical composition, and thus discussion of γ and p_2^0 with respect to chemical composition enables one to use Eq. (3.14) for the calculation of retention volumes. Vapour pressures are discussed explicitly in Section 3.3, and activity coefficients and molecular weights are discussed in Sections 3.4 and 3.5.

An idea of the order of magnitude of the quantities in Eqs. (3.13) and (3.14) can be suggested by an example. For ethyl acetate partitioning on dinonyl phthalate at 56°C,

$$T = 329°K$$
$$M_1 = 418 \; [C_6H_4(COOC_9H_{19})_2]$$
$$p_2^0 = 350 \; \text{Torr (from tables, see Section 3.3)}$$
$$\gamma = 0.52.$$

Substitution of these figures in Eq. (3.13) gives:

$$\beta = 183 \quad cc/g,$$

and in Eq. (3.14),

$$V_g = 152 \quad cc/g.$$

For most stationary phases other than high polymers, values of M_1 lie between about 100 and 1000. In normal gas chromatography, the vapour pressure of the solutes at column temperature may vary from a few millimetres to a few thousand millimetres. The result is that specific retention volumes usually lie between about 10 and 1000 cc/g. Table 3.1 gives a short list of partition coefficients measured by gas chromatography. The most notable property is the rapid increase in partition coefficient with increase in molecular complexity and boiling point of the solutes.

TABLE 3.1

SAMPLE PARTITION COEFFICIENTS[a] IN DIDECYL PHTHALATE

Solute	bp (°C)	Partition coefficient (a), at 105°C
n-Hexane	68.3	27.0
n-Heptane	98.4	57.6
n-Octane	125.6	121.0
n-Nonane	150.8	240.0
Methylcyclopentane	71.8	38.2
Cyclohexane	80.7	52.3
Methylcyclohexane	100.9	83.5
Methanol	64.6	12.6
Ethanol	78.3	20.9
Propanol-1	97.4	46.2
Butanol-1	117.7	107.0
Butanol-2	99.5	77.4
2-Methylpropanol-2	82.8	30.8

[a] See Pierotti et al. (4).

Equations (3.13) and (3.14) are implicit in many texts, for example, Glasstone (5), and Hildebrand and Scott (6), where the equation corresponding to the case in which the mole fraction of solute is not necessarily small is also given. An equation similar to Eq. (3.14) is given by Pierotti et al. (4) and by Porter et al. (7), in which the inverse molar volume of the solvent, N_1, replaces its molecular weight, M_1. The quantities N_1 and M_1 are connected by

$$N_1 = \frac{1000\varrho}{M_1} \quad \text{moles/l,} \tag{3.15}$$

so, substituting this into Eq. (3.13),

$$\beta = \frac{62.4 T_c N_1}{\varrho \gamma p_2{}^0}. \tag{3.16}$$

Using Eq. (3.1), this becomes

$$\alpha = \frac{62.4 T_c N_1}{\gamma p_2{}^0}, \tag{3.17}$$

which is the form used by the above authors. A similar equation is also used by Kwantes and Rijnders (8) in the calculation of activity coefficients. Equation (3.17) has the advantage that it gives the fundamental α rather than the derivative β, but for practical purposes it has the drawback that the determination of N_1 requires a knowledge of the density of the stationary phase.

(d) Approximations Involved in Equations (3.13), (3.14), and (3.17), and Their Effect

The equations given above relating β and V_g with solute vapour pressure take account of non-perfection in the solution phase, but imply that the vapour in the gas phase behaves as a perfect gas. Gas imperfection can, however, be sufficient to render the equations erroneous by several percent. The imperfection of gases or gas mixtures can be described in terms of *virial coefficients*, quantities the non-zero values of which describe the departure of the gas from Boyle's law in terms of a *virial series*. For example, the non-ideality of pure solute vapour (species 2) can be expressed by the equation:

$$p_2 = \frac{RT}{v_2} \left\{ 1 + \frac{B_{22}}{v_2} + \frac{C_{222}}{v_2{}^2} + \cdots \right\}, \tag{3.18}$$

where B_{22} is the "second virial coefficient," and C_{222} is the third virial coefficient, etc. of the vapour, and v_2 is its molar volume in the gas phase.

It can be shown by using forms of Eqs. (3.3) and (3.4) that include the second virial coefficients B_{22} for the solute and B_{32} for the mixture of solute and carrier gas (species 3), that the equation for the partition coefficient,

β', corrected for gas phase non-ideality is given by (*9, 10, 11, 12*):

$$\beta' = \frac{RT}{M_1 \gamma p_2^0} \exp\left[\frac{(v_2^0 - B_{22})p_2^0}{RT} + \frac{p(2B_{32} - v_2^\infty)}{RT} \right], \qquad (3.19)$$

where, in addition to previously defined quantities, v_2^0 is the molar volume of the pure liquid solute, v_2^∞ is its partial molar volume in infinite dilution in the solvent and p is the total pressure. Substitution of Eq. (3.13) enables one to compare β' with β,

$$\ln \frac{\beta'}{\beta} = \frac{p_2^0(v_2^0 - B_{22})}{RT} + \frac{p(2B_{32} - v_2^\infty)}{RT} \approx \frac{\beta'}{\beta} - 1, \qquad (3.20)$$

where the final form of writing is an acceptable approximation if, as is common, there is only a few percent difference between β' and β.

Values for second virial coefficients can be found in the literature, or can be calculated with fair accuracy from molecular parameters according to several molecular models (*13*). Table 3.2 gives some selected calculated values (*11*). In general, values of B_{22} for vapours used in GC at the temperatures at which they are likely to be chromatographed are of the order of -1000 ml/mole. In helium, values of B_{32} are small and positive, of the

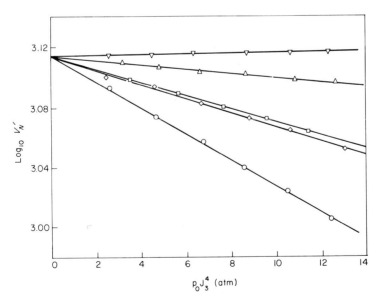

FIG. 3.2. Plot of $\log_{10} V_N$ for benzene in squalane as a function of average column pressure [$p_0 J_3^4$; J_3^4 is equivalent here to j defined in Eq. (2.35)] in various carrier gases; Cruickshank *et al.* (*12*).

order of $+30$ to $+100$ ml/mole, while in other carrier gases, they are invariably negative, becoming numerically larger in the range -100 to -1000 ml/mole the larger the molecule of the carrier gas and the larger the molecule of solute. Of the two terms in Eq. (3.20), the first is independent of total column pressure, while the second is proportional to it. At high pressures, the second term is numerically the greater, and it is in these circumstances that β' differs materially from β. The magnitude of the effect is calculable from the equations, and is best illustrated by a graph of retention versus average column pressure. Figure 3.2 (12) gives a plot of $\log_{10} V_N$ against average pressure for a solute in various carrier gases. It is seen that the error is less than 1% up to several atmospheres in helium, but in hydrogen, nitrogen, or heavier carrier gases, errors become greater than 1% with pressures greater than about 2 atm.

TABLE 3.2

SAMPLE SECOND VIRIAL COEFFICIENTS AT 25°C[a]

Solute	B_{22}	B_{32}		
		Helium	Nitrogen	Carbon dioxide
n-Pentane	—1033	+28	—135	—377
n-Hexane	—1468	+30	—164	—456
n-Heptane	—1968	+32	—192	—534
Benzene	—1326	+22	—149	—415
Cyclohexane	—1510	+25	—162	—451
2,2,3-Trimethylbutane	—1753	+31	—180	—498

[a] See Desty et al. (11).

The slopes of lines such as those of Fig. 3.2 enable second virial coefficients to be determined for physico-chemical purposes, and it is this, rather than the possible error produced in GC measurements, which has stimulated such extensive study of gas imperfections (9–12, 14–16). For this purpose, the pressure drop through the column must also be considered, leading to considerable elaboration of the equations. Second virial coefficients obtained from GC experiments are comparable in accuracy and consistency with those obtained by other means.

An explicit approximation is made in the derivation of Eq. (3.13) in neglecting the molar proportion of solute in the solution at Eq. (3.10). If this approximation is not made, the exact form of Eq. (3.10) is:

$$x_2 = \frac{w_2 M_1}{w_1 M_2} \left\{ \frac{1}{1 + (w_2 M_1 / w_1 M_2)} \right\} \approx \frac{w_2 M_1}{w_1 M_2} \left(1 - \frac{w_2 M_1}{w_1 M_2} \right). \qquad (3.21)$$

It is seen that the fractional error involved in neglecting the term in $(w_2 M_1 / w_1 M_2)^2$ is of the order of the value of x_2 itself. The effect of the finite mole fraction of solute in the solvent resembles the effect of the finite pressure of vapour on the velocity of the carrier gas discussed in Section 2.8(2) and, if there are no other factors involved, works in opposition to it. The theory is discussed in detail by Conder and Purnell (see Section 2.8). In addition, the presence of a finite concentration of solute in the solvent is likely to affect retentions by perturbing the value of γ, since the range of linearity of isotherm is small, especially when γ is much greater than unity; see Section 2.8(4).

3.3 EFFECT OF THE VAPOUR PRESSURE OF SOLUTES ON THEIR PARTITION COEFFICIENT

The vapour pressure of the solute affects the partition coefficient, and hence the retention volume, through the $p_2{}^0$ that appears in the denominator of Eq. (3.14), so that the larger the vapour pressure of a solute at the temperature of the column, the smaller is the partition coefficient. This is apparent from the sample results of Table 3.3. When the solutes and the stationary phase are such that there are no differences in activity coefficient from solute to solute, separation occurs solely on account of difference in $p_2{}^0$ between solutes.

In a general way, the higher the boiling point of a solute, the smaller its vapour pressure at a given temperature. Thus, when differences in vapour pressure are the main factor in producing a separation in a chromatographic column, the components will emerge in order of increasing boiling point. There are in fact many applications of this kind in gas chromatography, where differences in activity coefficients cannot be made to, or are not required to, enhance separations. In such cases, a knowledge of $p_2{}^0$ will enable one to determine, approximately at any rate, the retention volume and relative retention of two solutes with similar activity coefficients.

The vapour pressure of a solute is a very steep function of the temperature, with the result that the retention volume is similarly very much dependent upon temperature. It is important to select the right column temperature with respect to the solutes to be separated so that retention volumes should be neither too large nor too small. This requires knowledge of absolute values of vapour pressures at different temperatures, which may then be used in Eq. (3.13) or (3.14). As an illustration, consider the chromatography of n-heptane on di-isodecyl phthalate, for which it has been found that γ is virtually unity (8). Table 3.3 shows the vapour pressure

TABLE 3.3

VAPOUR PRESSURE AND PARTITION COEFFICIENT ON DI-ISODECYL PHTHALATE OF
n-HEPTANE AS A FUNCTION OF TEMPERATURE

Temperature (°C)	Vapour pressure (Torr)	β (cc/g)
25	46	905.0
75	360	135.0
95	700	75.7
105	940	56.3
115	1220	44.5
135	2010	28.9
150	2780	21.3

of n-heptane at various temperatures, and the partition coefficients β calculated from them by Eq. (3.13). Since specific retention volumes should normally be in the range 10–1000, it is seen from the table that the column should be operated between about 20° and 150°C, and probably somewhere in the middle of this range. In a mixture of wide boiling range, not all the components can give moderate retention volumes, and it is not generally practical to chromatograph at a fixed temperature a mixture of which the boiling range is greater than about 125°C, except when activity coefficients act so as to compress the chromatogram into a smaller range. For mixtures with greater boiling range, the programmed temperature technique described in Section 7.5 may be used.

An instructive guide to the temperature at which to chromatograph a mixture is found by considering the partition coefficient of any solute at its boiling point assuming unit activity coefficient. In these circumstances,

$p_2{}^0$ has the value of 760 Torr, so that Eqs. (3.13) and (3.14) become, substituting $\gamma = 1$,

$$\beta = \frac{82.2 T_B}{M_1}, \tag{3.22}$$

$$V_g = \frac{22,420}{M_1}. \tag{3.23}$$

For example, on didecyl phthalate, V_g is 50.3 for all solutes at their boiling point, and for n-heptane on didecyl phthalate, β is 68.4 at its boiling point (98°C). Since M_1 is generally of the order of 100 to 1000, the partition coefficient of a solute at its boiling point is usually suitable for practical chromatography. Columns designed for good column performance work better when partition coefficients are large, e.g., 100 to 1000, so that such columns are generally best operated some tens of degrees below the boiling points of the solutes. Capillary columns may operate 100°C or more below the boiling points.

At temperatures other than the boiling points of the solutes, vapour pressures must be sought or calculated. A knowledge of vapour pressure is required in many branches of technology, with the result that there are several useful compilations of such data, in which vapour pressures are given as functions of temperature either as tables, graphs, or formulae. Some useful sources of such data are given below:

"Handbook of Chemistry and Physics." Chemical Rubber Publ., Cleveland, Ohio (published annually).

Jordan, T. Earl, "Vapor Pressure of Organic Compounds." Interscience, New York, 1954.

Rossini, F. D., *et al.*, American Petroleum Institute Research Project 44. Selected values published for the American Petroleum Institute by Carnegie Press, Pittsburgh, Pennsylvania, 1953.

Timmermans, J., "Physico-Chemical Constants of Pure Organic Compounds." Elsevier, Amsterdam, 1950.

Stull, D. R., *Ind. Eng. Chem.* **39**, 517 (1947).

Other compilations to be found in the literature are referred to in the above. The compilation of Jordan gives many curves of vapour pressure against temperature for a large range of organic compounds.

For solutes of which the vapour pressures are not available in the literature, approximate values can generally be found by calculation, particularly if the boiling point is known. These can never be made exact, but are sufficiently useful to estimate the order of magnitude of retention volumes with some degree of accuracy and sometimes to make useful estimates of relative retentions. The vapour pressure of a solute is a function of its chemical composition and of temperature. The second of these can be treated fairly exactly, but the effect of composition is less predictable.

The variation of vapour pressure with temperature is described by the Clausius-Clapeyron equation. In the form relevant here, it is

$$\frac{d \ln p_2{}^0}{dT} = \frac{\varDelta H_v}{RT^2},$$ (3.24)

where $\varDelta H_v$ is the heat of vaporisation of the pure liquid solute. On integration, this gives

$$\ln p_2{}^0 = -\frac{\varDelta H_v}{RT} + A,$$ (3.25)

where A is a constant of integration. This equation possesses two parameters, $\varDelta H_v$ and A, and when these are known for a particular solute, the equation is known as a "Young's" equation for the vapour pressure. Equations of this kind are not accurate over large temperature ranges, since $\varDelta H_v$ is itself slightly dependent on temperature. Thus there are many kinds of vapour pressure equation containing more than two parameters that are more exact than Eq. (3.25). One such form, the "Antoine" equation:

$$\log_{10} p_2{}^0 = A - \frac{B}{t + C},$$ (3.26)

where t is the centigrade temperature, is very often used for quoting vapour pressure data, and can also be used for quoting retention data. This equation becomes identical with Eq. (3.25) if $C = 273$, but it is usual for heats of vaporisation to decline with increase in temperature, with the result that $C < 273$. Hala et al. (17) report the following empirical relations for the constant C:

(1) for hydrocarbons with n carbon atoms:

$$C = 271 - 7.6n,$$ (3.27)

(2) for other substances other than elements and substances boiling below $-150°C$:

$$C = 240 - 0.19t_B,$$ (3.28)

where t_B is the boiling point in °C.

In the absence of published data, the constants in the approximate Eq. (3.25) can be calculated from the boiling point of the solute, for this is connected with the heat of evaporation by Trouton's rule:

$$\frac{\Delta H_v}{T_B} \approx 22 \quad \text{cal}/(\text{mole } °\text{C}), \tag{3.29}$$

where T_B is the boiling point in °K. If Eq. (3.25) is considered at the boiling point of the pure liquid solute, $p_2^0 = 760$ Torr, so that

$$\ln 760 = 6.6 \approx \frac{-22}{R} + A = \frac{-22}{2} + A,$$

whence $A \approx 17.6$, and is a universal constant. Hence

$$\ln p_2^0 \approx \frac{-22 T_B}{RT} + 17.6,$$

or, using common logarithms and substituting the value of R,

$$\log_{10} p_2^0 \approx 7.7 - 4.8 \frac{T_B}{T}. \tag{3.30}$$

Equation (3.30) gives a very simple means of calculating the vapour pressure of a solute at any temperature given its boiling point. Its virtue is simplicity rather than accuracy, but it holds within a few per cent within some tens of degrees of the boiling point except for polar compounds such as alcohols, for which Trouton's constant is abnormal. Vapour pressures of various classes of organic substances at different temperatures are compared with values given by Eq. (3.30) in Table 3.4. It is seen that only for the alcohols is the approximation unusable.

Many other relations involving vapour pressure and boiling point and also relations including the critical parameters of vapours have been described. See, for example, Hala *et al.* (*17*).

The other variable of interest with regard to vapour pressures is chemical composition. The vapour pressure above a vapour is the pressure exerted when liquid and vapour are in equilibrium. In these circumstances, if the liquid is assumed incompressible and the vapour is assumed ideal, the difference in the free energies of liquid and vapour, each referred to a standard pressure, $P^\dagger$, is:

$$\Delta G^\dagger = G_{\text{gas}}^\dagger - G_{\text{liquid}}^\dagger = RT \ln \frac{p_2^0}{P^\dagger}. \tag{3.31}$$

TABLE 3.4

TESTS OF APPROXIMATION (3.30)

Substance	bp (°C)	VP at 50°C		VP at 100°C		VP at 150°C	
		calc	true	calc	true	calc	true
n-Hexane	68.3	407	400	—	—	—	—
n-Heptane	98.4	144	145	—	—	—	—
2,2,4-Trimethyl-pentane	99.2	138	140	—	—	—	—
n-Decane	174.1	10.5	7.5	83	70	398	380
Benzene	80.1	269	270	1380	1370	—	—
p-Xylene	138.3	37	33	251	235	1047	1030
n-Butylbenzene	183.1	7.9	5.3	64	53	316	300
Ethyl acetate	77.1	295	282	1470	1510	—	—
Diethyl carbonate	125.8	55	39	346	320	—	—
Methyl benzoate	199.5	4.5	2.0	39	30	204	197
Ethanol	78.4	288	222	1480	1690	—	—
Pentanol-2	119.7	69	32	426	350	—	—
Ethylene glycol	197.2	4.9	—	43	1.45	219	20

The difference between $G^{\ddagger}_{\text{liquid}}$ and $G^{\ddagger}_{\text{gas}}$ is that the former includes the interactions of all the molecules with the field of force provided by surrounding molecules, whereas the latter does not. Hence, $\Delta G^{\ddagger}$ is a measure of the forces acting on the molecules in the liquid state. It is clear that, in general, the bigger the molecule and the more polar groups between which specific electric interactions can occur, the smaller is the vapour pressure; this is familiar experience.

Detailed theories of intermolecular interactions in liquids are complex and incomplete. In the case of homologous series, however, each successive methylene group appears to add an almost constant increment to $\Delta G^{\ddagger}$. This can be shown by plotting the logarithm of the vapour pressure of the members of any one homologous series at any one temperature against the number of carbon atoms in the molecule (carbon number), as has been done by Pierotti *et al.* (*4*) and by Herington (*18*). Herington also quotes the relation:

$$\ln p_2{}^0 = A + Bn, \tag{3.32}$$

where n is the carbon number, and A and B are constants. Figure 3.3 (4) shows a plot of the logarithm of the vapour pressure against carbon number (or homolog number) for several different homologous series. It is seen that the lines corresponding to the different series all have very nearly the same slope, which indicates that the constant increment to the standard

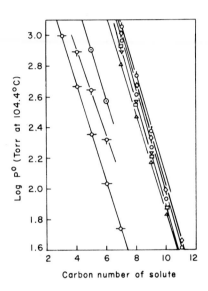

FIG. 3.3. Logarithms of vapour pressures of members of homologous series as a function of carbon number; Pierotti et al. (4). O, n-Alkanes; Ȯ, 2-methylalkanes; △, n-alkylbenzenes; ▽, n-alkylcyclopentanes; ☐, n-alkylcyclohexanes; ⧄, 1-alkenes; –O–, 1-alkanols; –Ọ–, 2-alkanols; ◇, 2-alkanones.

free energy change is independent of the end-group of the series. The constancy of this increment has been studied by Pierotti et al. (4), some of whose results are shown in Table 3.5. This shows the increments in $\log_{10} p_2^0$ for addition of one methylene unit, which for the several homologous series shown is about $0.35 \log_{10}$ units. The increments begin to deviate a little for the figures given for small carbon numbers, and generally constancy is obtained only above C_5 or above the first member of the series, whichever is first. The difference in vapour pressure between homologues can also be checked from the boiling points using Eq. (3.30), from which the increment in $\log_{10} p_2^0$ at temperature T is:

$$\log_{10} \frac{p_2^0}{p_3^0} = \frac{4.8(T_{B3} - T_{B2})}{T}. \tag{3.33}$$

TABLE 3.5

INCREMENTS IN $\log_{10} p_2^0$ AT 85°C (a) FOR ADDITION OF ONE CARBON ATOM IN A HOMOLOGOUS SERIES, (b) FOR CHANGE OF HOMOLOGOUS SERIES[a]

Homologous series	Increment in $\log_{10} p_2^0$
(a)	
n-Alkanes	0.35 ± 0.03
2-Methylalkanes	0.35 ± 0.03
3-Methylalkanes	0.37 ± 0.03
1-Alkanols	0.35 ± 0.03
2-Alkanols	0.34 ± 0.03
(b)	
n-Alkanes–1-alkanols	1.50 ± 0.15
n-Alkanes–2-methylalkanes	0.22 ± 0.05
2-Methylalkanes–2,2-dimethylalkanes	0.22 ± 0.05
n-Alkanes–3-methylalkanes	0.22 ± 0.05

[a] See Pierotti *et al.* (*4*).

TABLE 3.6

BOILING POINTS OF THE HEPTANES

Substance	bp (°C)
n-Heptane	98.4
3-Ethylpentane	93.5
3-Methylhexane	91.8
2-Methylhexane	90.1
2,3-Dimethylpentane	89.8
3,3-Dimethylpentane	86.1
2,2,3-Trimethylpentane	80.9
2,4-Dimethylpentane	80.5
2,2-Dimethylpentane	79.2
Cycloheptane	118.9
Ethylcyclopentane	103.5
Methylcyclohexane	100.9
cis-1,2-Dimethylcyclopentane	99.5
trans-1,2-Dimethylcyclopentane	91.9
trans-1,3-Dimethylcyclopentane	91.7
cis-1,3-Dimethylcyclopentane	90.8
1,1-Dimethylcyclopentane	87.8

As an example, the difference in boiling points between n-heptane and n-octane is about 27°C. From Eq. (3.33), the logarithm of the ratio of vapour pressures at 85°C is 0.36, which agrees well with the results of Pierotti *et al.* Note from Eq. (3.33) that the ratio of vapour pressures increases the lower the temperature. This point is discussed further in Section 3.10c.

The vapour pressures of branched-chain isomers of members of homologous series are always higher than those of the straight-chain isomers, so that their boiling points are lower, but it is not possible to correlate the vapour pressure with the amount of branching. Table 3.6 gives the boiling points of all the heptanes, from which it is seen that there are double-branched isomers with lower boiling points than a triple-branched isomer. Table 3.6 also includes the cyclic heptanes, and it is seen that these have higher boiling points than the alkanes. These trends apply to all hydrocarbons in homologous series. A result of branched-chain homologs having higher vapour pressures than the corresponding straight-chain compounds is that the addition of a methylene as a branch in the middle of a chain rather than at the end causes a smaller increment in $\log_{10} p_2^0$, as is shown by the last two entries in Table 3.5.

3.4. GENERAL THERMODYNAMIC EQUATIONS FOR MIXTURES

In detailed discussion of partition coefficients in terms of the mechanical interaction of the solute with solvent in the solution, it is most convenient to use the terms of the standard thermodynamic theory of non-electrolyte mixtures (*1–3, 6, 19*). Such equations as are required for our present discussion are given below.

(a) Chemical Potential of Ideal Solution

A definition of an ideal solution alternative to that of Section 3.2b is that its chemical potential is given by:

$$\mu_2^l = \mu_2^\ominus + RT \ln x_2, \tag{3.34}$$

where $\mu_2^\ominus$ is a constant but not that pertaining to $x_2 = 1$. Combination of this equation with Eqs. (3.3), (3.4), (3.5), and (3.7) yields the relation:

$$\mu_2^\ominus - \mu_2^0 = RT \ln \gamma, \tag{3.35}$$

which thus forms a more general definition of γ than that of Eq. (3.7).

A solution which is non-ideal obeys neither Eq. (3.3) nor (3.34), i.e., the chemical potential is not a linear function of $\ln x_2$, so that the vapour pressure is not a linear function of x_2. Reference to Fig. 3.1 shows that necessarily no non-perfect solution can be strictly ideal over any but an infinitesimal concentration range. The equations of the ideal solution can only be used in the case that x_2 is small enough that linearity can be assumed. Since this is the case in GC, the ideal equations are applicable.

(b) Thermodynamic Functions of Mixing and Excess Functions

The effect of forming a solution from solute and solvent can be described in terms of thermodynamic functions of mixing, i.e., the differences in the values of free energy, G, heat, H, or entropy, S, for the mixture and the sum of the corresponding values for the separate components. Thus, assuming 1 mole of mixture, and writing superscript M for a quantity of mixing for the binary mixture of solute and solvent,

$$G^M = G_{\text{mix}} - (x_1 G_1 + x_2 G_2), \tag{3.36}$$

$$H^M = H_{\text{mix}} - (x_1 H_1 + x_2 H_2), \tag{3.37}$$

$$S^M = S_{\text{mix}} - (x_1 S_1 + x_2 S_2), \tag{3.38}$$

$$\mu_i{}^M = \mu_{i(\text{mix})} - \mu_{i(\text{pure component})}. \tag{3.39}$$

The quantities of mixing for perfect and ideal solutions may be obtained using these equations together with Eqs. (3.3), (3.34), and the general relation:

$$G = \sum_i x_i \mu_i. \tag{3.40}$$

For the case of a perfect solution, Eqs. (3.3), (3.40), and (3.39) yield:

$$G^M = RT\{(x_1 \ln x_1 + x_2 \ln x_2)\}. \tag{3.41}$$

Application of the standard thermodynamic equation:

$$\Delta H = -T^2 \frac{\partial}{\partial T}\left(\frac{\Delta G}{T}\right) \tag{3.42}$$

to Eq. (3.41) yields:

$$H^M = 0. \tag{3.43}$$

A mixture which has zero heat of mixing is called "athermal." Perfect solutions are thus necessarily athermal.

For an ideal solution, the chemical potentials for the pure components are $\mu_i{}^0$, but the standard potentials for the mixture are $\mu_i{}^\ominus$. The quantity $\mu_i{}^M$ is thus given by:

$$\mu_i{}^M = (\mu_i{}^\ominus - \mu_i{}^0) + RT \ln x_i. \tag{3.44}$$

Substitution of Eq. (3.35) gives:

$$\mu_i{}^M = RT \ln \gamma_i x_i. \tag{3.45}$$

This, together with Eq. (3.40), yields:

$$G^M = RT\{x_1 \ln \gamma_1 x_1 + x_2 \ln \gamma_2 x_2\}, \tag{3.46}$$

and

$$-\frac{H^M}{RT^2} = x_1 \frac{\partial \ln \gamma_1}{\partial T} + x_2 \frac{\partial \ln \gamma_2}{\partial T}. \tag{3.47}$$

The difference between quantities of mixing as defined for an ideal solution and as defined for a perfect solution are called the *excess functions*, denoted by G^E, H^E, S^E, and μ^E. Eq. (3.45) and comparison of Eqs. (3.46) and (3.41), and (3.47) and (3.43), yield the results:

$$\mu_i{}^E = RT \ln \gamma_i, \tag{3.48}$$

$$G^E = RT\{x_1 \ln \gamma_1 + x_2 \ln \gamma_2)\}, \tag{3.49}$$

$$H^E = H^M. \tag{3.50}$$

In the above equations, the quantities of mixing apply to one mole of *mixture*. More relevant in GC are the values of the quantities per mole of *solute*; if these are designated $g_2{}^M$, $g_2{}^E$, $h_2{}^M$, and $h_2{}^E$, then:

$$g_2{}^M = RT\left\{\left(\frac{x_1}{x_2} \ln \gamma_1 x_1 + \ln \gamma_2 x_2\right)\right\}, \tag{3.51}$$

$$-\frac{h_2{}^M}{RT^2} = \frac{x_1}{x_2} \frac{\partial \ln \gamma_1}{\partial T} + \frac{\partial \ln \gamma_2}{\partial T}. \tag{3.52}$$

In the case of GC, in which $x_2 \to 0$, $x_1 \to 1$ and $\gamma_1 \to 1$, the first terms of both Eq. (3.51) and (3.52) converge to zero; if, as in previous sections, the subscript 2 is dropped from γ_2, the results are:

$$g_2{}^M = RT \ln \gamma x_2; \qquad g_2{}^E = RT \ln \gamma. \tag{3.53}$$

$$h_2{}^M = h_2{}^E = -RT^2 \frac{\partial \ln \gamma}{\partial T}. \tag{3.54}$$

3.5. ACTIVITY COEFFICIENTS FOR ALKANE SOLUTIONS

The activity coefficient of a solute reflects the way in which the environment of a molecule of the solute in solution differs from that of its fellow molecules in its own pure liquid. In the special case of GC, the solute in solution is so dilute that a solute molecule virtually never encounters its fellows, but only molecules of solvent.

There are two main ways in which the environment of a solute molecule in solution differs from that of its own liquid. First, the solvent molecules are of a different size and shape, so that they are subject to different kinds of geometrical restrictions on the conformations that they can adopt. Second, the intermolecular forces it forms with its solvent neighbours may differ from those it forms with its fellows in the liquid. Detailed theories of these matters (2, 20–22) almost always assume that the above two factors are independent, and contribute independently and additively to μ^E. Thus, we adopt the basic equation:

$$\ln \gamma = \ln \gamma \text{ (geometrical)} + \ln \gamma \text{ (energetic).} \qquad (3.55)$$

Since the second term here is assumed to be produced as a result of differences in energy, it is often written in terms of an interaction energy, χ, so that:

$$\ln \gamma = \ln \gamma \text{ (geometrical)} + \frac{\chi}{RT}. \qquad (3.56)$$

Substitution in Eq. (3.54) will show that χ is the heat of mixing of solute and solvent per mole of solute.

The case of athermal mixtures ($\chi = 0$) in which the component molecules are of different sizes has been studied widely in statistical mechanics. This case is that of mixtures of non-polar molecules, and in particular of mixtures of alkanes. The gas chromatography of alkane solutes in alkane solvents, where the solvent molecule is necessarily larger than the solute molecule, can be treated theoretically with considerable detail. In the usual treatment, the solution is assumed to occupy a lattice, and molecules are assumed to be able to adopt the form of chains, a particular link in each molecule of either solute or solvent occupying just one lattice site. Figure 3.4 illustrates such a scheme for a 2-dimensional square lattice, a solute molecule being two units long, and a solvent molecule being 8 units. The non-unit activity coefficient arises from the fact that a unit of a molecule bonded to a neighbouring unit on a neighbouring lattice site is restricted in the number of alternative lattice sites it can occupy because of similar restrictions of neighbouring molecules. The magnitude of these restrictions depends on the size of the molecules, since the ends of molecules are more free than their middles.

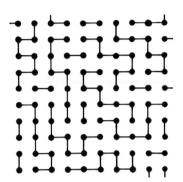

FIG. 3.4. Solvent molecules (long) and solute molecules (short) occupying a 2-dimensional square lattice. In this case, $z = 4$, and $r = 4$.

Analysis of the statistical problem yields an equation for G^M (*19, 23, 24*) from which can be derived the following equation for γ for the case that the mole fraction of solute, x_2, is small:

$$\ln \gamma = \ln \frac{1}{r} + \frac{z}{2} \ln \frac{rz/2}{r(z/2 - 1) + 1}. \qquad (3.57)$$

Here, the small molecule of solute is assumed to occupy one lattice site, while the solvent molecule occupies r, and the coordination number of the lattice is z. Values of γ are not very sensitive to the value of z when the latter is greater than about 6. Commonly, therefore, an equation is used in which z is assumed to be infinite (*25*):

$$\frac{G^M}{RT} = x_1 \ln \varphi_1 + x_2 \ln \varphi_2, \qquad (3.58)$$

where φ_1 and φ_2, instead of being *mole* fractions, in which case the mixture would be perfect [Eq. (3.41)], are *volume* fractions. For components of similar density, molar volume is proportional to molecular weight, so that:

$$\varphi_i = \frac{M_i x_i}{\sum_j M_j x_j}, \qquad (3.59)$$

where M is molecular weight. Substitution of Eq. (3.59) into Eq. (3.58), followed by differentiation and use of Eq. (3.48), leads to an equation for the solute activity coefficient,

$$\gamma = \frac{M_2}{M_1} \exp\left(1 - \frac{M_2}{M_1}\right). \qquad (3.60)$$

The approximation of uniform density is well within the accuracy of Eq. (3.58) itself for alkane mixtures. If the solvent is a mixture, e.g., a mixture of polymers or of higher hydrocarbons, Eq. (3.58) can be generalised to include a term for each component, and the resulting value of γ is:

$$\gamma = \frac{M_2}{M_{av}} \exp\left(1 - \frac{M_2}{M_{av}}\right), \tag{3.61}$$

where M_{av} is the average solvent molecular weight given by:

$$M_{av} = \sum_j x_j M_j. \tag{3.62}$$

Equation (3.60) is of direct relevance in GC using high molecular weight stationary liquids, since the product $M_1\gamma$ of Eq. (3.60) can be substituted in Eq. (3.13) or (3.14) for partition coefficient or specific retention volume. Furthermore, had the treatment of Section 3.2c been generalised to the case of a mixture of polymeric stationary liquids, M_{av} would have replaced M_1, so that Eq. (3.61) could be substituted similarly. In either case, the result is:

$$V_g = \frac{1.7027 \times 10^7}{M_2 p_2^0} \exp\left(\frac{M_2}{M_{av}} - 1\right). \tag{3.63}$$

M_{av} is in practice never less than twice M_2, and thus the total range of variation of the term in parentheses of Eq. 3.63 is comparatively small, i.e., from about $e^{-1/2}$ to e^{-1}. In particular, when $M_{av} \gg M_2$, the equation reduces to:

$$V_g \approx \frac{1.7027 \times 10^7}{M_2 p_2^0 e}. \tag{3.64}$$

The result is that specific retention volumes are only a shallow function of solvent molecular weight, and for solvents of molecular weight greatly exceeding that of any solute, retention is virtually independent of solvent molecular weight. The matter is treated in more detail in Fig. 3.5, which shows values of γ and $r\gamma$ calculated by Eq. (3.57) expressed as a function of r. It is apparent that when r is large, the product $r\gamma$ approaches an asymptotic value. The effect in practice is illustrated by Fig. 3.6, which presents values of V_g for n-hexane and n-heptane in n-alkanes plotted as a function of the carbon number of the alkane, using results from refs. (26) and (27). With carbon numbers of 30 or over, the variation of retention with carbon number is relatively slight.

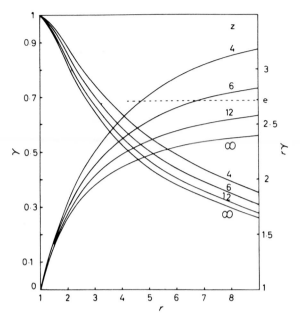

FIG. 3.5. Plots of γ and $r\gamma$ as calculated by the Miller-Guggenheim equation, Eq. (3.57), against r for various values of z.

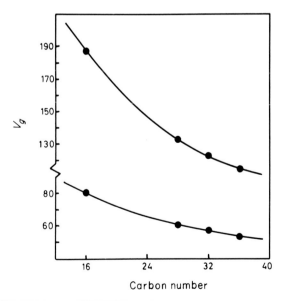

FIG. 3.6. Plot of V_g for n-hexane and n-heptane in various n-alkane solvents against carbon number of the solvent.

If Eq. (3.64) is assumed to hold, a calculation similar to that of Eq. (3.23) for the value of V_g at the solute boiling point yields the result:

$$V_g(T_b) \approx \frac{8250}{M_2} \qquad (8250 \equiv 22,420/e), \qquad (3.65)$$

which should apply for alkanes in alkane stationary liquids of high molecular weight. This very simple result both yields a simple approximate rule of greater practical validity than Eq. (3.23) and also gives a guide to the accuracy of the treatment of activity coefficients by means of lattice theory. The validity of the approximation is illustrated in Table 3.7, in which values

TABLE 3.7

Tests of Approximation (3.65) for Specific Retentions of Alkanes in Hexatriacontane at the Solute Boiling Point

Solute	bp	M_2	$V_g(T_b)$	$M_2 V_g(T_b)$
n-Nonane	150.8	128	65.3	8350
n-Octane	125.8	114	66.4	7800
3-Methylheptane	122.2	114	63.0	7190
2,3-Dimethylhexane	113.9	114	73.2	8350
2,2,4-Trimethylpentane	99.3	114	66.4	7560
n-Heptane	98.4	100	71.9	7190
3-Methylhexane	91.8	100	71.6	7160
2,3-Dimethylpentane	89.8	100	74.1	7410
n-Hexane	69.0	86	71.1	6110
2,3-Dimethylbutane	58.1	86	70.8	6100
n-Pentane	36.2	72	65.3	4700

of V_g for alkanes in n-hexatriacontane (C_{36}) at their boiling points, obtained by logarithmic interpolation from the results of Pease and Thorburn (27), are multiplied by M_2 for the alkane. The resulting product may be compared with the predicted figure of 8250. It is seen that the approximation is useful, although it predicts too large a value of V_g with light solutes. Detailed study shows that activity coefficients derived purely from lattice theory do not agree exactly with experiment, especially for the lower alkane solutes (2, 20, 21, 28), due to fundamental inadequacy of the model.

3.6. Retentions in Polar Solvents

(a) Introduction

The retentions of alkane solutes in alkane solvents are the only systems
for which there is a reasonably precise theory. For all other systems, a more
empirical approach must be used. In cases where the solvent is polar, the
term χ of Eq. 3.56 becomes large, and usually outweighs any minor geometrical effects on retention. However, the argument of the last section,
by which it was shown that retentions are but slightly dependent on solvent
molecular weight, holds throughout, with the result that retentions of
either polar or nonpolar solutes in polar stationary liquids are relatively
slightly affected by the molecular weight of the liquid. This is illustrated
in Fig. 3.7, in which the value of V_g at 120°C for three very different kinds
of solute in different polyethylene glycols is plotted against the average

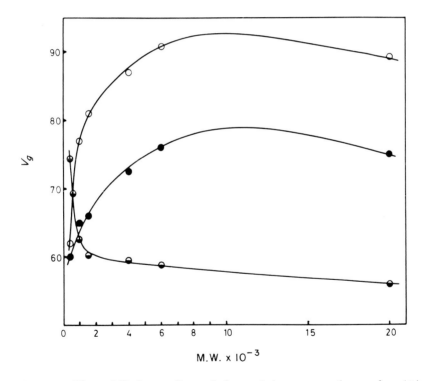

FIG. 3.7. Plots of V_g for an alkane, dodecane (O), an aromatic, p-xylene (●),
and an alkanol, n-butanol (◒) on polyethylene glycols, as a function of average
solvent molecular weight.

molecular weight of these polymeric stationary liquids. Between $M_1 = 1000$ and $M_1 = 20,000$, the variation in V_g does not exceed $\approx 15\%$.

In Sections 3.2 and 3.3, retention was discussed through the expression $p_2{}^0\gamma$, which appears in Eq. (3.14). This product is determined by:

  (a) the forces between solute molecules in the liquid solute, which thus determine the vapour pressure,

and

  (b) the comparison of forces acting on solute molecules first in their own liquid, and then in the dilute solution in the solvent.

The interaction of the solute molecules with their own liquid thus appears twice, once in the specification of $p_2{}^0$, and once in the specification of γ. In gas chromatography, the liquid solute is never present in the experiment. Furthermore, of all the systems involved; i.e., solvent, solution, solute vapour, and solute liquid, the last is by far the most difficult to describe theoretically, especially if it is polar. Yet another factor is that, in practical instances, vapour pressures of many important organic substances treated by GC are unknown. For all these reasons, the specification of retentions in terms of the product $p_2{}^0\gamma$ is inappropriate except for cases in which the thermodynamic parameters of the solute are well–known. Retentions of other solutes are best discussed, therefore, directly in terms of the processes involved when solute molecules equilibrate between the solvent and the vapour.

(b) Intermolecular Forces

Liquids and solutions cohere because of intermolecular forces between the molecules. It is convenient to divide these forces into four classes; detailed descriptions are given in refs. (6) and (13).

(1) *Electronic Dispersion.* This is the most universal intermolecular force. No accurate simple picture of this force can be given in classical (i.e., non-quantum mechanical) terms; it is approximately described as attraction between induced phase-coherent dipoles arising from electronic zero point energy (13). For practical purposes, the energy of dispersion interaction is given by the London formula:

$$\varepsilon_L = -\frac{3\alpha'\alpha''I'I''}{2r^6(I' + I'')}, \qquad (3.66)$$

where $'$ and $''$ refer to two cohering atoms each of polarisability α and ionisation potential I, with centres distant r. Dispersion forces exist between *all* atoms and molecules, and are responsible for the coherence of all molecules not possessing dipole moments. Though the London equation strictly applies only to atoms, it can be applied to molecules by summing the terms for each individual interaction of atoms in pairs, one from each molecule. It is seen from the factor of r^{-6} that dispersion forces (like all intermolecular forces) decrease very rapidly with increase in distance between the interacting centres. With complex organic molecules such as are encountered in gas chromatography, therefore, it may be considered that the coherence occurs mainly at the surfaces of the molecules. This idea is the basis for the use of the so-called "Kihara" potential (*29*), and has been considered in the context of GC by Littlewood *et al.* (*30, 31*).

(2) *Dipole–Dipole Interactions.* Pairs of dipoles in dipolar molecules in liquids tend to orient themselves with mutual attraction. The average energy resulting from this interaction is:

$$\varepsilon_D = -\frac{2\mu'^2\mu''^2}{r^6 kT},\tag{3.67}$$

where r is the distance between the centres of dipoles of moments μ' and μ''. Dipole moments of common organic groups are listed in Table 3.8, in Debye units (D; i.e., 10^{-18} esu–cm). There is in practice about a ten-fold range in dipole moments, so that Eq. (3.67) implies that there is a range of about 10^4 in the magnitude of dipolar forces. The magnitude of dispersion forces due to a single methylene group $-CH_2-$ is equivalent at or near room temperature to the dipolar force due to two dipoles of about 2D; i.e., in about the middle of the range. Essentially, it is this large range in

TABLE 3.8

DIPOLE MOMENTS OF COMMON ORGANIC GROUPS[a]

$RCH=CH_2$, alkene	0.4	R—Br, bromide	1.9
R—O—R, ether	1.15	R—I, iodide	1.8
R—O—Me, methyl ether	1.3	R—CO—OMe, methyl ester	1.9
R—NH_2, amine	1.4	R—CO—OR, ester	2.1
R—OH, alkanol	1.7	R—CHO, aldehyde	2.5
R—COOH, carboxylic acid	1.7	R—CO—R, ketone	2.7
R—F, fluoride	1.9	R—NO_2, nitroalkane	3.3
R—Cl, chloride	1.8	R—CN, nitrile	3.6

[a] In Debye units.

the magnitude of dipolar forces that enables different gas chromatographic columns to exhibit their selectivity.

(3) *Induced Dipole Interaction.* A permanent dipole in one molecule can induce a dipole in a neighbouring polarisable molecule, with resultant attraction; this is the mechanism by which a magnet attracts iron. The energy resulting from this interaction is:

$$\varepsilon_r = -\frac{\alpha' \mu''^2}{r^6}, \tag{3.68}$$

where α' and μ'' are as in Eqs. (3.66) and (3.67). Its magnitude is usually less than that of the other forces, but it becomes appreciable in gas chromatography of aromatic and halogenated molecules which have unusually large polarisabilities.

(4) *Hydrogen Bonds.* A special case of dipolar interaction is the interaction between hydrogen atoms bonded to oxygen, fluorine, or nitrogen (*32*) and certain polar groups known as "donors." The bond so formed is more directional than in other intermolecular forces, with the chemical bond between the O, F, or N and the hydrogen on one side, and the hydrogen bond between the hydrogen and the donor on the other side being more or less collinear. The hydrogen bond is thus halfway between a chemical bond and an intermolecular force. Hydrogen bonds are formed by hydrogen in order of stability $F-H > O-H > N-H$, of which the last two are most commonly relevant in GC. More important is the order of donor strength, which is greatest on the left:

It is apparent that the order of donor strength is different from the order of dipole moment. This is important in gas chromatography, since it implies that separation on the basis of hydrogen bond formation differs completely from separation on the basis of polarity.

As with other dipolar interactions, hydrogen bond association decreases with increase in temperature.

(c) The Process of Solution

Figure 3.8 illustrates for purposes of elementary explanation the process in which a solute enters a solvent. Both solute and solvent are shown as molecules in which the non-polar part is assumed to be a hydrocarbon residue, drawn as a zig-zag, and a polar grouping is drawn as a blob. The intermolecular forces are shown as lines. In all cases, entry of a solute molecule involves (i) rupture of intermolecular forces present in the solvent to make room for the solute, and (ii) formation of new forces incorporating the solute molecule.

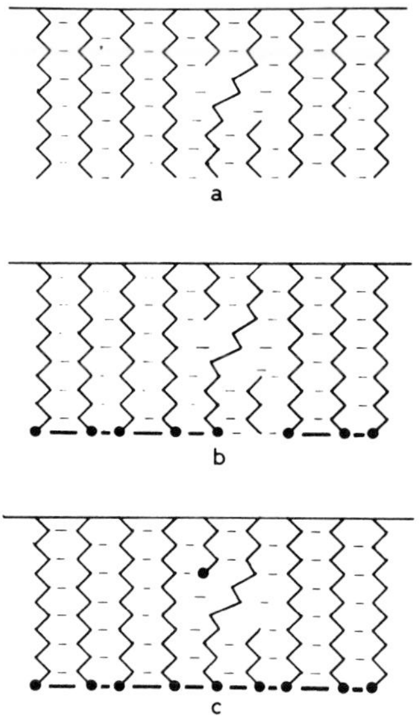

FIG. 3.8. Illustration of a solute molecule entering a solvent: (a) Alkane solute into alkane solvent; (b) alkane solute into polar solvent, polar group designated by large blob; (c) polar solute into polar solvent.

Figure 3.8a shows an alkane solute dissolving in an alkane solute. We assume that the total intermolecular forces are the sum of those between individual neighbouring unit parts of the molecules, and we consider a unit part to be one methylene group. The magnitude of the intermolecular forces is indicated in the figure, therefore, by the number of lines. It is clear that, in the entry of a solute molecule of n unit parts, n interactions are broken to make way for it, and $2n$ new units are formed. The difference of n unit interactions newly created is what contributes to the energy of solution. Since all methylene groups are similar, each new group in the solute adds a constant increment to the intermolecular energy. The total intermolecular energy change resulting from solution may therefore be written as $\sum_i \varepsilon_i$, where each term in the sum comes from each of the groups constituting the molecule. Assuming that intermolecular interactions in the vapour phase are neglected, the molar energy of solution, ΔU, is also, therefore, an additive function of the groups constituting the solute. The partition coefficient of the solute is related to the free energy of solution rather than the energy of solution. The detailed relation between the two is very complex, but it appears that as an approximate general rule (*33*), the free energy of solution is a linear function of the energy of solution, and therefore also of the heat of solution. Major exceptions to this rule occur when the intermolecular interactions are strongly directional, e.g., in the formation of hydrogen bonds, and minor exceptions are implied in other detailed relations between retention and structure described in later sections. The important result is that free energies of solution, and therefore also log V_g, are approximately additive properties of the constituent molecular groupings of the solute.

The fact that log V_g is a constitutive property of solute molecules, both in the case of alkanes and in general, plays a large part in GC. Its most obvious application is to homologous series, for which log V_g or log r is a linear function of carbon number. This relation holds with remarkable accuracy in all but highly cross-linked stationary liquids, and with all homologous series except, sometimes, for the lowest members. Examples of this relation are commonplace in the literature. Figure 3.9 shows an example, with esters of the higher fatty acids as solutes.

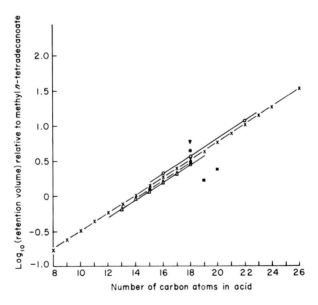

FIG. 3.9. Plot of the logarithms of the relative retentions of fatty acid esters against carbon number. Hawke *et al.*, *see* Section 12.6e. ✕, straight chain acids; △, iso-acids; ▲, -ante-iso-acids; ☐, multibranched acids; ○, mono-unsaturated acids; ●, diunsaturated acid; ▼, triunsaturated acid.

(d) Alkane Solutes in Polar Solvents

The solution of alkane solutes in polar solvents is illustrated in Fig. 3.8b. The entering alkane causes rupture of a polar-polar bond between two polar groups in the solvent, but it cannot compensate for this loss by forming polar-polar interactions itself. Alternatively expressed, solvent molecules in the polar solvent are associated, and entry of the alkane, in effect, dilutes the associated dipolar solvent molecules, thus diminishing the amount of association as with any other associated system on dilution. The free energy required thus to diminish association within the solvent must necessarily be detracted from the free energy of solution of the solute. The result is that retentions of alkanes in polar solvents are less than in corresponding non-polar solvents. The magnitude of the effect can be very much greater than the comparatively small changes in solution free energy imposed by changes in molecular size discussed in Section 3.5. Table 3.9 lists the specific retention volumes at 80°C of n-hexane in various stationary liquids. It is seen that the value can change some thirtyfold for stationary liquids in common use, and becomes very small for those liquids which contain a large proportion of polar groupings.

TABLE 3.9

SPECIFIC RETENTION VOLUMES OF n-HEXANE AND RELATIVE RETENTIONS OF SUCCESSIVE HOMOLOGUES IN DIFFERENT STATIONARY LIQUIDS[a]

Stationary liquids[b]	V_g [c] (ml/g)	$r_{z,z+1}$ [c]	$r_{z,z+1}$ [d]
Squalane	63.9	2.34	2.19
Hexadecanol	46.5	2.34	—
Dioctyl sebacate	48.3	2.28	2.2
Dodecanol	44.0	2.29	—
Dinonyl phthalate	36.9	2.34	2.14
Benzyl diphenyl	18.7	2.28	2.1
Tricresyl phosphate	16.9	2.14	—
Polyethylene glycol 400	5.1	1.89	1.73
1,2,3-tris(cyanethoxy)propane	1.6	1.75	1.62

[a] See Littlewood et al. (30, 35) and ref. (38).
[b] Arranged according to polar proportion.
[c] At 80°C.
[d] At 100°C.

Though the absolute retention of a given solute decreases greatly with progressive increase in the polar proportion of the solvent molecules, the relative retention of successive homologues, i.e., the extra energy gained from adding just one more methylene group to the solute, changes very much less. For many of the polar solvents in common use, the relative retention of successive homologues is virtually unchanged from its value in an alkane solvent. Values of this quantity, which is particularly relevant in discussion of the Retention Index (q.v. Section 3.6f), are also given in Table 3.9. It appears that the relative retention of successive homologues becomes materially reduced only when the solvent contains sufficient polar groups for appreciable cross-linking.

(e) Polar Solutes in Polar Solvents

The solution of a polar solute in a polar solvent is illustrated in Fig. 3.8c. In this case, the polar molecule causes disruption of the solvent as in the case of an alkane solute, but also the polar group of the solute is capable of forming specific electrical interactions with the polar groups of the solvent. If the partition coefficient of a given polar solute in a solvent is compared with that of the same solute in a non-polar solvent, the disruption of the solvent causes a decrease in partition coefficient, while the formation of specific interactions with the solute causes an increase. In practice, either of these two factors can be the greater, so that polar solutes can have partition coefficients which are either greater or less than their partition coefficients in a corresponding non-polar solvent. Since, however, an alkane solute can never form specific electrical interactions with the solvent so that its retention in a polar solvent is always less than in a non-polar one, the retention of a polar solute relative to an alkane is invariably greater in a polar solvent than in a non-polar one.

The contributions to the free energy of solution due to the dispersion forces discussed previously and the polar interactions discussed in this section are at least approximately independent, as implied by Eq. (3.56). The result of this is that the increments of retention caused by adding a methylene group to a polar solute are approximately the same as for a non-polar solute. Thus, the figures given for the relative retentions of successive homologues in Table 3.9 also hold approximately for homologous series of polar solutes. Departures from this approximate rule are, however, large enough to exceed experimental error (Section 3.6f).

All polar solvents in practical use contain molecules which consist partly of polar groups and partly of non-polar groups such as methyl or methylene. Different polar solvents can be characterised by three properties:

(1) The chemical nature of the polar groups,
(2) The proportions of polar groups in the solvent molecules,
(3) The relative conformation of polar and non-polar parts.

One these three properties, the third can be shown to have comparatively little effect on retentions; thus, mixed solvents compounded from different starting materials, but having the same concentrations of the same polar groups, induce similar retentions of all solutes (*34*). Therefore, retentions in polar solvents are largely determined by the nature and the proportions of the polar groups in the solvent.

In a series of papers, Littlewood and Willmott (*26, 34–36*) have investigated the effect of changing both the nature and concentration of the solvent polar group on retentions of different classes of polar solutes. They have restricted themselves to solvents in which the proportion of polar component is fairly small ($\approx 10\%$ w/w), in which case, the polar groups appear to act as thermodynamically ideal species. The effect of the polar groups in the solvent is studied from the ratio of V_g, the retention of a solute in a given polar solvent, to V_{go}, the retention of the same solute in a comparable non-polar solvent; this ratio is a function of the nature and concentration of the polar groups. If it is assumed that interactions between polar groups occur with the formation of complexes, e.g., quadrupoles or hydrogen-bonded structures, they can be treated thermodynamically as if they were chemical compounds, the Law of Mass Action being applied (*2*). On this basis, it is found that:

$$\frac{V_g}{V_{go}} = 1 + f(K_1, K_2, \ldots, K_i \ldots, C), \qquad (3.69)$$

where C is the concentration of polar component of the solvent and K_i are equilibrium constants for the formation of whatever complexes are formed as a result of association. For example, the association of alkanols by hydrogen bonding is assumed to occur by "Ideal Linear Association" (*3*), in which case the equilibrium constant for the hydrogen bonding is given by:

$$K_H = \frac{[(ROH)_{n+1}]}{[(ROH)_n][ROH]}. \qquad (3.70)$$

In Eq. (3.69), the second term on the RHS describes explicitly the extra retention conferred upon the retention of the solute by virtue of the presence of the polar part of the solvent.

The application of the above scheme for predicting the effect of polar groups is limited by the simplicity of the model used, but, nevertheless, four cases can be distinguished in which the model provides quantitative predictions of retentions:

(1) Solvents with weakly polar groups with dipoles up to about 1.15D (ethers) together with any solute and values of C up to about 5 moles/l. In this case,

$$\frac{V_g}{V_{go}} = 1 + K_w C, \tag{3.71}$$

where K_w is the constant of association between the polar group of the solvent and the polar group of the solute.

(2) Solvents and solutes of similar chemical type, e.g., alkanol solutes in alkanol solvents, cyanides in cyanides, ethers in ethers, etc. In this case, Eq. (3.71) applies.

(3) Solvents with strongly polar or strongly hydrogen-bonding groups, e.g., hydroxyl or nitrile solvents, and solutes with weaker interactions, e.g., halogenates, ethers, etc. In this case,

$$V_g = \frac{V_{go}}{r_a} \left\{ 1 + \frac{K_D}{2K_H} \left[(1 + 4K_H C)^{1/2} - 1 \right] \right\}, \tag{3.72}$$

where K_D is the equilibrium constant for interaction of the solute with unassociated solvent, and K_H is the equilibrium constant for the interaction of the solvent groups with one another. r_a for a given polar solvent is the ratio:

$$r_a = \frac{V_g \text{ (an alkane in a non-polar solvent)}}{V_g \text{ (the same alkane in the polar solvent)}} \tag{3.73}$$

and is always greater than 1. In this case, the relation between V_g and C is non-linear (see Section 7.4).

(4) Any solute in any solvent at limitingly small values of C. In these circumstances, the polar groups in the solvent are so dilute that their mutual association is negligible, and Eq. (3.71) holds. At higher values of C, however, neither Eq. (3.71) nor Eq. (3.72) may hold.

The application of Eqs. (3.71) and (3.72) is illustrated in Fig. 3.10, which shows a plot of V_g against C for a variety of solutes in a set of solvents compounded from squalane (non-polar) and 1-dodecanol (35). It is seen that the alkanol solutes give straight line plots of slope K in the alkanol solvents (case 2), while the alkene and the ether conform quantitatively

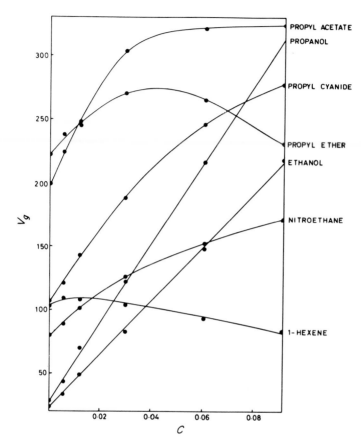

FIG. 3.10. Plot of V_g for various solutes against concentration of hydroxyl group in the solvent.

to case (3). It is noteworthy that in the case of species conforming to Eq. (3.72), the retention can show a maximum. Table 3.10 gives typical values of K for various common interactions, from which V_g/V_{go} can be calculated for any applicable solvent, given C. For the case that $V_g/V_{go} > 1$ solely on account of dipole-dipole interaction, a definite correlation can be made between the dipole moments of solute and solvent, and the extra retention they induce (26, 37).

(f) The Retention Index

Both for practical reasons, and for the theoretical reasons contained in the previous sections, it has long been common to regard the series of n-

TABLE 3.10

EQUILIBRIUM CONSTANTS FOR COMMON SPECIFIC INTERMOLECULAR INTERACTIONS[a]

Interaction	System studied, solute/solvent	$K(40°)$[b]	$K(80°)$[b]
—OH/—OH	n-Pentanol/1-dodecanol	4.11	1.48
—OH/—OH	n-Butanol/1-dodecanol	3.62	1.44
—CO—O—/—OH	Acetates/1-dodecanol	1.35	0.54
>O/—OH	Ethers/1-dodecanol	0.72	0.45
—OH/>O	Alkanols/methoxyhexadecane	0.68	0.34
—NO₂/—OH	Nitropropane/1-dodecanol	0.53	0.34
—X/—OH	Alkylhalides/1-dodecanol	0.52	0.35
—CN/—CN	Nitriles/lauronitrile	2.14	1.52
—OH/—CN	Alkanols/lauronitrile	1.33	0.83
—X/—CN	Alkylhalides/lauronitrile	0.92	—
>O/—CN	Propyl ether/lauronitrile	0.51	0.20
—CH=CH₂/—CN	Alkenes/lauronitrile	0.25	0.17

[a] See Littlewood and Willmott (35).
[b] Given in litres per mole.

alkanes as standard solutes in terms of whose retentions the relative retentions of other solutes can be expressed. Frequently, the retention of a given solute, x, relative to that of a given alkane of carbon number z is written r_{xz}; e.g., r_{x7} for x relative to n-heptane. A system of describing retentions relative to n-nonane has been described extensively by Evans et al. (39–42). A more subtle unit of relative retention using n-alkanes is the *Retention Index, I*, of Kovats et al. (43–46), which depends for its utility on the fact given in Section 3.6c, that the logarithm of the partition coefficient of a member of a homologous series is accurately a linear function of its carbon number. The index is defined by:

$$I = 100z + 100\left[\frac{\log_{10} V_{g(i)} - \log_{10} V_{g(z)}}{\log_{10} V_{g(z+1)} - \log_{10} V_{g(z)}}\right], \qquad (3.74)$$

where:

$V_{g(i)}$ is retention of the species of interest, i,

$V_{g(z)}$ is retention of the n-alkane eluted next before it,

$V_{g(z+1)}$ is retention of the n-alkane eluted next after it,

z is carbon number of the n-alkane of retention $V_{g(z)}$.

In this expression, the retentions, which are here written as specific retention volumes, can equally well be written as retentions r_i, r_z, r_{z+1}, relative to any one standard, or as lengths from the air peak on the chart paper, or time units, or any other of the units of Eq. (2.44) or (2.45), since the appropriate conversion factors cancel.

The significance of the Retention Index, which may initially seem obscure, can be appreciated by reference to Fig. 3.11. In Fig. 3.11a is shown a chromatogram of three components of interest shown as large peaks, together with three alkanes added as standards for relative retentions shown as little peaks. It is assumed that the scale of the abscissa, which can be length, time, volume, etc., is such that the distance of the first alkane from the point corresponding to the air peak is unity. In Fig. 3.11b, the chromatogram is re-plotted with an abscissa scale linear in the logarithm of the scale of Fig. 3.11a; logarithms to base 10 have been used. It is seen that here, the n-alkane peaks are equally spaced, as expected from Section 3.6c. The alkane peaks are thus seen to form regularly spaced "markers" on the chromatogram, to which the peaks of interest can easily be related.

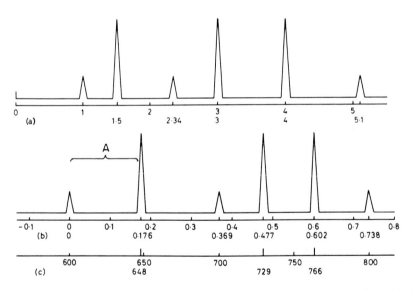

FIG. 3.11. Diagram to illustrate the significance of the Retention Index: (a) A chromatogram of three substances of interest (big peaks) with three alkane standards (little peaks), which we take to be C_6, C_7, and C_8 (in this example, the relative retention of successive alkanes is 2.34); (b) The same, re-drawn on a logarithmic scale of retention, so that the linear distance between any two peaks is proportional to the logarithm of their relative retention, and the distances between successive alkanes used as standards are constant; (c) In this, the scale has been changed so that the n-alkanes define the scale, there being 100 units between each.

For this purpose, it is convenient to change the scale of Fig. 3.11b so that the distance between two alkanes is a definite unit. Convention, following Kovats, makes 100 subunits between each alkane; each of such units is a unit of Retention Index as shown at Fig. 3.11c. Study of Eq. (3.74) will show that the expression on the RHS corresponds to the operations described above in relation to Fig. 3.11. First, all retentions are expressed logarithmically. The numerator inside the bracket gives, for the first of the peaks of interest, the distance A in Fig. 3.11b. The denominator inside the bracket changes the scale so that the distance between two alkanes is reduced to unity, and this is multiplied outside by 100 to form the subunits. Finally, the first term serves to ensure that the retention index of the n-alkane of carbon number z is $100z$.

TABLE 3.11

RETENTION INDICES OF SOME ALKANES IN A NON-POLAR STATIONARY LIQUID (SQUALANE)[a]

Substance	Retention index			
	40°C	60°C	80°C	100°C
n-Hexane	600	600	600	600
n-Heptane	700	700	700	700
n-Octane	800	800	800	800
2-Methylbutane	475	475	476	477
2-Methylpentane	570	570	570	571
2-Methylhexane	666	667	667	668
2-Methylheptane	765	765	765	765
3-Methylhexane	676	676	677	678
2,2-Dimethylpentane	625	626	627	—
2,3-Dimethylpentane	671	671	672	673
2,4-Dimethylpentane	(632)	630	630	631
3,3-Dimethylpentane	657	660	661	—
3-Ethylpentane	685	686	688	689
2,2,3-Trimethylbutane	638	641	—	—
2,2,4-Trimethylpentane	689	691	694	696
Toluene	742	751	753	—
$b = \log_{10} r_{n,n+1}$	0.457	0.42	0.37	0.34
$r_{n,n+1}$	2.86	2.63	2.34	2.19

[a] See "Gas Chromatography Abstracts" (38).

The advantages of the retention index lie in its properties given below. These can be illustrated from the sample retention indices given in Tables 3.11 and 3.12 (*38*).

(1) By definition the retention index of an *n*-alkane of carbon number *z* is 100*z* whatever the solvent.

(2) Retention indices of neighbouring members of homologous series differ by about 100 units. If the rule given in Section 3.6c that the relative retentions of successive homologues were the same for any homologous series in any solvent, the series of *n*-alkanes would necessarily be included as one of the series, and hence retention indices of homologues would invariably differ by multiples of 100 units. The tables show typically to what extent this rule holds; thus, in squalane, apart from isopentane, the differences in retention indices for the 2-methylalkanes are between 97 and 100. Similar consistency can be seen for alkanols in polethylene glycol. With initial homologues, however, the deviations are greater.

(3) Since change in homologue number changes the hundreds digit, but makes only a minor change in the other digits, the tens and units digits thus become characteristic of the particular homologous series. Thus, a 2-methyl alkane above isopentane is characterised by an index of 68 ± 2. This provides some measure of qualitative identification.

(4) The temperature variation of retention indices is generally smaller than that of relative retentions, and is very much smaller than that of absolute retentions (Section 3.10). Thus, retention indices retain their valuable invariance even if temperature control is imperfect.

3.7. General Relations between Partition Coefficient and Solute Structure

There are many structural features of solute molecules which have characteristic effects on retention, apart from those directly attributable to the specific electrical interactions described in the previous section. Some are described below.

(a) Retention Index and Solute Structure

Because the series of *n*-alkanes are used as standards for GC retentions, particularly in the Retention Index system, it is useful to regard organic solute molecules as derived from an alkane through a number of "unit operations," in which the alkane is transformed, either by replacing one or

TABLE 3.12

RETENTION INDICES OF COMPOUNDS IN POLAR STATIONARY LIQUIDS[a]

Substance	Retention index		
	60°C	80°C	100°C
(a) *Dinonyl phthalate (3,3,5-trimethylhexyl phthalate)*			
2-Methylbutane	474	474	475
2-Methylhexane	666	666	667
2-Methylheptane	764	764	765
3-Methylhexane	676	677	678
2,4-Dimethylpentane	628	629	630
2,2,4-Trimethylpentane	687	690	692
b	0.40	0.37	0.33
$r_{n,n+1}$	2.51	2.34	2.14
(b) *Polyethylene Glycol 400*			
1-Octene	853	852	852
Toluene	1083	1099	1107
n-Hexyl chloride	1073	1087	1094
Methyl ethyl ketone	979	992	1004
Ethyl acetate	948	954	963
n-Propyl acetate	1035	1043	1052
n-Butyl acetate	1130	1142	1149
Ethyl *n*-butyrate	1090	1104	1105
Ethyl *n*-valerate	1186	1200	1204
Ethyl *n*-hexanoate	1281	1297	1299
Nitropropane	1277	1298	1308
n-Propyl cyanide	1176	1199	1210
Methanol	1035	1041	1040
Ethanol	1069	1071	1072
n-Propanol	1167	1170	1171
n-Butanol	1270	(1278)	1273
n-Pentanol	1377	1383	1379
Allyl alcohol	1230	1247	1250

[a] See "Gas Chromatography Abstracts" (*38*).

other of its methyl or methylene groups by a different group, or by performing some simple structural change. For example, di-isopropyl ether can be regarded as derived from *n*-heptane by unit operations in which the central methylene of the heptane is replaced by oxygen, and in which each of the two resulting *n*-propyl groups are isomerised to *iso*-propyl groups. Very many organic compounds can be regarded this way, and though such derivations make chemical nonsense, it should be remembered that GC retentions depend on the molecular shape and on molecular groupings and not primarily on the chemical bonds in the solute molecule.

Each unit operation as described above causes either a given shape to be given to the molecule, or the replacement of a given polar group in the molecule, and as described in previous sections, either of these processes causes a characteristic, approximately constant, change in the free energy of solution. Thus, each unit operation causes a characteristic change in the retention index. In principle, therefore, the retention index of a compound can be calculated by relating the compound to an *n*-alkane of carbon number z, and adding to the number $100z$ the increments of retention index appropriate to the unit operations relating it to the alkane. Such an ideal scheme is useful if the number of unit operations is one, as is apparent from Tables 3.11 and 3.12. It may also be useful if the number is two, as will be apparent from Table 3.17, but because of its approximate nature, becomes virtually useless for more than three such operations. The idea of structural increments to a retention index has been used extensively, and its operation is described in further detail below.

(b) Effect of Chain Branching

The effect of branching of non-polar chains of methylene or methyl groups on retentions is of great importance, since much of the application of GC is to isomers of hydrocarbons and to other isomers differing only in the structure of their non-polar part.

In any set of isomeric alkanes of carbon number z, the *n*-alkane invariably has the largest partition coefficient, whatever the stationary liquid. Thus, retention indices of branched alkanes of carbon number z are always less than $100z$. A given simple structural change usually causes a change in the free energy of solution which is remarkably invariant, thus producing a constant percentage change in retention and a constant decrement in the retention index. The value of changes in retention caused by given types of branching is only slightly dependent on temperature, and only slightly dependent on the nature of the stationary liquid so long as the latter is

such that the relative retention of successive homologues in it is not appreciably different from that in a non-polar stationary liquid. Decrements in
retention index in an alkane solvent caused by simple structural changes in
which an alkane of given carbon number is changed into the listed branched
alkane of the same carbon number are listed in Table 3.13 (47); data
for monomethyl derivatives is averaged from measurements for several
carbon numbers; data for dimethyl derivatives from measurements of
octanes alone.

TABLE 3.13

RETENTION INDEX DECREMENTS FOR ALKANE BRANCHING[a]

Structural substitution	Decrement in I[b]
2-Methylalkane	—36
3-Methylalkane	—30
4-Methylalkane	—41
5-Methylalkane	—45
2,2-Dimethylalkane	—80
2,3-Dimethylalkane	—39
2,4-Dimethylalkane	—67
2,5-Dimethylalkane	—71
3,4-Dimethylalkane	—28

[a] See Schomburg (47).
[b] Units difference from n-alkane of same carbon number.

Since the stationary liquid, particularly if relatively nonpolar, has little
effect on the relative retention of branched and straight chain alkanes,
one can regard the alkane solute liquid as yet another stationary liquid.
The retention of the alkane in its own liquid is, of course, measured by the
inverse of vapour pressure of the liquid (see Section 3.2c). Thus, at any
temperature, the retention of alkanes would be expected to be approximately the inverse of their vapour pressures. This relation is studied in Table
3.14, which gives vapour pressures and retention of a variety of simple
alkanes in hexatriacontane relative to pentane. The last column shows "relative activity coefficients" calculated for a solute x from the product $p_x^0 r_{x5}$,
which is set equal to unity for n-pentane. It is apparent that there are no
gross changes in coefficient. Its tendency to rise with increasing solute molecular weight is a consequence of the overall size effect described in Section 3.5.

Close inspection of Table 3.14 shows that there are significant small variations in relative activity coefficient among isomers. For example, *n*-heptane has a fractionally larger vapour pressure than 2,2,4-trimethyl-pentane, but the latter is eluted considerably faster than the former. Similarly, the relative retentions of differently branched alkanes are slightly, but quite significantly, different in solvents containing large proportions of polar groups. There is at present no definite way of classifying this slight tendency of different alkanes to have different relative activity coefficients, but the empirical fact has often proved useful in separations of complex mixtures of alkanes; the mixture is chromatographed first on a

TABLE 3.14

RELATIVE RETENTION VOLUMES AND ACTIVITY COEFFICIENTS[a]

Solute	bp (°C)	vp	r in $C_{36}H_{74}$	γ_{rel} in $C_{36}H_{74}$
n-Pentane	36.07	2620	1.00	1.00
2,2-Dimethylbutane	49.74	1746	1.34	1.03
2,3-Dimethylbutane	57.99	1393	1.83	1.03
2-Methylpentane	60.27	1294	1.83	1.11
3-Methylpentane	63.28	1197	2.12	1.03
n-Hexane	68.32	990	2.42	1.09
2,2-Dimethylpentane	79.20	740	3.00	1.18
2,4-Dimethylpentane	80.50	710	3.08	1.20
2,2,3-Trimethylbutane	80.88	710	3.49	1.06
3,3-Dimethylpentane	86.06	590	4.13	1.08
2,3-Dimethylpentane	89.78	510	4.55	1.15
2-Methylhexane	90.05	510	4.27	1.20
3-Methylhexane	91.85	480	4.68	1.17
3-Ethylpentane	93.48	470	5.18	1.08
n-Heptane	98.43	405	5.73	1.13
2,2,4-Trimethylpentane	99.24	400	5.28	1.24
2,2-Dimethylhexane	106.84	310	6.57	1.29
2,5-Dimethylhexane	109.10	285	7.13	1.29
3,3-Dimethylhexane	111.97	260	8.49	1.19
n-Octane	125.67	165	13.42	1.18

[a] For alkanes in hexatriacontane at 78.5°C; see Desty and Whyman (48).

non-polar stationary liquid, and any non-resolved pairs are chromatographed again on a polar stationary liquid.

The actual retention ratio between first peak and last in a set of isomers
may not be very different on a polar stationary phase from that on a non-
polar one, as, for example, is seen from the results for heptanes given in
Table 12.8. The important thing, however, is that the relative retentions
on polar stationary phases have a good chance of being *different*, even if
not on average *greater*.

(c) *Partition Coefficient and Boiling Point*

One can construct relations between partition coefficient and boiling
point which are approximate, but nevertheless are of practical importance
both for the prediction of the order of magnitude of retentions and for the
prediction of relative retentions. Combination of Eqs. (3.14) and (3.30)
yields:

$$\log_{10} V_g \approx -0.5 - \log M_1 - \log \gamma + 4.8 \frac{T_B}{T} \qquad (3.75)$$

where

$$0.5 \approx 7.7 - \log_{10}(1.702 \times 10^7).$$

Alternatively, for cases where Eq. (3.57) is assumed to account for size
differences, combination of Eqs. (3.52), (3.57), (3.14), and (3.30) gives:

$$\log_{10} V_g \approx -0.9 - \log_{10} M_2 - \frac{\chi}{RT} + 4.8 \frac{T_B}{T}. \qquad (3.76)$$

In considering retention volumes relative to a standard, the constant terms
of Eqs. (3.75) and (3.76) are immaterial. In considering different homologous series of solutes, $\log M_2$ changes only slowly from solute to solute,
while the formation of successive homologues adds approximately constant
increments to T_B, as pointed out in connection with Eq. (3.33). Also, for
different homologous series in the same solvent, each series has an approximately constant, characteristic, value of χ. The result is that plots of
$\log V_g$, or plots of $\log r$ relative to any standard, versus boiling point,
yield approximately straight lines of approximately similar slopes for each
homologous series. Such a plot is shown in Fig. 3.12. It is apparent that the
pattern of parallel straight lines is obtained even for a stationary liquid
containing a large proportion of polar groupings. The same pattern holds
with even greater regularity of solvents of lesser polar component, though,
of course, the order of lines is different (*48*).

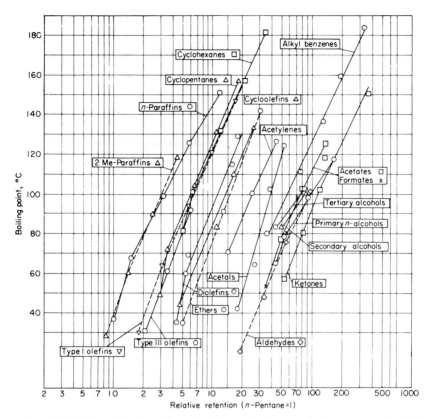

Fig. 3.12. Plots of the logarithm of relative retentions on β, β'-oxydiproprionitrile as a function of boiling point for various homologous series; from Tenney (49).

(d) Isomerism

Polar organic compounds can exhibit many kinds of isomerism, and, in general, different isomers give different retentions. Systematic correlation of change in retention with change in isomeric structure is very limited.

It appears to be general that, if an isomer (2) is capable of forming better *intra*molecular interactions within itself than another isomer (3), then the relative retention $r_{23} = r_2/r_3$ will be smaller in a polar solvent with which the intramolecularly interacting groups could otherwise interact than in a non-polar solvent in which there are no such intermolecular interactions with either isomer. An example of this is to be found in Section 12.7, where it is shown that o-disubstituted benzenes substituted with polar groups have relatively smaller retentions than their m- or p-isomers in the more polar solvents. A simple example is provided by the figures of Table 3.15

TABLE 3.15

RETENTIONS OF SUBSTITUTED PHENYLACETIC ACIDS[a]

4-Methoxyphenylacetic acid	*1.00*
3,4-Dimethylphenylacetic acid	3.13
4-Hydroxyphenylacetic acid	6.75
3-Methoxy-4-hydroxyphenylacetic acid	4.12
4-Hydroxy-3-methoxyphenylacetic acid	5.19

[a] On hydrogen bond donor stationary liquid (*50*).

(*50*), giving retentions of substituted phenylacetic methyl esters (PAME) relative to that of 4-methoxyphenylacetic acid in a polar polyester solvent. The addition of another neighbouring methoxy-group, to form 3,4-dimethoxy-PAME multiplies the retention by a factor of about 3, which is normal. The substitution of a hydroxyl rather than a methoxy produces a 6-fold increase in retention, which indicates the interaction of the hydroxyl group with the ester groups of the solvent. If, however, a hydroxyl group and a methoxy-group are substituted next to one another, the effect is scarcely greater than that of a methoxy alone, and less than that of a hydroxyl alone. The reason is that the methoxy–group and the hydroxyl group partake in strong intramolecular hydrogen bonding, with which the solvent can compete only poorly.

In the case of *n*-alkanes substituted with single polar groups, the retentions seem to be greatest, particularly in polar solvents, when the polar group is in the 1-position, and become less as the polar group moves towards the middle. This can be illustrated, for example, by the hexanols or heptanols. A similar rule appears to apply for series of isomers in which a polar group, e.g., ether or ester group, is flanked by two carbon chains the sum of whose carbon numbers is constant. These relations are displayed in Table 3.16, which gives retention indices of some series of such compounds in a non-polar and in three polar solvents. It can be seen that, in all cases, the retention index is greatest for the compound in which the polar group is at the end. The effect on the retention index of moving the solute polar group towards the middle of the molecule is greater for the polar solvent than for the non-polar solvent. These figures, and the values of $\varDelta I$ are discussed further in Section 3.9.

In general, *cis*- and *trans*-isomers are easily separable on at least one type of stationary phase, since in general, such isomers differ considerably both in shape and in dipole moment. For example, the decalins, *cis*- and

TABLE 3.16

RETENTION INDICES OF STRUCTURAL ISOMERS[a]

	1.I[b]	2.I[c]	3.I[d]	4.I[e]	5.ΔI (2–1)	6.ΔI (3–1)	7.ΔI (4–1)
Alkanols							
1-Pentanol	728	1354	878	1293	626	150	565
2-Pentanol	666	1211	793	1176	545	127	510
3-Pentanol	671	1194	798	1164	523	127	493
1-Heptanol	932	1543	1087	1496	611	155	564
2-Heptanol	868	1420	1003	1376	552	135	508
3-Heptanol	861	1395	995	1376	534	134	515
4-Heptanol	865	1378	993	1363	513	128	498
Esters							
n-Hexyl formate	884	1275	997	1339	391	113	455
n-Pentyl acetate	856	1231	964	1260	375	108	404
n-Butyl propionate	855	1198	951	1227	353	96	372
n-Propyl n-butyrate	844	1179	940	—	335	96	—
Ethers							
n-Propyl methyl ether	497	686	547	708	189	50	221
Di-ethyl ether	473	661	525	680	188	52	207

[a] See McReynolds (63).
[b] Apiezon L, 100°.
[c] Carbowax 400, 100°.
[d] Di-isodecyl phthalate, 120°.
[e] Ethylene glycol adipate, 120°.

trans-halogen disubstituted alkenes, and the simpler geometrical isomers of the alkenes are all easily separable on most columns. There are also, however, individual cases where separation is difficult, e.g., cis- and trans-3-heptene.

The resolution of optical isomers by GLC is difficult but can be achieved by using as solvent a strongly polar, optically active liquid, with which each optically isomeric solute can form slightly different polar interactions. Gil-Av et al. (51, 52) have produced complete separations of aminoacid derivatives in this way, using materials such as trifluoroacetyl-L-isoleucine lauryl ester as solvent, and using capillary columns in order to get sufficient column resolution. Optical isomers can also be resolved on solid stationary phases (53), though the use of GLC seems to be preferable in practice for this difficult problem.

TABLE 3.17

TYPICAL FIGURES TO TEST THE VALIDITY OF THE ADDITIVITY OF GROUP RETENTION
INDICES

(a) Sample retention indices[a]

No.	Solute	Retention index		
		I^b	I^c	I^d
1	1-Pentene	483	402	553
2	n-Propanol	513	662	1132
3	Allyl alcohol	504	672	1203
4	Propyl acetate	653	737	1032
5	Allyl acetate	638	737	1085
6	Butyl methyl ether	594	640	782
7	Ethylene glycol dimethyl ether	607	683	999
8	n-Butanol	620	759	1243
9	1,4-Butane diol	900	1170	2100
10	iso-Pentane	475	475	475
11	2-Butanone	552	648	891
12	3-Methyl-2-butanone	619	708	1008
13	Methylal	476	545	788
14	Methoxymethylal	654	745	1094
15	Dimethoxymethylal	826	937	1372

(b) Differences ΔI

(1) Compounds differing by 1 unsaturation

1–n-C_5	—17	2	53
3–2	—9	10	71
5–4	—16	0	53

(2) Compounds differing by replacement of —O— for —CH_2—

6–n-C_6	—6	40	182
7–6	+13	43	217

(3) Compounds differing by addition of a hydroxyl group

8–n-C_4	220	359	843
9–8	280	411	860

(4) Compounds differing by replacing —CO— for —CH_2—

11–n-C_4	152	248	491
12–10	144	233	533

(5) Compounds differing by addition of a methoxy group

6–n-C_4	194	240	382
14–13	178	200	306
15–14	172	192	378

[a] See McReynolds (63).　　　[c] Dioctyl sebacate.
[b] Apiezon L.　　　[d] Polyethylene Glycol 400 (Carbowax).

(e) *Bifunctional and Polyfunctional Compounds*

By the ideal principle given at the beginning of this section, the retention index of a polyfunctional organic compound of interest may be derived from that of a compound whose retention index is known simply by adding algebraically the sum of the increments of retention index due to each structural change required to convert the known compound to the compound of interest. In practice, however, the effect of structural and other perturbations such as discussed above on the incremental retention indices of structural groups, is sufficient to damage the utility of the ideal principle seriously. Illustrative figures are given in Table 3.17, which gives first the retention indices in three solvents of several compounds, and second, the difference between the indices of pairs of compounds differing by one unit operation, these differences being compared for different pairs. By the principle of additivity, all the differences corresponding to a given unit change should be the same. It can be seen that within the group of solutes chosen, which form a good cross-section of chemical types, there are cases where the rule works within the experimental error of $\approx \pm 5$, e.g., for double bonds or for ketones in Apiezon L or dioctyl sebacate. There are also cases, however, where the rule works badly, e.g., for hydroxyl groups in Apiezon L or ketones in polyethylene glycol 400. The conclusion is that though the additivity rule can often be used as a general guide to retention, it cannot be used indiscriminately. This implies qualification to the use of retention indices for general qualitative identification of unknown compounds; see Section 3.9.

3.8. CHOICE OF STATIONARY PHASE FOR A GIVEN MIXTURE

(a) *Criteria of Choice*

For a given mixture, the aim in choosing a stationary phase is to secure the required resolution of every component from every other component. The resolution of the column is a function of the column performance, the relative retention of the solutes, and the specific retentions, as described in Chapter 5, so that, if the column performance is given, all relative retentions and all specific retentions must be sufficiently large to secure the required separation. Thus, the two conditions to be satisfied in the choice of the stationary phase are:

(1) Adequate relative retentions between all pairs of solutes.
(2) Adequate retention volumes for all solutes except, possibly, one.

It is important to remember the second condition; it is no use choosing a stationary phase in which one component comes through a thousand times as fast as another if they both come through in virtually no time.

In the case of complex mixtures, it is not always possible to secure adequate relative retentions for all components, for there may be so many components that the chromatogram is crowded with components following one after the other, and no amount of care in the selection of the stationary phase can avoid overlaps. For example, even on a column of good performance, one will scarcely see the base line of the chromatogram of a sample of commercial gasoline from first peak to last. In such cases, it is common practice to use two or more columns with different stationary liquids in which overlapping peaks from the first column are fed into a second column designed to resolve them, and any overlapping peaks remaining on the second column are fed into a third if necessary. For complex mixtures, it is often possible to devise a "Group Separation" in which different chemical classes are separated into separate groups of peaks more or less independently of boiling point on columns which give grossly different activity coefficients for each class.

An important practical criterion of choice is that the stationary liquid be non-volatile at the temperature of operation of the column. For this reason, most of the stationary liquids which are used for high-temperature operation are polymers. This has the advantage that they are non-volatile, but has the drawback that the liquids are not precisely characterised, and therefore that partition coefficients are not exactly reproducible. The leakage of stationary liquid from the column is usually termed "bleed."

Another minor aim in the choice of stationary phase where more important factors are not decisive is that the chromatogram should occupy as small a range of retention volumes as possible, so that the first peaks are not too tall and narrow, and the last peaks are not too wide, shallow, and slow. Though this can always be overcome, if required, by temperature programming (Section 7.5), it is not always convenient to do so.

(b) Classification of Stationary Liquids

Though many hundreds of stationary liquids have been used by different workers, it is certain that all the separations that have hitherto been performed by gas chromatography could have been performed by one of a very moderate range of stationary liquids. Attempts to encourage the use of restricted range of solvents, in the hope that by using fewer solvents a large body of retention data for many solutes could be collected, have not been successful. It is therefore useful to try to achieve the lesser object of placing a stationary liquid, whatever its exact structure, into one of relatively few classes in a classification of solvents by their general retention behaviour. We choose here a classification into the following classes, which are:

(*1*) *Paraffinic*

(*2*) *Dilute*:
  (i) Polar
  (ii) Donor
  (iii) Hydroxyl

(*3*) *Concentrated*:
  (i) Polar
  (ii) Donor
  (iii) Hydroxyl

(*4*) *Specific*

Of the many stationary liquids which have been used, comparatively few are used frequently. The most frequently used stationary liquids are listed, together with their formulae and operating conditions, in Table 3.18.

(*1*) *Paraffinic.* Paraffinic stationary liquids are those containing neither polar groups nor particularly polarisable groups such as aromatic nuclei. Thus, they include all paraffins and mixtures of paraffins, and alkyl silicones. Graphitised carbon black, an adsorbent discussed in Chapter 4, is also in this class. The commonest paraffinic stationary liquids are squalane, the Apiezon greases, and some silicone greases. These are probably the most commonly used of all stationary phases.

The characteristics of non-polar stationary liquids are determined by the fact that retention occurs solely through dispersion forces, and thus the polarity of solutes does not influence their retention. The general behaviour of solutes on non-polar solvents can thus be summarised as below.

Alkanes separate according to size, as, for example, in the relation between carbon number and log V_g discussed in Section 3.6c. Among a set of isomers, the linear alkane has the greatest retention, and the general rule among branched alkanes is that the greater the branching, the smaller the retention (Table 3.13). This rule is, however, subject to systematic exceptions; for example, there are two doubly-branched heptanes with

TABLE 3.18

STATIONARY PHASES IN GENERAL USE

Stationary phase	Formula	Maximum operating temperature	Notes
(1) Non-Polar			
Liquid paraffin, *n*-alkanes	$CH_3—(CH_2)_n—CH_3$	Room–100	Commonly used on account of accessibility; maximum temperature depends on grade
Squalane	2,6,10,15,19,23-hexamethyltetracosane	150	A standard stationary phase
Vacuum pump oil, transformer oil		100–150	Commonly used on account of availability
Vacuum greases		300	For example, Apiezon products; commonly used for high-temperature work
Silicone oil		200	Commonly used; also phenylated silicones, e.g., pump oil
Silicone greases		300	Commonly used for high temperatures; may contain fillers which affect their properties

For the silicone structure:

$$\begin{array}{ccc} & Me & Me \\ & | & | \\ —O—Si—O—Si—O— \\ & | & | \\ & Me & Me \end{array}$$

Name	Structure		Description
Carbon		325	Generally similar to paraffins in the elution order it produces; provides specific acceleration of naphthenes; not generally used at high temperatures
(2) Dilute			
Alkyl aryl sulfonate		250	Household detergent is a useful general purpose stationary phase ready for pouring into a column tube
Di-isodecyl phthalate	—COOC$_{10}$H$_{21}$ —COOC$_{10}$H$_{21}$	150	General purposes
Dinonyl phthalate	—COOC$_9$H$_{19}$ —COOC$_9$H$_{19}$	150	Similar to the above
Dibutyl phthalate	—COOC$_4$H$_9$ —COOC$_4$H$_9$	100	Significantly more polar than the two above
Dioctyl sebacate	C$_8$H$_{17}$OCOC$_8$H$_{16}$COOC$_8$H$_{17}$	125	Generally similar to the phthalates, but not aromatic
Benzyl diphenyl	—CH$_2$—	100	
Tricresyl phosphate	(C$_6$H$_4$CH$_3$O)$_3$PO	125	Roughly similar to the above; all isomers are toxic, some very toxic

TABLE 3.18 (*Continued*)

Stationary phase	Formula	Maximum operating temperature	Notes
Dibenzyl ether	$-CH_2-O-CH_2-$ (with cyclohexyl rings)	50	The most polar in this class
Silica gel		300	See Chapter 4
Alumina		300	
(3) *Concentrated*			
Hexamethylphosphoramide	$CH_3-CH-\!-\!-CH-CH_3$ CH_2 CH_2 SO_2	Room	Common general purpose polar liquids not too polar to be used with alkanes; generally similar, but with significant small differences
Dimethylsulfolane	$CN-CH_2-CH_2$ $CN-CH_2-CH_2$ O		
β,β'-Oxydipropionitrile		100	
Various polyesters of dihydroxy compounds and dibasic acids, e.g., polyethylene glycol, adipic acid	$-CH_2-CH_2-O-CO-(CH_2)_4-CO-O-CH_2-CH_2-O-$	250	Extensively used as high-temperature polar stationary phases, especially for fatty acid ester analysis; properties can be altered at will by choosing suitable monomers
2,5-Hexanedione	$CH_3-CO-CH_2-CH_2-CO-CH_3$	Room	

Polyethylene glycols, M.W. 200–20,000	HO—CH$_2$—CH$_2$—[O—CH$_2$—CH$_2$—]$_n$OH	100–250	Extensively used for oxygenated and other polar solutes; the smaller the M.W., the greater the hydroxyl proportion
Dimethylformamide	HCONMe$_2$	Room	Has a rather low boiling point (152°C)
Diglycerol	[C$_3$H$_5$(OH)$_2$]$_2$O	150	Standard stationary phase suitable for analysis of alcohols, etc.
Glycerol	CH$_2$OH · CHOH · CH$_2$OH	100	Appreciably more polar than diglycerol
Erythritol	C(CH$_2$OH)$_4$	150	No retention of methylene groups

(4) Specific

Ethylene glycol–silver nitrate		50	Specific retention of alkenes in addition to ordinary polar properties
Benzyl cyanide–silver nitrate		50	As above, but solvent is less polar; more stable than the above
Perfluorocarbons			Retain other fluorocarbons, and have no retention of alkanes
Metal salts of higher fatty acids			Retain compounds which can form complexes with the metal, e.g., pyridines
Molecular sieves		300	Retain unbranched relative to branched alkyl groups

retentions smaller than the triply-branched 2,2-3-trimethylbutane. The author and co-workers have proposed the idea that log V_g is proportional to molecular surface area measured at a suitable contour around the molecule (*31*), and have illustrated this by showing a linear relation between log V_g and collision cross section in the gas phase, the latter being proportional to molecular surface area. According to this idea, branching decreases retention because it causes the molecule to become more compact, with a smaller surface-to-volume ratio.

Polar solutes also separate according to size, since their polarity is irrelevant. With polar molecules not containing halogen atoms, the size is very roughly proportional to molecular weight, so that for molecules of roughly the same shape, log V_g is proportional to molecular weight. Such a relation has been illustrated by the author (*30*). It is useful for prediction of orders of magnitude of retentions but cannot be considered as quantitative.

Though retentions in non-polar solvents are independent of solute polarity, the boiling points of pure liquid solutes are increased as a result of polar-polar interactions. Thus, there is no relation between the boiling points of polar solutes and their retentions. In general, for a mixture of a polar solute and a non-polar solute or less polar solute of about the same boiling point, the less polar substance will have the greater retention, since it necessarily has a larger molecule than the polar substance in order to have a comparable vapour pressure. As an example, the relative retention of methanol (bp 66) and *n*-hexane (bp 68°C) in squalane is about 7, the methanol being eluted first.

Though the differences between different alkane solvents are small, they are quite significant. For example, in comparing squalane and *n*-hexadecane, it is found that the retentions of solutes of large density, e.g., those containing halogen atoms, relative to alkane solutes, are greater in squalane than in *n*-hexadecane (*26*). Thus, the retention indices of halogenates are greater in squalane. Such changes in relative retentions produced by changing from one non-polar solvent to another may amount to as much as 20% and thus are useful in avoiding overlaps, but they do not appear to have been studied systematically.

(*2*) *Dilute.* These are solvents in which the majority of the molar volume is occupied by non-polar groups, but in which there are also some polar groupings. They include many organic esters, alkanols and ethers. Their retention characteristics are determined by the fact that they have polar groups with which polar solutes can interact, but not so many as to make a strongly cross-linked solvent lattice, the internal pressure of which is such as to exclude non-polar molecules.

Alkanes separate in dilute polar solvents in very much the same manner as in non-polar solvents, except that specific retentions are somewhat smaller, as described in Section 3.6d.

The retention of *polar* solutes is determined in part by size, as in a non-polar solvent, but, in addition, there is a term in $\log V_g$ contributed by the specific interaction between solute and solvent polar group. With this, one can distinguish usefully three classes of solvent polar groups:

(*i*) Those with purely polar groups, e.g., nitro-groups or nitriles. These provide a large extra retention for polar solutes but do not retain selectively compounds with hydroxyl groups, or those which are hydrogen bond donors.

(*ii*) Those with hydroxyl groups, which provide a very large extra retention for solutes with hydroxyl groups, and very considerable extra retention for solutes which are hydrogen bond donors.

(*iii*) Those with groups which can act as hydrogen bond donors, e.g., ether groups. These have a moderate polarity and thus confer moderate extra retention on polar solutes, but interact very strongly with solutes which have hydrogens capable of forming hydrogen bonds.

The practical distinction between these three groups is best illustrated by the figures of Table 3.19. Here, four solutes have been chosen which all have very similar retentions on a non–polar stationary liquid. In the purely polar solvent, palmitonitrile, all are separated, with the purely polar solute having by far the largest retention. In the hydroxyl solvent, all are sepa-

TABLE 3.19

SPECIFIC RETENTION VOLUMES IN FOUR DIFFERENT SOLVENTS OF FOUR SOLUTES WHICH OVERLAP ON A NON-POLAR SOLVENT

	I[a]	II[b]	III[c]	IV[d]
1-Pentene	83.2	62.9	32.0	85.5
Diethyl ether	89.5	85.7	45.7	88.3
Ethyl cyanide	87.2	521	99.5	170
tert-Butanol	92	390	320	200

[a] *n*-Hexadecane.
[b] Palmitonitrile.
[c] *n*-Hexadecanol.
[d] Methoxyhexadecane.

rated, with the alkanol solute having three times the retention of its neighbour, which is the polar solute. In the donor solvent, the polarity is insufficient to separate the weakly polar alkene and ether, but provides considerable extra retention for the polar solute, and even more for the alkanol solute. The difference between the two, however, is not so extreme as with the hydroxyl solvent.

(*3*) *Concentrated.* These are solvents in which a large proportion of the molar volume is occupied by polar groups, which thus interact strongly. Such solvents include many polymeric stationary liquids, e.g., the polyethylene glycols, and many polyesters. The behaviour of polyesters depends on the length of the methylene chains of the diacids and dialcohols forming their monomers. When these are long, e.g., butylene glycol sebacates, they approximate to "dilute" solvents. When they are short, e.g., ethylene glycol adipate, they are more "concentrated."

Alkanes and other hydrocarbons have very small retentions in these solvents, for the reason described in Section 3.6d. Thus, they are generally unsuitable for hydrocarbon analysis, unless it is to separate alkanes as a group from other solutes which are polar. In these solvents, the relative retention of successive homologues is less than the value which pertains to non-polar solvents.

Polar solutes have considerable retentions in these solvents, and it is for these that they are principally used. In general, however, the values of V_g even for the most polar or strongly hydrogen-bonding solutes are less than in many solvents with more dilute polar groups. For example, V_g for *n*-propanol is greater in 1-dodecanol than in polyethylene glycol.

Because rates of diffusion tend to be smaller in concentrated polar solvents, column efficiencies tend to be poorer than otherwise.

(*4*) *Specific Solvents.* In certain cases, the solvent can consist of, or contain, a chemical reagent which can react specifically with a particular class of solute in a specifically chemical manner, unlike any of the intermolecular interactions considered hitherto. Thus, if silver nitrate is dissolved in a stationary liquid, alkenes and dienes have anomalously large partition coefficients due to the formation of complexes between the silver and the double bond (*54*). The effect is more marked for 1-alkenes than for others. Other examples of this kind of specific behaviour are the large activity coefficients of *o*-alkyldiphenyls on aromatic stationary phases through steric hindrance (*55*); the separation of pyridines on glycerol (*56*); or the separation of amines and other compounds on columns using metal salts of higher fatty acids as stationary phase (57). Such specific chemical effects are obviously very useful in practice, but are not amenable to a general theoretical treatment.

(c) The Ordering of Stationary Liquids

The dividing lines between different classes in any classification of stationary liquids are inevitably imprecise, and thus several authors (30, 58–61) have attempted instead to arrange stationary liquids in some sort of order based on some particular trend in retention behaviour. Rohrschneider (61) used the relative retention of alkenes and their corresponding alkanes as a criterion by which to classify stationary liquids. In a non-polar stationary liquid, alkenes have the smallest retention relative to their alkanes, and in other liquids, their relative retention is greater. A list of stationary liquids (Table 3.20) in order of the alkene/alkane relative retention was thus produced, with non-polar liquids at one end, and the concentrated polar liquids at the other.

TABLE 3.20

STATIONARY LIQUIDS ARRANGED IN ORDER OF RELATIVE RETENTION OF BUTADIENE AND BUTANE[a]

Stationary liquid	Relative retention
Squalane	0.83
Silicone Oil	0.95
1-Chloro-octadecane	1.07
Ethoxy lauryl alcohol	1.68
Dibutyl formamide	1.93
Dibenzyl ether	1.97
n-β-Hydroxypropylmorpholine	2.22
1,2-Butylene glycol sulphite	2.30
Epoxypropylmorpholine	2.55
Diethylformamide	2.81
Benzyl cyanide	2.92
Acetylacetone	3.48
Polyethylene Glycol 600	3.85
Dimethylformamide	4.01
Propylene glycol carbonate	4.25
n-(Methylacetyl)-β-aminopropionitrile	4.59
Oxydipropionitrile	5.93

[a] See Rohrschneider (61).

The value of a given ordered list of stationary liquids depends solely on the invariance of the order produced, since if the order applies only to the criterion by which the order was produced, it has no relevance in predicting retention patterns for other classes of solutes. In practice, the order in terms of alkene/alkane retention has a fair measure of generality. For example, Rohrschneider (58, 59) showed that the order produced by the alkene/alkane criterion was the same as that produced by arranging stationary phases according to the specific retention of an alkane in them (30). Thus, the order of Table 3.20 is generally similar to that of Table 3.9. The generality of any order based on a single criterion is, however, very limited, as the author has illustrated (30), and is obvious, for example, from Fig. 3.10.

In order to enlarge the scope of empirical methods of describing the retention behaviour of a solvent in terms of numerical parameters, Rohrschneider has considered the use of more than one criterion. Taking the viewpoint that the difference in retention of a solute between a non-polar liquid and a polar solvent is due to specific forces each of which contribute independently to the free energy of solution in the polar solvent, he has assumed that the difference, ΔI, in retention index of a solute between its value in a given polar solvent and a non-polar one is given by:

$$\Delta I = \sum_i a_i x_i, \qquad (3.77)$$

where a is a number characteristic of the solute, and x is characteristic of the solvent. There are thus several terms of the type ax, each of which represents roughly the effect of a particular type of intermolecular force. The number of such terms may be two or three (58, 59), or as many as five (62). The parameters a, for given solute types, and x, for given solvents, are obtained empirically from a limited number of retention measurements, and, using these values, Rohrschneider finds that retention indices of other solutes in the given solvents can be predicted to within about 10 RI units. Clearly, the more terms that are taken in Eq. (3.77), the better can be the prediction.

When solvents have been arranged according to a single criterion, i.e., by using Eq. (3.77) with one term only, the position assumed by a given solvent has often been referred to as its "Polarity." The fact that better fits between Eq. (3.77) and practice can be obtained by taking more than one term, and also the more physically-based discussion of Section 3.6, makes it clear that there can never be any single numerical parameter called "Polarity" with a precise meaning.

3.9. QUALITATIVE ANALYSIS

The retention of a solute, being characteristic of its chemical nature, can in principle be used for its qualitative identification. Since, however, a single retention value can only be identified to within about $\pm 2\%$, which usually is equivalent to 2 or 3 retention index units, the number of individual compounds that can be distinguished by a single measurement is rather small. Nevertheless, cases in which a compound has been identified from within a limited range of possibilities are commonplace in the literature.

The scope of qualitative identification by retention measurements can be increased by chromatographing a mixture of interest, usually with alkane standards incorporated, on two or more columns. The retentions of each component on each column are measured; thus, each compound is characterised by two or more numbers, and not merely one. The normal practice is to choose the columns so that one is non-polar and the other or others are polar. On the polar columns, the retentions relative to alkanes of solutes with polar groupings will be greater than the similar relative retentions on the non-polar column, and the extra retention engendered by the polar/

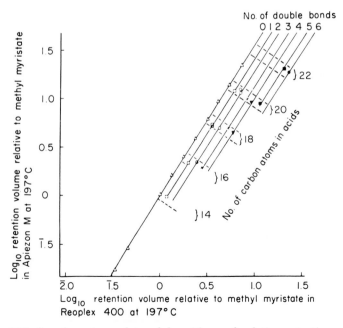

Fig. 3.13. Complementary plots of logarithms of relative retentions on two different stationary liquids for fatty acid esters; from James (64).

polar interactions can be correlated with values previously determined for various simple polar groups.

The value of the use of retentions or relative retentions in each of two solvents can be displayed by plots in which the logarithms of the retentions or relative retentions on one solvent are plotted against those on the other. In such a case, since the addition of a methylene group to a solute adds a constant increment to the logarithms, members of a homologous series will lie on a straight line. Because different functional groups have different free energies of interaction in each of the solvents, different homologous series will lie on different straight lines. Examples of plots of this type are shown in Figs. 3.13 and 3.14. In Fig. 3.13, the relative retentions of fatty

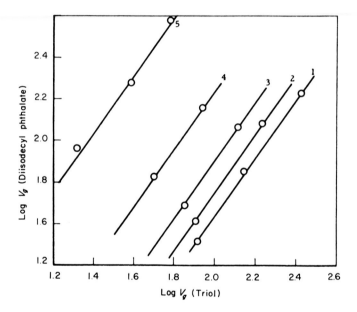

FIG. 3.14. Comparison of logarithms of retention volumes of solutes in different stationary liquids; points due to solutes in a given homologous series lie on straight lines; from Pierotti *et al.* (*4*). 1, 1-alkanols; 2, *sec*-alkanols; 3, *tert*-alkanols; 4, alkanones; 5, *n*-alkanes.

acid esters in Apiezon L are plotted against those in a polyester solvent, Reoplex 400. The presence of a double bond in the fatty acid ester produces an increment in the logarithm of its retention in the polar solvent, thus causing homologues with a single double bond to be displaced to the right of those for the saturated esters. Further double bonds provide further increments, thus producing a set of parallel straight lines. Measurement of the retention of an unknown ester in each solvent enables one to place on the graph a characteristic point. The number of double bonds is then given by the particular line on which the point lies, and the homologue number is given by its position on the line. A similar example, using specific retention volumes, is given in Fig. 3.14.

In plots such as those of Fig. 3.13 or 3.14, the lines have a slope of unity if the relative retention of successive alkanes is the same in both solvents; this is normally so for solvents of not too great a proportion of polar groups, (see Table 3.9). If the relative retention of successive homologues is less in one solvent than in the other, the lines have a slope different from unity being more inclined to parallelism with the axis of the solvent in which the relative retentions of successive homologues are greatest.

The above technique, in which functional groups in solutes are identified from the increments to the free energy of solution produced as a result of their interaction with different kinds of solvents, can also be used through study of the retention index. The retention index of a polar substance is always greater in a polar solvent than in a non-polar one, and the difference, ΔI, is approximately characteristic of the solute. The values of I and of ΔI can thus be used to characterise a compound; a value of ΔI gives the same information as a particular homologue line of Figs. 3.13 and 3.14, while the actual value of I gives the position on the line, and helps define the homologue number when the homologous series has been identified. The use of ΔI values becomes greater if a third or fourth solvent is used, since these provide further values of ΔI, giving either a greater degree of certainty in identification, or identification from within a larger range of possibilities. The use of values of ΔI can be illustrated using the figures given in Table 3.16. It is seen from the last three columns of the Table that alcohols, esters, and ethers have approximately the characteristic values of ΔI that are tabulated in Table 3.21.

TABLE 3.21

VALUES OF ΔI SUMMARISED FROM TABLE 3.16[a]

	$\Delta I(2-1)$	$\Delta I(3-1)$	$\Delta I(4-1)$
Alcohols	540	130	520
Esters	360	100	410
Ethers	190	50	210

[a] $\pm \approx 20$ units.

In most practice, the values of ΔI which may be used to characterise a particular polar group are by no means independent of structure, and such values can only be used with some degree of certainty because variations between values of ΔI for different groups are usually greater than the variations due to the position of the group in the molecule. The "fine structure" of the small but significant differences in ΔI resulting from structural changes have recently been studied systematically by Walraven (65) for methyl esters of fatty acids, using data from Schomburg (66) and others. As an example, he has studied ΔI for the series of carbomethoxy-alkanes in which the carbomethoxy group is located on each position of the alkane, varying between the 1-position and the central position. Values of ΔI decrease some 10–20% of their total value as the carbomethoxy group is moved inwards. This can be seen from the figures of Table 3.16, of which those in Table 3.21 are averages. More clearly, however, it can be seen from a plot given by Walraven (Fig. 3.15), which is similar in type to those of Fig. 3.13 or 3.14, but in which lines have been drawn connecting the points corresponding to the series of positional isomers. It is seen that the positional isomers give points which lie on straight lines. The pattern of lines is one in which the variation of ΔI with homologue number is shown by straight

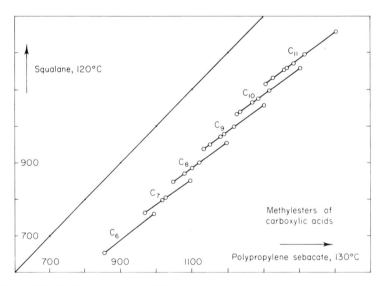

FIG. 3.15. To illustrate fine variation of relative retentions in two stationary liquids as a function of detailed solute structure. Instead of points for all isomers of a given carbon number lying on the same straight line as those of successive homologues, points for positional isomers occupy lines of slightly different slope, giving an "imbricated" pattern; from Walraven (65).

lines (not in the diagram) which connect the points due to successive homologues of similar structure. The large–scale value of ΔI is shown by the
distance of the whole pattern from the line of unit slope through the origin,
and the small-scale variation of ΔI with structure within each homologue
number is shown by the set of parallel straight lines. Such plots have been
called (65, 67) "imbricated," using a word which means "in the conformation of roofing tiles"; the relevance is obvious. These plots can be used in
many instances to display a small scale fine structure on the pattern of
retention values; the large-scale pattern is produced by the polar groups
of the molecule and the fine structure resulting from differences due to the
differences in conformation of different isomers.

In general, the use of GC for qualitative identification is of restricted
scope; first, because considerable care is required to identify retentions,
either as indices, relative retentions, or specific retentions, with sufficient
accuracy; second, because the identification is rarely unambiguous; and
third, because other methods, e.g., spectroscopic, are more specific. The
possibility of identification by GC retentions remains, however, and there
are several cases, e.g., where samples are too small for spectroscopic examination, where the GC method has been used successfully (e.g., 68, 69).

3.10. Effect of Temperature on Partition Coefficients

(a) Thermodynamic Equations

The effect of temperature on V_g is best studied through Eq. (3.14).
On the RHS of this, γ and p_2^0 are temperature-dependent, their temperature
dependence being given by Eqs. (3.54) and (3.24), respectively. By taking
logarithms of both sides of Eq. (3.14) and subsequent substitution, the
variation of V_g with temperature is thus shown to be:

$$\frac{d \ln V_g}{dT} = \frac{1}{RT^2} (-\Delta H_v + h_2^E). \qquad (3.78)$$

One can therefore write:

$$\frac{d \ln V_g}{dT} = \frac{-\Delta H_s}{RT^2}, \qquad (3.79)$$

where:

$$\Delta H_s = \Delta H_v - h_2^E. \qquad (3.80)$$

As written here, both ΔH_v and ΔH_s are positive; thus, ΔH_v is the heat of *vaporisation*, and not the heat of *condensation*, which would be $-\Delta H_v$. The quantity ΔH_s may thus be called the *heat of evaporation* of the dilute solute from the solution. Its corresponding negative may be called the *heat of solution*. Here, we discuss the positive heats.

By using Eq. (3.13) in place of Eq. (3.14), an equation for the temperature dependence of β is obtained:

$$\frac{d \ln \beta}{dT} = \frac{1}{RT^2} (-\Delta H_s + RT). \tag{3.81}$$

Also, it is possible to substitute Eq. (3.1) into Eq. (3.81) in order to obtain the temperature variation of α. The result involves the temperature coefficient of density, which is the negative of the coefficient of expansion of the stationary liquid; letting this be η, the result is:

$$\frac{d \ln \alpha}{dT} = \frac{1}{RT^2} (-\Delta H_s + RT - RT^2\eta). \tag{3.82}$$

All of Eqs. (3.79), (3.81), and (3.82) have been used by various workers (*7, 26, 70*), and sometimes the quantities in brackets on the RHS of Eqs. (3.81) and (3.82) have been called "heats of solution." Academic thermodynamics seems to provide no guide as to usage. All three of the coefficients of $1/RT^2$ in Eqs. (3.79), (3.81), and (3.82) are slightly dependent on temperature. The term RT in (3.81) accounts for the effect on the heat of evaporation of considering the change in volume of the gas phase with temperature, and the term $RT^2\eta$ in Eq. (3.82) similarly accounts for the change in volume of the stationary phase. However, neither of these terms completely accounts for the temperature dependence of the heat of evaporation. For practical purposes in GC, therefore, the term "heat of evaporation" is best given to ΔH_s as defined by Eq. (3.79), since the relation between ΔH_s and ΔH_v is easily studied, and also V_g is the quantity most easily accessible in GC.

(*b*) *Variation of V_g with Temperature*

Rearrangement of Eq. (3.79) yields:

$$\frac{d \ln V_g}{d(1/T)} = \frac{\Delta H_s}{R}, \tag{3.83}$$

so that a plot of $\ln V_g$ against $1/T$ should yield a line of slope $\Delta H_s/R$. Because of the relative constancy of ΔH_s with temperature, such a line is normally substantially straight over temperature ranges of some tens of degrees, and curvature is apparent only over very wide temperature ranges. An example of such a plot is shown in Fig. 3.16 (70).

From the slopes of lines such as are shown in Fig. 3.16, heats of evaporation can be obtained. Table 3.22 shows some typical values (26). In general, heats of evaporation exhibit many of the same regularities as do the free energies. Thus, heats of evaporation increase with increasing molecular size, and, as with free energies, addition of successive similar structural units to the solute molecule produces constant increments in ΔH_s.

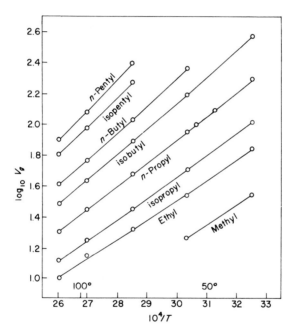

Fig. 3.16. Typical plot of log V_g against inverse temperature. Lines are for alkanols in silicone oil; from Littlewood et al. (70).

The general range of heats of evaporation in GC is from about 6 to about 15 kcal/mole, and, on the whole, the compounds with smaller heats of evaporation will be chromatographed at comparatively low temperatures. Using these figures in Eq. (3.81), it is found that for every one degree (°C) change in column temperature, the value of V_g changes on the order of 3%. Thus, for accurate measurements of partition coefficients, column temperatures are required to be controlled within close limits, e.g., at least ±0.1°C.

TABLE 3.22

VALUES OF ΔH_v, ΔH_s, AND h_2^E FOR VARIOUS SOLUTES

Solute	ΔH_s [a]	ΔH_v	h_2^E [b]
n-Pentane	6.42	6.36	−0.06
n-Hexane	7.43	7.44	+0.01
n-Heptane	8.38	8.48	+0.10
Carbon tetrachloride	7.34	7.38	+0.04
Di-n-propyl ether	7.98	8.20	+0.22
Ethyl iodide	6.6	7.38	+0.8
Ethyl formate	5.72	7.42	+1.70
Ethyl acetate	6.75	8.22	+1.47
Methyl ethyl ketone	6.53	8.40	+1.87
Ethanol	6.22	9.8	+3.6
n-Propanol	6.66	11.1	+4.4
n-Butanol	6.83	(11.1)	(+4.3)

[a] For solutes in a non-polar solvent (n-hexadecane).
[b] Values are given in kilocalories per mole.

(c) Variation of Relative Retentions with Temperature

The temperature variation of the relative retention of two solutes is easily studied by reference to plots of V_g against $1/T$ such as are shown in Fig. 3.16, since the distance apart of any two lines gives the logarithm of the relative retention. In the common case that both heats of evaporation and free energies of evaporation increase with molecular complexity, the lines higher up the graphs such as Fig. 3.16 have steeper slopes, so that with many solutes, the pattern of lines is slightly fan shaped. This is just visible in the figure. The consequence of this is that as a general rule, *the lower the temperature, the larger the relative retention.* For very many substances and very many systems, this rule holds, and is of great practical importance. An incomplete separation at one temperature can often be improved at a lower temperature. Of particular general importance is the relative retention of successive alkanes, the logarithm of which forms the denominator of the expression for the Retention Index, and is frequently designated b. As pointed out in Section 3.6d, b changes relatively little for

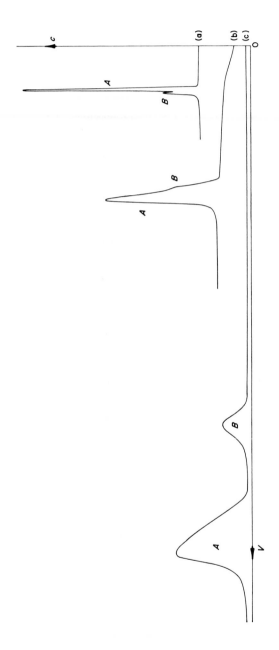

Fig. 3.17. Chromatograms of 2 parts of *n*-propanol (*A*) to 1 part of 3-methyl- hexane (*B*) at (a) 100°C, (b) 50°C, (c) 22°C, on didecyl phthalate.

different stationary liquids other than those which have many cross-linked polar interactions and also applies to homologous series other than alkanes. The values of b as a function of temperature given in Table 3.11 are, therefore, applicable to the majority of common stationary liquids.

When studied in detail, it is found that the general rule that ΔH_s increases with retention is inexact and subject to specific deviations. There are very many cases where neighbouring lines of $\log V_g$ against $1/T$ for different solutes of close retentions have different slopes and thus inevitably cross at some given temperature. The practical consequence of this is illustrated in Fig. 3.17, which shows a mixture of an alkane and an alkanol chromatographed at three different temperatures, with consequent inversion in the order of elution.

The detailed variations in the proportionality of ΔH and ΔG have been studied by Littlewood (26), Willmott (71), and Walraven (65). The detailed relation between retention and its temperature variations can be displayed by plotting the entropy of evaporation, calculated by the equation:

$$\Delta S = \frac{\Delta H - \Delta G}{T}, \tag{3.84}$$

against the free energy of evaporation, ΔG, calculated from V_g at a given temperature by the equation:

$$\Delta G = RT \ln V_g. \tag{3.85}$$

At a given temperature, each solute gives a point, as is illustrated by the example in Fig. 3.18. The general trend is for ΔG, ΔH, and ΔS to be roughly proportional to one another, all increasing with increase in retention. Thus, the general trend on the figure is for points to lie on a line crossing the figure from bottom left to upper right. Such a line is given by homologous series, and especially by the n-alkanes, which are used as reference. Significant variations in the proportionality of ΔH and ΔG are shown by points being off the line.

In general, the entropies of solution for solutes which interact with the solvent by creating hydrogen bonds are anomalously large, as is shown in the figure for the alkanol solutes. The result is, therefore, that these have anomalously large values of ΔH for a given retention, and the variation of their retention with temperature is abnormally high. This is illustrated by Fig. 3.17, which shows that as the temperature is raised, it is the alkanol which overtakes the alkane, and not vice-versa.

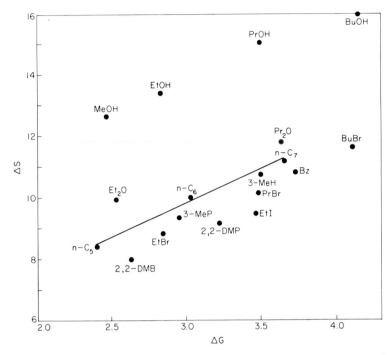

FIG. 3.18. Entropy of solution against free energy of solution for various solutes in palmitonitrile (26). ΔG in kcal/mole; ΔS in cal/mole/°K. DMB is dimethyl butane; DMP is dimethyl pentane; MeH is methyl hexane; MeP is methyl pentane.

The major characteristic of solutes other than those which form hydrogen bonds is that the greater the degree of branching of the solute molecule, the smaller the entropy, and therefore, the smaller the heat of solution in relation to the free energy. Thus, the greater the density or the greater the branching, the smaller the variation in retention with temperature. As an example, one may consider the relative retention of the linear n-heptane and the branched 2,2,4-trimethyl pentane (Section 3.7b, Table 3.14). At fairly low temperatures, these separate easily, with the branched octane appearing first. As the temperature rises, however, the retention of the n-heptane decreases faster than that of the 2,2,4-trimethyl pentane, so that their separation becomes less, till at or near 100°C they fail to separate at all. The detailed relation between ΔH and ΔG shown by the plot of Fig. 3.18 can also be demonstrated as the formation of imbricated lines (Section 3.9), when retentions of variously branched alkanes at one temperature are plotted against those at another temperature. This method has been used by Walraven, again to show that, in general, the variation of the retention of alkanes with temperature decreases, the greater the branching.

It should be noted particularly that the relation between retention and its temperature variation does not necessarily involve the polarity of the solute.

The retention indices of solutes whose points on figures such as Fig. 3.18 are above the line for alkanes *decrease* with increase in temperature, and those of solutes whose points lie below the line *increase* with increase in temperature.

(d) Variation of Activity Coefficient with Temperature

The variation of γ with temperature is described by Eq. (3.54), which shows it to be characterised by the value of $h_2{}^E$. Values of this quantity, calculated from the difference of values of ΔH_s determined chromatographically and values of ΔH_v obtained from vapour pressure data (Section 3.3), are given in Table 3.22.

For alkanes in an alkane solvent, it is seen that $h_2{}^E$ is within experimental error of zero, thus confirming the thesis of Section 3.5 that such solutions are virtually athermal. Thus, the activity coefficients discussed in detail in Section 3.5 are virtually independent of temperature. For polar solutes in an alkane solvent, ΔH_v is invariably greater than ΔH_s, with the results that $h_2{}^E$ is positive, and activity coefficients decline with increase in temperature. In general, there is a rough proportionality between $g_2{}^E$ [Eq. (3.53)] and $h_2{}^E$, with the result that when $h_2{}^E$ is positive, the corresponding activity coefficient is large. Thus, there is a general rule that large activity coefficients become less large the higher the temperature. In general, the use of conditions involving large activity coefficients is undesirable in GC, since they lead to non-linearity of isotherms at very small concentrations, and for this reason, and because a large activity coefficient implies relative insolubility of the solute in the solvent, very small samples must be used. The capacity of a given column for a solute interacting with a large activity coefficient can therefore often be improved by raising the temperature of operation.

In the case of solutes dissolving in a non-polar solvent, as for the figures of Table 3.22, the value of $h_2{}^E$ is closely related to the magnitude of the heat of specific interactions in the liquid solute. Thus, the values for the alkanols are virtually equal to the heat of hydrogen bonding in the liquid alkanols.

In the case of polar solvents, alkanes or weakly polar solutes dissolve with large activity coefficients, but also give positive values of h_2^E. The general rule, therefore, that increase in temperature leads to decline in activity coefficients applies both ways; i.e., in all cases where solute and solvent are of widely different chemical natures.

REFERENCES

1. Guggenheim, E. A., "Thermodynamics," 3rd ed., p. 246. North-Holland Publ., Amsterdam, 1957.
2. Prigogine, I., "The Molecular Theory of Solutions," North Holland Publ., 1957.
3. Prigogine, I., and Defay, R., "Chemical Thermodynamics" (D. H. Everett, transl.). Longmans, Green, New York, 1954.
4. Pierotti, G. J., Deal, C. H., Derr, E. L., and Porter, P. E., *J. Am. Chem. Soc.* **78**, 2989 (1956).
5. Glasstone, S., "Textbook of Physical Chemistry," 2nd ed., p. 702. Macmillan, New York, 1943.
6. Hildebrand, J., and Scott, R. L., "Solubility of Non-Electrolytes," 3rd ed., p. 22, Am. Chem. Soc. Monograph No. 17. Van Nostrand (Reinhold). Princeton, New Jersey, 1950.
7. Porter, P. E., Deal, C. H., and Stross, F. H., *J. Am. Chem. Soc.* **78**, 2999 (1956).
8. Kwantes, A., and Rijnders, G. W. A., *in* "Gas Chromatography 1958," Proceedings of the Second Symposium, Amsterdam, May, 1956 (D. H. Desty, ed.), p. 125. Academic Press, New York, 1958.
9. Windsor, M. L., and Young, C. L., *J. Chromatog.* **27**, 355 (1967).
10. Cruickshank, A. J. B., Windsor, M. L., and Young, C. L., *Proc. Roy. Soc. (London)* **A295**, 271 (1966).
11. Desty, D. H., Goldup, A., Luckhurst, G. H., and Swanton, W. T., "Gas Chromatography 1962," Proceedings of the 4th International Symposium (M. van Swaay, ed.), p. 67. Butterworth, London, 1963.
12. Cruickshank, A. J. B., Gainey, B. W., and Young, C. L., "Gas Chromatography 1968," Proceedings of the 7th International Symposium (C. L. A. Harbourn, ed.). Institute of Petroleum, 1969.
13. Hirschfelder, J. O., Curtiss, C. F., and Bird, R. B., "Molecular Theory of Gases and Liquids," 2nd ed. Wiley, New York, 1964.
14. Cruickshank, A. J. B., Windsor, M. L., and Young, C. L., *Proc. Roy. Soc. (London)* **A295**, 259 (1966).
15. Everett, D. H., *Trans. Faraday Soc.* **61**, 1637 (1965).
16. Luckhurst, G. R., *J. Chromatog.* **16**, 543 (1964).
17. Hala, E., Pick, J., Fried, V., and Vilim, O., "Vapour-Liquid Equilibrium." Pergamon Press, New York, 1960.
18. Herington, E. F. G., *in* "Vapour Phase Chromatography," Proceedings of the First Symposium, London, May, 1956 (D. H. Desty, ed.), p. 7. Academic Press, New York, 1957.
19. Guggenheim, E. A., "Mixtures." Oxford Univ. Press, London and New York, 1952.
20. Flory, P. J., Orwoll, R. A., and Vrij, A., *J. Am. Chem. Soc.* **86**, 3507 (1964).
21. Flory, P. J., Orwoll, R. A., and Vrij, A., *J. Am. Chem. Soc.* **86**, 3515 (1964).

22. Bellemans, A., *Advan. Chem. Phys.* **2**, Chapter 3 (1967).
23. Miller, A. R., *Proc. Cambridge Phil. Soc.* **39**, 54 (1943).
24. Guggenheim, E. A., *Proc. Roy. Soc. (London)* **A183**, 203 (1944).
25. Flory, P., *J. Chem. Phys.* **10**, 51 (1942).
26. Littlewood, A. B., *Anal. Chem.* **36**, 1441 (1964).
27. Pease, E. C., and Thorburn, S., *J. Chromatog.* **50**, 344 (1967).
28. Martire, D., "Gas Chromatography 1966," Proceedings of the Sixth International Symposium (A. B. Littlewood, ed.), p. 21. Institute of Petroleum, 1967.
29. Pitzer, K. S., *J. Am. Chem. Soc.* **77**, 3427 (1955).
30. Littlewood, A. B., *J. Gas Chromatog.* **1**, 16 (1963).
31. Dyson, N., and Littlewood, A. B., *Trans. Faraday Soc.*, **63**, 1895 (1967).
32. Pimental, G. C., and McClellan, A. L., "The Hydrogen Bond." Freeman, San Francisco, California, 1960.
33. Pople, J. A., *Discussions Faraday Soc.* **15**, 35 (1960).
34. Littlewood, A. B., and Willmott, F. W., *J. Gas Chromatog.* **5**, 543 (1967).
35. Littlewood, A. B., and Willmott, F. W., *Anal. Chem.* **38**, 1031 (1966); Dyson, N., Thesis, Newcastle upon Tyne, 1968.
36. Littlewood, A. B., and Willmott, F. W., *Anal. Chem.* **38**, 1076 (1966).
37. Kovats, E., and Weisz, P. B., *Ber. Bunsenges. Phys. Chem.* **69**, 812 (1965).
38. Data Sub-Committee of the Gas Chromatography Discussion Group *in* "Gas Chromatography Abstracts, 1966," p. 233. Institute of Petroleum, London, 1967.
39. Guiochon, G., *Anal. Chem.* **36**, 1672 (1964).
40. Evans, M. B., *J. Chromatog.* **12**, 2 (1963).
41. Evans, M. B., and Smith, J. F., *J. Chromatog.* **8**, 541 (1962).
42. Evans, M. B., and Smith, J. F., *J. Chromatog.* **8**, 303 (1962).
43. Kovats, E., *Advan. Chromatog.* **1**, 229 (1965).
44. Cremer, E., and Gruber, H. L., *J. Chromatog.* **3**, 8 (1965).
45. van den Dool, H., and Kratz, P. D., *J. Chromatog.* **11**, 463 (1963).
46. Wehrli, A., *Promotionsarbeit (Zurich)* No. 3032 (1961).
47. Schomburg, G., *J. Chromatog.* **23**, 1 (1966).
48. Desty, D. H., and Whyman, B. H. F., *Anal. Chem.* **29**, 320 (1957).
49. Tenney, H. M., *Anal. Chem.* **30**, 2 (1958).
50. Van den Heuvel, W. J. A., *J. Chromatog.* **25**, 29 (1966).
51. Gil-Av, E., Feibush, B., and Charles-Sigler, R., "Gas Chromatography 1966," Proceedings of the 6th International Symposium (A. B. Littlewood, ed.), p. 227. Institute of Petroleum, 1967.
52. Feibush, B., and Gil-Av., E., *J. Chromatog.* **5**, 257 (1967).
53. Klemm, L. H., and Reed, D., *J. Chromatog.* **3**, 364 (1960).
54. Bradford, B. W., Harvey, D., and Chalkley, D. E., *J. Inst. Petrol.* **41**, 80 (1955).
55. Beaven, G. H., James, A. T., and Johnson, E. A., *Nature* **179**, 490 (1957).
56. Anderson, J. R. A., *J. Am. Chem. Soc.* **78**, 5692 (1956).
57. Barber, D. W., Phillips, C. S. G., Tusa, G. F., and Verdin, A., *J. Chem. Soc.* p. 18 (1959).
58. Rohrschneider, L., *J. Chromatog.* **17**, 1 (1965).
59. Rohrschneider, L., *Z. Anal. Chem.* **211**, 18 (1965).
60. Maier, H. J., and Karpathy, O. C., *J. Chromatog.* **8**, 308 (1962).
61. Rohrschneider, L., *Z. Anal. Chem.* **170**, 256 (1959).
62. Rohrschneider, L., *J. Chromatog.* **22**, 6 (1966).

63. McReynolds, W. O., "Gas Chromatographic Retention Data." Preston Technical Abstracts Co., Evanston, 1966.
64. James, A. T., *J. Chromatog.* **2**, 552 (1959).
65. Walraven, J. J., Doctoral Thesis, Einthoven, 1968.
66. Schomburg, G., *Z. Anal. Chem.* **200**, 360 (1964).
67. Walraven, J. J., Ladon, A. W., and Keulemans, A. I. M., *Chromatographia* **1**, 195 (1968).
68. McCarthy, A. I., Wyman, H., and Palmer, J. K., *J. Gas Chromatog.* **2**, 121 (1964).
69. Merritt, C., Walsh, J. T., Robertson, D. H., and McCarthy, A. I., *J. Gas Chromatog.* **2**, 125 (1964).
70. Littlewood, A. B., Phillips, C. S. G., and Price, D. T., *J. Chem. Soc.* p. 1480 (1955).
71. Willmott, F. W., Ph. D. Thesis, Newcastle upon Tyne, 1967.

Chapter 4

Adsorbent Stationary Phases

4.1. THEORY OF ADSORBENTS IN GAS CHROMATOGRAPHY

Although the great majority of gas chromatography uses liquid stationary phases, there is also considerable use of solid stationary phases onto the surface of which vapours are adsorbed. There are several applications in which gas-solid chromatography (GSC) has advantages over gas-liquid chromatography (GLC), e.g., in analysis of permanent gases. The advantages and drawbacks of GSC are summarised at the end of the chapter.

(a) Adsorption Type

The adsorption of vapours onto surfaces can be classified into two main classes: (i) *physical adsorption*, in which the vapours are held on the surface of the adsorbent by physical forces similar in nature to the intermolecular forces discussed in the last chapter, and (ii) *chemisorption*, in which the vapour forms a chemical bond with the surface. The distinction between these two types of adsorption is closely analogous to that between physical intermolecular forces and chemical interatomic forces in a three-dimensional system. In general, physical adsorption is relatively weak, and the bonds between vapour and surface are formed and broken easily and rapidly. Chemisorption usually occurs by a process which requires considerable activation energy, and thus tends to occur at higher temperatures than are necessary for physical adsorption, and at higher temperatures than are used in most gas chromatography, e.g., 300°C. Furthermore, adsorption and desorption may be slow. Gas chromatography, therefore, uses physical adsorption almost exclusively. One of the drawbacks to GSC is that if it is used at too high a temperature, chemisorption may replace the physical adsorption, causing either sluggish and broad peaks, or, more probably, chemical reaction of the vapours being chromatographed. This occurs

particularly on adsorbents which also act as chemical catalysts, e.g., silica/
alumina.

The isotherm of interaction of a vapour with any adsorbent is necessarily
non-linear, since the surface can become saturated. Isotherms for different
systems can, however, differ widely in shape. Two extreme examples are
given in Fig. 4.1. In case (a) the adsorbent has a large capacity for solute

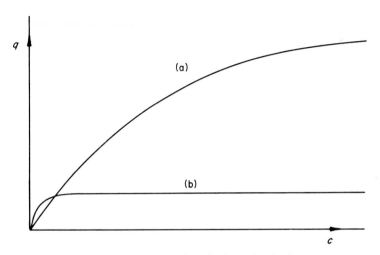

Fig. 4.1. Extreme examples of adsorption isotherms.

before saturation occurs, and a comparatively large region of approximate
linearity. In case (b), the adsorbent is "stronger" in that the initial slope
of the isotherm is steeper, but it is very easily saturated, so that the region
of approximate linearity is small. The great majority of GSC is done using
the elution technique, which works satisfactorily only with an approximately linear isotherm. Thus, an adsorbent satisfying case (a) would be
suitable, but not one satisfying case (b). In general, chemisorbents operate
according to case (b), with a small capacity but very great adsorbent
strength, thus providing an additional reason for their unsuitability.

The region of an isotherm which is relevant in GC depends on the values
of c inside a zone of vapour in the column; in particular, the greatest value
of c for the majority of the column length depends on the sample size.
With practical adsorbents such as are discussed in the next section in practical analytical columns, e.g., of $\frac{1}{2}$ cm diameter, isotherms are such that
vapour samples of the order of milligrams span a considerable portion of
the isotherm and include a region showing considerable curvature. The
result of this is broadened and asymmetrical peaks. On the other hand,

samples of the order of micrograms span only a small region of concentration, in which range the isotherm is substantially linear, so that symmetrical
peaks are obtained. Adsorption chromatography can, therefore, be considered in two "scales"; first, there is "large scale" operation, in which
curvature of the isotherm is relevant, and second, there is "small scale"
operation, in which only the bottom end of the isotherm is relevant, where
it is substantially linear. Effective elution chromatography uses only the
latter.

(b) The Mechanism of Physical Adsorption

In some ways, the physical adsorption of molecules onto a surface has
simpler mechanics than the solution of molecules into a solvent, and mechanical models have greater practical relevance. The statistical mechanics
of the problem has been considered by many authors (1–5) using different
models for the process.

The interaction of a molecule with a surface can be represented by a
curve such as that of Fig. 4.2, which shows the energy of the system consist-

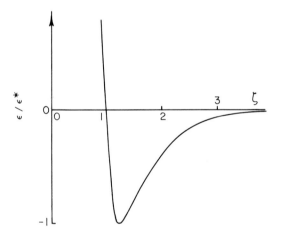

FIG. 4.2. Typical interaction potential for a molecule and a surface.

ing of a vapour molecule and a surface as a function of the perpendicular
distance between the two. At large separations, there is an attractive
force, necessarily decreasing asymptotically to zero at infinite separation,
and increasing as the separation decreases. At small separations, there is a
repulsive force, which increases more rapidly than the attractive force at
yet smaller separations, and serves to prevent the vapour molecule and

the surface from coalescing. The result is that the vapour molecule is most stable at a given distance from the surface, where the attractive and repulsive forces balance.

Curves such as that of Fig. 4.2 are commonplace in considering interactions not only with adsorbents, but also between molecules in solution and in imperfect gas phases. It is often found that there are large numbers of different systems for which the general shape of the potential energy curve is the same, individual systems being completely defined merely by characteristic values of depth and position of the minimum. In such a case, the potential energy curve can be written:

$$\frac{\varepsilon}{\varepsilon^*} = f\left(\frac{z}{z_0}\right) \equiv f(\zeta), \tag{4.1}$$

where the depth of the energy well ε^* and the separation z_0 are characteristic of an individual system, but the function f, which defines the shape of the curve, is the same for many systems. A set of systems conforming to this regime is called conformal, and $\zeta = z/z_0$ is the *reduced separation*.

Given a particular potential energy curve f, one may calculate by statistical mechanics the number of molecules, n, adsorbed on the surface. The complexity of the calculation and the result depends on the sophistication of the model chosen. For example, if there is no interaction between the adsorbed molecules, and if they are spherical and small, it can be shown that (1):

$$\frac{n}{A} = \frac{p}{RT} \cdot z_0 \int_1^\infty [\exp(-\varepsilon^* f(\zeta)/kT) - 1] \, d\zeta, \tag{4.2}$$

where n is the number of molecules adsorbed on an area A of adsorbent, and p is the pressure of adsorbate. Equation (4.2) predicts a linear relation between p and n, i.e., a linear isotherm. Thus, it and other such equations are useful in discussing the bottom part of the isotherm only, and thus in chromatography only for the treatment of small samples. In the derivation of Eq. (4.2), it is assumed that the adsorbate molecules do not interact. Incipient saturation leading to isotherm curvature is regarded in this discussion as interaction of the molecules.

Further analysis of Eq. (4.2) depends on the exact form of f, and various analytical forms have been studied in the literature. In all practical cases, increase in ε^* leads to increased adsorption, and increase in temperature to decreased adsorption, as is described below. The forces contributing to ε^* are similar in nature to the intermolecular forces described in Section

3.6. In all cases, there are dispersion forces acting between adsorbent and adsorbate. In addition, either the adsorbate or the adsorbent can be polar or abnormally polarisable, and in the case of adsorbents, there is the special possibility that they may be ionic. The possible forces contributing to ε^* can, therefore, be summarised by Fig. 4.3 (*1, 5*).

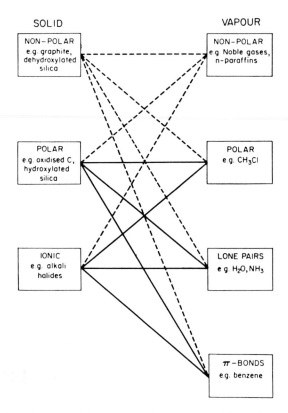

FIG. 4.3. Classification of interactions between a solid surface and a vapour molecule. Dispersion forces shown by broken lines; specific electrical interactions by full lines (*1, 5*).

(c) Retention Units in GSC

Retention units only have useful meaning in GSC in the case that isotherms are linear, since only then do they have any invariance. There are two ways in which retentions can be expressed. In one way, the adsorbent can be regarded exactly as is a liquid, and the concentration of adsorbate in the adsorbed phase is defined as the weight of adsorbate per unit weight of adsorbent. Thus q is defined, and hence a partition coefficient β can be defined as in Eq. (1.1) or Section 3.2, and a specific retention volume can be defined as in Eq. (3.2). The use of the partition coefficient for GSC defined in this manner has been suggested by Janak (6). Hanlan and Freeman (7) have pointed out that the quantity β for an adsorbent is the same as the "adsorption volume" of a physical adsorbent as defined by Steele and Halsey (8, 9), which is the difference between the actual volume of an evacuated container containing the adsorbent and the volume calculated by assuming the gas laws to hold when a gaseous adsorbate is introduced. This concept, in one form or the other, is used generally in theories of physical adsorption.

The alternative unit in which to express adsorbent retention is in terms of weight of adsorbate per unit area of adsorbent surface, rather than weight per unit weight of adsorbent, and is defined by:

$$V_s = \frac{\text{weight of adsorbate per m}^2 \text{ of adsorbent}}{\text{weight of adsorbate per cc of gas phase}}. \tag{4.3}$$

Reference to Eq. (4.2) and the discussion around Eq. (3.13) will show that p/RT of the RHS of Eq. (4.2) is the number of molecules per unit volume of the gas phase, while n/A is the number of molecules per unit surface of the adsorbed phase. Thus, the second term of the LHS of Eq. (4.2) is in fact equal to V_s.

(d) Homogeneity of Adsorbents

An adsorbent on which all adsorption sites are identical is said to be *homogeneous*, in which case, ε^* for a given vapour is the same over the whole adsorbent surface. In general, adsorbents are not homogeneous, so that some sites are more "active," i.e., give larger values of ε^* than others. In this case, the first molecules to be adsorbed by a surface tend to go on the more active sites, and succeeding molecules are forced to occupy less and less active sites. The practical effect of this is that the isotherm becomes non-linear even in the region of concentration where saturation non-linearity is absent. Indeed, in ordinary practice, using adsorbents not specially prepared so as to be homogeneous, non-linearity from heterogeneity is far more important than that from incipient saturation. It can be shown that even on a heterogeneous adsorbent to which a statistical distribution of values of ε^* is attributed, there is still a region of concentration near zero in which the isotherm is substantially linear (i.e., the isotherm can be expanded in a Taylor series), though this region is smaller than for a homogeneous adsorbent. Nevertheless, for practical purposes, it is desirable that adsorbents be as homogeneous as possible.

(e) Thermodynamics of Adsorption

Adsorption occurs with evolution of energy, and thus occurs with evolution of heat which may, if desired, be measured calorimetrically. Also, the partition coefficient of adsorption, β or V_s, is related with temperature by an equation of the type of the van't Hoff isochore:

$$\frac{\partial \ln V_s}{\partial T} = \frac{\Delta H_s}{RT^2}, \qquad (4.4)$$

where ΔH_s is the heat of adsorption (10–13). There is thus a linear relation between the logarithm of the partition coefficient of adsorption and inverse temperature. An illustration of this relation for various permanent gases on charcoal (12) is given in Fig. 4.4.

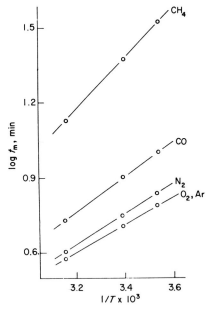

Fig. 4.4. Plots of logarithm of retention time against inverse temperature for gases chromatographed on charcoal. From Greene and Pust (12).

A non-homogeneous adsorbent is characterised by the fact that the heat of adsorption is a function of the amount adsorbed, being greater the smaller the extent of adsorption. Several workers have determined heats of adsorption both by gas chromatography and by calorimetric methods, and in cases where there are no complications, the two methods agree.

In general, heats of adsorption for a given molecule tend to be rather greater than corresponding heats of solution in stationary liquids. This is illustrated, for example, in Table 4.1, which compares heats of adsorption on graphitised carbon black (*14*) (see below), and heats of solution in hexadecane (*15*).

TABLE 4.1

HEATS OF SOLUTION AND HEATS OF ADSORPTION COMPARED

Solute	Heat of adsorption[a]	Heat of solution[b]
n-Pentane	8.7	6.4
n-Hexane	10.6	7.4
n-Heptane	12.5	8.4
n-Propanol	8.1	6.7
n-Butanol	9.9	6.8
Ethyl acetate	10.1	6.8
Carbon tetrachloride	8.9	7.3
Diethyl ether	8.1	6.4
Benzene	9.8	7.4

[a] In graphitised carbon black (kilocalories/mole); see Kiselev (*14*).
[b] In *n*-hexadecane (kilocalories/mole); see Littlewood (*15*).

Another factor which can cause heats of solution to vary with coverage is intermolecular interaction between solute molecules leading to attraction, e.g., in the adsorption of polar or hydrogen-bonding molecules. Thus, on a homogeneous adsorbent, the heat of adsorption of alkanols increases with surface coverage due to intermolecular hydrogen bonding. Heats of hydrogen bonding obtained in this way can be compared with those obtained by other methods, e.g., from solution (*14, 16, 17*).

4.2. ADSORBENTS USED IN GAS CHROMATOGRAPHY

(a) Carbon

Carbon has been used extensively as an adsorbent in GC since its inception. It is simplest to use any of a variety of types of "Activated Charcoal," which are usually prepared by suitable steam treatment of vegetable charcoals at moderate temperatures. Such materials have large surface areas with many fine pores, and are extremely heterogeneous; because of their large surface area, retentions tend to be very large indeed, so that such columns are normally used at temperatures very much higher than the boiling points of the substances to be separated. Thus, they tend to be used for separation of permanent gases at or near room temperature. This application is exemplified in Section 12.1.

If charcoal or other carbons are treated at temperatures of about 3000°C, structural changes take place converting the carbon into poly-hedra with homogeneous basal graphite faces. Carbon of this form, called "Graphitised Carbon Black," has a relatively small surface area, is almost homogeneous, and is much more suitable for use in GC for any but simple empirical applications. Because of its relative inactivity, it need not be used at high temperatures, and thus is available for use with large organic molecules at temperatures either below or around their boiling points. Graphitised carbon black has been studied extensively by Kiselev and his school (14, 18–21). Since its structure contains no double bonds, its inter-action with vapours is solely by dispersion forces, and relations between retention and structure thus resemble those for solutes in non-polar liquid solvents. Because of the homogeneity of the system, symmetrical GC peaks with reproducible retentions are easily obtained. In the case of homologues, linear relations are obtained between $\log V_s$ and homologue number, and, as with solution systems, $\log V_s$ is found to be approximately given by the sum of contributions from the structural elements of the vapour molecule (8, 13, 22, 23).

Since interaction on graphitised carbon black is solely through dispersion forces, retentions are not a function of solute dipole moment, but, as with non-polar stationary liquids, are dependent more on molecular size. Kiselev has pointed out that there is also a correlation between molecular polaris-ability and either ΔH_s or $\log V_s$. With the compounds used by Kiselev, however, there is also an approximately linear relation between molar volume and polarisability. Thus, for organic compounds of C, H, and O, retention index on carbon black is roughly proportional to molecular size.

Adsorption on a surface differs from solution in that it is "one-sided," interaction of the vapour molecule occurring from one side only and not from all the way round. Petov and Shcherbakova (19) have, therefore, calculated the magnitude of the interaction of complex vapour molecules with the surface by summation of the force due to the separate atoms in the vapour with the surface, using known polarisabilities and distances from the atom to the surface. In this way, retentions of compounds as complicated as the terpenes could be correlated with their structure with some measure of accuracy. A practical consequence of the fact that interaction on carbon is "one-sided" is that solute molecules such as naphthenes, whose ability to bend and conform closely with the surface is restricted, have smaller relative retentions with respect to solutes not so constrained on carbon than in solvent phases. The fact that naphthenes are thus accelerated with respect to alkanes as compared with solvents has frequently been found useful in hydrocarbon analysis.

(b) Silica

Silica gel as normally encountered, e.g., by preparation from silicate solutions, is a powerful adsorbent of large specific surface area, and crude silica gel has been used considerably for simple separations of gases at temperatures well above their boiling point. Ordinary silica gel, however, is ill defined, and as an adsorbent it is extremely heterogeneous. Furthermore, it ordinarily contains large quantities of water, and the surface is covered in hydroxyl groups.

Ordinary silica gel consists of an agglomeration of small globules of silica, between which are pores of width of the order of some tens of microns. Adsorption forces are different at curved surfaces from those at flat surfaces, and since the small pores necessarily contain many regions of curvature of random small radius, it is these that cause the heterogeneity. The heterogeneity can, therefore, be removed by increasing the average pore diameter, with consequent reduction in total surface area. Pore size can be increased by treatment of the gel with steam under pressure at high temperatures, e.g., 800–900°C. Kiselev (24) shows chromatograms of samples of hydrocarbons chromatographed on silica gels hydrothermally treated so as to give progressively larger pores, and these illustrate the greater symmetry obtained from gels of larger pore size.

Both untreated and hydrothermally treated silica gels contain water and hydroxyl groups, and thus the retention properties resemble those of stationary liquids containing hydroxyl groups, i.e., selective retention of alkanols and all other solutes with which hydrogen bonds can be formed. Water can be removed from silica gel by progressive heating, though removal of water is accompanied by changes in the structure of the adsorbent. Hydroxyl groups on the surface of the silica cannot be completely removed with heat, even at the highest temperatures. In order to remove all possibility of hydrogen bonding to silica, therefore, the silica must be modified chemically as described in the next section.

(c) Molecular Sieves

Molecular sieves are aluminosilicates in which the crystalline lattice is unusually open, so that it contains holes several angstroms across (25). Though they occur naturally, they may also be made synthetically. Different types containing different sizes of hole can be prepared; most commonly encountered are 4A, 5A and 13X.

The most characteristic use of molecular sieves in GC is provided by sieve 5A, in which the holes are such that they will contain linear chains of methylene groups, but not any branched chains. Thus, they are used extensively as "subtractors" for removing n-alkyl compounds from branched alkyl compounds. This subtraction effect works both for alkanes (26, 27), and for other chemical types such as alkenes or alkanols (28).

Molecular sieves are also useful in the separation of permanent gases. Particularly common is their use for separation of oxygen from nitrogen, the latter having more than twice the retention. In such cases, separations do not occur exclusively through the "sieving" action, the molecular sieve acting simply as a weakly polar, rather heterogeneous adsorbent.

(d) Porous Polymers

Recently, microporous organic polymers have been prepared in which the pores are large enough that gas can diffuse into them. Thus, the materials can be used in gas chromatographic columns in granular form, where they pack uniformly and act as adsorbents with comparatively large specific areas. The products at present described are cross-linked polyaromatic structures; e.g., from styrene and vinyl benzene, and by using monomers with polar groupings, polymers with these groupings on their surfaces can also be produced (29–32).

Microporous organic polymers produce excellent columns for the separation of common gases at or near room temperature, and their use is increasing (33, 34). They may be used at higher temperatures for the analysis of liquids (35). A particular characteristic is that water is eluted reversibly from the polymers, giving a symmetrical peak. Furthermore, the presence of water vapour in the carrier gas does not modify the performance of the polymers, as is often the case with inorganic adsorbents (see below). Because the materials are reproducible and stable, retentions of vapours are reproducible. Unlike many other common adsorbents, therefore, retention data for vapours on microporous polymers has some measure of invariance (29, 30).

4.3. Modification of Adsorbents

The retention properties of adsorbents can be influenced greatly by material already adsorbed on their surfaces; indeed, in practice, considerable care is required to obtain a clean adsorbent not already modified in some way. Frequently, adsorbents for use in GC are intentionally modified by non-volatile liquids, solids, or volatile substances present in the carrier gas.

(a) Liquid Modifiers

If an adsorbent is treated with a small proportion of a non-volatile liquid such as any of those previously described as stationary liquids, the liquid is adsorbed in preference to any vapour which might be used and forms a stable layer on the surface. If the adsorbent is heterogeneous, the liquid will tend to occupy the sites of greatest activity, leaving empty those of lesser activity, with the result that the adsorbent becomes more homogeneous. In practice, this renders chromatographic peaks more symmetrical. The use of small proportions of squalane (1.5%) to modify an active charcoal in order to enable it to produce symmetrical peaks was first described by Eggertsen et al. (36), and this technique has been described frequently since. For example, Scott (23) describes the use of silicone oil to modify alumina for the better separation of C_1–C_5 hydrocarbons.

Since heats of adsorption are in general larger than heats of solution for a given vapour, the vapour interacts with a modified adsorbent by adsorption on unmodified sites rather than by solution in the modifier, unless the modifier is present in such quantity as to swamp the adsorbent. Thus, a modified adsorbent gives retention behaviour characteristic of the adsorbent rather than of the modifier. For example, modified carbon black still causes naphthenes to be accelerated relative to alkanes (36) as described in Section 4.2a.

An extension of the modification of adsorbents is the use of a small proportion of a polar stationary liquid, e.g., polyethylene glycol, to poison completely any adsorptive sites on a support used for partition columns. In contrast to the above case, the aim here is to prevent the adsorbent from modifying the retention properties of a non-polar stationary liquid (Section 7.3).

A somewhat different technique of adsorbent modification, in which the modification is chemical, has been described by White et al. (37–40). In this, the adsorbent is a montmorillonite clay which has been modified by replacing the inorganic ion with an organic amine containing long alkyl

chains. Thus, the authors used a commercial product in which the amine
is the dioctodecyl dimethylammonium ion. The result of this is a product
which is essentially an adsorbent with a particularly uniform surface, but
which, on account of the large proportion of methylene chain, behaves
partly as a paraffinic partition liquid. With alkanes and naphthenes, symmetrical peaks are obtained, and separations are generally in order of boiling
points. With aromatic compounds, however, unsymmetrical peaks with
sharp front profiles are obtained, indicating ordinary adsorption with
Langmuir type isotherms. The conclusion is that the interaction of the
paraffins is with the alkyl groups, but the interaction of the aromatics is
with the interior of the adsorbent. Of practical significance is the fact that
the aromatics are very strongly selectively retained relative to the alkanes,
as is shown by the figures of Table 4.2.

TABLE 4.2

COMPARISON OF THE RETENTION OF ALKANES, NAPHTHENES, AND AROMATICS ON
ALKYLATED MONTMORILLONITE[a]

Solute	Relative retention volume on alkylated montmorillonite at 80°C	Specific retention volume on alkylated montmorillonite at solute bp	Specific retention volume on paraffin oil at solute bp
Benzene	1.00	139	66.3
Toluene	1.69	94	77.8
o-Xylene	—	78	66.7
Hexane	0.10	15.5	62.9
Cyclohexane	0.17	21.2	83.7
Heptane	0.20	15.2	63.0

[a] See White (37) and White and Cowan (38).

(b) Modification by Salts

C. G. Scott and C. S. G. Phillips have shown that alumina, silica, and
aluminosilicas can be modified by treatment with inorganic salts, e.g.,
alkali halides or hydroxides (41–43). Such modification may be done simply
by forming a slurry of the adsorbent with a solution of the salt, followed

by evaporation of the water and heat treatment to whatever temperature may be required. Baking temperatures may be of the order of 200–400°C, and the proportion of modifier may be from about 5–40%.

As with liquid modifiers, one effect of the salt is to reduce the surface area of the adsorbent and to improve the homogeneity of what remains. Thus it enables symmetrical peaks of organic compounds to be obtained at temperatures which are not too high. In general, it appears that with alkali halide modifiers, organic compounds can usually be eluted at their boiling points and even below (42).

Salt modifiers used in such large quantities as are used by Scott and Phillips produce considerable variation in the retention properties of the columns. The effect of altering the proportion and chemical nature of the modifier can most simply be studied from the variation in retention index of some suitable polar or polarisable solute, e.g., benzene. In general, increase in the proportion of modifier increases the retention index of a polar vapour, though a curve of retention index vs. modifier concentration may show a minimum. In such a case, presumably, polar groups on the unmodified adsorbent and ions in the modifier interact to form comparatively stable and inert complexes, with which polar vapours cannot effectively compete in competitive equilibria.

In general, it appears that the effect of a modifier in increasing the retention indices of polar materials increases with the polarisability of the ions. This is illustrated in Table 4.3 (41) for alumina modified by sodium salts. The extra retention of the benzene and heptene is greatest on the iodide-modified adsorbent, and least with that modified by hydroxide.

TABLE 4.3

RETENTIONS OF HYDROCARBONS RELATIVE TO n-HEPTANE ON ALUMINA AT 100°C MODIFIED WITH SODIUM HYDROXIDE AND HALIDES[a]

Modifier	Cyclohexane	2,2,4-Trimethyl pentane	1-Heptene	Benzene
NaOH	0.36	1.21	1.34	1.05
NaCl	0.28	1.28	1.80	1.97
NaBr	0.27	1.32	2.00	3.00
NaI	0.30	1.37	2.31	3.90

[a] From Scott (41).

Phillips and Scott find that salt modified columns can be reproduced to give retentions within about 10%, but probably different batches of adsorbent would cause greater deviations, and it seems likely that reproducibility depends rather critically on the technique of preparation.

(c) Modification by Volatile Material

Volatile adsorbates can modify adsorbents in a similar manner to nonvolatile ones. By far the most ubiquitous modifier is water vapour, which is strongly adsorbed by most adsorbents, particularly those with polar groups and those which are heterogeneous. In such cases, the attachment of the water is so strong at temperatures used for the chromatography of organic compounds that the vapour pressure of water above its adsorbed layer is negligible and the adsorption is frequently described as "irreversible." If an adsorbent with adsorbed water is baked at a temperature higher than its normal operating temperature, the water is progressively removed, with consequent increase in retention volumes at the normal temperature of operation which may easily amount to as much as tenfold. In many cases, separations are thereby improved (44). The effect of water vapour on retentions of substances on alumina has been studied in detail by Halasz and Heine (45), who have compared retentions on alumina using a dry carrier gas and a carrier gas moistened to a given vapour pressure with water. The water vapour reduces retentions and, because of the competition between the water and a vapour for adsorption sites, the linear relation between the logarithm of retention and inverse temperature breaks down. Thus, reduction in temperature may in some cases produce a *fall* in retention, rather than the usual rise, since reduction in temperature may favour adsorption of extra water more than the adsorption of extra vapour. Change of water content of an adsorbent may also change relative retentions by altering the proportion of hydroxyl groups. For example, water on Molecular Sieve 5A can cause inversion in the usual order of elution of methane and carbon monoxide (46). When permanent gases are analysed by gas adsorption chromatography, a different permanent gas must necessarily be used as carrier gas; this is also adsorbed by the adsorbent, so that the chromatography is a function of the carrier gas. Greene and Roy (47) have found that the heavier the carrier gas, the shorter are retention times for a mixture of permanent gases and light hydrocarbons. The effect may be very marked. Thus, methane was found to have a retention time of 34 minutes with helium as carrier gas, 15 minutes with air as carrier gas, and 5 minutes with acetylene as carrier gas.

4.4. Use of Gas Chromatography to Study Adsorbents

The properties of adsorbents are frequently conveniently studied from their chromatographic behaviour when they are packed in columns. The determination of adsorption isotherms by GC has been studied quite extensively. There are several methods.

(a) By Frontal Analysis

James and Phillips (48), and Perrett and Purnell (49) have used a frontal technique (Sections 1.1, 7.7) for the determination of adsorption isotherms. The adsorbent is packed into a column and a stream of carrier gas is passed through it. At a measured instant the carrier gas is mixed with a measured concentration of a vapour, e.g., by diverting it through a saturator held at a known temperature, and the mixture is passed through the column. Before the column of adsorbent is in equilibrium with the vapour, it strips it out of the carrier gas, and the detector at the far end of the column shows no response. When all the adsorbent is in equilibrium with the vapour, the latter breaks through the far end of the column, and a step shows on the recorder. The time taken from the start to the break-through, the flow rate, and the vapour pressure of the vapour enable one to calculate the amount of vapour adsorbed. By repeating this procedure at different vapour pressures, e.g., by altering the temperature of the saturator, different points on the isotherm are obtained.

Nelsen and Eggertsen (50) have modified the procedure of James and Phillips in order to determine surface areas of adsorbents by a modification of the B.E.T. method. This method makes use of the fact that when a vapour is adsorbed on any adsorbent at or near its boiling point, adsorption proceeds with ease till a monomolecular layer is formed, after which there is a reduction in the rate of adsorption. This reflects in the shape of the isotherm, and by a suitable method of plotting, given the area of a single absorbed molecule, the surface area may be determined. The modification of the above authors is essentially merely the use of helium as a carrier gas and nitrogen as the adsorbed vapour, with the column at liquid nitrogen temperature. The results obtained closely resemble those obtained by the standard vacuum apparatus for B.E.T. area determinations. The authors find that it is also possible to use butane and ice in place of nitrogen and liquid nitrogen, but, as is generally recognised, B.E.T. areas obtained with large molecules may differ from those obtained from nitrogen.

(b) By Elution in Vapour at Constant Concentration

Other methods of determining adsorption isotherms all use in one way or another the general equation:

$$V = Wf'(c) + V_M , \tag{4.5}$$

(see, e.g., Huber and Keulemans, *51*), where the isotherm is denoted by the equation $q = f(c)$, and $f'(c) = dq/dc$. This equation is a consequence of the conservation equation of DeVault, and is easily proved from the discussion of Section 2.2. For a linear isotherm, $f'(c) = \beta$, and thus Eq. (4.5) becomes Eq. (2.12). In the elution technique for determining isotherms (*52, 53*) the adsorbent is packed in a column designed for ordinary elution chromatography, and the carrier gas contains a constant concentration of adsorbate passing continuously, e.g., by using a saturator as in the frontal technique. The concentration of adsorbate is then momentarily either slightly increased by ordinary injection of a small sample of the adsorbate, or momentarily decreased by simple injection of a small sample of clean carrier gas. Thus a positive or negative peak, respectively, is gener-

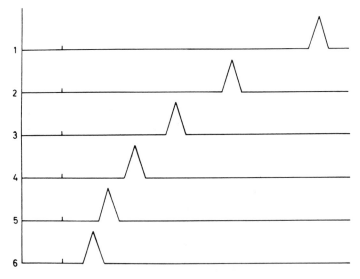

Fig. 4.5. To illustrate how adsorption isotherms can be obtained by elution of a perturbation in a stream of vapour at constant concentration. Chromatogram 1 is that of vapour eluted in pure carrier gas. Chromatograms 2–6 are those of small samples of the vapour using carrier gas containing successively greater steady concentrations of the same vapour.

ated and eluted through the column. From the elution time, flow rate, etc., the quantity $f'(c)$ can be obtained. By repeating the experiment at other constant concentrations of adsorbate, a set of values of $f'(c)$ as a function of c may be obtained, and from these, the isotherm may be constructed. In the normal case, $f'(c)$ decreases monotonically as c increases; Fig. 4.5, therefore, illustrates a typical set of chromatograms at values of c increasing down the set; retentions become less the greater is c.

(c) From an Unsymmetrical Elution Peak

Both the methods described above for isotherm determination involve a separate experiment for determination of each point on the isotherm. Since the shape of a single elution peak is determined by the isotherm, several authors (54–58) have sought to relate the shape of the peak with the shape of the isotherm, so that in this way the whole isotherm may be obtained from a single chromatographic run. For every value of c, there is a unique value of $f(c)$ and $f'(c)$, and therefore for a zone of infinitesimal width of a given concentration c inside the peak, there is a unique speed of elution. Such zones of constant concentration are conveniently called "characteristic points," following Gluekauf (54) and Conder (58), and by studying the movement of characteristic zones, together with considerations of conservation, comparatively simple equations and constructions relating peak shape and isotherm shape can be derived.

The calculation of isotherms from peaks as first presented was over-simplified by omitting many complications, e.g., non-equilibrium in the peak formation, gas compressibility, non-instantaneous input peak profiles, and considerations due to the volume change within the peak due to sorption. Nevertheless, isotherms in good agreement with those obtained by static means can be obtained.

(d) From a Non-Sharp Front

The case of a non-sharp front, in which either a carrier gas carrying a lower concentration of adsorbate is replaced by a higher concentration (for isotherms of the type of Fig. 1.7), or a carrier gas carrying a higher concentration of adsorbate is replaced by one carrying a lower concentration (for isotherms of the type of Fig. 1.6), is easier to treat theoretically than that of a single elution peak. Conder (58) has recommended the use of such elution fronts for isotherm determination and has studied the theory in detail.

4.5. Comparison of GSC and GLC

The principal advantages and drawbacks of GSC compared to GLC are given below.

(a) Advantages of GSC

(1) *Speed of Equilibration.* Physical adsorption is generally quicker than the process of solution. Thus, there is more rapid equilibration between gas and solid phase than between gas and liquid phase. The discussion of Chapter 6 shows that this can lead to greater column performance, and greater separative ability. This advantage is most relevant in those columns which are specifically designed for high performance, e.g., open tube "Capillary" columns, and such columns embodying adsorbents can be both fast and efficient (59, 60) (Section 7.3).

(2) *Specific Relative Retentions.* The one-sided nature of the inter-molecular forces between adsorbents and adsorbates enables retentions to be differentiated on a basis different to that occurring in solution. The practical use of this, however, is impeded by drawback (2) given in Section 4.5b.

(3) *High Temperature Operation.* The ability of adsorbents (usually heterogeneous) to act as columns at temperatures very much greater than the normal boiling points of the adsorbates is an advantage in the analysis of gases.

(4) *Involatility.* Unlike many solvents, adsorbents do not have a vapour pressure at high temperatures and thus do not "bleed."

(5) *Use in Capillary Columns.* Since adsorbents are stable up to very high temperatures, they can often be incorporated into glass capillary columns as they are made (see Section 7.3).

(6) *Use in Displacement and Frontal Analysis.* The curvature of isotherms is used specifically in displacement and frontal analysis (see Section 7.7). These techniques can use large samples, since, in their application, solute concentrations necessarily span the curved regions of the isotherm.

(b) Drawbacks to GSC

(1) *Small Quantities.* In the elution technique, sample quantities must necessarily be small in order to secure symmetrical peaks.

(2) *Irreproducibility.* Considerable skill is required to reproduce a given adsorbent.

(3) *Restricted Range.* The range of easily available adsorbents is more restricted than the corresponding range of solvents.

(4) *Restricted High-temperature Operation.* Many adsorbents cannot be used at high temperatures because of the possibility of chemisorption and chemical reaction.

(5) *Liability to Contamination.* The fact that adsorbents are so easily modified by contaminants is in practice a serious drawback to their use.

REFERENCES

1. D. H. Everett, "Gas Chromatography 1964," Proceedings of the Fifth International Symposium (A. Goldup, ed.), p. 219. Institute of Petroleum, 1965.
2. Ash, S. G., Everett D. H., and Findenegg, A., *Trans. Faraday Soc.*, **64**, 2645 (1968).
3. Barker, J. A., and Everett, D. H., *Trans. Faraday Soc.* **58**, 1608 (1962).
4. Steele, W. A., and Halsey, G. D., *J. Chem. Phys.* **22**, 979 (1954).
5. Hanlan, J. F., and Freeman, M. P., *Can. J. Chem.* **37**, 1575 (1959).
6. Janak, J., *Collection Czech. Chem. Comm.* **18**, 798 (1953).
7. Hanlan, J. F., and Freeman, M. P., *Can. J. Chem.* **37**, 843 (1959).
8. Steele, W. A., and Halsey, G. D., Jr., *J. Chem. Phys.* **22**, 979 (1954).
9. Steele, W. A., and Halsey, G. D., Jr., *J. Phys. Chem.* **59**, 57 (1955).
10. Cremer, E., and Muller, R., *Z. Elektrochem.* **55**, 217 (1951).
11. Cremer, E., and Prior, F., *Z. Elektrochem.* **55**, 66 (1951).
12. Greene, S. A., and Pust, H., *J. Phys. Chem.* **62**, 55 (1958).
13. Habgood, H. W., and Hanlan, J. F., *Can. J. Chem.* **37**, 843 (1959).
14. Kiselev, A. V., "Gas Chromatography 1964," Proceedings of the Fifth International Symposium (A. Goldup, ed.), p. 238. Institute of Petroleum, 1965.
15. Littlewood, A. B., *Anal. Chem.* **36**, 1441 (1964).
16. Kiselev, A. V., *Discussions Faraday Soc.* **40**, 205 (1965).
17. Belyakova, L. D., Kiselev, A. V., and Kovaleva, N. V., *Anal. Chem.*, **56**, 1517 (1964).
18. Poshkus, D. P., *Discussions Faraday Soc.* **40**, 195 (1965).
19. Petov, G. M. and Shcherbakova, K. D., "Gas Chromatography 1966," Proceedings of the Sixth International Symposium (A. B. Littlewood, ed.), p. 50. Institute of Petroleum, 1967.
20. Kiselev, A. V., *Zh. Fiz. Khim.* **38**, 2753 (1964).
21. Kiselev, A. V., *Advances in Gas Chromatography* **4**, 113 (1967).
22. Cremer, E., Symposium on the Use of Physical Chemical Methods for Analysis. Freiburg, West Germany, April, 1959.
23. Scott, C. G., *J. Inst. Petrol.* **45**, 118 (1959).
24. Kiselev, A. V., "Gas Chromatography 1962," Proceedings of the Fourth International Symposium (M. van Swaay, ed.), p. xxxiv. Butterworth, London, 1962.

25. Barrer, R. M., *Ber. Bunsenges, Phys. Chem.* **69**, 786 (1965).
26. Brenner, N., and Coates, V. J., *Nature* **181**, 1401 (1958).
27. Whitham, B. T., *Nature*, **182**, 391 (1958).
28. Brenner, N., Ciepelinski, E., Ettre, L. S., and Coates, V. J., *J. Chromatog.* **3**, 230 (1960).
29. Hollis, O. L., and Hayes, W. V., "Gas Chromatography 1966," Proceedings of the Sixth International Symposium (A. B. Littlewood, ed.), p. 57. Institute of Petroleum, London, 1967.
30. Hollis, O. L., *Anal. Chem.* **38**, 309 (1966).
31. Hollis, O. L., and Hayes, W. V., *J. Gas Chromatog.* **4**, 235 (1966).
32. Johnson, J. F., and Barrall, E. M., *J. Chromatog.* **31**, 547 (1967).
33. Cross, R. A., *Nature* **211**, 409 (1966).
34. Havelena, E. J., Jr., and Hutchinson, K. A., *J. Gas Chromatog.* **6**, 419 (1968).
35. Cockle, N., and Fitch, G. R., *Chem. Ind. (London)* **1966**, 1970 (1966).
36. Eggertsen, F. T., Knight, H. S., and Groennings, S., *Anal. Chem.* **28**, 303 (1956).
37. White, D., *Nature* **179**, 1075 (1957).
38. White, D., and Cowan, C. T., *Trans. Faraday Soc.* **54**, 557 (1958).
39. White D., and Cowan, C. T., "Gas Chromatography 1958," Proceedings of the Second Symposium, Amsterdam, (D. H. Desty, ed.), p. 116. Academic Press, New York, 1958.
40. Hughes, M. A., White, D., and Roberts, A. L., *Nature* **184**, 1796 (1959).
41. Scott, C. G., "Gas Chromatography 1962," Proceedings of the Fourth International Symposium (M. van Swaay, ed.), p. 36. Butterworth, London, 1962.
42. Scott, C. G., and Phillips, C. S. G., "Gas Chromatography 1964," Proceedings of the Fifth International Symposium (A. Goldup, ed.), p. 266. Institute of Petroleum, London, 1965.
43. Phillips, C. S. G., and Scott, C. G., "Progress in Gas Chromatography" (J. H. Purnell, ed.), p. 1212. Wiley (Interscience), New York, 1968.
44. Karlsson, B. M., *Anal. Chem.* **38**, 668 (1966).
45. Halasz, I., and Heine, E., *Advances in Chromatography* **4**, 207 (1967).
46. Champeix, L., "Chromatography and Methods of Immediate Separation" (G. Parissakis, ed.), p. 395. Union of Greek Chemists, Athens, 1966.
47. Greene, S. A., and Roy, H. E., *Anal. Chem.* **29**, 569 (1957).
48. James, D. H., and Phillips, C. S. G., *J. Chem. Soc.*, p. 1066 (1954).
49. Perrett, R. H., and Purnell, J. H., *J. Chromatog.* **7**, 455 (1962).
50. Nelsen, F. M., and Eggertsen, F. T., *Anal. Chem.* **30**, 1387 (1958).
51. Huber, J. F. K., and Keulemans, A. I. M., "Gas Chromatography 1962," Proceedings of the Fourth International Symposium (M. van Swaay, ed.), p. 26. Butterworth, London, 1962.
52. Peterson, D. L., and Helfferich, F., *J. Phys. Chem.* **69**, 1283 (1965).
53. Stalkup, F. I., and Kobayashi, R., *Am. Inst. Chem. Eng. Paper* **9**, 121 (1963).
54. Gluekauf, E., *J. Chem. Soc. (London)* **1947**, 1302.
55. Gregg, S. J., and Stock, R., "Gas Chromatography 1958," Proceedings of the Second International Symposium (D. H. Desty, ed.), p. 90. Butterworth, London, 1958.
56. Huber, J. F. K., and Keulemans, A. I. M., "Gas Chromatography 1962," Proceedings of the Fourth International Symposium (M. van Swaay, ed.), p. 26. Butterworth, London, 1962.

57. Cremer, E., *Monatsh. Chem.* **92**, 112 (1961).
58. Conder, J. R., "Progress in Gas Chromatography" (J. H. Purnell, ed.), p. 209. Wiley (Interscience), New York, 1968.
59. Halasz, I., Hartmann, K., and Heine, E., "Gas Chromatography 1964," Proceedings of the Fifth International Symposium (A. Goldup, ed.), p. 38. Institute of Petroleum, London, 1965.
60. Halasz, I., and Heine, E., "Progress in Gas Chromatography" (J. H. Purnell, ed.), p. 153. Wiley (Interscience), 1968.

Chapter 5

Column Performance—Fundamentals

5.1. Introduction

It was pointed out in Chapter 1 that the separation of two substances depends on the relative retention and the column performance. The former is discussed in the two preceding chapters. The two following chapters describe the column performance, which determines the width of peaks relative to their retention volume.

It is simplest to imagine that a zone of vapour is put into a column instantaneously, as in Section 2.2, so that at the beginning of the elution it takes the form of a very narrow band which in the ideal case is infinitely narrow. This broadens while being eluted from one end of the column to the other. The problem is to define the degree of broadening by a suitable number, to find out the factors upon which the broadening depends, and finally to produce quantitative relations connecting the broadening with the factors which produce it. There are two ways of approaching this problem. The logical method, which is also the most useful, considers what happens to a band of vapour as it passes through the column in terms of the kinetics of vapour molecules as they move in and out of the stationary phase, a motion which is controlled by diffusion and by the geometry of the column. This method will be considered in the next chapter. Historically, however, it happened that another method of treatment came first, in which a very artificial model of the chromatographic column, the "Plate" model, was used, and which provided the number (number of theoretical plates) by which column performance is defined. The "Plate Theory" was first given in connection with liquid-liquid partition chromatography by Martin and Synge (1) and was subsequently developed by Mayer and Tompkins (2) and others. The discussion below also makes extensive use of papers by Klinkenberg and Sjenitzer (3) and by Gluekauf (4).

5.2. Plate Theory

Martin and Synge (1) imagine a chromatographic column divided along its length into a number of separate zones each of which is of such a length that within it there is complete equilibration of the vapour between the gas and the stationary phases. The zones, called "Theoretical Plates," form the imaginary basis of the model on which the plate theory is founded, and their length in the column is referred to as the "Height Equivalent to the Theoretical Plate," H.E.T.P., or the "Plate-Height." A similar model is used in describing the performance of distillation columns, but as is shown later, the theoretical plate in a chromatographic column and that in a distillation column do not have the same significance, though they may be defined in the same way.

Let us adopt the plate model of the column (Fig. 5.1) and imagine that at the beginning of the chromatography, a particular vapour is all contained in the first plate (Fig. 5.1a). On passing an incremental volume of carrier gas, δV, some of the vapour in the gas phase is swept onto the second plate, where it equilibrates with the stationary phase (Fig. 5.1b). Meanwhile, what remains in the stationary phase in the first plate equilibrates with the clean carrier gas that has entered. On passing further increments of carrier gas this process repeats (Fig. 5.1c) and slowly the

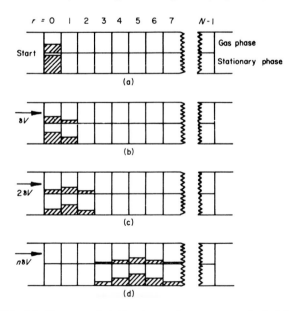

Fig. 5.1. Progress of elution in a column composed of plates.

vanguard of the vapour moves along the column while the concentration in the first plate becomes smaller and smaller till virtually none remains, and the whole zone has effectively moved along the column (Fig. 5.1d). The way in which the vapour is distributed among the plates after passage of a given number of increments of carrier gas depends on the amount of vapour transferred at each incremental passage. This in turn depends upon the relative cross sections occupied by the phases and upon the partition co-efficient. Using mainly the notation of James and Martin (5, 6), let

H = height equivalent to the theoretical plate (cm),

a = cross-sectional area of column occupied by the gas phase (cm^2),

b = cross-sectional area of column occupied by the stationary phase (cm^2),

α = partition coefficient defined in Section 3.1 (number),

c = concentration of vapour in the gas phase (g/cc),

δV = incremental volume of carrier gas (cc),

and we shall find the proportion of the contents of any plate moved into the following plate by passage of a single incremental volume, δV. The total vapour content of any plate is the sum of the contents of the gas phase and the stationary phase. The weight of vapour in the gas phase of one plate is the gas volume of the plate multiplied by the concentration in the gas phase, which is Hac. The concentration in the stationary phase is αc, so that the weight of vapour in the stationary phase is $Hb\alpha c$. Hence, the total weight of solute in the plate is $Hc(a + \alpha b)$. The passage of δV will remove from the plate a mass of vapour $c\delta V$. Hence the proportion of vapour moved out of the plate on passing δV (p) is

$$p = \frac{\delta V}{H(a + \alpha b)}. \tag{5.1}$$

Note that this is only the amount moved *out*, and does not take into account the vapour moved *in* from the previous plate.

Using Eq. (5.1), we now consider the distribution that results after a given number of incremental volumes (n) has been passed, assuming that before elution all the vapour is in the first plate. The distribution resulting from elution, expressed as a function of the concentrations existing in plates numbered from zero upwards (serial number of plate being r, the first plate being $r = 0$) and as a function of the number of incremental volumes, is tabulated for small values of the variables in Table 5.1. The amount of vapour has been normalised so that it is represented by a mass of unity. After passage of one increment δV, p is transferred from plate 0

TABLE 5.1

Number of incremental volumes δV (n)	Serial number of plate (r)						
	0	1	2	3	4	5	6
0	1						
1	q	p					
2	q^2	$2qp$	p^2				
3	q^3	$3q^2p$	$3qp^2$	p^3			
4	q^4	$4q^3p$	$6q^2p^2$	$4qp^3$	p^4		
5	q^5	$5q^4p$	$10q^3p^2$	$10q^2p^3$	$5qp^4$	p^5	
6	q^6	$6q^5p$	$15q^4p^2$	$20q^3p^3$	$15q^2p^4$	$6qp^5$	p^6

to plate 1, leaving $1 - p$ in plate 0. Let $1 - p = q$. In the next passage of δV, a proportion p of the p already present in plate 1 is transferred from plate 1 to plate 2, giving p^2 in plate 2; from this transfer there remains pq in plate 1. Also, a proportion p of the q already present in plate 0 is transferred to plate 1, giving a further pq in plate 1. Thus plate 1 contains $2pq$. Plate 0 contains a proportion q of the q originally present, and thus contains q^2. In succeeding passages, this process is repeated, i.e., a proportion p from the contents of plate $r - 1$ is transferred to plate r, and a proportion q remains, the total contents of the plate being the sum of that remaining and that added by transfer from the previous plate. Study of Table 5.1 will make it evident that the amount in the rth plate after the nth incremental passage is

$$X \cdot p^r q^{(n-r)}$$

where the coefficient X is the sum of the coefficients of the terms above and to the upper left in the table. For small numbers, these coefficients are obtainable from "Pascal's Triangle," which is constructed in this way. The coefficients are those of the expansion of the binomial $(p + q)^n$ as a power series, and in general, the rth coefficient is given by the equation

$$X = \frac{n!}{r!(n - r)!}. \tag{5.2}$$

Hence, the mass distribution of the vapour among the plates as a function of r after the passage of n incremental volumes is

$$w(n, r) = \frac{n!}{r!(n-r)!} \, p^r q^{(n-r)} \tag{5.3}$$

where $w(n, r)$ is the proportion of the mass of vapour in the rth plate after passage of $n\delta V$.

The distribution of Eq. (5.3) is very common, and arises in many cases where some dependent property results from the repetition of a number of steps each of which has a given chance (p) of success or failure. First described by Newton, it is called the "Binomial Distribution," since the terms of the binomial expansion satisfy it. As a linear isotherm is assumed, w is proportional to c, the concentration in the gas phase of the plate, so that Eq. (5.3) is essentially the equation of the peak in the column as a function of r after a given amount of elution.

A little algebraic transformation of Eq. (5.3) is necessary to bring it into convenient analytical form, and this is done later in order to study the shapes of the peaks predicted by the plate theory. However, the retention volume and broadening of peaks can be obtained from familiar properties of binomial distributions without the necessity of obtaining the actual equation for the chromatogram.

In connection with any distribution there is a *mean*, $\bar{r}$, which is a point on the abscissa, r, such that a vertical line drawn through it bisects the area of the distribution, and there is a *standard deviation*, σ, or *variance*, σ^2, which measures the extent to which the distribution is spread out from the mean. These quantities are defined by the equations:

$$\bar{r} = \int r w(r) \, dr \tag{5.4}$$

and

$$\sigma^2 = \int (r - \bar{r})^2 w(r) \, dr. \tag{5.5}$$

For a binomial distribution it can be shown that (see, for example, Margenau and Murphy (7), Section 12.4)

$$\bar{r} = np \tag{5.6}$$

and

$$\sigma^2 = nqp. \tag{5.7}$$

Substituting Eq. (5.1) in Eq. (5.6) to obtain an expression for the mean,

$$\bar{r} = \frac{n\delta V}{H(a + \alpha b)}, \tag{5.8}$$

we obtain the serial number of the plate which has the same quantity of vapour on either side, i.e., the plate which bisects the area of the peak in the column. In the circumstances in which chromatography is normally used, it will appear that the distribution is nearly symmetrical with one maximum, so that the plate $\bar{r}$ is also the plate at which the concentration is the maximum. Also, the product $n\delta V$ is the total volume of eluting carrier gas passed, V, so that

$$\bar{r} = \frac{V}{H(a + \alpha b)}. \tag{5.9}$$

The product $\bar{r}H$ is the distance of the $\bar{r}$th plate from the beginning of the column, i.e., the distance of the peak maximum from the beginning of the column. Hence

$$V = x(a + \alpha b), \tag{5.10}$$

where V and x are the same symbols as used in Chapter 2. When x is equal to the length of the column, l, V is the volume of gas passed for the maximum to appear at the end of the column, i.e., the retention volume, $V_R{}^0$. Hence

$$V_R{}^0 = l(a + \alpha b). \tag{5.11}$$

This, using αb instead of the identical $m\beta$, is identical with the corresponding equation for the retention volume derived by the theory of Section 2.3 (Eq. 2.11). Hence, provided that the assumption that the peaks are symmetrical is valid, both theories give the same result.

The broadening can be obtained from the standard deviation, which, for the binomial distribution, is given by Eq. (5.7). In the most realistic interpretation of gas chromatography by means of the plate theory, p is small, so that q is approximately equal to unity. Thus the variance, σ^2, has the same form as the mean,

$$\sigma^2 = \frac{nq\delta V}{H(a + \alpha b)} \approx \frac{V}{H(a + \alpha b)}. \tag{5.12}$$

In order to obtain an expression for the broadening produced by the column, we require the standard deviation when the peak emerges from the column, that is, when $V = V_R{}^0$. Thus, substituting Eq. (5.11) for $V_R{}^0$,

$$\sigma^2_{(r)} = \frac{l(a + \alpha b)}{H(a + \alpha b)} = \frac{l}{H} = \mathcal{N}, \tag{5.13}$$

where $\mathcal{N}$ is the number of plates in the column and the subscript to σ indicates its units. The last equality of Eq. (5.13) derives from the fact that the product of the height of a plate and the number of plates equals the length of the column. The quantity defining the column performance is not the standard deviation itself, which increases continuously with either the plate-number of the length of the column, but, as stated in Section 1.3, the ratio of the standard deviation to the mean. Thus the measure of the performance is given by

$$\frac{(\bar{r})^2}{\sigma^2_{(r)}} = \frac{(V_R{}^0)^2/H^2(a + \alpha b)^2}{l/H} = \frac{l^2/H^2}{l/H} = \frac{l}{H} = \mathcal{N}. \tag{5.14}$$

In this equation, neither standard deviation nor mean is in units easily accessible to measurement. However, if both numerator and denominator of the extreme L.H.S. of Eq. (5.14) are multiplied by $H^2(a + \alpha b)^2$, the plate units are changed into volume units by virtue of Eq. (5.9), so that $\sigma_{(r)}$ becomes $\sigma_{(V)}$ and $\bar{r}$ becomes $V_R{}^0$, and

$$\frac{(V_R{}^0)^2}{\sigma^2_{(V)}} = \mathcal{N}. \tag{5.15}$$

Equation (5.15) is the fundamental justification of the plate theory. In Chapter 1, the criterion of column performance was defined as the ratio of the retention volume to the standard deviation of a peak produced by the column. The equation shows that the square of this quantity is in fact equal to the number of theoretical plates, so that the number of theoretical plates provides a number characteristic of column performance. This criterion is widely used, though the idea of the theoretical plate is in fact rather far removed from a directly measurable criterion of performance. The plate theory can do no more, for it cannot continue by making any predictions about the height of the theoretical plate in terms of column parameters, and the plate model of the chromatographic column is a model based solely on the answer it is required to give, which is Eq. (5.15). However, the notion of the theoretical plate is now so well established that it is convenient to express performances in terms of "Number of Plates," even in discussions in which it is fully recognised that there are no such things as plates, either in theory or practice. In all such cases, the plate number is defined by Eq. (5.15).

5.3. Peak Shape from Plate Theory

In Eq. (5.3), $w(n, r)$ is the amount of solute in plate r after the passage of n incremental volumes δV. If, as is normally the case, the zone of solute covers many plates, $w(n, r)$ can be considered as a function of a continuous variable r which is related to x, the distance from the start of the column, by the equation $Hr = x$ $(x \gg H)$. In this case, w is proportional to c or q, the concentrations in gas or liquid phases, since, by definition, there is equilibrium inside each plate and the isotherm is assumed to be linear. Thus, for a column with $\mathscr{N}$ plates, the quantity $Kw(n)$ for a value of r given by $\mathscr{N} - 1$ ($\mathscr{N} - 1$ rather than $\mathscr{N}$ since the serial number of the first plate is zero), where K is a normalising constant, is the equation of the chromatogram as it emerges from the end of the column, and $K'w(r)$ at a given value of n is the equation of the zone inside the column after an elution volume $n\delta V$ has been passed.

Equation (5.3) cannot be plotted with ease in the algebraic form given except for small values of n and of r and except after specification of p and q. Normally, n and r are by no means small, and, as will be seen shortly, it is not convenient to give specific values to p and q. There are several different analytically convenient approximations to Eq. (5.3), the accuracy and applicability of which depend on the relative values of n, r, p, and q. One of these, to be described below, is generally applicable in chromatography.

In the case that $\bar{r}$ is sufficiently large that $1/\bar{r}$ may be neglected compared to unity, it can be shown that, as $n \to \infty$,

$$w(r) = \frac{1}{\sqrt{2\pi}\ \sigma_{(r)}} \exp[-(r - \bar{r})^2/2\sigma_{(r)}^2], \qquad (5.16)$$

where $\sigma_{(r)}$ is given by Eq. (5.7). In these conditions, p is small in such a manner that $\bar{r} = np$ is finite as $n \to \infty$. Equation (5.16) is that of the well-known "Gaussian Distribution," and the conditions required for it are usually satisfied in gas chromatography. When $w(r)$ is plotted against r, it appears as a symmetrical peak whose maximum at $r = \bar{r}$ (Fig. 5.2). In this distribution, it can be shown that the standard deviation, $\sigma_{(r)}$, is represented by the half-width of the peak drawn at the points of inflection, which occur at points 0.607 up the height of the peak (Fig. 5.2). The quantity $1/(2\pi)^{1/2}\sigma_{(r)}$ is a normalising constant such that the area of the peak is unity. Hence, the equation of a zone of vapour of mass w in the column is

$$c(r) = \frac{w}{\sqrt{2\pi}\ \sigma_{(r)}} \exp[-(r - \bar{r})^2/2\sigma_{(r)}^2]\ \text{(g/plate)}. \qquad (5.17)$$

This can also be written as a function of x rather than of the plate-number,

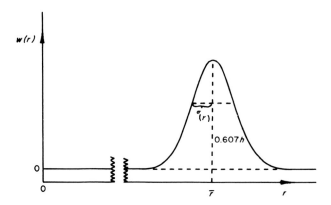

FIG. 5.2. Plot of a Gaussian peak.

so long as the unit of the standard deviation is changed correspondingly:

$$c(x) = \frac{w}{\sqrt{2\pi}\,\sigma_{(x)}} \exp[-(x - \bar{x})^2/2\sigma^2_{(x)}] \ (\text{g/cm}). \qquad (5.18)$$

Since the peak is symmetrical, the concentration of an emerging zone can also be expressed in volume units:

$$c(V) = \frac{w}{\sqrt{2\pi}\,\sigma_{(V)}} \exp[-(V - V_R^0)^2/2\sigma^2_{(V)}] \ (\text{g/cc}), \qquad (5.19)$$

where V_R^0 is the retention volume. Note that the fact that the peak as given by any of Eqs. (5.16)–(5.19) is symmetrical justifies $\bar{r}$ being identified with $r_{\max}$ in the derivation of Eq. (5.11). The maximum value of $c(V)$ for a peak in the column is when $r = \bar{r}$, and is given by:

$$c_{(\max)} = \frac{1}{\sqrt{2\pi}\,\sigma_{(V)}}$$

for unit weight of vapour. Since $\sigma^2_{(V)} \propto V$ [Eq. (5.12)], the relation between the maximum concentration of a peak and its position in the column is:

$$c^2_{(\max)} \propto \frac{1}{V} \propto \frac{1}{x}. \qquad (5.20)$$

This equation is used in Section 2.8.

5.4. COMPARISON OF THEORETICAL PLATES IN CHROMATOGRAPHY
AND DISTILLATION

The expression of the performance of chromatographic columns in terms of the number of plates invites comparison with the similar term used in fractional distillation. Though the definition of the theoretical plate is the same in both cases, the number of plates required to perform a separation to a given degree of purity is very much greater in chromatography than in distillation, as has been pointed out by Herington (8) and others. Van Deemter, Zuiderweg, and Klinkenberg (9) have given a graph (Fig. 5.3) showing the number of plates required to obtain two products of 99.7% purity from 50–50 mixtures of two components as a

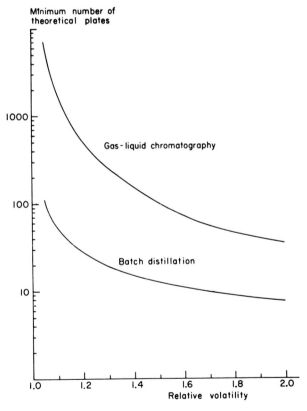

FIG. 5.3. Comparison of the number of plates required for a given separation by gas chromatography and by distillation. The curves show the number of plates required as a function of relative retention (G.C.) or relative volatility (distillation) to obtain fractions of 99.7% purity from an equimolar mixture. From van Deemter *et al.* (9).

function of the relative retention for gas chromatography and relative volatility for distillation. As expected (see Section 5.6), the number of plates required rises as the relative retention approaches unity, but the over-all number of plates required in chromatography is very much greater. Herington considers that the number of plates required in chromatography is about the square of the number required in distillation for the same degree of separation. The reason for this large difference is simple; in chromatography, only the part of the column occupied by the solutes is effective in performing the separations, and most of the column is empty most of the time; but, in distillation, all the column is working all the time in separating the components of the mixture.

Figure 5.3 shows that the very high plate-numbers achieved in chromatography are deceptive to those who are used to thinking of separations in terms of distillation, though it should be emphasised that a plate in gas chromatography, although it may mean less than a plate in distillation, is very much easier to attain and to operate. Thus, though a distillation column of 100 plates is comparable with a chromatographic column of 10,000 plates for separation and analysis of small samples, the chromatographic column is much easier to construct and operate than the corresponding distillation column. A 10,000-plate chromatographic column could be used for the analysis of a small sample of a mixture in a few minutes, but a distillation column at 100-plate efficiency would require a long time on total reflux, with careful temperature control, and the allowable take-off rate would be very small. Chromatography also has the advantage that there is no equivalent of the "Hold-up Volume" of the distillation column, and no chasers are required.

5.5. Methods of Determining Plate-Numbers

The plate-number of a column may be found from a chromatogram by making measurements equivalent to the standard deviation and the retention of a peak, and by calculating the number of theoretical plates by Eq. (5.15). This equation is true whatever the units of the retention and the standard deviation so long as they are the same, and thus, for the greatest convenience, the quantities are measured as distances on the chromatogram as it appears on the strip-chart. Four methods for measuring plate-numbers have been reported:

(1) Measure L, the distance on the chart from the point corresponding to the start of the chromatogram to the peak maximum, and measure

the standard deviation of the peak, $\sigma_{(L)}$. From these, the plate number will be given by:

$$\mathcal{N} = \frac{L^2}{\sigma_{(L)}^2}. \tag{5.21}$$

This method was suggested by James and Martin (5).

(2) An adaptation of the above method measures L and the peak-width half-way up the peak. If this latter quantity is $\omega_{1/2}$, the plate number is

$$\mathcal{N} = 5.54 \frac{L^2}{\omega_{1/2}^2}. \tag{5.22}$$

A simple calculation will show that $\omega_{1/2}^2$ is equal to $5.54 \; \sigma_{(L)}^2$, where $5.54 \equiv 8 \ln (2)$. This method is illustrated in Fig. 5.4.

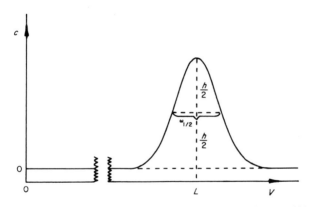

FIG. 5.4. Plate-number from retention and peak width at half-height.

(3) Draw tangents to the points of inflection of the peak, and produce the base line across the bottom of the peak (Fig. 5.5). A simple calculation shows that the distance AB (M) on the baseline between the points where the two tangents intersect it is of length $4\sigma_{(L)}$. Hence, if L is also measured, the plate-number is given by:

$$\mathcal{N} = 16 \frac{L^2}{M^2}. \tag{5.23}$$

This method has been recommended by Desty et al. (10).

(4) Measure the area of the peak, A; the height of the peak, h; and the retention distance, L; in such units as to make the quantity hL/A unitless. Thus, h and L could both be in centimetres, and A in cm². In this

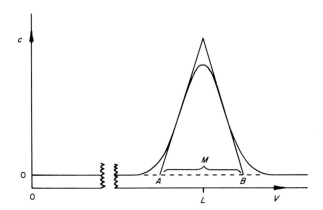

FIG. 5.5. Plate-number from retention and inflectional tangents.

case, a simple calculation will show that the number of plates is given by:

$$\mathcal{N} = 2\pi \left(\frac{hL}{A} \right)^2. \tag{5.24}$$

This method was suggested by James and Martin (5).

Of these, the first is too slow for practical use, since there is no easy construction for measuring $\sigma_{(L)}$. The fourth method demands some means of measuring area, such as a planimeter, and also involves the measurement of two lengths in addition, so this is relatively slow, though it has occasionally been used. Methods (2) and (3) are both quick and easy to use, and the choice between them probably depends on personal preference. Each involves the measurement of two distances; method (2) involves making a construction (the point half-way up the peak); method (3) involves drawing three constructional lines, and probably the two methods take about an equal time. There is possibly more personal error involved in drawing the tangents than there is in measuring $\omega_{1/2}$, and therefore method (2) might be expected to be more reliable. However, consistent results are easily obtained with method (3).

5.6. PURITY OF SEPARATION OF PAIRS OF SOLUTES

The separation of two solutes has been described in terms of their relative retention and the plate-number of the column with respect to the two solutes. As illustrated by Fig. 1.4, both of these are relevant in determining the over-all separation, and this section describes quantitatively

the way in which they do this. The over-all separation can be described by
the percentage purity of the zones as they emerge from the column, but,
since in most cases of interest the purity will be nearly 100%, it is more
useful to define the percentage impurity rather than the purity.

Figure 5.6 shows two slightly overlapping peaks, and it is evidently
not possible to choose any two points on the volume axis between which
an absolutely pure sample of either component could be obtained. In the
figure shown, a nearly pure sample of A could be obtained between the
limits V_1 and V_2; and of B between V_3 and V_5, but no single cut can be
made so that material to the right is nearly pure A and to the left nearly

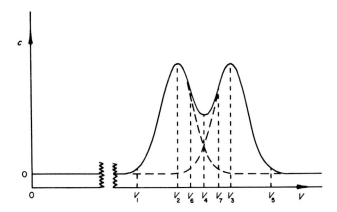

FIG. 5.6. Two overlapping peaks.

pure B. In the case shown, where the area-proportions of A and B are
equal, the sum of the impurity fractions obtained to the left and right of a
single cut is a minimum when the impurity fractions are equal, and, in the
case of two symmetrical peaks, the cut should be at the minimum of the
col* between the peaks. Thus, the best possible single cut to obtain the
purest possible samples of both A and B is at V_4. Gluekauf (4) has studied
the impurity fractions in this case as a function of the number of plates
and the retention volumes of the two components. If the retention volumes
are V_2 and V_3, and the number of plates is $\mathcal{N}$, and if the impurity fraction
of either component is $\eta_{1:1}$, Gluekauf gives:

$$\eta_{1:1} = 0.5 - \mathrm{erf}\left[\frac{\sqrt{\mathcal{N}}(\sqrt{V_3} - \sqrt{V_2})}{\sqrt[4]{V_2 V_3}}\right], \qquad (5.25)$$

* The word "col" is defined as a depression in a mountain chain.

where

$$\text{erf}(x) = \frac{1}{\sqrt{2\pi}} \int_0^x \exp(-\xi^2/2) \, d\xi. \qquad (5.26)$$

The error function, $\text{erf}(x)$, is tabulated in many sources, for example in the "Handbook of Physics and Chemistry" (Section 3.3). A plot of $0.5 - \text{erf}(x)$ [sometimes called the complementary error function, erfc (x)] is given in Fig. 5.7. As expected, its value drops sharply as x increases.

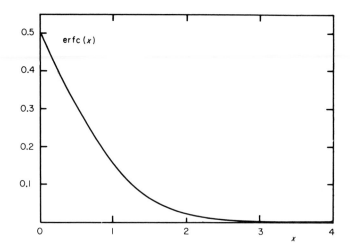

FIG. 5.7. Plot of erfc (x) against x.

Reference to tables shows that it becomes less than 0.01 (1%) when x exceeds 2.33 and less than 0.1% when x exceeds 3.08. Gluekauf (4) has given a plot of impurity fraction $\eta_{1:1}$ against plate-number $\mathcal{N}$ with the ratio of the retention volumes as parameter (Fig. 5.8). This enables any two of $\eta_{1:1}$, $\mathcal{N}$, and the ratio of retention volumes to be related with the third.

Equation (5.25) holds with accuracy only for cases in which the ratio of the retention volumes does not differ too much from unity, for, when this is not so, each peak will have a different value for $\mathcal{N}$. However, with ordinary columns with performances of the order of thousands of plates, impurity fractions will be quite negligible before this factor begins to produce error in the use of Eq. (5.25). A little simplification of Eq. (5.25) makes it easier to use in the absence of a graph, and shows its structure more clearly. Let the ratio of the retention volumes of two solutes be

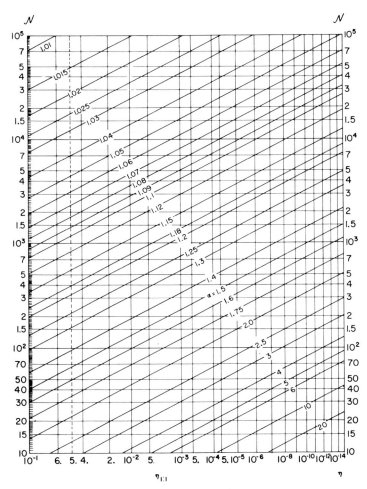

Fig. 5.8. Diagram giving the impurity fraction (abscissa) as a function of the number of plates (ordinate) with the ratio of retention volumes as parameter (4). From A. I. M. Keulemans, "Gas Chromatography." Van Nostrand (Reinhold), Princeton, New Jersey, 1957.

expressed by a number greater than unity, and let

$$\frac{V_3}{V_2} = 1 + x, \qquad (5.27)$$

so that if the ratio is, for example, 1.2, then $x = 0.2$. In terms of x, Eq. (5.25) can be approximately rewritten

$$\eta_{1:1} = \mathrm{erfc}\left(\frac{x\sqrt{\mathcal{N}}}{2}\right). \qquad (5.28)$$

As with Eq. (5.25), this equation assumes equal peaks and a single cut at the col between them. It applies so long as impurity fractions are small.

It is useful to show a few examples of the use of Eqs. (5.25) and (5.28) to give an idea of the order of magnitude of the quantities involved. Table 5.2 gives the relation between plate-number and impurity fraction for different ratios of retention volumes, measurements having been made from Fig. 5.8. Figure 5.9 shows pairs of solutes as they would appear on chromatograms with impurity fractions corresponding to the columns in Table 5.2.

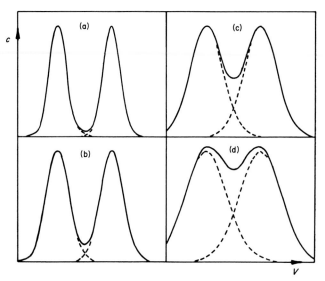

FIG. 5.9. Illustrations of overlapping peaks with given impurity fractions (see Table 5.2): (a) Impurity fraction 0.1%; (b) impurity fraction 1.0%; (c) impurity fraction 5%; (d) impurity fraction 10%.

When the areas or the amounts of material of the two peaks are not the same, Eq. (4.25) needs modification. Let the overlapping peaks contain material in each amounting to m_2 and m_3, and let a cut be made at such a place on the abscissa that the impurity fractions of each component in the other are the same, $\eta_{m_2:m_3}$. In this case,

$$\eta_{m_2:m_3} = \eta_{1:1} f, \tag{5.29}$$

where f is a numerical factor. This factor has been studied by Said (11), who gives graphs relating f with m_2/m_3. It is a roughly symmetrical function of $\log m_2/m_3$, approximately parabolic around $m_2/m_3 = 1$, where it has its

TABLE 5.2

NUMBERS OF PLATES REQUIRED TO OBTAIN GIVEN IMPURITY FRACTIONS FROM PAIRS
OF SUBSTANCES WITH GIVEN RATIOS OF RETENTION VOLUMES

Ratio of retention volumes	Impurity fraction (%)			
	0.1	1.0	5.0	10.0
1.01	4×10^5	2×10^5	1.2×10^5	7×10^4
1.05	1.6×10^4	9000	4500	2800
1.1	4200	2400	1200	700
1.2	1200	640	320	190
1.4	340	190	79	54

maximum value of unity. In the range most likely to be of practical interest, $1/10 \leq m_2/m_3 \leq 10$, f lies between 0.85 and unity. In most applications, therefore, it can be assumed that $\eta_{m_2:m_3} \approx \eta_{1:1}$.

The formulae so far given assume that two overlapping zones are separated by making the best possible single cut. In preparative work, a more likely procedure is to make two cuts, one each side of the col, for example, V_6 and V_7 in Fig. 5.6, and to discard the portion between the cuts. In this way, impurity fractions can be greatly reduced on account of the rapid decline in the value of erfc (x) with increase in x. A calculation derived from Eqs. (5.15) and (5.19) will show that for a peak of retention volume $V_R{}^0$, and plate-number $\mathscr{N}$, the proportion of its area beyond a cut made at $V^\dagger$, which may be either greater or less than $V_R{}^0$, is

$$\text{erfc}\left\{ \frac{|V_R{}^0 - V^\dagger| \sqrt{\mathscr{N}}}{V_R{}^0} \right\}. \tag{5.30}$$

This equation can be used, if required, to determine impurity fractions resulting from arbitrarily made cuts. Note that if $V_R{}^0 - V^\dagger = \frac{1}{2}xV_R{}^0$, Eq. (5.30) gives Eq. (5.28).

Equation (5.28) is instructive in that it shows the relative importance of plate-number and the ratio of the retention in determining the over-all separation of two solutes. Whereas the quantity x appears to the first power in the argument of the error function, the plate-number appears only to the power of $\frac{1}{2}$. Thus, doubling x is equivalent to multiplying the plate-number by 4, and the over-all separation is more sensitive to a change in the ratio of retention volumes than to a change in the plate-number.

Another means of defining the separation of the solutes is by the "Resolution" of two peaks. This quantity (12) has been accepted by the IUPAC committee in their preliminary proposals (13), and is defined by

$$R = \frac{2(L_3 - L_2)}{M_3 + M_2}, \tag{5.31}$$

where L_2, L_3, M_2, and M_3 are the distances L and M defined in Fig. 5.5 for each peak. The resolution, R, is easily related with the more precise impurity fraction. For two close peaks we shall assume $\mathcal{N}_2 = \mathcal{N}_3$, and $M_2 = M_3$; in this case, substitution of Eqs. (5.15), (5.27), and (5.23) yields

$$R = \frac{x\sqrt{\mathcal{N}}}{4}, \tag{5.32}$$

so that

$$\eta_{1:1} = \text{erfc } 2R \tag{5.33}$$

if the impurity fraction is small.

5.7. The Influence of Gas Hold-up on Resolution

The retention of solutes enters the definitions of impurity fraction and resolution as the ratio V_3/V_2. It is important to realise that this ratio is always smaller than the relative retention, for V_2 and V_3 each contain the gas hold-up,

$$\frac{V_3}{V_2} = \frac{V_M + W\beta_3}{V_M + W\beta_2} = \frac{1 + k_3}{1 + k_2}, \tag{5.34}$$

where symbols are as in Chapter 2. In a case when the gas hold-up is comparable with retention volume, there will be a considerable difference between V_3/V_2 and the relative retention, r_{23}, so that many more plates are required to obtain a given resolution than would be anticipated from the relative retention. It is seen that the larger the numerical value of the partition ratio, k, the closer the ratio V_3/V_2 is to the limiting value, r_{23}. The distinction between relative retention and the ratio of retention volumes in determining the resolution can easily be included in the equations of the previous section, for

$$x = \frac{1 + k_3}{1 + k_2} - 1 = \frac{k_3 - k_2}{1 + k_2} = (r_{23} - 1)\frac{k_2}{1 + k_2}, \tag{5.35}$$

so that, for close peaks, omitting the distinction between k_2 and k_3,

$$R = (r_{23} - 1)\frac{k}{1+k} \cdot \frac{\sqrt{\mathcal{N}}}{4}$$ (5.36)

and

$$\eta_{1:1} = \text{erfc}\,\frac{1}{2}\left\{(r_{23} - 1)\frac{k}{1+k} \cdot \mathcal{N}^{1/2}\right\}.$$ (5.37)

These relations have been discussed by Golay (*14*), Purnell (*15*), and by Loyd *et al.* (*16*). It is apparent that when k is large, Eqs. (5.36) and (5.37) tend towards Eqs. (5.38) and (5.32), since $(r_{23} - 1) \to x$ and $k/(1 + k) \to 1$. At the other limit, it is apparent that as $k \to 0$, $R \to 0$, whatever the values of $\mathcal{N}$ or r_{23}. This corresponds to the circumstance referred to in Section 3.8, in which one might well fail to resolve two solutes with a very large relative retention on a very efficient column if both of them are virtually insoluble in the stationary phase. In practice, there is usually an optimum value of k, but, since this is determined by considerations such as the time required for the analysis and other variables concerned with the mechanism of column performance, it is discussed in the following chapter.

References

1. Martin, A. J. P., and Synge, R. L. M., *Biochem. J.* **35**, 1358 (1941).
2. Mayer, S. W., and Tompkins, E. R., *J. Am. Chem. Soc.* **69**, 2866 (1947).
3. Klinkenberg, A., and Sjenitzer, F., *Chem. Eng. Sci.* **5**, 258 (1956).
4. Gluekauf, E., *Trans. Faraday Soc.* **51**, 34 (1955).
5. James, A. T., and Martin, A. J. P., *Analyst* **77**, 915 (1952).
6. James, A. T., and Martin, A. J. P., *Biochem. J.* **50**, 679 (1952).
7. Margenau, H., and Murphy, G. M., "The Mathematics of Physics and Chemistry," 2nd ed. Van Nostrand, Princeton, New Jersey,1956.
8. Herington, E. F. G., *in* "Vapour Phase Chromatography," Proceedings of the First Symposium, London, May, 1956 (D. H. Desty, ed.), p. 30. Academic Press, New York, 1957.
9. Van Deemter, J. J., Zuiderweg, F. J., and Klinkenberg, A., *Chem. Eng. Sci.* **5**, 271 (1956).
10. Committee Recommendations, *in* "Vapour Phase Chromatography," Proceedings of the First Symposium, London, May, 1956 (D. H. Desty, ed.), p. xi. Academic Press, New York, 1957.
11. Said, A. S., *J. Gas Chromatog.* **1**, (6) 20 (1963).
12. Jones, W. L., and Kieselbach, R., *Anal. Chem.* **30**, 1590 (1958).
13. "Recommendations on Nomenclature and Presentation of Data in Gas Chromatography." See "Gas Chromatography 1960," Proceedings of the 3rd Symposium. Butterworth, London, 1961.
14. Golay, M. J. E., *Nature* **182**, 1146 (1958).
15. Purnell, J. H., *J. Chem. Soc.*, p. 1268 (1960).
16. Loyd, R. J., Ayers, B. O., and Karasek, F. W., *Anal. Chem.* **32**, 698 (1960).

Chapter 6

Column Performance—Mechanisms

6.1. Broadening Factors and Column Variables

The principal criteria of quality in analytical columns are:

(1) plate-number, or column performance,
(2) resolution,
(3) time required for analysis.

The purpose of this chapter is to relate these criteria with all possible variables involved in the design and operation of columns, so that it is possible to design a column suitable for any particular analysis. There are many column variables each of which can influence all the criteria given above, and which in many cases affect the way in which another column variable influences the criteria; in other words, the column variables do not act independently. The description of the effect of column variables on the chromatography, therefore, is complicated and involves a large number of items of information.

In order to provide a formal scheme for the discussion, the ideal column defined in Chapter 1 will be taken as standard, for this is the best possible column as judged by the above criteria, in that two vapours with a relative retention infinitesimally different from unity are perfectly resolved in an infinitesimal time. Real columns depart from this standard in all three criteria, but in order to simplify the argument, we shall regard the first criterion as paramount, and the second two as subsidiary.

Real columns differ from the ideal column in that a zone of vapour broadens during elution. We shall specify the model of the column so that it contains a number of independent items each of which contributes to the broadening. The broadening factors each produce a variance σ_i^2 on an instantaneously introduced zone of sample, and we assume that they may be combined by the same rule that applies in the addition of the effects of independent sources of random error upon a distribution,

$$\sigma_{\text{total}}^2 = \sum_i \sigma_i^2. \tag{6.1}$$

This equation is valid for all broadening factors which act independently, but fails when the action of one broadening factor affects another. In the discussion of this chapter, the broadening factors are independent except for the "coupling" of the effects of lateral mass-transfer described in Section 6.5 and for non-linear isotherms. In all other parts of the discussion, Eq. (6.1) is valid. Its use is discussed by Klinkenberg and Sjenitzer (1), among others.

The broadening of a peak expressed as a variance can be related with the plate height, H, or the plate number, $\mathcal{N}$, by the equations of Chapter 5. The various relations between variances in different units, plate height, and plate number that will be used in this chapter are given below, using Eq. (5.15) and equations of Chapter 2:

$$\sigma_{(V)} = (a + m\beta)\sigma_{(x)} = a(1 + k)\sigma_{(x)} = \dot{V}\sigma_{(t)} = ua\sigma_{(t)}, \tag{6.2}$$

$$(1 + k)\sigma_{(x)} = u\sigma_{(t)}, \tag{6.3}$$

$$\frac{\sigma_{(V)}^2}{(V_R{}^0)^2} = \frac{H}{l} = \frac{1}{\mathcal{N}}, \tag{6.4}$$

$$\frac{\sigma_{(x)}^2}{x} = H = \frac{l}{\mathcal{N}}. \tag{6.5}$$

It is apparent from Eqs. (6.4) and (6.5) that the plate height is proportional to the peak variance, so that Eq. (6.1) implies that each broadening factor may be regarded as adding a term to H. This idea is used throughout this chapter.

The expressions for the variances due to each broadening factor each contain a number of terms and parameters describing the column variables, so that the column variables can be related to the criteria of quality of the column through the specification of the broadening factors. The broadening factors to be discussed are:

(1) Non-zero rate of longitudinal diffusion of the vapour in the gas phase.

(2) Non-infinite rate of equilibration of the vapour with the stationary phase.

(3) Factors depending on the geometry of the column packing.

(4) Non-linearity of isotherms.

(5) Non-zero concentration of vapour in the gas phase.

(6) Unsharp input distribution of vapour.

(7) Non-zero time constant of the recording system.

Complementary to these are the column variables which affect the column performance either directly or through their effect on one or more of the broadening factors listed above:

(1) Column length (l).

(2) Flow rate ($\dot{V}$ or u).

(3) Partition coefficient (β).

(4) Mass of stationary phase per unit length of column (m).

(5) Pore volume per unit length of column (a).

(6) Temperature (T).

(7) Carrier gas.

(8) Size and shape of particles of column packing.

(9) Column diameter.

(10) Pressure drop across the column (P_i/P_o).

(11) Mass of vapour (w).

Sections 6.2 to 6.8 give the theory of the broadening factors. Following this, the effect of each of the column variables is discussed in Sections 6.9 to 6.20, using the broadening factors as the basis of discussion.

The actual broadening of a peak is measured by the standard deviation, σ, rather than by the variance σ^2, so that it is apparent from Eq. (6.1) that the broadening produced by several broadening factors operating together is less than the sum of the broadenings produced by each, since

$$(\sum_i \sigma_i^2)^{1/2} < \sum_i \sigma_i. \tag{6.6}$$

This is reasonable. A molecule of vapour slowed down relative to the mean on account of the operation of one broadening factor may well be speeded up by the operation of another, and vice versa, so that the total broadening is not as great as would be calculated by simple addition of the standard deviations due to each factor.

Equation (6.1) has a very important application in the general design of gas chromatographic equipment, for it shows that the total broadening produced by the operation of several broadening factors together is very much dominated by the factor giving the largest individual broadening. Consider, for example, two broadening factors which individually would contribute standard deviations of 10 and 2 cc. The broadening produced by both together is $(104)^{1/2} = 10.2$ cc, so that even though the major broadening factor is only 5 times the minor, it contributes 98% to the total broadening, and the effect of the minor broadening factor is virtually negligible. In practical chromatography, this observation implies that in order to improve the over-all performance, it is more important to reduce the largest broadening factor than any other, and given that at least some broadening is inevitable, it is best to design and operate an apparatus so that all broadening factors are more or less equal. When a good column is used in bad conditions, it is the badness of the conditions that determines the performance, not the excellence of the column, and when a bad column is used in good conditions, it is the badness of the column and not the excellence of the conditions that determines the performance.

The reader who is primarily interested in the practical features of column design and operation but not in the theoretical background can omit Sections 6.2–6.6 inclusive and assume the results quoted in Section 6.9.

6.2. Broadening Due to Longitudinal Diffusion in the Gas Phase

A narrow and concentrated zone of vapour, such as is introduced into the beginning of a column, in time diffuses into a wider and less concentrated zone. This diffusion occurs whether the zone is stationary or being eluted through the column. The effect of this longitudinal diffusion on a zone as it is eluted through the column is shown in Fig. 6.1.

To calculate the variance produced by longitudinal diffusion, we assume the elution of the vapour does not affect the diffusion by adopting a length

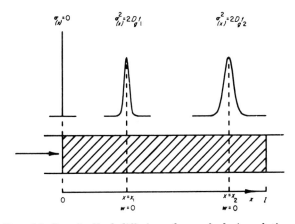

FIG. 6.1. Longitudinal diffusion of a peak during elution.

coordinate, w, the units of which are the same as those of x, but the zero of which is always at the peak maximum, as indicated in Fig. 6.1. We assume that the diffusion obeys the one-dimensional diffusion equation,

$$D_g \frac{\partial^2 c}{\partial w^2} = \frac{\partial c}{\partial t}, \tag{6.7}$$

where D_g is the diffusion coefficient of the vapour in the carrier gas, and c, t, and w are as previously defined. The boundary condition for an initial delta-function distribution is

$$t = 0, \qquad c = \delta(w). \tag{6.8}$$

The solution to Eqs. (6.7) and (6.8) is

$$c(w, t) = \frac{1}{2(\pi D_g t)^{1/2}} \exp(-w^2/4D_g t). \tag{6.9}$$

By comparison with Eq. (5.16), it is seen that $c(w, t)$ is a Gaussian function of w with a mean at $w = 0$ and a variance of

$$\sigma_{(x)}^2 = \sigma_{(w)}^2 = 2D_g t. \tag{6.10}$$

This equation for the diffusional spread of a sharp zone in one dimension is well known, and is sometimes referred to as Einstein's law of diffusion.

In the case of an open tube column such as a capillary column, Eq. (6.10) is accurate. With a packed column, however, there are two complications. First, the diffusion is not precisely along the column axis, but along the tortuous paths between, or also possibly through, the particles of packing. Since the tortuous path is necessarily longer than the straight path along the column axis, the effect of the diffusion is thereby reduced. Van Deemter et al. (2) therefore applied to the RHS of Eq. (6.10) a constant less than unity called the "Tortuousity," γ. A second complication is that any given route of the gas through the packing contains comparatively wide regions where the gas moves slowly, and also comparatively narrow regions where the gas moves fast. When the longitudinal diffusion is averaged for such paths, the net average differs from that which would have been obtained for uniform flow (3, 4). The effect of the constricted flow is also to modify the RHS of Eq. (6.10) by a constant; it is convenient, therefore, to include both effects in the constant γ.

Equation (6.10) applies only to the portion of the vapour in the gas phase. An exactly similar equation applies in principle to the portion of the vapour dissolved in the stationary phase as has been recognised, for example, by Khan (5). It appears, however, that longitudinal diffusion in the stationary phase is always small enough to be negligible in comparison with other broadening effects. Since, therefore, only diffusion in the vapour phase is significant, the variance produced on the total sample of vapour is given by Eq. (6.10) multiplied by the proportion of vapour in the gas phase, which is $1/(1 + k)$, where k is the partition ratio. Applying this and the correction γ, Eq. (6.10) becomes:

$$\sigma^2_{(x)} = \frac{2D_g\gamma t}{1 + k} = \frac{2D_g\gamma V}{\dot{V}(1 + k)} = 2D_g\gamma \frac{x}{u} \tag{6.11}$$

where the other forms of writing are derived using the equations of Chapter 2. In volume units, the variance is:

$$\sigma^2_{(V)} = \frac{2D_g\gamma a(a + m\beta)V}{\dot{V}}. \tag{6.12}$$

It should be noted that the broadening produced in an initially sharp peak by longitudinal diffusion is symmetrical, so that the formulae given in Chapter 2 for retention volume and retention time are unaffected by this source of diffusion so long as measurements are made to the peak maximum.

6.3. Broadening Due to Non-Instantaneous Equilibration of Vapour

(a) Qualitative Explanation

In linear chromatography, which is to be assumed in all the following discussion, the ideal equation $q = \beta c$ should be replaced by

$$q = \beta c f(t), \tag{6.13}$$

where $f(t)$ is some function attaining the value of unity only when the time t is large, since, in a real column, the vapour does not equilibrate instantaneously. The way in which the operation of Eq. (6.13) leads to peak broadening is illustrated in Fig. 6.2, in which the column is idealised as in Fig. 1.1, and a peak produced as a result of the ideal equation $q = \beta c$ is compared with the peak produced as a result of Eq. (6.13). In ideal chromatography, the ratio q/c is constant at every point inside the zone of vapour, so that the distributions in each phase are similar in shape, and differ only

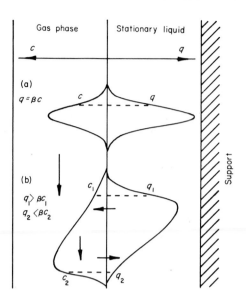

Fɪɢ. 6.2. Comparison of (a) peak shapes in ideal chromatography with (b) those broadened by non-instantaneous equilibration of the vapour with the stationary phase.

in the factor β along the ordinates. In non-ideal linear chromatography, however, q/c is no longer constant. As soon as the front profile of the zone in the gas phase meets a clean region of stationary phase, vapour starts to dissolve, but equilibrium is not reached at once, so that in the front profile the ratio q/c is less than β, and as a result undissolved vapour in the gas phase moves further along the column than it would in the ideal case. At the rear profile of the zone, the reverse happens; as the zone in the gas phase moves along, vapour leaves the stationary phase to try to maintain equilibrium, but cannot do so instantaneously, so that $q/c > \beta$, and vapour remains in the stationary phase longer than it would have done had the column been ideal. Throughout the zone, the vapour is always trying to keep up with equilibrium, but can never quite do so before the zone in the gas phase has moved on. The result of this on the shape of the peaks is illustrated in the figure, where it is seen that the different conditions in the two profiles require that the peaks are asymmetrical as shown, and broader than in the ideal case.

(b) Quantitative Theory

The quantitative study of broadening due to slow equilibrium, or finite rate of mass transfer, is similar in kind to the calculation given in Section

2.3 in which the equation of the chromatogram is obtained from the conservation equation, a relation between q and c, and the initial conditions. In linear non-ideal chromatography, the only difference is the substitution of Eq. (6.13) for Eq. (1.1). The problem has been studied by many authors, including Gluekauf (6), Lapidus and Amundsen (7), Klinkenberg and Sjenitzer (1), Thomas (8), and with special reference to gas chromatography by van Deemter et al. (2), Golay (9, 10), Young (11), Funk and Houghton (12) and Kucera (13). Similar results obtained by the stochastic theory are given by Giddings and Eyring (14) and by Beynon et al. (15).

In this discussion we shall consider only the case that Eq. (6.13) takes the form

$$q = \beta c(1 + K'e^{-Kt}), \tag{6.14}$$

in which equilibrium is reached exponentially. The differential equation corresponding to this is:

$$\frac{dq}{dt} = K(\beta c - q), \tag{6.15}$$

and describes a first order reaction of the vapour between the phases with a rate constant K. It is indicated below that this equation generally applies in gas chromatography.

As in Section 2.3, Eq. (6.15), together with Eq. (2.5) and the initial conditions:

$$q(0, x) = 0, \qquad c(V, 0) = \delta(V) \tag{6.16}$$

may be solved to give expressions for c and q as a function of any two of the variables x, t, and V. The solutions for c and q are:

$$c(V, x) = \frac{K}{\dot{V}} \left(\frac{m\beta x}{V - ax} \right)^{1/2} I_1 \left\{ 2 \frac{K}{\dot{V}} [m\beta x(V - ax)]^{1/2} \right\}$$

$$\times \exp\left[-\frac{K}{\dot{V}} (m\beta x - ax + V) \right] + \exp\left(-\frac{K}{\dot{V}} m\beta x \right) \delta(V - ax) \tag{6.17}$$

and

$$q(V, x) = \frac{\beta K}{\dot{V}} I_0 \left\{ 2 \frac{K}{\dot{V}} [m\beta x(V - ax)]^{1/2} \right\} \exp\left[-\frac{K}{\dot{V}} (m\beta x - ax + V) \right], \tag{6.18}$$

where, in addition to the symbols used in Chapter 2, $I_0(z)$ and $I_1(z)$ are the Bessel functions of the zeroth and first order of purely imaginary argument iz, and are tabulated in many sources, e.g., "Handbook of Chemistry and Physics" (16).

The second term in Eq. (6.17) represents the original input distribution swept through the column at the same speed as the carrier gas, and decaying exponentially. The rate of decay is normally so great that this term is negligible after the first few millimetres of the column, and the term will not be considered further.

When the argument of the Bessel functions in Eqs. (6.17) and (6.18) is large,

$$I_n(z) \approx \frac{e^z}{(2\pi z)^{1/2}},$$

(6.19)

which holds within about 1% or less for $z > 10$. If this approximation is substituted into the first term of Eq. (6.17),

$$c(V, x) \approx \frac{K^{1/2}}{(4\pi \dot{V})^{1/2}} \cdot \frac{(m\beta x)^{1/4}}{(V - ax)^{3/4}} \exp\left[-\frac{K}{\dot{V}}(\sqrt{m\beta x} - \sqrt{V - ax})^2\right].$$

(6.20)

The equation of the chromatogram of a peak emerging from a column of length l is $c(V)$ for $x = l$. In this case, the two terms in the exponent in Eq. (6.20) are equal when $V = V_R^0$ from Eq. (2.11). The equation for the chromatogram may therefore be written:

$$c(V) \approx \frac{K^{1/2}}{(4\pi \dot{V})^{1/2}} \cdot \frac{(V_R^0 - V_M)^{1/4}}{(V - V_M)^{3/4}}$$

$$\times \exp\left[-\frac{K}{\dot{V}}(\sqrt{V_R^0 - V_M} - \sqrt{V - V_M})^2\right].$$

(6.21)

If it is now assumed that the effective total width of the peak is only a small fraction of its retention, so that we need consider the chromatogram only in the region where $V_R^0 - V$ is small compared to V_R^0, the approximation:

$$(\sqrt{z} - \sqrt{z + \Delta z})^2 \approx \frac{(\Delta z)^2}{4z}$$

(6.22)

may be substituted in Eq. (6.21), yielding:

$$c(V) \approx \frac{K^{1/2}}{(4\pi \dot{V} V')^{1/2}} \exp\left(-\frac{K(V_R^0 - V)^2}{4 \dot{V} V'}\right).$$

(6.23)

Comparison with Eq. (5.19) shows that this is the equation of a Gaussian curve with a variance of

$$\sigma_{(V)}^2 = \frac{2 \dot{V} V'}{K},$$

(6.24)

and a mean of $V_R{}^0$. Thus, in conditions in which approximations (6.19) and (6.22) are valid, the result of the finite rate of mass-transfer is to broaden the delta-function input distribution into an approximately Gaussian distribution with the same mean as if the broadening factor were absent. In these conditions, therefore, retention volumes remain unaffected. In length units, the variance is

$$\sigma_{(x)}^2 = \frac{2kux}{(1+k)^2 K}, \tag{6.25}$$

where k is as in Chapter 2, u is the linear flow rate, and x is the position of the mean.

It is apparent from Eq. (6.23) that the broadening is appreciable even when the asymmetry is not, for otherwise it would not be possible to make approximations giving a finite variance belonging to a symmetrical distribution.

(c) Specification of the Rate Constant, K

There are several ways in which a non-infinite rate constant in Eq. (6.15) may be conceived, of which three will be considered here:

(1) Slow diffusion of vapour in the stationary phase.
(2) Slow diffusion of vapour in the gas phase.
(3) A process akin to chemical reaction at the interface of the phases.

These three are illustrated in Fig. 6.3a, b, and c, and all three together in Fig. 6.3d.

(d) Slow Diffusion in the Stationary Phase

A finite time is required for vapour in the stationary phase to diffuse to and from the interface between the phases. When this is the only factor, $q = \beta c$ at the interface, but within the stationary phase there is a concentration gradient in which the concentration is too small in the front profile and too large in the rear profile of a peak, as shown in Fig. 5.3a.

It may be shown that the effect of slow diffusion within the stationary phase is equivalent to a first order reaction at the surface, so that Eq. (6.15) holds (2). The rate constant, K, may be seen intuitively to be proportional to the area of the surface, A, the diffusion coefficient of the vapour in the stationary phase, D_l, and inversely proportional to the thickness of the liquid layer, d_f. Furthermore, since the larger the volume of the stationary phase per unit length of column (m/ρ), the more vapour must diffuse

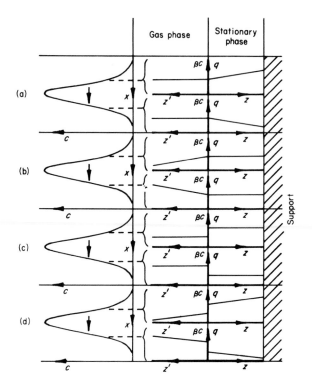

FIG. 6.3. Concentrations of vapour as a function of a coordinate in cross sections of the gas phase and the stationary phase in the front and rear profiles of peaks for various possible causes of non-equilibrium: (a) Non-instantaneous diffusion through the stationary phase. (b) Non-instantaneous diffusion through the gas phase. (c) Discontinuity in chemical potential at the surface of the stationary phase. (d): (a), (b), and (c) operating together.

to increase the average concentration a given amount, the rate constant is also inversely proportional to this. Thus, the expression for K is:

$$K \propto \frac{\varrho A D_l}{m d_f}. \tag{6.26}$$

The constant of proportionality has been assumed by van Deemter, $et\ al.$ (2) to be the constant which is obtained if the rate constant is determined by diffusion into an even layer of stationary phase of constant thickness d_f; in this case the constant is $\pi^2/4$. The authors use this constant, at the same time recognising that it applies only to an ideal case, since in a real packed column, the thickness of stationary phase is by no means constant.

With this value of the constant, and also making use of the fact that if d_f is assumed constant,

$$Ad_f = m/\varrho, \tag{6.27}$$

then the value of the rate constant is given by:

$$K = \frac{\pi^2}{4} \frac{D_l}{d_f^2}. \tag{6.28}$$

Thus the variance due to the operation of slow diffusion in the stationary phase is:

$$\sigma_{(V)}^2 = \frac{8}{\pi^2} \cdot \frac{d_f^2 \dot{V} V'}{D_l}, \tag{6.29}$$

or

$$\sigma_{(x)}^2 = \frac{8}{\pi^2} \cdot \frac{d_f^2 u}{D_l} \cdot \frac{kx}{(1+k)^2}. \tag{6.30}$$

(e) *Slow Diffusion of the Vapour in the Gas Phase*

A finite time is required for vapour molecules in the middle of the carrier gas stream to diffuse to the surface of the stationary phase, as illustrated in Fig. 6.3b. The problem is more complicated than in the previous case, since, in addition to the lateral diffusion, the characteristics of viscous flow are such that gas streams in different parts of the cross section of the gas phase are moving at different speeds.

In the case of a cylindrical tube such as a capillary column, the problem of determining the magnitude of the dispersion in the vapour phase can be regarded in three successive steps, the final result applying to real capillary columns:

(1) Dispersion because of the viscous flow in a tube without stationary phase.

(2) Dispersion also considering a stationary phase in which equilibrium is instantaneous.

(3) Dispersion also considering a stationary phase in which equilibrium is non-instantaneous.

The first of these has been considered by Taylor (17) for cylindrical tubes and by Aris (18) for tubes of arbitrary cross section. The dispersion caused by viscous flow in cylindrical tubes can be explained as follows. Vapour in the tube flows faster in the centre than at the outside, so that if we imagine a distribution of vapour initially constant across the tube, the action of the flow of gas is to move the centre of the distribution further along the tube than the outside; a contour of constant concentration initially planar is distorted by the flow into a paraboloid, as shown in Fig. 6.4. This process, if allowed to continue undisturbed, would produce a very large variance in an initially compact distribution averaged across the tube, but the dispersion is reduced by the action of lateral diffusion, by which

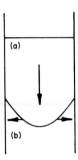

FIG. 6.4. Flow and diffusion in a cylindrical tube. An initially planar concentration contour as at (a) is distorted by viscous flow into the paraboloid (b). If the contour is in a region with more concentrated vapour behind it, lateral diffusion occurs as indicated by the horizontal arrows. If the contour is in a region with less concentrated vapour behind it, lateral diffusion occurs against the arrows.

regions of great concentration in the centre of the tube in the front profile diffuse into regions of small concentration at the edges, and regions of great concentration at the edges of the tube in the rear profile diffuse into regions of small concentration at the centre. If the rate of lateral diffusion (considered independently of longitudinal diffusion) is fast compared to the flow of gas, the dispersion due to viscous flow is nullified. Taylor has calculated that the dispersion for cylindrical tubes of radius r is

$$\sigma^2_{(x)} = \frac{r^2 u x}{24 D_g} \tag{6.31}$$

where u is the average linear flow rate, and Golay, also giving the above result, finds that the dispersion for rectangular tubes with sides z and y $(y \gg z)$ is

$$\sigma^2_{(x)} = \frac{4z^2 u x}{105 D_g}. \tag{6.32}$$

Golay has considered the next two stages of the argument. In the case that there is a retentive stationary phase in which equilibrium is instantaneous, the variance produced in cylindrical columns is

$$\sigma^2_{(x)} = \frac{1 + 6k + 11k^2}{(1 + k)^2} \cdot \frac{r^2 u x}{24 D_g} \tag{6.33}$$

and in flat rectangular columns is

$$\sigma^2_{(x)} = \frac{1 + 6k + 51k^2/2}{(1 + k)^2} \cdot \frac{4z^2 u x}{105 D_g}. \tag{6.34}$$

In these equations, the expressions in k have their smallest values when $k = 0$, indicating that the retentive stationary phase increases the variances due to viscous flow.

Finally, Golay (10) has considered the additional effect of slow diffusion in the stationary phase, and finds that it adds a further variance independently of lateral diffusion in the gas phase, in accord with Eq. (6.1). In the case of cylindrical tubes, this variance is

$$\sigma^2_{(x)} = \frac{k^3}{6(1 + k)^2} \cdot \frac{r^2 u x}{\alpha^2 D_l}, \tag{6.35}$$

where α is the partition coefficient defined by Eq. (3.1). This equation becomes identical with Eq. (6.30) after suitable transformation, with the constant $8/\pi^2$ replaced by the constant $\frac{2}{3}$. The variance for flat rectangular tubes is

$$\sigma^2_{(x)} = \frac{2k^3}{3(1 + k)^2} \cdot \frac{z^2 u x}{\alpha^2 D_l}. \tag{6.36}$$

(f) Processes Equivalent to Chemical Reaction at the Interface

There is little, if any, experimental evidence in gas chromatography for the effect of a discontinuity in chemical potential at the interface between the phases, though experience in other fields of science suggests that such a discontinuity must be present. Interfacial resistance can be accounted for in gas chromatography by assuming a first order reaction at the surface, as described by Eq. (6.15), in which the rate constant is given by (5, 19):

$$K = \frac{Ak_2}{a_2}, \tag{6.37}$$

where k_2 is the rate constant for the desorption of the vapour from the stationary phase, a_2 is (proportional to) the area of the column cross section occupied by the stationary phase, and A is the surface area of stationary phase per unit length of column. A similar term, proposed to account for possible non-instantaneous diffusion of vapour through a stagnant film of gas on the surface of the stationary phase, has been given by Jones [see Kieselbach (20)].

(g) Comparison of Magnitudes of Different Variances

The relative magnitudes of the variances produced by lateral diffusion in each phase of a capillary column can be demonstrated by dividing Eq. (6.33) by Eq. (6.35) to give:

$$\frac{\sigma^2_{(x)g}}{\sigma^2_{(x)l}} = \frac{3}{48} \cdot \frac{r^2}{d_f^2} \cdot \frac{D_l}{D_g} \cdot \frac{1 + 6k + 11k^2}{k}, \tag{6.38}$$

where the additional subscripts to the variances refer to gas and liquid phase. The corresponding equation for packed columns cannot be specified exactly, but may be assumed to have the same form with different constants, d_f being interpreted as an average, and r being replaced by half the average interstice dimension.

When k is of the order of unity, as is common in capillary columns operated for rapid analysis or for optimum resolution per second (Section 6.14), the orders of magnitudes of quantities in Eq. (6.38) can be seen by simplifying it to the approximation:

$$\frac{\sigma^2_{(x)g}}{\sigma^2_{(x)l}} \approx \frac{r^2}{d_f^2} \cdot \frac{D_l}{D_g}. \tag{6.39}$$

Values of D_g are of the order of 10^{-2} to 10^{-1} cm²/sec in most carrier gases; values of D_l for the sort of vapours and the sort of stationary liquids used in gas chromatography have been little studied, but the evidence is that they are of the order of 10^{-7} to 10^{-6} cm²/sec, decreasing with increase in the viscosity of the solvent. Thus the ratio D_l/D_g is of the order of 10^{-5}. In capillary columns, d_f is small compared to r in order to minimise σ and for other reasons discussed in other parts of this chapter, and therefore the ratio of r^2/d_f^2 is large. In much current usage, d_f is of the order of the wavelength of light, e.g., 10^{-5} to 10^{-4} cm (0.1 to 1 μ), and r is of the order of 10^{-1} cm, so that the ratio is of the order of 10^3. In these circumstances, therefore, Eq. (6.39) shows that $\sigma_g{}^2 \approx 10\sigma_l{}^2$, and that diffusion in the gas phase is the more important. For large values of k, Eq. (6.38) shows that the relative importance of gas diffusion becomes still greater. This is shown for capillary columns by Desty and Goldup (21), who find that the variance due to mass transfer increases with increase in retention volume. This subject is discussed further in Sections 6.12 to 6.14.

With packed columns, the circumstances may be different, especially when the packing contains much stationary phase. It is found in practice that on most common porous packings with of the order of 10% by weight of stationary phase, d_f is of the order of 10^{-3} cm, while r interpreted as half the average linear dimension of an interstice is of the order of 10^{-2} cm. In this case, the ratio r^2/d_f^2 is only of the order of 10^2, so that for $k \approx 1$, $\sigma_g^2 \approx 10^{-3}\sigma_l^2$, and virtually all the dispersion of the peak is caused by diffusion in the stationary phase. These considerations led van Deemter et al. (2) to ignore diffusion in the gas phase. When, however, packed columns are made with small proportions of stationary phase and operated with such large values of β that k is large in spite of the small value of m, the circumstances may be such that gaseous diffusion in packed columns is no longer negligible, as is shown in results given by Kieselbach (20).

(h) The Range of Validity of Approximations (6.19) *and* (6.22)

When approximations (6.19) and (6.22) fail, the peaks are not Gaussian and the equations given for the variances also fail.

Transformation of the argument of the Bessel function in Eq. (6.17) for the case that $x = l$ yields:

$$z \approx 2Kkt_M, \tag{6.40}$$

where t_M is the gas hold-up time. For packed columns, use of the typical figures given in Section 6.3(g) together with Eq. (6.28) shows that K is of the order of 10^{-1} to 10^0 sec^{-1}. In much current practice, t_M is of the order of 10 to 100 sec, depending on the column length and the flow rate, so that it is apparent from Eq. (6.40) that with short columns, fast flow rates, and/or small values of k, z may well be less than 10, so that there are conditions in common use in which Approximation (6.19) may be invalid.

With capillary columns, K is much larger; if it is assumed that σ_g provides the only significant peak dispersion due to mass-transfer, use of typical figures together with Eqs. (6.25) and (6.33) show that K is of the order of 10 to 10^2 sec^{-1}. On the other hand, very much smaller values of k are commonly used with capillary columns, e.g., $k = 0.05$ is not unreasonable. In these circumstances also, therefore, Approximation (6.19) may be invalid.

Similar considerations will also show that Approximation (6.22) is also invalid for peaks with small values of k. The result is that either with excessively small values of k, or with large linear flow rates, or with columns in which, for one reason or another, K is excessively large, the corresponding peaks are unsymmetrical with sharp front profiles. This observation is commonplace in gas chromatography, and, though it may sometimes be due to other causes, e.g., a sluggish recording system, there are many cases where it is not. In these circumstances, retention times measured to peak maxima fail to obey the equations of Chapter 2, and retention volumes calculated from such retention times do not have their characteristic invariance.

6.4. The General Non-Equilibrium Theory

(a) "Non-Equilibrium" as a Point Function

The last section described how the effect of non-infinite lateral diffusion in either phase could be related with the resultant dispersion of a chromatographic zone. The method used depends on the solution of differential equations for c subject to boundary conditions imposed by the exact problem, and becomes intractable for all but the simplest sets of such conditions. A very powerful method of calculating the dispersions of chromatographic zones for a much wider variety of conditions than is possible by exact analytical methods has been developed by Giddings (22–24). An account of this is given below.

Section 6.3a and Fig. 6.2 show that it is the lack of instantaneous equilibrium between the phases which causes dispersion of zones. While a zone is being eluted *along* the column, there is a continuous flux *across* the column from phase to phase. In Giddings' treatment, this motion between the phases is regarded as being at right angles to the average direction of flow of the mobile phase, i.e., at right angles to the column axis. Such motion is called *lateral*. In the general treatment, the contents of the column is divided into a set of phases, 1, 2, . . . , i, which is usually just two, one mobile phase and one stationary phase, but may be more if required. Thus, the method can be applied also to simultaneous or consecutive adsorption and solution, or to counter-current extraction, etc., if required.

In each of the phases, there are lateral fluxes of solute. In any element of volume of a given phase i, the rate of accumulation of solute expressed as rate of change of concentration, $\partial c_i/\partial t$, can be specified in terms of a conservation equation similar in kind to that described in Section 2.2. This concentration can change on three counts:

(1) Because there is a longitudinal concentration gradient and the phase

is moving. If the phase is moving with longitudinal velocity v_i, and the longitudinal axis is z, the contribution to $\partial c_i/\partial t$ from this source within the element of volume is $v_i \, \partial c_i/\partial z$ (see Section 2.2).

(2) Because of the lateral flux discussed above. Let this be s_i.

(3) Because of longitudinal diffusion. The contribution to $\partial c_i/\partial t$ from this source is given by the LHS of Eq. (6.7).

Adding these three terms, the resulting conservation equation is:

$$\frac{\partial c_i}{\partial t} = s_i - v_i \frac{\partial c_i}{\partial z} + D_i \frac{\partial^2 c_i}{\partial z^2}. \tag{6.41}$$

Of these three terms, the last is normally small, since the concentration gradient along the column even at the steepest part of the peak is small compared to the lateral gradients, and the relaxing effect of longitudinal diffusion on this gradient is small compared to the relaxing effect of the lateral diffusions on lateral gradients. Thus, the third term can in the present context be neglected.

The major characteristic of Giddings' treatment consists in the recognition that, though the lateral concentration gradients may be large, they apply over short distances, and thus the local concentrations c_i, which are functions of lateral position, are never very different from the values they would have if there were complete lateral equilibrium. It is therefore possible to define two kinds of concentration; first, the actual values, c_i, as above, and second, equilibrium values, $c_i{}^*$, related with the actual values by:

$$c_i = c_i{}^*(1 + \varepsilon_i) \tag{6.42}$$

where ε_i is a number assumed to be small compared to unity, and is called the *non-equilibrium*. Every point in any phase in the column inside a peak has a definite value of ε_i, which is thus a point function. The advantage of the assumption that ε_i is small is that longitudinal concentration gradients can be expressed in terms of the $c_i{}^*$'s rather than the c_i's without material error. Since the $c_i{}^*$'s are not functions of lateral position within the cross-section of any phase, the mathematical problem is thus enormously simplified. The c_i's are relevant only in consideration of lateral gradients, and are considered through the ε_i's. One can thus re-write Eq. (6.41), also omitting the last term:

$$\frac{\partial c_i{}^*}{\partial t} = s_i - v_i \frac{\partial c_i{}^*}{\partial z}. \tag{6.43}$$

With the new assumption, the LHS of this equation can now be related with the average rate of migration of the solute through the column, i.e., the speed of motion of the peak; let this quantity be $\bar{u}$:

$$\frac{\partial c_i^*}{\partial t} = -\bar{u}\,\frac{\partial c_i^*}{\partial z}. \tag{6.44}$$

In this equation, terms due to longitudinal diffusion are again omitted. Eliminating the time derivative between Eqs. (6.43) and (6.44), the result is an equation for the s_i:

$$s_i = (v_i - \bar{u})\,\frac{\partial c_i^*}{\partial z}. \tag{6.45}$$

This equation states the intuitively reasonable result that if a particular phase is moving at a different rate (v_i) from that of the average rate of the solute $(\bar{u})$, the disparity in solute must necessarily be made up by lateral mass transfer (s_i). For stationary phases, $v_i = 0$.

We shall assume here that the flux producing s_i is due solely to diffusion and not to other slow processes such as chemical reaction or slow mass transfer across interfaces (Section 6.3d). If the lateral diffusion coefficient in phase i is D_i, then, from the ordinary diffusion equation:

$$s_i = D_i\,\nabla^2 c_i. \tag{6.46}$$

Since we are now dealing with the *lateral* diffusions which are caused directly by lateral non-equilibrium described by ε_i, we substitute for c_i by Eq. (6.42) to give:

$$s_i = c_i^* D_i\,\nabla^2 \varepsilon_i. \tag{6.47}$$

Elimination of s_i now yields an equation for ε_i:

$$\nabla^2 \varepsilon_i = (v_i - \bar{u})\,\frac{1}{D_i c_i^*}\,\frac{\partial c_i^*}{\partial z} \equiv (v_i - \bar{u})\,\frac{1}{D_i}\,\frac{\partial \ln c_i^*}{\partial z}. \tag{6.48}$$

Since the lateral diffusion is assumed to occur solely in a plane at right angles to the axis, the Laplacian operator is never in more than two dimensions, which symmetry may often reduce to one. Equation (6.48) is a case of Poisson's equation, solutions of which are extensively studied in mathematical physics and engineering.

Analytical solutions of Eq. (6.48) to give ε_i as a function of lateral coordinates can be obtained given the boundary conditions applicable to the circumstances of the particular column under study. The boundary conditions can be divided into five possible classes (22, 24):

(i) The sum of non-equilibrium over a whole cross-section must necessarily equal zero; thus:

$$\sum_i c_i^* \int \varepsilon_i \, dA = 0,$$ (6.49)

where the summation is over all phases, and the integrations over the area occupied by each phase.

(ii) There are no concentration gradients normal to a boundary through which there is no mass-transfer, e.g., a column wall or the surface of a non-absorbent or non-adsorbent particle. Thus at these surfaces,

$$\frac{\partial \varepsilon_i}{\partial w} = 0,$$ (6.50)

where w is a coordinate normal to the boundary.

(iii) Solute transports either side of a phase boundary must be identical, whence:

$$D_i c_i^* \frac{\partial \varepsilon_i}{\partial w} = D_j c_j^* \frac{\partial \varepsilon_j}{\partial w}.$$ (6.51)

(iv) In the usual case that there is no resistance to transport at a phase boundary, non-equilibria either side of the boundary are identical:

$$\varepsilon_i = \varepsilon_j.$$ (6.52)

(v) Conditions imposed by any symmetry in the column. For example, in an open cylindrical tube, there is a radial symmetry so that lateral position can be specified by a single radius variable, r. In such a case,

$$\frac{\partial \varepsilon_i}{\partial r} = 0 \quad \text{when} \quad r = 0.$$ (6.53)

(b) Non-Equilibrium and Plate-Height

Consider a cross-section of a column at right angles to its axis inside a zone of solute. The total flux of solute J per unit area through the cross-section is the sum of all such fluxes one for each phase:

$$J = \sum_i \int^{a_i} c_i v_i \, da_i,$$ (6.54)

where a_i is the fraction of the total column cross-section occupied by phase

i; i.e., $\Sigma_i \, a_i = 1$. Substituting for c_i by Eq. (6.42), this flux can be divided into two parts:

$$ J = \sum_i \int^{a_i} c_i{}^* v_i \, da_i + \sum_i c_i{}^* \int^{a_i} \varepsilon_i v_i \, da_i . \qquad (6.55) $$

In this, the first part is the flux which would pertain if there were no non-equilibrium and no consequent dispersion, and describes the passage through the cross-section of a zone unaffected by any lateral mass-transfer considerations. The second term is that part of the flux due to the non-equilibrium. Formally, such a flux can be related *via* a constant of the nature of a diffusion coefficient according to Fick's law with the overall concentration gradient along the column, $\partial \langle c \rangle / \partial z$, where $\langle c \rangle$ is the average concentration in all phases, defined as the sum of the masses of solute in all phases divided by a unit volume of column containing all phases. Let us make this relation, calling the diffusion coefficient $\mathscr{D}$, so that:

$$ \mathscr{D} = \frac{\sum_i c_i{}^* \int \varepsilon_i v_i \, da_i}{\partial \langle c \rangle / \partial z} . \qquad (6.56) $$

This procedure acquires value if the quantity $\mathscr{D}$ has any useful invariance, which we now study. In the case that there is a single mobile phase, the sum in Eq. (6.56) contains only one term for which $v_i \neq 0$. In this case, using g for mobile phase:

$$ \mathscr{D} = \frac{c_g{}^* \int \varepsilon_g v_g \, da_g}{\partial \langle c \rangle / \partial z} = \frac{c_g{}^* \int \varepsilon_g v_g \, da_g}{\partial \langle c^* \rangle / \partial z} = \frac{c_g{}^*}{\langle c^* \rangle} \cdot \frac{\int \varepsilon_g v_g \, da_g}{\partial \ln \langle c^* \rangle / \partial z} ; \qquad (6.57) $$

the substitution of $\langle c^* \rangle$ for $\langle c \rangle$ is here exact and not merely approximate, on account of Eq. (6.49). Equation (6.48) shows that $c_i{}^*$ appears in the expression for ε_i for any phase only in the form $\partial \ln c_i{}^* / \partial z$ and thus this is a factor in ε whatever the boundary conditions. But in linear chromatography, where $c_i{}^* \propto c_j{}^*$ at any part of the zone for any pair of phases,

$$ \frac{\partial \ln c_i{}^*}{\partial z} = \frac{\partial \ln c_j{}^*}{\partial z} = \frac{\partial \ln \langle c^* \rangle}{\partial z} . $$

Hence the factor $\partial \ln c_i / \partial z$ in ε_i cancels with the similar factor in $\mathscr{D}$. Thus $\mathscr{D}$ is independent of position and of concentration gradient, and is therefore invariant and equivalent to a true diffusion coefficient.

In its effect on a zone, $\mathscr{D}$ is a longitudinal diffusion coefficient similar in kind to that of Section 6.2; i.e., the effect of the non-equilibrium due to *lateral* diffusions D_i is *as if* there had been a *longitudinal* diffusion. The relation between variance and longitudinal diffusion is given by Eq. (6.10). Applying this, therefore, the result is:

$$\frac{\sigma^2_{(x)}}{t} = H\bar{u} = \frac{c_g^*}{\langle c^* \rangle} \cdot \frac{\int \varepsilon_g v_g \, da_g}{\partial \ln\langle c \rangle / \partial z}, \tag{6.58}$$

where also the relation with H is given, using a simple extension of Eq. (6.5). Equation (6.58) thus enables H to be calculated from ε, which in turn can be calculated from Eq. (6.48) and the boundary conditions pertaining to the particular problem. The use of these two equations, therefore, provides a very general method of calculating variances and equivalent plate-height contributions for a large variety of models of columns, and the simplicity of the method is such that the models can afford to be complicated enough to be realistic. The method is exemplified below.

(c) Example

To prove Eq. (6.33) for the dispersion produced in the gas phase in a zone moving through an open tube of radius r_o coated with a retentive layer for which the partition ratio is k. The area occupied by the retentive layer is considered negligible, so that the whole of the cross-section of the column is occupied by the gas phase.

Let the flow velocity averaged across the tube be u. As a result of the paraboloidal flow illustrated in Fig. 6.4, the velocity v_g at a radius r from the tube centre is:

$$v_g = 2u\left(1 - \frac{r^2}{r_0^2}\right). \tag{6.59}$$

The average rate of migration of the vapour, $\bar{u}$, is $u/(1 + k)$, by Eq. (2.17). Thus, the equation for the non-equilibrium in the gas phase, ε_g, using the form of V for a single radial variable is:

$$V^2\varepsilon_g \equiv \frac{1}{r}\frac{\partial}{\partial r} r \frac{\partial \varepsilon_g}{\partial r} = \frac{1}{D_g}\frac{\partial \ln c_g^*}{\partial z}\left\{2u\left(1 - \frac{r^2}{r_0^2}\right) - \frac{u}{(1+k)}\right\}. \tag{6.60}$$

Straightforward integration of this yields:

$$\varepsilon_g = \frac{u}{D_g}\frac{\partial \ln c_g^*}{\partial z}\left\{\frac{(1+2k)r^2}{4(1+k)} - \frac{r^4}{8r_0^2}\right\} + g_0 \ln r + g_1, \tag{6.61}$$

where g_0 and g_1 are integration constants. One boundary condition is the symmetry condition that $\partial \varepsilon_g / \partial r = 0$ when $r = 0$; this immediately gives

$g_o = 0$. Two other boundary conditions are first that the non-equilibrium in the retentive layer, ε_l, equals that in the gas phase, ε_g, at the interface, and second that the sum of non-equilibrium over a cross-section is zero. These conditions are:

$$\varepsilon_l = \varepsilon_g(r_o) \tag{6.62}$$

and

$$k\varepsilon_l + \frac{1}{\pi r_0{}^2} \int_0^{r_0} 2\pi r \varepsilon_g \, dr = 0. \tag{6.63}$$

Solution of Eqs. (6.61), (6.62), and (6.63) gives the three unknowns g_1, ε_g, and ε_1, of which ε_g is relevant here:

$$\varepsilon_g = \frac{u}{4D_g} \cdot \frac{\partial \ln c_g{}^*}{\partial z} \left\{ \frac{r^2(1 + 2k)}{(1 + k)} - \frac{r^4}{2r_0{}^2} - \frac{r_0{}^2}{6} \cdot \frac{(2 + 8k + 9k^2)}{(1 + k)^2} \right\}. \tag{6.64}$$

Application of Eq. (6.57) gives the following expression for $\mathscr{D}$; note the cancellation of $\partial \ln c_g{}^*/\partial z$ with $\partial \ln\langle c^*\rangle/\partial z$:

$$\mathscr{D} = \frac{u^2 r_0{}^2}{48 D_g} \cdot \frac{c_g{}^*}{\langle c^*\rangle} \cdot \left\{ \frac{1 + 6k + 11k^2}{(1 + k)^2} \right\}. \tag{6.65}$$

In this case, $c_g{}^*/\langle c^*\rangle$ is the proportion of vapour in the mobile phase, which is $1/(1 + k)$ [compare text above Eq. (6.11), where the same factor is used; essentially for the same reason]. Hence, using Eq. (6.58):

$$\sigma_{(x)}^2 = 2\mathscr{D}t = 2\mathscr{D}x/\bar{u} = \frac{uxr_0{}^2}{24 D_g} \left\{ \frac{1 + 6k + 11k^2}{(1 + k)^2} \right\},$$

which is Eq. (6.33).

6.5. Broadening Factors Dependent on the Geometry of Packing

(a) The Geometry of Columns

In every chromatographic column, the velocity of the carrier gas is uneven across the column cross section. In the case of a capillary column, there is a simple parabolic velocity profile, while in a packed column, there is a complicated profile determined by the exact arrangement of the particles. As illustrated in the previous section, the existence of this non-uniform velocity distribution causes dispersion. Similarly, dispersion produced by slow processes in the stationary phase depends on the exact shape of the phase.

The connection between the geometry of the phases in a column and the dispersion they produce is particularly easily studied by the general non-equilibrium theory. Thus, the calculation of dispersions in the gas phases for different flow profiles is similar to the example given in Section 6.4c, with different forms for Eq. (6.59) and different boundary conditions, but without other change. Calculations for various geometries have been made, mainly by Giddings et al. (22–32) and also by the author (33). In general, the equation for the contribution to H due to non-infinite lateral mass-transfer takes the form:

$$H = \frac{\sigma^2_{(x)}}{x} = \frac{au}{D_g} \{1 + bf(k)\}, \tag{6.66}$$

where a and b are constants determined by the geometry and k is the partition ratio. Thus, H is proportional to the average flow rate and inversely proportional to a lateral diffusion coefficient. Tables of equations for H in the general format of Eq. (6.66) are given by Giddings (22, 30) and by the author (33) for many geometrical models of columns. Giddings lists equations for liquid phase dispersion, gas phase dispersion, and various cases where there might be rate processes at an interface. The author gives equations for different flow profiles such as might be expected in imperfectly packed columns.

Contributions to the dispersion due to non-infinite diffusion in the liquid phase are calculable for capillary columns, where the liquid phase may approach the ideal of a smooth layer of given thickness; in this case Eq. (6.35) gives the required result and has been confirmed in practice. For packed columns, the geometry of the stationary liquid is usually so complex that no tractable theoretical shape provides a realistic model. However, in the case that the liquid consists of a support consisting of spheres in contact, as in packed glass beads, Giddings gives the appropriate equation for dispersion (30), which has been confirmed in practice (31).

The contribution to dispersion due to the geometry of the flow pattern of the mobile phase has been studied in considerable detail and is of practical importance, since the dispersion occurring in the gas phase is the largest dispersing factor in the more efficient packed columns. In general, the flow pattern of gas through the packed column is complex and very uneven; thus, in any one channel of the packing some gas will be virtually stationary while other gas will be moving with several times the average speed. Were the final chromatographic zone to reflect this velocity profile, peaks would be very broad indeed. What happens is that the very large dispersion which would be produced by the uneven flow profile alone is relaxed by the processes of lateral diffusion described above, so that material diffuses laterally between the very different streamlines of the carrier gas. The effect is to reduce the dispersion to the values calculated by either the precise theory of Section 6.3 or by the approximate but practically valid theory of non-equilibrium. Giddings (22) has divided the possible kinds of lateral mass-transfer into five groups:

(i) *Trans-channel* transfer, which occurs across single interstices, and is the main transfer involved when vapour equilibrates between the gas phase and the liquid on the particles of packing.

(ii) *Trans-particle* transfer, within porous particles.

(iii) *Short-range interchannel* transfer between a large channel and a neighbouring smaller channel.

(iv) *Long-range interchannel* transfer between groups of channels distant by a few particle diameters.

(v) *Trans-column* transfer between totally different parts of the cross-section of the column, due to flow differences caused by uneven packing density in different parts of the packing, or due to "wall effects."

In ordinarily packed columns, lateral mass-transfer occurs in all the above categories, except, of course, (ii), in the case of impermeable packing materials. In general, the further apart in the cross-section are two regions between which the average gas velocity differs, the larger is the distance over which lateral mass-transfer must occur in order to relax the dispersing effect of the uneven flow. Thus, when there are wall effects or uneven packing, these become the dominant contributor to gas-phase dispersion (33). In the case of preparative scale columns of large diameter, there is no doubt that uneven packing across the column causes most of the dispersion. The author concludes (33) that this is also true for the majority of ordinarily packed analytical columns in current use.

When lateral mass-transfer occurs in the process of equilibration between the phases, the dispersion is a function of k, with the contribution to the plate-height increasing asymptotically to a given value as k increases. When lateral mass-transfer occurs during relaxation of flow unevenness on a scale larger than that pertaining to equilibration between the phases, e.g., in the trans-column effect, the contribution to H is independent of k (33); i.e., $b = 0$ in Eq. (6.66). Thus, a column which is inefficient through bad packing is inefficient for all solutes, while in a well packed column, there is a value of k for which the plate number has a pronounced minimum (see Section 6.12).

A particularly important geometrical feature of columns conveniently treated by the non-equilibrium theory is that of coiling (34–36). If it is assumed that the coiling of a column has no effect on the homogeneity or permeability of the packing, the broadening is given by:

$$H = \frac{\sigma_{(x)}^2}{x} = \frac{7ur^4}{12R^2\gamma D_g},\qquad (6.67)$$

where r is the radius of the column, R is the radius of the helix into which the column is wound, and γ is the tortuosity factor (Section 6.2). With ordinary analytical columns in which $r \ll R$ and r is small, the effect is small, but with wide columns, e.g., preparative columns, even a single right-angled bend may produce a very large variance, and render useless any other precautions taken to secure a small total variance.

(b) The Coupling Effect

Hitherto, we have assumed that any lateral mass-transfer in a column has occurred by molecular diffusion, the rate of which is independent of the flow of gas through the column. However, in any packed column, there is also lateral mass-transfer as a result of the bulk flow of gas, since any gas coming up against a particle of packing is forced to go round it to get to the other side, and in so doing it moves sideways. This constitutes lateral mass-transfer. Mass transfer of this sort may be called "hydrodynamic" as opposed to molecular. Golay (37) and the author (38) have referred to this kind of flow as "anastomosis," the word being borrowed from physiology, where it refers to the complicated interconnections of blood capillaries.

Anastomosis occurs by the random motion of given stream lines through any of the many possible routes through the packing, just in the same way that molecular diffusion occurs by the random passage of molecules along paths determined by collisions with their fellows. The result is that the lateral mass-transfer produced by anastomosis obeys Fick's law, and can be described by a quantity similar to a diffusion coefficient. Lateral mass-transfer can, therefore, occur simultaneously by molecular diffusion and by hydrodynamic diffusion.

The effect of simultaneous diffusions is obtained by adding their coefficients. The coefficient of hydrodynamic diffusion is proportional to the average carrier gas speed, u, and also to the average particle diameter,

d_p, since the larger the particles, the larger the step sideways taken by a streamline in bypassing the particle. This coefficient adds to D_g in augmenting lateral mass-transfer. The effect of this on plate-height can best be seen by revising Eq. (6.66) to include the extra term:

$$H = \frac{au}{D_g + \alpha u d_p} \{1 + bf(k)\},\qquad(6.68)$$

where α is a constant. It is seen that the extra lateral diffusion serves to reduce the plate-height, and thus to improve the column performance at fast flows.

The coupling of simultaneous mass-transfers breaks the rule implied by Eq. (6.1), since in this case the diffusions add in the denominator of the expression for H rather than in the numerator. Giddings (39) has studied the effect in detail by a more general treatment than that given here (22, 40), and refers to it as the "coupling" effect. Harper and Hammond (55), and the author (38) have demonstrated the effect experimentally, and have confirmed Eq. (6.68). The exact value of the constant α, which determines the comparative importance of the two kinds of mass-transfer depends on the packing; values between 0.1 and 0.25 have been reported.

6.6. Effect of the Linearity of Isotherms on Broadening

Calculations of peak shapes and variances in non-ideal gas chromatography with a non-linear isotherm equivalent to those of the previous sections have not been made because of the mathematical complexity. If a particular non-linear isotherm is specified, however, the system of differential equations defining the chromatography can be set up, and these can be solved numerically, if not analytically. Funk and Houghton (12) have demonstrated this using a digital computer with the isotherm:

$$c = K_1 qP + K_2 q^2 P^2,\qquad(6.69)$$

where P is the total pressure and K_1 and K_2 are constants.

The case of non-linear ideal chromatography has been considered by DeVault (41). Imagine a zone of vapour with any form of input distribution, e.g., a Gaussian distribution, and consider the chromatography of this in a column in which the vapour has a Langmuir-type isotherm (Fig. 1.6). The front of the front profile of the distribution is at a small concentration, and will start to be eluted through the column at a speed determined by the initial slope of the isotherm. Regions of greater concentration, however, move more rapidly, thus leading to unsymmetrical peaks as described in Section 2.9. If the curvature of the isotherm is considerable, or the column is of sufficient length, the difference in speeds of the front profile and the maximum may be such as would make the peak maximum overtake the front profile, if such a situation were possible or had any meaning. In the case of an ideal column, DeVault shows that the peak maximum crowds up on the front profile until the front profile eventually becomes infinitely sharp, and the equation of the chromatogram contains a discontinuity. This discontinuity moves through the column at a speed determined by the isotherm and the height of the discontinuity, while the rear profile, the concentration in which is always small, moves at a slower speed determined by the initial slope of the isotherm. A similar argument applies in the case of the anti-Langmuir isotherm, the discontinuity now being in the rear profile. In either case, the sharp profile moves at a different speed to the diffuse profile with the result that, though the column is ideal, the zone broadens during its elution. This contrasts with the case of ideal chromatography with a linear isotherm.

In practice, the above processes applying to ideal columns are modified by anastomosis, diffusion, and non-instantaneous equilibrium, with the result that the discontinuity becomes diffuse, and after a certain period of elution a steady state is set up on which, on the one hand, the column is trying to produce a discontinuity on account of the curvature of the iso-therm, and on the other hand, diffusional and rate processes are tending to make the sharp profile more diffuse. If the elution takes longer than is required to establish the steady state, as is common, additional length to the column does not affect the shape of the sharp front, but, of course, increases the diffuseness of the diffuse front. This is seen clearly in Fig. 6.5, where, in the first two peaks, the elution is too fast and the isotherms

FIG. 6.5. Chromatogram illustrating steady-state sharp rear profiles to peaks eluted from columns with very curved anti-Langmuir type isotherms. After James and Phillips (42). Methyl, ethyl, n-propyl, and n-butyl acetates on tricresyl phosphate at 56°C.

are insufficiently curved for the rear profile to reach the steady state, the third peak is intermediate, and, with the fourth peak, there is a rear profile the width of which is determined solely by diffusion, together with a long diffuse front profile.

The factors described in Section 2.8 which cause retention volumes to shift when concentrations of vapour are not effectively infinitely small also cause broadening. The effect of vapour concentration on dispersion has been studied systematically by Bosanquet (43) and by Bosanquet and Morgan (44), using frontal techniques (Section 7.7). In practice, the effect of finite vapour concentration is similar to that of a non-linear isotherm.

6.7. Broadening Due to the Input Distribution of the Vapour

So far the discussion has assumed that the sample is introduced to the input to the column in an infinitely sharp zone. In practice this is impossible, since the zone of vapour occupies a finite volume at least equal to the volume of pure vapour at the inlet pressure, and usually greater because of dilution with the carrier gas. As discussed in Section 2.8, two extreme input distributions are: (1) a plug of gas of constant concentration (Fig. 2.6a); (2) a distribution of great initial concentration, subsequently falling exponentially (Fig. 2.6b). Of these, the first results when the sample injector has a finite volume equal to the volume of the plug which is completely swept out without mixing by one such volume of carrier gas; the second results when the vapour and the carrier gas can mix freely in the sample injector, so that it requires more than one passage of carrier gas to clean the sample injector cavity. In practice, the actual distribution usually lies between these.

For practical purposes, it is important to know the effect of the volume of the input distribution on the column performance. This may be done as follows. Let the input distribution have a variance σ_I^2, let the column produce a variance of σ_C^2, and let the variance of a peak produced by the column on the input distribution have a variance of σ_T^2, all in volume units. Then, by Eq. (6.1):

$$\sigma_T^2 = \sigma_C^2 + \sigma_I^2. \tag{6.70}$$

Substituting for σ_C^2 with Eq. (5.15),

$$\sigma_T^2 = \sigma_I^2 + \frac{(V_R^0)^2}{\mathcal{N}}, \tag{6.71}$$

where $\mathcal{N}$ is the true plate-number of the column. If $\sigma_I{}^2$ is known, therefore, the variance of the resulting peak may be determined.

In practice, a plate-number resulting from the column and input distribution combined would be measured from the chromatogram by the equation:

$$\mathcal{N}' = \frac{(V_R{}^0)^2}{\sigma_T{}^2}, \tag{6.72}$$

where $\mathcal{N}'$ is a phenomenological quantity less than $\mathcal{N}$. If this is substituted into Eq. (6.71), the result is:

$$\mathcal{N}' = \mathcal{N} \cdot \frac{(V_R{}^0)^2}{\mathcal{N}\sigma_I{}^2 + (V_R{}^0)^2}. \tag{6.73}$$

This shows clearly the effect of the input distribution on the performance of the apparatus as a whole. As $\sigma_I \to 0$, $\mathcal{N}' \to \mathcal{N}$; as σ_I increases, $\mathcal{N}'$ decreases, until when σ_I is sufficiently large that $\mathcal{N}\sigma_I{}^2 \gg (V_R{}^0)^2$, $\mathcal{N}'$ is inversely proportional to the variance of the input distribution.

Further light may be thrown on Eq. (6.73) by dividing the right-hand side by $(V_R{}^0)^2$, resubstituting the left-hand side in Eq. (6.72), and rearranging, to give:

$$\frac{\sigma_T}{V_R{}^0/\sqrt{\mathcal{N}}} = \left[\frac{\sigma_I{}^2}{(V_R{}^0)^2/\mathcal{N}} + 1 \right]^{1/2}. \tag{6.74}$$

If the right-hand side of this is plotted against $\sigma_I\sqrt{\mathcal{N}}/V_R{}^0$ (Fig. 6.6), the result is independent of the true plate-number of the column or the retention volume of the vapour. When σ_I is small in relation to $V_R{}^0/\sqrt{\mathcal{N}}$, $\sigma_T = V_R{}^0/\sqrt{\mathcal{N}}$, which is its smallest value. As σ_I rises in relation to $V_R{}^0/\sqrt{\mathcal{N}}$, σ_T rises compared to $V_R{}^0/\sqrt{\mathcal{N}}$. It is seen from the curve that if

$$\sigma_I < \approx 0.2 \frac{V_R{}^0}{\sqrt{\mathcal{N}}} = 0.2\sigma_C, \tag{6.75}$$

then the effect of the input distribution on the performance is negligible. In the case of plug flow in which the volume of the plug is V_I,

$$\sigma_I = V_I/3, \tag{6.76}$$

so that Inequality (6.75) becomes:

$$V_I < \approx 0.6 \frac{V_R{}^0}{\sqrt{\mathcal{N}}}. \tag{6.77}$$

This equation was calculated in this connection by van Deemter, *et al.* (2), and has been frequently quoted. It should be noted that there is no special significance in the factor 0.6 (the above authors, in fact, quote 0.5), which is

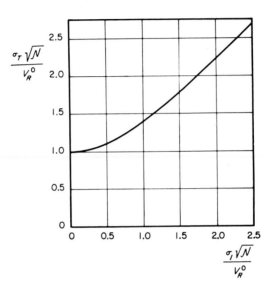

FIG. 6.6. Plot of $\sigma_T \sqrt{\mathcal{N}}/V_R^0$ against $\sigma_I \sqrt{\mathcal{N}}/V_R^0$ according to Eq. (6.74).

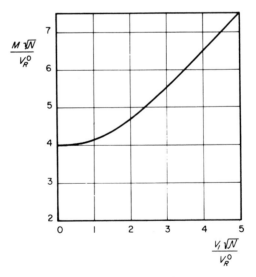

FIG. 6.7. Plot of $M \sqrt{\mathcal{N}}/V_R^0$ against $V_I \sqrt{\mathcal{N}}/V_R^0$ according to van Deemter *et al.* (2).

merely a coefficient providing a threshold below which the effect of the input distribution is less than a certain amount.

The above treatment, though simple, suffers from the defect that σ_T is hard to specify when the effect of the sample injector is so bad that the resulting peak is appreciably flat-topped. This is avoided in the more complicated treatment given by van Deemter *et al.* (2), who use the quantity M as constructed in Fig. 5.5 in place of σ_T, and plot $M\sqrt{\mathcal{N}}/V_R{}^0$ against $V_I\sqrt{\mathcal{N}}/V_R{}^0$ in place of Fig. 6.6 (Fig. 6.7). It is observed that the plots are virtually identical apart from the scales, and give exactly the same information in slightly different ways.

6.8. Broadening Due to the Time Constant of the Detecting System

The possibility of a time lag between the true effluent concentration in the detector and the indication of this concentration by the recorder is a factor in the chain of events between the introduction of a sample and the measurement of the results, although it is not really a broadening factor produced by the chromatographic process. For example, in Fig. 6.8, the peak which should appear as in (a) may appear as in (b) or (c), in which the lag in the recording system causes too small a reading when the concentration is rising and too large a reading when the concentration is falling. In gas chromatography, we are interested in the effect of this lag on three parameters of the chromatogram, (a) the position of the peak maximum, (b) the variance, and (c) the peak area, for quantitative analysis. Aspects of the problem have been studied by Schmauch (45) and by Johnson and Stross (46).

Lag between effluent concentration and its registration can arise in several ways, e.g.:

(1) Non-zero detector volume in which complete mixing occurs (45, 46). The detector takes time to fill and to empty, during which periods the concentration in the detector lags behind that emerging from the column.

(2) Non-zero detector volume in which different parts of the sensing element of the detector sense different regions of the volume of the detector, not all of which can contain vapour at the true effluent concentration (45). This applies, for example, to catharometers consisting of wires coaxially in a tube carrying the effluent and (presumably) to gas density balances.

(3) When the sensing element of the detector is fed by diffusion, as

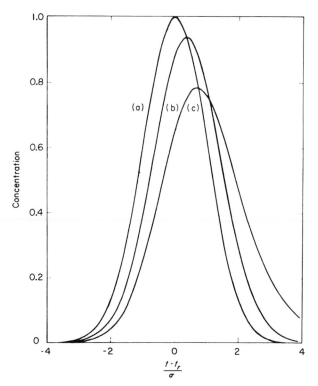

FIG. 6.8. (a) Plot of a Gaussian peak $[c(t)]$ emerging from a column. (b), (c) Plots of $z(t)$ for $k/\sigma = 0.4$, 1.0. From Schmauch (45).

when it is placed in a short side-arm leading from the tube carrying the column effluent (45).

(4) When the remaining portion of the transducer, e.g., the recorder, is sluggish (46).

In cases (1), (3), and (4), which are in practice the most common, the lag in the detecting system can be specified by a time constant, k, defined such that if the concentration is suddenly changed from a value c_0 to c_1 at $t = 0$, the reading of the recorder is given by

$$c_1 - c = (c_1 - c_0)e^{-t/k}. \tag{6.78}$$

If $c(t)$ is the effluent concentration, and $z(t)$ is the concentration recorded by a detector obeying the above equation, then $z(t)$ and $c(t)$ are related by the usual first order equation,

$$\frac{dz(t)}{dt} = \frac{1}{k}\,[c(t) - z(t)]. \tag{6.79}$$

Making use of the condition that in practice, $z(t) = c(t)$ when $t = 0$, the general solution to Eq. (6.79) is:

$$z(t) = \frac{e^{-t/k}}{k} \int c(t) \exp t/k \, dt. \tag{6.80}$$

In the case that the effluent appears as a Gaussian distribution, $c(t)$ can be written:

$$c(t) = \frac{A}{\sigma(2\pi)^{1/2}} \exp[-(t_R - t)^2/2\sigma^2] \tag{6.81}$$

and Eq. (6.81) substituted into Eq. (6.80) gives an explicit equation for $z(t)$. This cannot be expressed analytically, but $z(t)$ may be plotted with the aid of tables of the error function, or may be expanded as a series. Curves for $z(t)$ as a function of $(t_R - t)/\sigma$ for two values of k/σ are given in Fig. 6.8 (45). It is apparent from Eq. (6.79) that the maximum of all such curves lies on $c(t)$.

The effect of the detector time constant on the maximum of the recorded peak is indicated in Fig. 6.8. When, for a given peak, $k \ll \sigma$, it may be shown by expansion of Eqs. (6.80) and (6.81) that the apparent added retention time is approximately equal to k, the time constant of the recording system. The above condition usually holds in practice; if it does not, then the effect of the detector lag can be found only by calculation.

The effect of the lag of the detecting system on the apparent variance of a peak is most easily assessed using Eq. (6.1). The detector lag superimposes a broadening process described by an exponential curve [Eq. (6.78)] on the real effluent distribution. The variance due to this is easily shown to be equal to k^2. Thus, if the variance of the real distribution is σ^2 and that of the recorded distribution is σ'^2, then

$$\sigma'^2 = \sigma^2 + k^2. \tag{6.82}$$

The effect of the detector lag on the peak area is very simply described — there is none, for the areas of $z(t)$ and $c(t)$ are equal. Thus quantitative analysis is not affected by the lag.

The total dispersion of a peak produced by the column, and also by all the various extra-column devices such as those considered in this and the previous section can be studied by the same methods as are used in electrical engineering for the study of the effect of filters. A general survey of extra-column broadening in these terms has been given by Sternberg (47).

6.9. Equations for Plate–Height

Having now discussed the broadening factors and the variances they produce, we now start to discuss the effect of individual column variables on the column performance, the resolution, and the time of analysis. Each of the common types of chromatographic column is subject to a different selection of broadening factors. For each, therefore, there is a different summation of variances which effectively describes the overall plate-height. Here, we shall distinguish three column classes for which there are classical equations for plate-height. We follow normal practice in including in the equations only the broadening factors due to the column itself, and assuming linear isotherms.

(a) Packed Columns with Large Proportions of Stationary Liquid

Columns in this category are the most commonly used for routine purposes, being stable and robust, but they do not give the best performance. With these, the major contributions to dispersion are longitudinal diffusion and slow mass-transfer in the stationary phase. Addition of Eqs. (6.11) and (6.30), followed by substitution in Eq. (6.5) to give an equation for H yields:

$$ H = (A) + \frac{2\gamma D_g}{u} + \frac{8}{\pi^2} \cdot \frac{d_f{}^2}{D_l} \cdot \frac{k}{(1+k)^2} \cdot u. \qquad (6.83) $$

This equation was first given by van Deemter *et al.* (*2*), and usually carries van Deemter's name. In the original treatment a flow independent term A was added. Though this term has no theoretical foundation, it may arise from extra-column broadening; see Section 6.11d. The symbol A is in general use for discussing flow-independent contributions to H.

(b) Packed Columns with Small Proportions of Stationary Liquid

Columns in this category are made with a small proportion of stationary liquid in order to avoid slow diffusion in the liquid becoming the dominant contributor to H at fast flows, and are thus used in applications where good performance and high speed are required (see Section 6.13). In the circumstance that performance is not completely dominated by stationary phase diffusion, there remain four significant broadening factors:

(1) Flow-unevenness on a large scale relaxed by coupled hydrodynamic and molecular diffusion [Eq. (6.68)].
(2) Longitudinal diffusion [Eq. (6.11)].

(3) Short range trans-channel mass-transfer in the gas phase during equilibration of the phases [Eq. (6.66)]. The magnitude of this term is greater the larger the channels, and is roughly proportional to the square of the particle diameter, d_p.

(4) What remains of the slow mass-transfer in the stationary phase [Eq. (6.30)]. In this case, the constant term can scarcely be specified.

Adding together the variances for these four factors, in the order quoted, the resultant equation for H is:

$$H = \frac{Ku}{D_g + \alpha u d_p} + \frac{2\gamma D_g}{u} + \frac{K' d_p{}^2}{D_g} \cdot f(k) \cdot u + \frac{K'' d_f{}^2}{D_l} \cdot \frac{k}{(1+k)^2} \cdot u,$$

(6.84)

where K, K', and K'' are constants, the effective values of which are discussed in later sections.

(c) Capillary Columns

In open-tube columns, e.g., capillary columns, anastomosis is absent, while longitudinal diffusion in the gas phase and lateral diffusion in both phases may be important. The three variances are given by Eq. (6.11) substituting unit tortuosity, Eq. (6.33), and Eq. (6.35). Together with Eqs. (6.1) and (6.5) these yield:

$$H = \frac{2D_g}{u} + \frac{1 + 6k + 11k^2}{24(1+k)^2} \cdot \frac{ur^2}{D_g} + \frac{k^3}{6(1+k)^2} \cdot \frac{ur^2}{\alpha^2 D_l}.$$

(6.85)

This equation is given by Golay (*10*), and often carries his name.

6.10. Effect of Column Length on Performance

It may be seen from any of the equations given for σ in the preceding sections that $\sigma^2_{(x)} \propto x$, and therefore that H is a constant and independent of the length of the column. This justifies the use of the idea of theoretical plates. It is shown in Section 6.18, however, that H is only constant throughout the column or independent of the column length when the pressure drop across the column is small. The result is that usually the plate-number is rather less than proportion to its length. For example, DeWet and Pretorius (*48*) find that a packed column of 500 cm length has the equivalent of 2404 plates, and that a similarly constructed column of

5000 cm length operated similarly has the equivalent of 17,605 plates, which is considerably less than 10 times as many as the shorter column. Few workers have investigated the relation between $\mathcal{N}$ and l in circumstances where the pressure drop is not significant, possibly because the linear relation is considered axiomatic. Scott (49), however, shows that $\mathcal{N} \propto l$ at least up to $\mathcal{N} = 20,000$, $l = 50$ feet if the ratio of inlet to outlet pressure is reduced by means of an outlet choke.

In connection with column length, it should be emphasised that though the column performance is measured by $\mathcal{N}$, the resolution (column properties other than length being constant) is proportional to $(\mathcal{N})^{1/2}$, so that the resolution is proportional to the square root of the length. Thus, double the resolution requires four times the length.

6.11. Effect of Flow Rate on Performance

The carrier gas flow rate has a large effect on the performance of a column, and this variable has been extensively studied.

(a) Packed Columns; Thick Liquid Layer

The term A of the van Deemter equation, Eq. (6.83), does not include the flow rate, the second term contains it in the denominator, and the third term contains it in the numerator. Thus, for a general discussion of the effect of flow rate, the equation can be simplified to:

$$H = A + \frac{B}{u} + Cu, \tag{6.86}$$

where A is a constant,

$$B = 2\gamma D_g, \tag{6.87}$$

and

$$C = C_l = \frac{8}{\pi^2} \cdot \frac{k}{(1+k)^2} \cdot \frac{d_f^2}{D_l}, \tag{6.88}$$

and are in principle not functions of flow rate. Equation (6.86) was first given by Keulemans and Kwantes (50). It is the equation of a hyperbola, the general shape of the positive part of which is shown in Fig. 6.9. The curve has a minimum in the H.E.T.P. when

$$H = A + 2(BC)^{1/2} \tag{6.89}$$

at a flow rate of

$$u = (B/C)^{1/2}. \qquad (6.90)$$

For best column performance in a given column, this flow rate is an optimum. It is apparent that longitudinal diffusion is important at slow flow rates, when the vapour resides for a long time in the column, while non-equilibrium is important at fast flow rates, in which case there is little time for equilibration before the zone has passed on. It can be seen that C matters at fast flow rates, B matters at slow flow rates, and all matter at or near the optimum flow rate.

Experimental curves of H.E.T.P. as a function of flow rate have been given by many authors (49–54) and the general shape of such curves is that of Fig. 6.9. Typical experimental curves are shown in Fig. 6.10 (51).

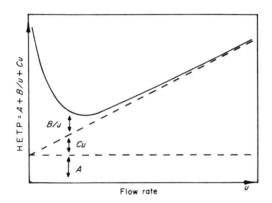

FIG. 6.9. Theoretical plot of Eq. (6.86).

Equation (6.86) is useful in the discussion of column design for two reasons: (a) it gives a concise description of the variation of efficiency with flow rate, and (b) it can be used to eliminate the flow rate as a variable, so that the discussion of the other column variables can be made entirely in terms of the parameters A, B, and C, subject to the limitations of the equation discussed above. In order to determine values of A, B, and C from experimental data, it is necessary to determine plate-heights (Section 5.5) as a function of flow rate. The parameters may then be conveniently obtained by standard methods of numerical analysis or by a graphical technique. A suitable graphical technique is:

Plot H against u (Fig. 6.9). Construct the asymptote to the curve at fast flow rates by placing a transparent straight edge in the approximate position of the asymptote, and adjusting it until the vertical distance between the straight edge and the curve is inversely proportional to the flow rate. This operation is easily performed if the plot is made on finely squared paper. The intercept of the asymptote on the ordinate $u = 0$ is

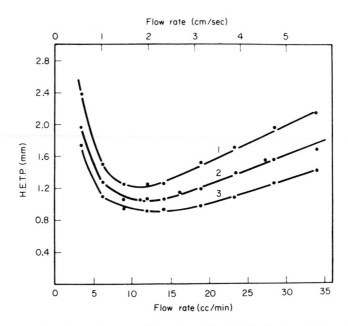

FIG. 6.10. Experimental curves illustrating Eq. (6.86). 1, 2-methyl pentane; 2, n-heptane; 3, n-octane. From Littlewood (*51*).

A, B is the constant product of the flow rate and the distance between asymptote and the curve, and C is the slope of the asymptote.

Values of A, B, and C differ widely according to the design and operation of the columns. The following tabulation gives the orders of magnitude of the quantities for packed columns of the type commonly used in analysis:

$$A \approx 0\text{–}1 \text{ mm}$$

$$B \approx 10 \text{ mm}^2/\text{sec}$$

$$C \approx 0.001\text{–}0.01 \text{ sec}$$

$$H_{\min} \approx 0.5\text{–}2 \text{ mm}$$

$$u_{\text{opt}} \approx 1\text{–}10 \text{ cm/sec}$$

(b) *Packed Columns; Thin Liquid Layer*

In this case, H is given by Eq. (6.84), and can be abbreviated to:

$$H = \frac{Ku}{D_g + \alpha u d_p} + \frac{B}{u} + C_g u + C_l u, \qquad (6.91)$$

where C_g pertains to the gas phase and C_l to the liquid phase. Of the terms in this equation, the term involving slow diffusion in the liquid phase is, by hypothesis, relatively small. Also, in ordinary practice, the third term, describing short-range mass-transfer in the gas phase, e.g., across channels, is small compared to the first term which describes larger-scale effects relaxed by coupled molecular and hydrodynamic diffusion. The variation of H with flow rate, therefore, is dominated by the first two terms.

At fast flows $\alpha u d_p \gg D_g$ with the result that the first term becomes approximately a constant "A term," while at slow flows, so that $D_g \gg u d_p$ with the result that the first term approximates to a term proportional to flow rate, as in the "C term" of the van Deemter equation. The net result is that a plot of H against u resembles that of Fig. 6.9 except that at fast flows, the plot begins to flatten out to the asymptotic value given by the dominating first term, i.e., $K/\alpha d_p$. The flow at which the effect of coupling begins to cause flattening of the H vs. u curve depends in detail on the values of the parameters. If it is assumed that the second two terms of Eq. (6.91) can be completely neglected, which is nearly true for diatomaceous earth packings with less than about 5% by weight of stationary liquid, the only remaining parameters are K and α.

Values of α have been studied in a gas chromatographic context by Giddings (22), by Harper and Hammond (55), and by Littlewood (38), and by others in chemical engineering, in which it is closely related to the coefficient of radial diffusion in fixed beds. Values vary with packing between $\alpha = 0.1$ (22) and about $\alpha = 0.25$ (38). The result of this in ordinary columns is that the effect of the coupling on the shape of the plot of H against u is apparent when $u > 5$ cm/sec in heavy gases such as nitrogen, where D_g is small, or when $u > 20$ cm/sec in gases such as hydrogen or helium, where D_g is large (38, 55). A typical plot of H against u showing the coupling effect is given in Fig. 6.11 (38).

The use of columns at fast flow rates where hydrodynamic diffusion couples with molecular diffusion in relaxing flow unevenness has the advantage that the number of theoretical plates spanned per unit time by the solute is thereby augmented. Thus, the resolution achieved per unit time is increased (Section 6.14). It may be argued that rather than alleviate the effects of bad packing by thus using fast flows, it would be better to improve the packing. This counsel of perfection, however, has hitherto proved impractical.

Values of K in Eq. (6.91) or (6.84) depend on the degree of flow unevenness. At flows slow enough that hydrodynamic diffusion is negligible, and in packed columns where dispersion due to short-range trans-channel mass-transfer is small, the coefficient of u in the equation for H is virtually

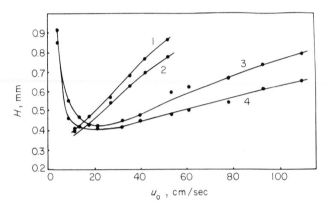

FIG. 6.11. Typical plot of H against u showing tendency of H to flatten out at very fast flows; the curves fit Eq. (6.91) rather than Eq. (6.86). Lines 1 and 2 are for solutes in nitrogen carrier gas; lines 3 and 4 are for solutes in hydrogen carrier gas (38).

equal to K/D_g. Indeed, in much of the literature in which the coupling effect is not considered, the quantity K/D_g is called C_g. These conditions apply in most practical packed columns operated at flow rates not too far above the values for minimum H. Values of K and of K/D_g for various of the more efficient packed columns described by several authors in the literature are tabulated by the author (33). A summary of typical values of K, K/D_g, and C_l for packed columns is given in Table 6.1. Values of both K/D_g and C_l are of the order of milliseconds, and the figures show that in packed columns operating with light liquid loading, the gas phase and liquid phase terms can be of comparable magnitude (see Section 6.3g).

In detailed studies of column dispersion, it is often required to separate C_g from C_l in the term for H which is proportional to u. This may be done by using successively in the column under study either two different carrier gases, or one carrier gas at two different pressures, comparing the dispersions given by each, and using the fact that $C_g \propto 1/D_g$, but C_l is constant (28, 33, 56–59).

TABLE 6.1

VALUES OF K, K/D_g, AND C_l FOR TYPICAL PACKED COLUMNS OF GOOD PERFORMANCE[a]

Support	Stationary liquid	Proportion of liquid (% w/w)	Diameter (mm)	K (cm² × 10⁵)	K/D_g (ms)		C_l (ms) (solute in brackets)	Reference
					H₂	N₂		
"Chromosorb"	Polyether	5	2.2	15	0.4	—	0.3 (n-C₅)	57
"Chromosorb"	Polyether	30	2.2	30	0.8	—	2.4 (n-C₅)	57
"Sil-o-Cel"	Octadecane	10	5	11	0.2	1.0	0.3 (n-C₄)	56
"Sil-o-Cel"	Octadecane	20	5	20	0.5	2.2	0.8 (n-C₅)	56
Celite	Hexadecane	10	4.5	20	0.7	2.7	1.3 (n-C₆)	33
Celite	Hexadecane	10	6	40	1.2	4.5	1.6 (n-C₅)	33

[a] See Eq. (6.91).

(c) Capillary Columns

The principal difference between capillary columns and packed columns as regards H against u curves is the absence in the former of any term to do with uncertain geometry of packing. For capillary columns, the equivalent of Eq. (6.91) is derived from Eq. (6.85), and is:

$$H = \frac{B}{u} + (C_g + C_l)u. \qquad (6.92)$$

This equation gives a plot similar to that of Fig. 6.9, with $A = 0$. Many examples are given by Desty and Goldup (21).

There is special interest in this equation in the case that the layer of stationary phase is thin enough that the term for diffusion in the stationary phase is negligible, so that $C_l = 0$ and:

$$H = \frac{2D_g}{u} + \frac{1 + 6k + 11k^2}{24(1 + k)^2} \cdot \frac{ur^2}{D_g}. \qquad (6.93)$$

From this, it is easily found (60) that when k is small,

$$
\begin{aligned}
H_{\min} &= 0.57r && [0.57 = (1/3)^{1/2}], \\
u_{\mathrm{opt}} &= 6.9D_g/r && [6.9 = (48)^{1/2}],
\end{aligned}
\qquad (6.94)
$$

and when k is large,

$$
\begin{aligned}
H_{\min} &= 1.9r && [1.9 = (11/3)^{1/2}], \\
u_{\mathrm{opt}} &= 2.1D_g/r && [2.1 = (48/11)^{1/2}].
\end{aligned}
\qquad (6.95)
$$

If the above assumption is justified, as is discussed in Section 6.3(d), typical values for a capillary column of 1 mm diameter would be

$$
\begin{aligned}
H_{\min} &\approx 0.2\text{–}1 \quad \mathrm{mm}, \\
u_{\mathrm{opt}} &\approx 5\text{–}10 \quad \mathrm{cm/sec},
\end{aligned}
$$

and these figures appear to be typical of current practice.

(d) Other Broadening Factors Dependent on Flow Rate

The variance due to the detector can be divided into two parts, that due to the time required to sweep out the volume of the detector cavity (σ_D), and that required for the transducer to respond (σ_T). It is apparent that

$$\sigma_{(t)D} \propto \frac{1}{\dot{V}}, \qquad \sigma_{(t)T} = \text{const},$$

and

$$\sigma_{(V)D} = \text{const}, \qquad \sigma_{(V)T} \propto \dot{V}. \qquad (6.96)$$

Therefore, for peaks that come through in a fast *time* on account of a fast flow rate, the variance due to the transducer is of primary importance, but for peaks which come through in a small *volume*, whether the flow rate be slow or fast, the variance due to the detector volume is of primary importance.

6.12. EFFECT OF PARTITION COEFFICIENT ON PERFORMANCE

(a) Packed Columns

The partition coefficient affects the performance of packed columns largely through its effect on the parameter C of Eq. (6.86). There is a small effect on B, since in general the larger the partition coefficient, the more complex the vapour molecule, and the smaller the value of D_g. This effect is rarely significant, however, since it is small in any case, and flow rates are commonly greater than optimum.

The expression for C_l, Eq. (6.88), contains the partition coefficient explicitly in the form

$$\frac{k}{(1 + k)^2} \equiv \frac{a/m \cdot \beta}{(a/m + \beta)^2}.$$
(6.97)

The expression has a maximum when $k = 1$, tends to zero as k tends to zero, and tends to $1/k$ as k becomes large. In packed columns, k is generally considerably greater than unity (see Section 2.4), so that because of the above expression, C_l decreases with increase in partition coefficient. The fall of C with increase in k for $k > 1$ is somewhat diminished by the fact that it is generally the larger molecules which are the more retained, and these tend to have larger values of D_l, which also appears on the denominator of the expression for C_l. However, the variation of D_l is considerably smaller than the variation of k with retention. The net result is that when C_l is the dominating broadening factor, the larger the retention volume, the smaller the plate-height. An example of this in practice can be seen from Fig. 6.10.

In packed columns with light liquid loading conforming to the regimens of Eq. (6.84) as discussed in Section 6.11b, the terms containing k are numerically small compared to the first term. In these circumstances, therefore, the plate-height is found to be virtually independent of reteution.

(b) Capillary Columns

Study of Eq. (6.85) on the same lines as are used above for packed columns shows that if gas diffusion is the dominant broadening factor at fast flow rates, then the plate-height should increase with increase in k, but that if diffusion in the stationary phase is dominant, then capillary columns should show the same characteristics as packed columns. The former conditions have been demonstrated in practice by Scott and Hazeldean (61) and by Desty and Goldup (21), both sets of authors giving results in which C increases as k increases. In this case, families of curves such as are shown for packed columns in Fig. 6.10 are reversed, as in Fig. 6.12.

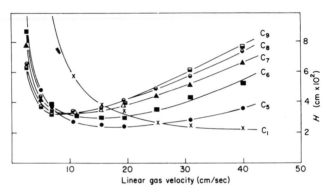

FIG. 6.12. Experimental plots of plate-height of peaks due to n-alkanes against linear gas velocity in a capillary column (75°C). Note that in contrast to the similar plot of Fig. 6.10, the greater the retention of the vapour, the larger the plate-height at large flow rates. From Desty and Goldup (21). $C_x = n - C_x H_{2x+2}$.

(c) Partition Coefficient and Other Broadening Factors

The effect of the detector time constant on peaks eluted quickly in the early part of the chromatogram is greater than that on those eluted with greater $\sigma_{(t)}$ in the later parts of the chromatogram. In this way, the detector tends to make H appear to decline with increase in partition coefficient.

Another factor is that vapours with large partition coefficients are usually the less volatile members of a mixture, and so may require a larger volume of carrier gas in which to evaporate in the sample injector. This, however, does not affect H as a function of β, since $\sigma_{(V)}$ is in any case larger the larger the value of β.

A less obvious factor of frequent occurrence is that substances with large retention volumes tend to have non-linear isotherms, especially when their activity coefficients are considerably greater than unity. This produces asymmetrical peaks together with an increase in plate-height, as described in Section 6.5. The effect can be reduced by reducing the sample size (Section 6.19), increasing the temperature (Section 6.15), or by choosing a different stationary phase (Section 3.8).

6.13. Effect of the Proportion of Stationary Phase on Performance

For a given support, the weight of stationary phase per centimetre of column (m) affects the column performance through its effect on C_l of Eq. (6.88), which contains the quantity m explicitly [expression (6.97)], and also implicitly in d_f, the average thickness of the stationary phase layer. In the circumstance that $k \gg 1$, th part of C_l containing m explicitly reduces to approximately $1/k$. At the same time it appears that d_f is roughly proportional to m, so that from Eq. (6.88), the net result is that $C \propto m$ approximately.

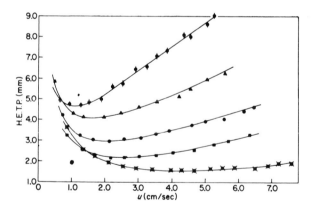

Fig. 6.13. Plate height as a function of flow rate with the proportion of stationary phase as parameter. From Duffield and Rogers (*62*). 2,3-Dimethylbutane on polyethylene glycol 400 at 25°C. ◆, 50% w/w P.E.G.; ▲, 43%; ●, 34%; ■, 25%; ✖, 18%.

The improvement in performance with decrease in m has been reported many times; e.g. by Duffield and Rogers (*62*), whose graph of H as a function of u with m as parameter is shown in Fig. 6.13. Several authors have pointed out the advantage of using small values of m in the construction of columns with small plate-height, and Scott (*49*), and Cheshire and Scott

(*53*) amongst others have constructed packed columns with large plate-numbers the prime feature of which is a small value of m.

An advantage of the use of small values of m is that C_l is small, so that flow rates may be increased without much loss in performance, and so analyses may be performed more rapidly. This property has commonly been recognised, but if m is reduced below a certain value, though performance increases, resolution does not, as is described in the following section.

Apart from the considerations of the next section, there are certain drawbacks to using small proportions of stationary phase which may make it desirable to sacrifice the smaller plate-height obtained thereby. As has been pointed out by Scott (*49*) and by Golay (*63*), if m is reduced, the sample size must be reduced in proportion to avoid raising the concentrations of solute in either phase. This may necessitate samples being so small that a very sensitive detector is necessary, or that important trace components are missed.

A further drawback to columns with small quantities of stationary phase is that, if a small weight of stationary phase is removed by evaporation, the proportion so removed is comparatively large, and there is a significant change in retention volumes. Thus, columns with small values of m tend to have short working lives.

Yet another drawback is associated with the fact that the supports of packed columns are rarely completely inert, and, if m is small, the adsorptive properties of the support are comparable with the retention produced by the solvent. This factor is discussed fully in Section 7.2.

In conditions in which mass transfer is largely determined by diffusion in the gas phase, and when k is large, C is nearly independent of the proportion of stationary phase, as is shown for capillary columns by Desty and Goldup (*21*).

6.14. Effect of k on Resolution and Analysis Time

We have described in the previous two sections how the column performance generally increases with increase in β and decrease in m. Large values of β associated with ordinary values of m, however, cause large values of k, and with ordinary flow rates cause excessive retention times. Also, small values of m associated with ordinary values of β cause small values of k, with the result that the column resolution may suffer even when the performance is good, as described in Section 5.7. Thus when retention time and resolution must be considered in addition to column performance, the considerations of the previous sections require enlarging. The matter is discussed most easily by choosing k as an independent variable.

(a) Effect of k on Resolution

The resolution defined by Eq. (5.31) contains k explicitly in Eq. (5.36), in the form:

$$R \propto \frac{k}{1 + k}. \tag{6.98}$$

Thus, if the relative retention and the plate-number remain constant, R is more or less constant and nearly equal to its greatest value when k is large, but becomes smaller as k declines. Because of this, therefore, it is desirable to use conditions in which k is large, e.g., low temperature, large value of m, and large value of β. This inevitably implies long analysis time.

Ordinary packed columns usually operate with relatively large values of k, and capillary columns operate with small values of k. Purnell (*64, 65*) has pointed out that the whole advantage of the enormous plate-numbers given by capillary columns may be lost if they are operated in conditions in which k is fractional. This may be seen by comparing the analyses on a capillary and on a packed column of a mixture with a wide range of values of β, using the typical values of k quoted in Section 2.3, i.e.,

> Capillary $k = 0.2$ to 20,
>
> Packed $k = 2$ to 200.

The effect of k on the resolution operates only on the very fastest peaks in the case of the packed column. On the capillary column, the effect of k on slow peaks is again small, but on fast peaks, however, the effect is such that most of the advantage of the large plate-number is lost. For example, with a vapour which gives $k = 0.2$ on a capillary column and $k = 2$ on a packed column, the capillary column must have $(2/3)/(0.2/1.2)^2 = 16$ times as many plates in order to provide the same resolution. In many chromatograms shown in the literature, the value of k for rapid peaks is even less than 0.2, with the result that, for these peaks, the resolution on a column capable of hundreds of thousands of plates may be poorer than that on quite a short packed column having only of the order of 1000 plates. The operation of k on resolution independently of plate-number is shown in Fig. 6.14, in which are constructed the chromatograms of a mixture

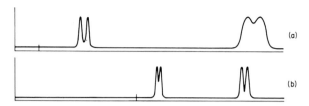

Fig. 6.14. Chromatograms of two close volatile vapours and two close less volatile vapours, (a) on a column of relatively poor performance but operating at large values of k, (b) on a column of relatively good performance, but operating at small values of k. The chromatograms have been constructed as for the separation of 1-pentene, n-pentane, 2-methylhexane, and 2,3-dimethylpentane, (a) on a column with 2000 plates, $k = 2$ for n-pentane, (b) on a column with 20,000 plates, $k = 0.2$ for n-pentane. The vertical line on each chromatogram represents the position of an air peak, i.e., $k = 0$.

of two close vapours with small values of β and two close vapours with large values of β (a) on a column with large m but relatively small plate-number, which separates the volatile pair but not the involatile pair, and (b) on a column such as a capillary column, which separates the involatile pair but not the volatile pair.

In order to try to avoid the complication that the relation between resolution and plate-number also involves k, some workers (66, 67) use a scheme of description involving "effective theoretical plates," the number of which, n, is related to the number of theoretical plates already defined in Section 5.2 by the relation:

$$n = \left(\frac{k}{1+k}\right)^2 \mathscr{N}.$$ (6.99)

n is always thus less than $\mathscr{N}$. The relation between R and n is [cf. Eq. (5.36)]:

$$R = (r_{23} - 1)(n)^{1/2}/4,$$ (6.100)

which does not involve k. The "Height Equivalent to an Effective Theoretical Plate," HEETP, h, can also be defined as l/n. The quantities h and n pertain to a given separation, and have limited use in discussing individual separations. The quatities H and $\mathscr{N}$ are characteristic of the column; thus in this chapter, the whole of the discussion is in terms of these.

(b) Effect of k on Analysis Time

According to the principles considered so far, the analysis time can be made arbitrarily small by any of several ways, e.g., increasing the flow rate, reducing m, or reducing β by raising the temperature. In all such cases, however, reduction in analysis time less than a certain threshold results in loss of resolution. It is therefore more appropriate to consider analysis time in relation to the resolution as a function of other variables. For example, Loyd et al. (68) consider the quotient R_{23}/t, where t is the retention time of either of two close components 2 and 3; this is the amount of resolution produced per unit time. Golay (37), and, in effect, Purnell and Quinn (69) consider R^2/t, which is more invariant. Apart from considerations of invariance, any such function may be considered, depending on the relative importance of R and t. The quantity R^n/t^m for any positive values of n and m as a function of k always has a maximum or greatest value at a specific value of k.

If, in Eq. (5.36), R is divided by the retention time, t, the result is:

$$\frac{R_{23}}{t} = (r_{23} - 1) \cdot \frac{k}{(1+k)^2} \cdot \frac{\sqrt{\mathcal{N}}}{t_M}, \qquad (6.101)$$

where t_M is the gas hold-up time. Loyd et al. assume that $\mathcal{N}$ is independent of k, and from the above equation they find that R/t has a maximum value when $k = 1$. When k increases greater than unity, the retention time increases faster than the improvement in resolution; when k decreases less than unity, the loss of resolution more than outweighs the gain in retention time.

The assumption made above that $\mathcal{N}$ is independent of k is unreasonable, as is apparent from Section 6.12. Golay (37), Purnell and Quinn (69), Scott and Hazeldean (61), and others have considered equations also containing assumed relations between $\mathcal{N}$ and k.

It is reasonable to assume that the flows at which any function of resolution per unit time will be maximised will be fast enough that longitudinal diffusion can be neglected. Therefore, in discussing packed columns in which the dispersion due to geometrical effects and coupled relaxation is negligible, e.g., in cases where C_l is dominant, and in discussing capillary columns, one can assume (69) that $H = Cu$. Rearranging Eq. (5.36), and substituting this form for H, we obtain:

$$R^2 = \frac{\mathcal{N}}{16} \cdot \frac{k^2(r_{23}-1)^2}{(1+k)^2} = \frac{l}{16Cu} \cdot \frac{k^2(r_{23}-1)^2}{(1+k)^2}.$$

If now the equation $u = l(1 + k)/t$ [derived from Eq. (2.16)] is substituted, the result is:

$$\frac{R_{23}^2}{t} = (r_{23} - 1)^2 \cdot \frac{k^2}{4C(1+k)^3}. \qquad (6.102)$$

Thus, R_{23}^2/t is independent both of column length and flow rate; hence the statement above that this particular function of R and t was the most invariant. In such a case, doubling the column length requires one to double the flow to keep the same analysis time, with consequent doubling of the plate-height. The number of plates and the resolution are thus unchanged.

If it is assumed that C is independent of k, R_{23}^2/t as given by Eq. (6.102) has a maximum at $k = 2$, and the required time of analysis is:

$$t = \frac{27CR_{23}^2}{(r_{23} - 1)^2} . \tag{6.103}$$

As an example of the use of this equation, let us assume that two components have a relative retention of $r_{23} = 1.1$, and that we require the minimum time for their separation to the extent of 4 standard deviations; this separation is approximately that of Fig. 5.9b. Substitution in Eq. (5.31) shows that 4σ separation corresponds to $R = 1$. The minimum time required by Eq. (6.103) is thus $27C/0.1^2 = 2700C$ sec. Using a typical value of $C = 0.005$ sec (Table 6.1), this gives a minimum analysis time of 13.5 sec.

Discussion of the minimisation of R^2/t can be improved by incorporating a known functional relation between C and k. Thus, Purnell and Quinn (69), and Scott and Hazeldean (61) have considered the case of a capillary column, in which C_g and C_l are given by Eqs. (6.33) and (6.35). In this case, the optimum value of k is also a function of the partition coefficient, α [see Eq. (6.35)]. When α is large, k has an optimum value close to 2, and for values of k greater than the optimum, the ratio t/R_{23}^2 increases but slowly. Also, Eq. (6.103) holds approximately. When α is small, the optimum value of k is also small, e.g., $k \approx 0.1$ when $\alpha \approx 10$, but, as a result of these excessively small optimum values of k, the corresponding minimum value of t/R_{23}^2 is very much larger, and furthermore the minimum is deeper, so that the ratio t/R_{23}^2 increases rapidly as k departs from the optimum value. On all counts, therefore, it is recommended that for optimum values of t/R_{23}^2, the partition coefficient should be as large as practical.

In columns conforming to Eq. (6.84) where geometrical factors predominate, the plate number is virtually independent of k and α. The connection between resolution and plate number, however, still involves k through Eq. (5.36). The optimum value of R/t is thus still given by $k = 1$ from operation of Eq. (6.101). At moderate flows where diffusion is predominantly molecular, the plate-height is approximately proportional to u. In this case, R^2/t is invariant as described by Eq. (6.102), there is a maximum in

R^2/t at $k = 2$, and Eq. (6.103) applies. At very fast flows where lateral diffusion is predominantly hydrodynamic, the plate-height rises asymptotically to the value of $K/\alpha d_p$.* In this case, R^2/t increases continuously with flow rate, but R itself is subject to a greatest value. In principle, therefore, increase in flow secures more rapid analysis *ad infinitum* so long as the resolution corresponding to the asymptotic value is adequate. In practice, however, mass-transfer terms due to equilibration between the phases inevitably supervene at very fast flows.

6.15. Effect of Temperature on Performance

Change of temperature affects performance principally through the change that it causes in the partition coefficient. With packed columns in which C_l predominates, as the temperature is reduced, the partition coefficient increases, and hence the value of C decreases as described in Section 6.12, thus improving the performance. Operating against this is the fact that as the temperature decreases, the diffusion coefficient D_l also decreases, thus tending to increase the value of C. In most practice, it appears that the effect of the increase in partition coefficient easily outweighs the effect of the increase in diffusion coefficient, so that performances improve as the temperature lowers. This is reasonable on theoretical grounds, for the changes in partition coefficient and in diffusion coefficient with temperature are both processes described by an equation of the form of Eq. (3.79), and the heat of solution of the vapour is always greater than the activation energy of diffusion.

With capillary columns, decrease in the value of k may improve the performance if gas diffusion is the dominant factor in mass transfer, as is illustrated by Fig. 6.12. In this case, increase in temperature should improve the performance both on this account, and on account of the change in diffusion coefficient. Desty and Goldup (*21*) present results that show that for a given vapour the value of C decreases considerably with increase in temperature, but that for a given partition coefficient, the changes in performance are small, and probably dominated only by the comparatively small temperature coefficients of diffusion.

With packed columns in which relaxed flow unevenness is the dominating factor, performance at moderate flow rates improves with increase in tem-

---

* α is here the constant describing hydrodynamic diffusion; cf. α used for partition coefficient immediately above.

perature (51, 62), presumably also because of the increase in the gas diffusion coefficient.

The influence of the temperature of the sample injector on the efficiency of a gas-chromatograph has been studied by Pollard and Hardy (70), who have plotted the effective plate-height against the introducer temperature (Fig. 6.15). When the temperature of the introducer is below the boiling

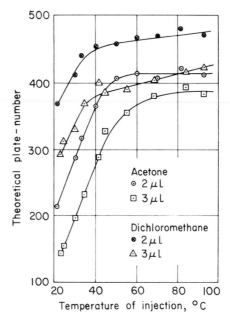

Fig. 6.15. Plate-number as a function of the temperature of the sample injector, with sample as parameter. From Pollard and Hardy (70).

point of the sample, the input distribution is broadened because of the time taken for the sample to evaporate and the volume of carrier gas required to contain the vapour. As the temperature of the sample injector rises, the plate-number rises, till at a high enough temperature the value of the plate-number becomes nearly constant, at which stage the variance due to the input distribution has become small compared to the broadening produced by the column. The authors observe that the larger the sample, the worse is the broadening due to a cool sample injector, since evaporation takes longer, and more gas is required to contain the vapour. With preparative columns, sample injectors require special design to enable evaporation to occur rapidly (Section 7.6).

General recognition of the above effect has led to the recommendation that sample injectors should be heated to a temperature higher than that of the column by means of a "Flash Heater." The exact temperature is found only by experience, but probably it need not be more than 50°C higher than the column temperature. Note that it is more reasonable to relate the temperature of the sample injector to the temperature of the column rather than to the boiling points of the components of the mixtures to be analysed, since, though it is true that the higher the boiling point of the vapour the greater will be the broadening in a cool sample injector, this extra broadening is swamped by the column broadening if the column temperature is also low.

In cases where vapours have non-linear isotherms on partition columns, the column temperature may have a dominant influence on the performance through its effect on the non-linearity. If there is an anti-Langmuir type non-linearity caused through the variation of a large activity coefficient with concentration (Section 6.5), the non-linearity frequently becomes less at higher temperatures, since large activity coefficients tend to decrease with increase in temperature, just as most solubilities rise with temperature.

6.16. Effect of Carrier Gas on Performance and Speed

In packed columns in which m is sufficiently large that the effect of lateral diffusion in the gas phase is negligible, the carrier gas affects the performance through its effect on the parameter B of Eq. (6.86), since the lighter and smaller the molecules of the carrier gas, the greater is the diffusion coefficient of vapours within it. Thus, at fast flow rates, where B is only a minor factor in determining the plate-height, the carrier gas has little effect on the performance, while at slow or optimum flow rates, where B is a major factor, the heavier the carrier gas, the better the performance. This is well shown by results given by Bohemen and Purnell (52), who give plots of plate-height against flow rate for the same vapour on the same column, but using different carrier gases (Fig. 6.16). The heavy gases nitrogen and argon give much smaller plate-heights at slow flow rates than does hydrogen, while at faster flow rates the performances approach each other. Values of B for hydrogen and for nitrogen are not exactly in the ratio of the diffusion coefficients of the vapour in the two gases because of the inaccuracy of Eq. (6.86).

The case of columns in which gas phase mass-transfer dominates is in contrast to the above case, for with these, the *lateral* diffusion *suppresses* dispersion at *fast* flows, while in the previous case, *longitudinal* diffusion *increases* dispersion at *slow* flows. The result is that in packed columns in which dispersion is caused by relaxed uneven flow, performances at fast flows are better the faster diffusion can occur; i.e., in light carrier gases. This is clearly shown from Fig. 6.11, where the lines for nitrogen lie above the lines for hydrogen, in contrast to Fig. 6.16.

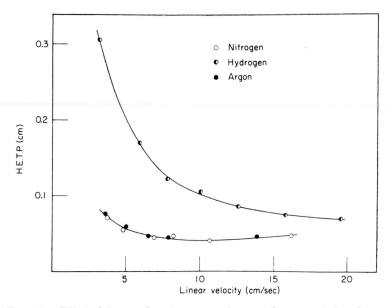

Fɪɢ. 6.16. Effect of change of carrier gas on column performance at slow flow rates. The plots of plate-height against flow rate are made in similar conditions apart from change in the carrier gas. From Bohemen and Purnell (*52*).

In the case that the variation of the performance with flow rate is given accurately by Eq. (6.92), and the minimum flow rate is given by Eq. (6.89) with or without $A = 0$, then a change in carrier gas changes B and C in opposite directions, a lighter carrier gas increasing B but decreasing C. If $C_l \gg C_g$, the product BC is constant, so that, from Eq. (6.89), the carrier gas does not affect the minimum plate-height, but, from Eq. (6.90), the use of a lighter carrier gas causes an increase in the optimum flow rate. If the conditions are such that the above argument applies, therefore, analysis times may be reduced without loss of resolution by using a light carrier gas, e.g., hydrogen. These observations acquire more significance when discussed in connection with the pressure drop across the column in Section 6.18.

6.17. Effect of Column Diameter on Performance

If the column diameter is not less than approximately 2 or 3 mm, the general trend is for the plate-height to increase with increase in the column diameter. Most workers find that between about 3 mm and about 30 mm the rise in plate-height is small (71–73). For example, Dimbat et al. (71) find that a sixfold increase in column diameter requires only a 50% increase in column length to maintain the same plate-number at the same linear flow rate, using firebrick as a packing support.

The variation of performance with diameter in wide (>15 mm diameter) packed columns has been studied by several workers (26, 72, 74–79). In principle, if a wide column were perfectly evenly packed, it would be equivalent to many narrow columns in parallel, and thus plate-height would be independent of diameter. In practice, there are many reasons why this is not so (79). Almost certainly, the major factor which causes wide columns to have greater plate-heights than narrow ones is the fact that flow–unevenness across wide columns is not as easily relaxed as across narrow columns (26, 75, Section 6.5a). Thus, the trans-column contribution to C_g increases rapidly with increase in diameter till at large diameters it swamps all other contributions to H.

The existence of a trans-column contribution to C_g implies that there is necessarily flow–unevenness between widely separated streamlines. If it were possible to devise methods for packing wide columns evenly, this contribution to H would be removed. Giddings and Fuller (78) have shown that if a granular packing material is poured into an open tube, a certain amount of size segregation occurs as it beds down, with larger particles on average going to the outside. This is consistent with the work of Huyten et al. (72), who found that the flow was faster at the outside of a wide column than in the middle. Methods of packing in which the material is sieved into the column have been recommended (80), though they do not appear to have been evaluated, and no consistent method of ensuring even packing seems to have been proved.

Wide columns are normally used for preparative purposes and are thus used with large samples. In this case, there are several other factors leading to further increase in plate-height (Sections 6.19, 7.6). Apart from the volume occupied by the sample, there is also the fact that when the sample dissolves in the stationary liquid in the front of a zone the heat of solution is evolved, and when it evaporates at the rear, the heat of solution is absorbed. In a narrow column, the heat is quickly dissipated laterally, but in a wide column this is not so, and the centre of the column inside the peak becomes warmer than its surroundings. The central regions of the zone are thus accelerated and the average plate-height raised (74, 77). Peters and Euston show (77) by using thermistors located at different parts of the tube diameter that the temperature rise may be as much as 4°C.

The effect of column diameter in capillary columns is considered in Sections 6.11(c) and 6.18(c).

6.18. Effect of Pressure Drop across the Column on Performance and Analysis Time

(a) Qualitative Considerations

When the ratio of pressures across the column is considerably greater than unity, there is a velocity gradient in the column, and, since the plate-height is a function of the flow rate, equivalent theoretical plates in different parts of the column have different heights. The measured plate-height is therefore an average value. The velocity gradient can be minimised by the use of coarse packings, short columns, or slow flow rates, but all these involve loss in performance, and for a good performance an appreciable pressure drop is necessary. As columns become longer, the effect of the pressure drop becomes greater, and in the limit, further addition to the column length may not add to the plate-number. At this stage, an ultimate limit to the performance of a column of given design is reached. If it is required to design a column to perform separations of very close peaks, the column will necessarily be long, and it is important that it be designed so that its useful length is limited as little as possible by considerations of pressure drop.

(b) Modification of the van Deemter Equation

In this subsection, we describe the effect of the pressure drop in a column on the measured plate-height, mainly following Giddings et al. (81) and Golay (10).

When there is a pressure drop across the column, the plate height as given by Eqs. (6.86), (6.91), or (6.92) becomes a function of x, the position of the plate in the column. We shall study the effect of this for a column with separate C_g and C_l terms, and we shall also consider an "A" term, so that we assume:

$$H(x) = A + \frac{B(x)}{u(x)} + (C_g(x) + C_l)u(x). \qquad (6.104)$$

This can be simplified by making use of the fact that D_g, the diffusion coefficient of the vapour in the gas, is inversely proportional to the pressure, so that

$$D_{g(o)}P_o = D_g(x)P(x),   \qquad (6.105)$$

where $D_{g(o)}$ and P_o are the values at the column outlet. This equation, together with Eqs. (2.18), (2.22), (6.87) for B, and (6.84) for C_g, yields:

$$H(x) = A + \frac{B_o}{u_o} + C_{g(o)}u_o + C_l u(x),   \qquad (6.106)$$

where B_o and $C_{g(o)}$ are the values relevant at the outlet. The B and C_g terms are thus independent of x. This is because the greater the pressure, the slower the gas, and therefore the longer the time available for diffusion; however, the diffusion coefficient is proportionately smaller, and these two factors exactly cancel one another.

The measured plate-number is defined by:

$$\mathscr{N} = \frac{V^2}{\sigma^2_{(V)}} = \frac{t^2}{\sigma^2_{(t)}}.   \qquad (6.107)$$

When there is a pressure drop, however, $\mathscr{N}$ defined in this way is not equal to l/H, for H is not constant. Let us define a new phenomenological quantity, $\mathscr{H}$, such that

$$\mathscr{H} = \frac{l}{\mathscr{N}} = \frac{l\sigma^2_{(t=tR)}}{t_R^2} = \frac{l(1+k)^2\sigma^2_{(x=l)}}{u_o^2 t_R^2},   \qquad (6.108)$$

where the last form of writing follows from Eq. (6.3). We shall now find an equation for $\mathscr{H}$ [Eq. (6.114)] equivalent to Eqs. (6.86) or (6.92) for H.

The variance $\sigma^2_{(x)}$ is given as a function of x alone by Eq. (6.5). Differentiation of this gives:

$$\frac{\partial(\sigma^2_{(x)})}{\partial x} = H(x),   \qquad (6.109)$$

which applies at any point in the column. The variance is also a function of the pressure, for as the peak moves along the column into regions of smaller pressure, it expands. The dependence of the variance on the pressure alone may be specified by $\partial(\sigma^2_{(x)})/\partial(P^2)$, which is given by:

$$\frac{\partial(\sigma^2_{(x)})}{\partial(P^2)} = -\frac{\sigma^2_{(x)}}{P^2},   \qquad (6.110)$$

since by Boyle's law $\sigma_{(x)}$ is inversely proportional to the pressure. The total differential $d(\sigma^2_{(x)})/dx$ is obtained from Eqs. (6.109) and (6.110):

$$\frac{d(\sigma^2_{(x)})}{dx} = H(x) - \frac{\sigma^2_{(x)}}{P^2} \cdot \frac{d(P^2)}{dx}, \tag{6.111}$$

and reference to Eq. (2.24) shows that $d(P^2)/dx$ is constant. The solution to Eq. (6.111) for the case of a sharp input distribution, the peak from which is just being eluted from a column of length l, is:

$$\sigma^2_{(x=l)} = \frac{1}{P_o^2} \int_0^l P^2(x)H(x)\,dx. \tag{6.112}$$

This may be substituted in the extreme right-hand side of Eq. (6.108), and the retention time, t_R, is given by Eq. (2.33). The result is:

$$\mathscr{H} = \frac{j^2}{lP_o^2} \int_0^l P^2(x)H(x)\,dx, \tag{6.113}$$

where j is given by Eq. (2.35). The integral may be evaluated substituting for P^2 by Eq. (2.27) and for H by Eq. (6.106). The result is that

$$\mathscr{H} = (A + B_o/u_o + C_g u_o)g(P_i, P_o) + jC_l u_o, \tag{6.114}$$

where

$$g(P_i, P_o) = \frac{9\{(P_i/P_o)^4 - 1\}\{(P_i/P_o)^2 - 1\}}{8\{(P_i/P_o)^3 - 1\}^2}, \tag{6.115}$$

which varies monotonically between unity when $P_i = P_o$, and 9/8 when $P_i/P_o \to \infty$. Equations (6.114) and (6.115) are given by Giddings (*81*).

By differentiating Eq. (6.114) with respect to u_o, using the equations of Section 2.4 to give the relation of P_i and u_o, and setting the result equal to zero, the optimum value of u_o and the minimum value of $\mathscr{H}$ may be found. The equations show that the minimum value of $\mathscr{H}$ is generally greater than the minimum value of H as given by Eq. (6.89) except in the limiting case that $P_i = P_o$. Thus, the effect of the pressure drop is usually deleterious to the performance of the column, and it is desirable to design columns so as to minimise the pressure drop per plate. This adds a fourth criterion of quality to the three given at the beginning of Section 6.1, and the theory of it is considered below.

(c) *The Design of Columns with Regard to the Effect of*
     Pressure Drop–Performance Index

We have assumed so far that the best possible column by which all others are compared is the ideal column, in which broadening factors are absent. Such a column is impossible in practice, but it is also impossible in principle, for a column must have a finite channel for the passage of gas; diffusion across this cannot occur instantaneously, and if diffusion occurs across it, diffusion must also occur along it. The best possible real column, therefore, is one which allows longitudinal and lateral diffusion in the gas phase, but does not suffer from anastomosis or slow mass-transfer in and out of the stationary phase. The plate-height in a cylindrical column of this type is given by the first two terms of Eq. (6.85) for capillary columns. If Eq. (6.105) is applied to Eq. (6.85), the pressures being turned into the equivalent flow velocities, the result is:

$$H = \frac{2D_{g(o)}}{u_o} + \frac{u_o r^2 f(k)}{D_{g(o)}}, \qquad (6.116)$$

where

$$f(k) = \frac{1}{24} \cdot \frac{1 + 6k + 11k^2}{(1 + k)^2}, \qquad (6.117)$$

from which it is seen that H is independent of x, and is independent of the pressure drop across the column. Hence $\mathcal{H}$ has its smallest value, and the pressure drop has the least possible deleterious effect on the performance. In this case,

$$H_{\min} = 2\sqrt{2} \cdot r\sqrt{f(k)}. \qquad (6.118)$$

This optimum holds in all parts of the column. In this case, therefore, a pressure drop across the column, even if large, does not cause some parts to operate at lower efficiency than others, as has been emphasised by Giddings, and by Sternberg *et al.* (*82–85*).

In contrast to an ideal column, a real column has three finite quantities:

(1) peaks with a non-zero variance,
(2) a non-zero time of analysis,
(3) a non-zero pressure drop.

All these quantities are zero in the ideal column, and are essentially undesirable, but in a real column none can be avoided, and any attempt to reduce one of them by changing the operating or design variables in any conceivable way always results in an increase of one of the others, as the reader may check. It appears, therefore, that there is a positive function of (1), (2), and (3) which has a minimum but non-zero value for the best possible real column operating optimally and which is greater for every other real column. Such a function has been sought by Golay (9, 10, 37, 63), from whom the following treatment is derived.

The value of $\mathcal{H}$ in terms of H_{min} and the pressure drop for the best possible real column is given by Eq. (6.113), which becomes:

$$\mathcal{H} = \frac{j^2}{lP_o^2} \int_0^l P^2(x) H_{min} \, dx = \frac{j^2 H_{min}}{lP_o^2} \int_0^l P^2(x) \, dx. \qquad (6.119)$$

The second form of writing results from the fact that for this column, H is not a function of x. Substituting Eq. (2.27) and integrating, this becomes:

$$\mathcal{H} = gH_{min} = 2\sqrt{2} \cdot gr\sqrt{f(k)}, \qquad (6.120)$$

so that, at worst, $\mathcal{H}$ is no greater than $9H/8$, and the difference between $\mathcal{H}$ and H can be regarded as due solely to the operation of expansion of the peak as described by Eq. (6.110). The radius of the tube in Eq. (6.120) can be converted into quantities relevant in the specification of (1), (2), and (3) above by the equation for the flow of a compressible gas of viscosity η through a cylindrical tube of radius r and length l, which is:

$$u_0 = \frac{r^2(P_i^2 - P_o^2)}{16l\eta P_o}. \qquad (6.121)$$

If r is eliminated between Eqs. (6.120) and (6.121), and u_0 is substituted by Eqs. (2.17) and (2.33), the result is:

$$\eta = \frac{\mathcal{H}^2}{64l^2} \cdot \frac{t_M}{f(k)} \cdot \frac{16(P_i^3 - P_o^3)^3}{27(P_i^4 - P_o^4)^2} = \frac{1}{64\mathcal{N}^2} \cdot \frac{t_M}{f(k)} \cdot \frac{16(P_i^3 - P_o^3)^3}{27(P_i^4 - P_o^4)^2}. \qquad (6.122)$$

This is the required equation relating performance ($\mathcal{N}^2$), analysis time ($\propto t_M$), and pressure drop. If the equation is written in the form:

$$1 = \frac{1}{64\eta} \cdot \frac{1}{\mathcal{N}^2} \cdot \frac{t_M}{f(k)} \cdot \frac{16(P_i^3 - P_o^3)^3}{27(P_i^4 - P_o^4)^2}, \qquad (6.123)$$

then the right-hand side is invariant for a real column operating optimally, and is independent of the length of the column. Golay has called this expression the "Specific Performance Index," which is identically equal to unity for the best possible real column, but is greater than unity for all others. As laid out in Eq. (6.123), the first factor is a constant and the following three factors are the functions of (1), (2), and (3) referred to above. The smaller the value of the Specific Performance Index (S.P.I.) for a real column, the smaller will be the increase in average plate-height at optimum flow rate when the column is lengthened to such a degree that the pressure ratio becomes large.

The specific performance indices of capillary columns are much smaller than those of packed columns, often approaching the ideal of unity. This is partly because of their greater permeability, and partly because anastomosis is absent. The result is that the pressure drop per plate is very much smaller, and, even though the plate-height in capillary columns is not smaller than that in packed columns, very large plate-numbers can be attained by using very great lengths without having excessive pressure drops. Thus capillary columns of up to a mile long and having as many as 10^6 theoretical plates have been constructed, whereas packed columns usually require excessive pressure drops when they are longer than about 50 feet or have more than 20,000 to 30,000 plates. The performance indices of packed columns can often be improved by using a coarser grade of packing material, as has been shown by Bohemen and Purnell (52); there is therefore a case for making columns which are to be very long of a coarser grade of material than would be used to obtain the smallest optimum plate-height. In such a case, the gain on permeability may more than offset the loss on plate-height.

In a sense, the specific performance index is a more complete specification of column quality than the plate number, but, like the plate number, it suffers by being characteristic of the column rather than of the separation, as was discussed in Section 6.14. Some attempt to produce a parameter which defines the quality of the resolution also considering the pressure drop in a column has been given by Halasz et al. (86). The discussion, however, remains incomplete.

6.19. Effect of Mass of Sample on Performance

In most cases, the greater the mass of sample chromatographed, the smaller the performance of the apparatus. For example, Bohemen and Purnell (52) have plotted the apparent plate-height of a column against sample size, and obtain straight-line plots for each component of a mixture (Fig. 6.17). There is no definite reason for the linearity, and such a relation

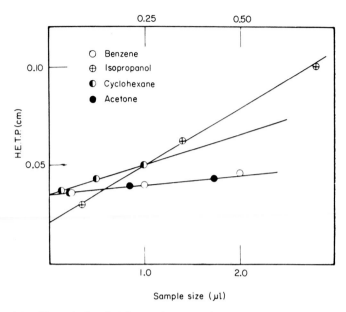

FIG. 6.17. Plot of plate-height against sample size for various vapours. Lower scale for isopropanol, upper scale for the other vapours. From Bohemen and Purnell (*52*).

is not always found; most workers, however, agree on the sign of the slope of the lines.

Sample size affects the column performance mainly through the effect of the input distribution of vapour (Section 6.7), the volume of vapour in the gas phase, and the non-linearity of isotherms (Section 6.6).

The sample size can affect the input distribution in two ways, firstly, because the sample produces a finite volume of vapour, and secondly because if the sample is a liquid, it requires a finite time to evaporate. The second is a technological problem which may be effectively solved for analytical columns by using a heated sample injector, as described in Section 6.15.

The effect of the finite volume of vapour on performance as a function of other column variables has been studied by DeWet and Pretorius (*87*). Also, a general theory of the most efficient use of preparative columns has been given by Pretorius *et al.* (*88–90*).

The results may be interpreted simply in terms of Fig. 6.6 and equations from Section 6.7, using the premise that $\sigma_I{}^2$ is proportional to the mass of sample.

(a) *Effect of the Proportion of Stationary Phase on the Variation of Performance with Sample Size*

With a small sample, performance is best when the proportion of stationary phase is small. However, the smaller the proportion of stationary phase, the smaller the retention volume. From Fig. 6.6, the smaller the retention volume, the smaller the threshold value of σ_I less than which broadening due to sample size is negligible. Hence, with a small proportion of stationary phase, performance falls sharply with increase in sample. With a large proportion of stationary phase, however, though the plate-number for small samples is smaller, retention volumes are larger, so that the threshold for σ_I is larger, and performance does not fall so rapidly with increase in sample size. This argument is illustrated in Fig. 6.18 by the results of DeWet and Pretorius (*87*).

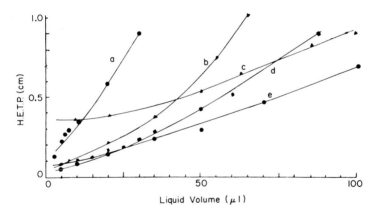

FIG. 6.18. Plot of plate-height against sample size with proportion of stationary phase as parameter. With small values of m, the plate-height with small samples is small, but it increases rapidly with increase in sample. With large values of m, the variation of plate-height with sample is much less steep. (a) 10% w/w stationary liquid; (b) 20%; (c) 44.5%; (d) 25%; (e) 35%. From DeWet and Pretorius (*87*).

(b) *Effect of Partition Coefficient on the Variation of Performance with Sample Size*

The greater the partition coefficient of a vapour, the larger is V_R, and hence, as above, the smaller the effect of quantity. This is illustrated from the results of DeWet and Pretorius in Fig. 6.19 for benzene and toluene.

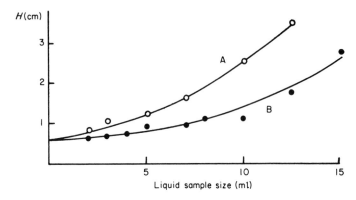

F$_{IG.}$ 6.19. Plot of plate-height against sample size with partition coefficient as parameter: (A) benzene, (B) toluene. The latter, having the greater retention volume, gives peaks the plate-height equivalent to which increases more slowly with increase in sample. After DeWet and Pretorius (87).

(c) Effect of the Plate-Number of the Column on the Variation of Performance with Sample Size

Again making use of Fig. 6.6, the larger the plate-number, $\mathscr{N}$, the smaller the threshold of sample size greater than which sample size causes the performance to deteriorate, and the greater the proportional deterioration produced by a given sample.

If it is assumed that all the broadening due to sample size is accounted for by the volume of the vapour, a relation between the broadening and the sample size is easily calculable in terms of the retention volume of the vapour and the plate-number of the column. If the sample of molecular weight M weighs w mg, then its volume at $t°C$ is:

$$V_I = \frac{22.4w(t + 273)}{273M}, \tag{6.124}$$

which, for quantities of the order of milligrams will normally be of the order of cubic centimetres. For example, 5 mg of n-hexane at 40°C has a volume of 1.5 cc. This may then be related with the variance of the peak by Fig. 6.7, or Eq. (6.77) may be used to check whether or not the sample size is large enough to have a material effect on the column performance. For example, in a column of 2000 plates in which n-hexane has $V_R = 500$, the threshold value of V_I according to Eq. (6.77) is 11 cc, so that the threshold sample size is between 30 and 40 mg.

Whereas the above effect of sample size can be accurately assessed, other effects cannot. The way in which the results of DeWet and Pretorius agree with their theoretical predictions based on the premise that only the vapour volume is relevant suggests that, in their circumstances, other effects are small. DeWet and Pretorius, however, have aimed more at testing the theory than at attempting to separate the maximum sample sizes in a given column; for example, their vapours were usually diluted with carrier gas to prevent their concentration becoming too great. When large samples are put into a column, broadening due to their concentration and due to non-linear isotherms inevitably occurs (see Section 7.6).

An exception to the general rule given at the beginning of this section is given by Bethea and Smutz (91), who have reported experiments in which the plate-height shows a minimum when expressed as a function of sample size; with large samples, performance declines with increase in sample as described above, but with very small samples, the performance declines with *decrease* in sample. The probable reason for this is that the authors used column of which the supports were slightly adsorptive, and when the sample was small enough that the adsorption was not completely masked by solution of the sample in the partitioning liquid, excessively broadened peaks were obtained.

REFERENCES

1. Klinkenberg, A., and Sjenitzer, F., *Chem. Eng. Sci.* **5**, 258 (1956).
2. Van Deemter, J. J., Zuiderweg, F. J., and Klinkenberg, A., *Chem. Sci.* **5**, 271 (1956).
3. Knox, J. H., and McLaren, L., *Anal. Chem.* **36**, 1477 (1964).
4. Boyack, J. R., and Giddings, J. C., *Arch. Biochem. Biophys.* **100**, 16 (1963).
5. Khan, M. A., *Nature* **186**, 800 (1960).
6. Gluekauf, E., Barker, K. H., and Kitt, G. P., *Discussions Faraday Soc.* **7**, 199 (1949).
7. Lapidus, L., and Amundsen, N. R., *J. Phys. Chem.* **56**, 984 (1954).
8. Thomas, H. C., *Ann. N.Y. Acad. Sci.* **49**, 161 (1948).
9. Golay, M. J. E., *Anal. Chem.* **29**, 928 (1957).
10. Golay, M. J. E., *in* "Gas Chromatography 1958," Proceedings of the Second Symposium, Amsterdam, May, 1958 (D. H. Desty, ed.), p. 36. Academic Press, New York, 1958.
11. Young, J. F., *in* "Gas Chromatography," I.S.A. Symposium, 1957 (V. J. Coates, H. J. Noebels, and I. S. Fagerson, eds.), p. 15. Academic Press, New York, 1958.
12. Funk, J. E., and Houghton, G., *Nature* **188**, 389 (1960).
13. Kucera, E., *J. Chromatog.* **19**, 237 (1965).
14. Giddings, J. C., and Eyring, H., *J. Phys. Chem.* **59**, 416 (1955).
15. Beynon, J. H., Clough, S., Crookes, D. A., and Lester, G. R., *Trans. Faraday Soc.* **54**, 705 (1958).

16. "Handbook of Chemistry and Physics." Chemical Rubber Publ., Cleveland, Ohio, published annually.
17. Taylor, G., *Proc. Roy. Soc.* **A219**, 186 (1953).
18. Aris, R., *Proc. Roy. Soc.* **A235**, 67 (1956).
19. Giddings, J. C., James, M. R., and Eyring, H., *Anal. Chem.* **37**, 612 (1965).
20. Kieselbach, R., *Anal. Chem.* **32**, 880 (1960).
21. Desty, D. H., and Goldup, A., "Gas Chromatography 1960," Proceedings of the Third International Symposium (R. P. W. Scott, ed.), p. 162. Academic Press, New York, 1961.
22. Giddings, J. C., *J. Chromatog.* **5**, 46 (1961).
23. Giddings, J. C., "Dynamics of Chromatography; Principles and Theory," Dekker New York, 1965.
24. Giddings, J. C., *J. Chem. Phys.* **31**, 1462 (1959).
25. Giddings, J. C., *Anal. Chem.* **34**, 1186 (1962).
26. Giddings, J. C., and Jensen, G. E., *J. Gas Chromatog.* **2**, 290 (1964).
27. Giddings, J. C., *Ber. Bunsenges. Phys. Chem.* **69**, 773 (1965).
28. Giddings, J. C., *Anal. Chem.* **37**, 1580 (1965).
29. Giddings, J. C., *J. Chromatog.* **3**, 443 (1960).
30. Giddings, J. C., *Anal. Chem.* **35**, 439 (1963).
31. Giddings, J. C., Mallik, K. L., and Eikelberger, M., *Anal. Chem.* **34**, 1026 (1962).
32. Giddings, J. C., *J. Chromatog.* **5**, 60 (1961).
33. Littlewood, A. B., "Gas Chromatography 1964," Proceedings of the Fourth International Symposium (A. Goldup, ed.), p. 77. Institute of Petroleum, 1965.
34. Giddings, J. C., *J. Chromatog.* **3**, 520 (1960).
35. Giddings, J. C., *J. Chromatog.* **16**, 494 (1964).
36. Giddings, J. C., *Anal. Chem.* **37**, 1580 (1965).
37. Golay, M. J. E., *Nature* **182**, 1146 (1958).
38. Littlewood, A. B., *Anal. Chem.* **38**, 2 (1966).
39. Giddings, J. C., *Nature* **184**, 357 (1959).
40. Giddings, J. C., and Robison, R. A., *Anal. Chem.* **34**, 885 (1962).
41. DeVault, D., *J. Am. Chem. Soc.* **65**, 532 (1943).
42. James, D. H., and Phillips, C. S. G., *J. Chem. Soc.* p. 1066 (1954).
43. Bosanquet, C. H., *in* "Gas Chromatography 1958," Proceedings of the Second Symposium, Amsterdam, May, 1958 (D. H. Desty, ed.), p. 107. Academic Press, New York, 1958.
44. Bosanquet, C. H., and Morgan, G. O., *in* "Vapour Phase Chromatography," Proceedings of the First Symposium, London, May, 1956 (D. H. Desty, ed.), p. 35. Academic Press, New York, 1957.
45. Schmauch, L. J., *Anal. Chem.* **31**, 225 (1959).
46. Johnson, H. W., and Stross, F. H., *Anal. Chem.* **31**, 357 (1959).
47. Sternberg, J. C., *Advan. Chromatog.* **2**, 205 (1966).
48. DeWet, W. J., and Pretorius, V., *Anal. Chem.* **32**, 1396 (1960).
49. Scott, R. P. W., *in* "Gas Chromatography 1958," Proceedings of the Second Symposium, Amsterdam, May, 1958 (D. H. Desty, ed.), p. 189. Academic Press, New York, 1958.
50. Keulemans, A. I. M., and Kwantes, A., *in* "Vapour Phase Chromatography," Proceedings of the First Symposium, London, May, 1956 (D. H. Desty, ed.), p. 15. Academic Press, New York, 1957.

51. Littlewood, A. B., *in* "Gas Chromatography 1958," Proceedings of the Second Symposium, Amsterdam, May, 1958 (D. H. Desty, ed.), p. 23. Academic Press, New York, 1958.

52. Bohemen, J., and Purnell, J. H., *in* "Gas Chromatography 1958," Proceedings of the Second Symposium, Amsterdam, May, 1958 (D. H. Desty, ed.), p. 6. Academic Press, New York, 1958.

53. Cheshire, J. D., and Scott, R. P. W., *J. Inst. Petroleum* **44**, 74 (1958).

54. Desty, D. H., Godfrey, F. M., and Harbourn, C. L. A., *in* "Gas Chromatography 1958," Proceedings of the Second Symposium, Amsterdam, May, 1958 (D. H. Desty, ed.), p. 200. Academic Press, New York, 1958.

55. Harper, J. M., and Hammond, E. G., *Anal. Chem.* **37**, 486 (1965).

56. Perrett, R. H., and Purnell, J. H., *Anal. Chem.* **35**, 430 (1965).

57. DeFord, D. D., Loyd, R. J., and Ayers, B. O., *Anal. Chem.* **35**, 426 (1963).

58. Perrett, R. H., and Purnell, J. H., *Anal. Chem.* **34**, 1336 (1962).

59. Giddings, J. C., and Schettler, P. D., *Anal. Chem.* **36**, 1483 (1964).

60. Desty, D. H., Goldup, A., and Whyman, B. H. F., *J. Inst. Petrol.* **45**, 287 (1959).

61. Scott, R. P. W., and Hazeldean, G. S. F., "Gas Chromatography 1960," Proceedings of the Third International Symposium (R. P. W. Scott, ed.), p. 144. Academic Press, New York, 1961.

62. Duffield, J. J., and Rogers, L. H., *Anal. Chem.* **32**, 340 (1960).

63. Golay, M. J. E., *in* "Gas Chromatography," I.S.A. Symposium, 1957 (V. J. Coates, H. J. Noebels, and I. S. Fagerson, eds.), p. 1. Academic Press, New York, 1958.

64. Purnell, J. H., *Nature* **184**, 2004 (1959).

65. Purnell, J. H., *J. Chem. Soc.* p. 1268 (1960).

66. Halasz, I., Hartmann, K., and Heine, E., "Gas Chromatography 1964," Proceedings of the Fourth International Symposium, (A. Goldup, ed.), p. 38. Institute of Petroleum, 1965.

67. Desty, D. H., Goldup, A., and Swanton, W. T., "Gas Chromatography 1961" (N. Brenner, J. E. Callen, and M. D. Weiss eds.), p. 105. Academic Press, New York, 1962.

68. Loyd, R. J., Ayers, B. O., and Karasek, F. W., *Anal. Chem.* **32**, 698 (1960).

69. Purnell, J. H., and Quinn, C. P., "Gas Chromatography 1960," Proceedings of the Third International Symposium (R. P. W. Scott, ed.), p. 184. Academic Press, New York, 1961.

70. Pollard, F. H., and Hardy, C. J., *Chem. Ind. (London)* p. 1145 (1955).

71. Dimbat, M., Porter, P. E., and Stross, F. H., *Anal. Chem.* **28**, 290 (1956).

72. Huyten, F. H., Beerson, W. van, and Rijnders, G. W. A., "Gas Chromatography 1960," Proceedings of the Third International Symposium (R. P. W. Scott, ed.), p. 224. Academic Press Inc., New York, 1961.

73. Baker, W. J., Norlin, H. L., Zinn, T. L., and Wall, R. F., *Am. Chem. Soc. Div. Petrol. Chem. Preprints* **2**, No. 4, D43 (1957).

74. Rose, A., Royer, D. J., and Henley, R. S., *Separ. Sci.* **2**, 229 (1967).

75. Hargrove, G. L., and Sawyer, D. T., *Anal. Chem.* **38**, 1634 (1966).

76. Gordon, S. M., Krige, G. J., and Pretorius, V., *J. Gas Chromatog.* **2**, 285 (1964).

77. Peters, J., and Euston, C. B., *Anal. Chem.* **37**, 649 (1965).

78. Giddings, J. C., and Fuller, E. N., *J. Chromatog.* **7**, 255 (1962).

79. Giddings, J. C., *J. Gas Chromatog.* **1**, 12 (1963).

80. Keulemans, A. I. M., "Gas Chromatography 1966," Proceedings of the Sixth International Symposium (A. B. Littlewood, ed.), p. 211. Institute of Petroleum, 1967.

81. Giddings, J. C., Seager, S. L., Stucki, L. R., and Stewart, G. H., *Anal. Chem.* **32**, 867 (1960).

82. Sternberg, J. C., and Poulson, R. E., *Anal. Chem.* **36**, 58 (1964).

83. Sternberg, J. C., *Anal. Chem.* **36**, 921 (1964).

84. Giddings, J. C., *Anal. Chem.* **36**, 741 (1964).

85. Giddings, J. C., *Anal. Chem.* **35**, 353 (1963).

86. Halasz, I., and Heine, E., "Progress in Gas Chromatography" (J. H. Purnell, ed.), p. 153. Wiley (Interscience), 1968.

87. DeWet, W. J., and Pretorius, V., *Anal. Chem.* **32**, 169 (1960).

88. Gordon, S. M., and Pretorius, V., *J. Gas Chromatog.* **2**, 196 (1964).

89. Gordon, S. M., Krige, G. J., and Pretorius, V., *J. Gas Chromatog.* **2**, 241 (1964).

90. Gordon, S. M., Krige G. J., and Pretorius, V., *J. Gas Chromatog.* **2**, 241 (1964).

91. Bethea, R. M., and Smutz, M., *Anal. Chem.* **31**, 1211 (1959).

Chapter 7

The Preparation and Use of Columns

7.1. Preparation of Packed Columns

The packing material in a partition column is a mixture of a support and a stationary liquid. This mixture is packed into the column tube, and then the column is pre-conditioned. Adsorbents for use in adsorption columns usually require some kind of treatment before packing (Section 4.3). All these operations require as much art as science, and it is not possible to describe exact techniques by which workers could reproduce similar columns. General instructions for column packing, however, are standard, and are described below.

(a) Supports

Table 7.1 lists in rough order of importance the supports that have most often been used in gas chromatography; the great majority of work has been done using the first two. Relevant notes on the supports are given below.

Kieselguhr was used by James and Martin (1) in their original work on gas partition chromatography. They used a commercial calcined and extracted brand, Celite (Johns Manville Company) of Californian origin, which is the most commonly used brand of all the kieselguhrs. This product is largely used as a filter aid in industrial filtration, as a white filler in paper, etc., and as a component of thermal insulation material. Kieselguhr is largely composed of silica, but contains small quantities of other oxides (Table 7.2), which have an important effect on its use as a support (Section 7.2). It may absorb up to about 40% by weight of stationary liquid without becoming unduly sticky, but with such a proportion, it is not freely flowing.

Firebrick can hold a larger proportion of stationary phase than kieselguhr without becoming sticky, and material with up to 40% of liquid is

TABLE 7.1

GAS CHROMATOGRAPHIC SUPPORTS

Support	Reference
Diatomaceous earth	*1* and many others; for reviews, see *2, 3*
Crushed firebrick	*4* and many others
Glass beads	*5, 6, 7*
Glass powder	*8, 9, 10*
Metal helices	*11, 12*
Sodium chloride	*9, 10, 13, 14*
Mixed salts contained in domestic detergent	*15, 16, 17*
Powdered Teflon	*18, 19*
Carborundum	*20*
Sintered glass wafers	*21*
Crushed white tile	*22*

freely flowing. This is a great advantage over kieselguhr in the rapid manufacture of columns. It has the drawback that its mechanical strength is smaller than that of Celite, so that its granules are rather easily reduced to fine powder. It is general experience that columns prepared using firebrick give slightly smaller plate-heights than those using kieselguhr with the same mesh size and same proportion of stationary liquid.

Glass beads are manufactured in sizes down to at least 0.1 mm diameter, and the smaller sizes are used in gas chromatography. Glass powder is different in that its particles are not spherical; it is familiar in the laboratory for the manufacture of sintered glass apparatus. The maximum proportion by weight of stationary liquid on beads of about 0.1 mm diameter is

TABLE 7.2

COMPOSITION OF CALCINED DIATOMACEOUS EARTH[a]

SiO_2	91.0%
Al_2O_3	4.6
Fe_2O_3	1.9
CaO	1.4
MgO	0.4
Volatile	0.3
Other	0.4

[a] From Hull *et al.* (*2*).

about 2 to 3%. This is very much smaller than for kieselguhr or firebrick, but since the packing density of glass beads is about 8 times that for kieselguhr and 4 times that for firebrick, the disparity in volume proportions is very much less. The surface area of glass beads is of the order of 0.1 m²/g, which is much smaller than that of kieselguhr or firebrick, though, again, on account of the difference in packing densities, the ratio of surface area of support to weight of stationary liquid on glass beads is comparable with that on kieselguhr or firebrick.

Metal helices are normally used for packing distillation columns. They have a restricted use in gas chromatography, since they have practically no adsorptive properties. They are too openly packed and hold too little stationary liquid for common use.

Desty and Harbourn (16) have used a commercial domestic detergent as a column packing, in which case the partitioning agent is the alkylaryl sulfonate, and the support is the mixture of inorganic salts composing the remainder of the product. Decora and Dineen (17) have extracted the organic detergents from domestic detergent, and have used the granular residue as a convenient support for any other stationary liquid phase. This material is very absorptive, and can contain up to 70% by weight of liquid before becoming sticky.

In order for a support to produce a column packing which will produce an efficient column, it is necessary that the liquid phase does not penetrate too deeply into fine pores in the support structure, since diffusion into and out of these is slow, leading to a large value of C_l (Section 6.11). Ideally, the support should consist of hard particles with a rough surface in which to contain the stationary liquid and impermeable centres. Several workers have modified diatomaceous earth support materials to try to approach this ideal. In one technique (23), the granular support is heated to a temperature of about 1200°C, at which temperature it sinters slightly, the smaller pores becoming closed. There is at the same time a desirable reduction in surface area, thus reducing any adsorptive activity of the support. Another technique is to use glass beads as the basis of a support, and to provide these with a suitable rough surface. Kirkland (24, 25) describes a technique for coating the beads with silica, using fibrillar boehmite as the "glue" to stick the small particles of silica to the surface of the beads. This surface can then be used directly as an adsorbent, or alternatively it can be used to absorb a stationary liquid. Halasz and Horvath (26, 27) describe a technique for coating glass beads with ferric oxide or alumina. In yet another technique, the surface of the glass beads is roughened by etching (28). All these techniques for improving supports enable packings to be prepared which give the advantages of a small C term (Section 6.11), i.e., analyses which can be both efficient and fast.

Diatomaceous earth supports of various kinds, including types in which fine pores have been eliminated by some form of calcination, are commercially available from many sources. Non-diatomaceous earth supports, e.g., polytetrafluoroethylene, glass beads, etc., are also commercially available. Supports in general have been reviewed by Ottenstein (29).

(b) Preparation of Column Material

The support and the stationary liquid must be blended carefully if the resulting material is to be used to make a column which is efficient. It is important that the support contains no fines, since these tend to impede the process by which the packing beds down into the column. Most commercial diatomaceous earths provided specifically for gas chromatography have already had their fines removed. Crude kieselguhr, or Celite, however, contains a large proportion of fines which must be removed, e.g., by sedimentation, before use (30).

The weight proportion of stationary liquid in the column material affects the properties of the column as described in Section 6.13. In most normal practice, proportions of about 10% w/w liquid/Celite give columns in which C_l is comparable with C_g, and thus give a relatively small plate-height. Calcined diatomaceous earth supports have a larger packing density, and thus the proportion of stationary liquid should normally be smaller, e.g., 3%. Larger quantities of liquid, e.g., up to about 40% on Celite, give columns of smaller efficiency but larger capacity. By using larger proportions of stationary liquid, any effects on retentions due to the surface either of the liquid or of the support become relatively smaller, and thus larger proportions of stationary liquid should be used if accurate values of retentions are to be used or determined. If specific retention volumes or partition coefficients are to be used, the proportion of stationary liquid to support should be determined accurately, so that the weight of stationary liquid in a column can be determined from the weight of packing in it.

By far the commonest method of blending is by *slurrying*. The support is weighed out, and a sufficient quantity of volatile solvent in which the stationary liquid is miscible or at least soluble is added to make a slurry. The stationary liquid is added, and the slurry is continuously stirred while the solvent is evaporated, e.g., in a stream of hot air. When all the solvent is substantially removed, the column material is shaken for some time, e.g., half an hour.

Other methods of blending are by simple mixing for a prolonged period (1), by spraying the liquid onto the support by an atomiser, and by impregnating the support while it is packed into a column (31). There seems to be little difference in the product provided by these choices (32), and thus they provide no advantage over the slurrying technique, which is easiest.

(c) Packing the Column

Packing materials composed of adsorbents, of partition liquids on firebrick, or of small proportions of liquids on kieselguhr, are completely freely flowing, and may be poured into the column tube. Packing materials with large (e.g., >20%) proportions of liquid on kieselguhr, and most of those using other less porous supports, are more or less sticky and require assistance in bedding down into a column. The flow of sticky material into the column tube is accelerated by vibrating the column, e.g., by holding the column against a rapidly rotating spindle one segment of which has been cut away, or against a domestic massage vibrator. In addition, it is often desirable to tamp the packing down into the tube with a close-fitting rod. Experience in such tamping enables one to judge and reproduce the packing density with reasonable accuracy. The intensity of vibration is also a relevant factor. Too weak a vibration is insufficient for the sticky particles to bed down evenly. With too strong a vibration, the amplitude of the motion in the particles is so great that the packing expands. There is thus an optimum, which is normally found by experience. The above phenomenon has been confirmed and studied in connection with the packing of powders by Macrae et al. (33).

In practice, it is generally found that the nature of the column tube affects the efficiency with which the vibration can cause the packing to bed down. Thus, columns in glass or other acoustically resonant material can usually be made to give smaller plate-heights than columns in soft copper or other acoustically dead materials using the same packing. The achievement of a good efficiency from a given packing remains, however, something of an art.

(d) Conditioning of the Column

A newly packed column invariably contains small quantities of residual solvent from the preparation of packing material, together with water condensed from the atmosphere and other volatile contaminants; these may be removed by heating the column in a stream of carrier gas in a gas-chromatographic apparatus until the base-line remains steady. Cooper *et al.* (*34*) then continue heating the column until the base-line begins to drift again due to volatilisation of stationary liquid, in order to determine the maximum operating temperature of the column. The final weight of a column should be recorded after a preliminary heat-treatment to remove superfluous volatiles, which may otherwise lead to appreciable error in calculating the mass of stationary liquid. Littlewood (*6*) has found that the efficiency of a column (using glass beads) may be improved by heating a new column in the absence of a stream of carrier gas up to a temperature where the stationary phase is appreciably volatile. The stationary liquid is held by surface tension around points of contact of particles of support, and, since all its surfaces are concave, it tends to equilibrate itself so that all surfaces have the same curvature. If the support is carefully size-graded, this has the result that each point of contact holds the same amount of liquid, thus producing less randomness in the distribution of stationary liquid.

7.2. REACTIVITY OF SUPPORTS IN PACKED COLUMNS

Ideally, the support in a packed column is inert; but in practice it may cause chemical reaction of the vapours either between themselves or with the stationary liquid, it may produce tailing, or it may influence retention volumes. All these effects are generally attributed to the adsorptive properties of the support; the reactions are caused through heterogeneous catalysis, the tailing through superimposition of the usual asymmetrical peak shape produced on adsorbents, and the change in retention volumes through the addition of the adsorption to the partition. It should be recalled that the supports mainly used in gas partition chromatography are largely composed of silica, which, when activated, is also used as an adsorbent in gas adsorption chromatography.

The adsorptive properties of various supports have been studied and commented on by many workers; see reviews by Ottenstein (*29*), Hesse (*35*), and Blandenet and Robin (*36*). The relevance of the adsorption is clearly shown in Fig. 7.1, which shows a chromatogram of a mixture of the five hexane alkanes taken on a column of pure Celite kieselguhr at 0°C (*37*). Similar results are obtained by Bens (*38*).

Of the common supports, there is fairly general agreement that firebrick is more adsorptive than Celite. Firebrick is generally brown in colour, and it has been thought that brown firebricks, presumably containing much

iron, are more adsorptive than colourless samples. Hishta *et al.* (7) consider
that glass beads are much less adsorptive than either kieselguhr or firebrick,
but this is not universal experience, and, as indicated in Section 7.1, there is
no obvious reason why it should be so; for example, Naves (9, 10) finds that
glass powder used as a support causes the catalytic isomerisation of terpenes.

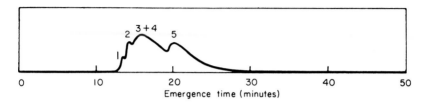

FIG. 7.1. Chromatogram of a mixture of the hexanes on a column of pure Celite
kieselguhr at 0°C. Eggertsen and Knight (37). 1, 2,2-Dimethylbutane; 2, 2,3-dimethyl-
butane; 3, 2-methylpentane; 4, 3-methylpentane; 5, *n*-hexane.

The choice of support has much more effect on the chromatography of
polar compounds than on that of less reactive compounds such as hydrocarbons. Thus, petroleum hydrocarbons can normally be analysed on all
but the most adsorptive columns, which would produce bad tailing of other
compounds. This is illustrated by Fig. 7.2, which shows two peaks taken

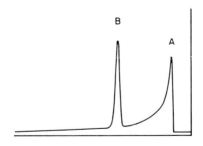

FIG. 7.2. Peaks due to ethanol (A) and octane (B) taken from a chromatogram
made on a column of silicone 550 on 42–50 mesh firebrick, temperature 130°C. Re-
drawn from Johns (39), omitting peaks due to other components.

from a chromatogram (39) run on a column of silicone 550 fluid on kieselguhr. The hydrocarbon peak is narrower than the alcohol peak, even though
its retention volume is more than twice as great. The effect of the adsorption of the support diminishes when the stationary liquid is itself polar.
There are two reasons for this; first, that the stationary liquid saturates
the active sites of the support as described below, and second, that polar

substances are more soluble in polar stationary liquids, so that the relative importance of the adsorption in the total retention is smaller.

An interesting effect of the tailing influence of the support is reported by Baker *et al. (32)*. With either firebrick or kieselguhr, the plate-height shows a minimum as a function of the proportion of stationary liquid applied to the support. At a concentration greater than the minimum, the plate-height rises as usual with increase in the proportion of stationary phase (Section 6.13); at concentrations smaller than the minimum, the broadening produced through the influence of adsorption presumably outweighs the further reduction in plate-height because of the reduction of the thickness of the liquid layer. This observation is consistent with the variation of plate-height with sample size found by Bethea and Smutz (Section 6.19).

The adsorption of the support can affect retention volumes both relative and specific; with polar stationary liquids, the effect is complicated by a competitive equilibrium between the support, the stationary liquid, and

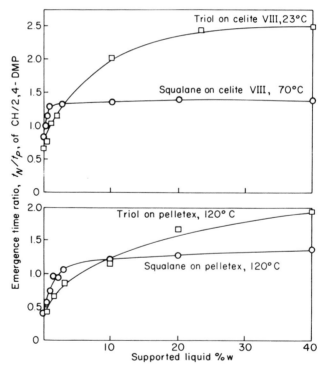

FIG. 7.3. Ratio of retention times, t_N/t_P, of cyclohexane (CH) and 2,4-dimethyl-pentane (2,4-DMP) as a function of proportion of stationary phase for Triol and squalane on Celite and Pelletex. Eggertsen and Knight *(37)*.

the solute. The effect is most powerfully demonstrated by experiments in which relative retention volumes are studied as a function of the proportion of stationary liquid on a support. This can be illustrated by the results for alkanes and naphthenes by Eggertsen and Knight (37). On some pure adsorbents, including silica and carbon, naphthenes have greater activity coefficients than alkanes, and on nearly all partitioning liquids, alkanes have greater activity coefficients than naphthenes. Thus, the authors have investigated the relative retentions of cyclohexane and 2:4-dimethylpentane, which have virtually identical vapour pressures, so that retention times are in inverse ratio to activity coefficients. When the proportion of stationary liquid is small or zero, the naphthene appears first, but, as the proportion increases, it is selectively retained till, at greater proportions, the alkane appears first. This is shown in Fig. 7.3 by plotting the ratio of the retention times, $t_{naphthene}/t_{paraffin}$, as a function of the proportion of stationary liquid on the adsorbent. It is seen that both on Celite and on charcoal (Pelletex) the components change their order of elution at a given concentration of stationary liquid, as is shown by the plots crossing the ordinate $t_N/t_P = 1$. When squalane is used as stationary phase, the concentration at which the partition swamps the adsorption is smaller than when a polar stationary liquid, e.g., Triol, is used, since the hydrocarbons are much more soluble in the former. It will be noted that an adsorptive kieselguhr column with a very small proportion of squalane acts similarly to the squalane-Pelletex columns described in Section 4.3. They differ in that the adsorptive capacity of kieselguhr is very small, so that, though the selective acceleration of the naphthenes might otherwise be useful, the over-all retention is very small.

The above type of behaviour, in which retentions are shown to depend on the proportion of stationary liquid, has been reported frequently in the literature. For example, Evans and Smith (40) show that the effect can cause a shift of as much as 100 units in the retention indices of alkanols. Even supports like polytetrafluoroethylene can affect retentions by a sort of sieving effect.

It is apparent that the adsorptive properties of supports are nearly always undesirable. Cures may be put into four categories:

(1) Enveloping the support.
(2) Neutralisation of adsorption sites.
(3) Permanent removal of adsorption sites.
(4) Saturation of adsorption sites.

(1) *Enveloping the Support.* This was first done by Ormerod and Scott

(41), who coated a support made of firebrick by silvering it in the same way as mirrors are silvered, using the Rochelle salt process, in which a solution of ammoniacal silver nitrate and Rochelle salt containing the firebrick is slowly warmed. This process is repeated until the support has gained between 40 and 100% of its weight in silver. Microscopic examination shows that the silver forms a coherent layer over the particles of support, and the treated support may then be mixed with stationary liquid in the usual way. The treatment of the support can make a great difference in the chromatography of polar compounds, especially using non-polar stationary phases. A drawback of this method is that sulfur compounds and amines attack the silver. The authors' attempts to prepare corresponding gold-treated supports failed.

(2) *Neutralisation of Adsorption Sites.* It is commonly accepted that the adsorption sites on siliceous supports consist of Si—OH groups, together with Al—OH and Fe—OH groups where the other elements are present. These are acidic, and indeed, the reactions caused by supports, e.g., isomerisation of olefins and terpenes, and the dehydrogenation of alcohols, are all acid-catalysed reactions. Thus several workers have tried the effect of various kinds of alkali pre-treatment to the support. For example, Holmgren (42) reports that alcohol dehydrogenation may be prevented by using a support which has merely been treated with sodium carbonate solution for 10 minutes, and Tornquist (43) describes how tailing may be removed if the support is pre-treated with 3% potassium hydroxide solution. Mitzner and Jacobs (44) find that this treatment reduces chemical reactivity, but does not eliminate it. They find also that alcohol dehydrogenation may occur on capillary columns prepared in untreated tubing, but that, if the tubing is rinsed out with detergent solution, followed by caustic potash, rinsing water, methanol, acetone, chloroform, and benzene, the reactivity is removed.

Other workers have pre-treated supports with acid. Thus, Villalobos (18) finds that tailing in analyses of H_2S—SO_2—NH_3 mixtures is reduced by acid treatment, and Kirkland (45) finds that tailing of polar compounds on kieselguhr may be reduced by slurrying the kieselguhr with concentrated hydrochloric acid, followed by alkali and water washing. Zlatkis et al. (46) find it advantageous to pre-treat firebrick or kieselguhr with hot aqua regia for a considerable period. This detaches "peninsulas" from the main body of large particles, thus producing a mixture of roughly spherical granules and fines; the latter are then elutriated out, and the former are neutralised with alkali before use.

(3) *Permanent Removal of Adsorption Sites.* Since many adsorption sites on supports are associated with —OH groups, a chemical reagent for such groups effectively reduces the adsorption. The methylchlorsilanes have been used by several workers for this purpose, since they replace —OH groups with inert Me—Si groups. A common technique (e.g., (47)) is to pack the support into a tube, and pass dimethyldichlorsilane vapour in a stream of nitrogen through it. The support is then treated with methanol, removed from the tube, and dried, after which it is ready for the preparation of the column packing, as described in Section 7.1.

The use of dimethyldichlorsilane may be criticised, since it is difunctional, with the result that, if it reacts with only one active site, one active halogen atom remains. Perrett and Purnell (48) have found that a more satisfactory method of pre-treatment for the removal of adsorption is to reflux the support in a 5% solution of hexamethyl disilazane, $Me_3SiNHSiMe_3$ in petroleum pentane. This has the advantages that the labile hydrogens are replaced by the monofunctional Me_3Si-group, and the reagent is easier to handle than methylchlorsilanes. The extent of reaction may be studied by monitoring the ammonia which is produced. In practice, it appears that there is little to choose between the use of a trimethyl silyl derivative and a dimethyl silyl derivative. Any remaining active active function on a dimethyl derivative is easily removed by forming its methoxy derivative with methanol vapour. Silylated supports are commercially available and are usually prepared using dimethyldichlorosilane.

No silylation treatment, however thorough, removes all trace of adsorptive properties from a support, either because the silanes cannot reach every site, or because some of the adsorption does not result from hydroxyl groups. However, any remaining adsorption can usually be removed by treating the silanised support with a small proportion, e.g., 0.1%, of a hydroxylated stationary liquid, e.g., polyethylene glycol (48), as described below.

(4) *Saturation of Adsorption Sites.* Adsorption sites may be effectively deactivated by saturating them with any compound of chemical type similar to the solutes the adsorption of which is required to be inhibited. Such a saturating compound may be either volatile or non-volatile. A common practice is to add to the stationary liquid a small proportion, e.g. 0.1%, of some polar solvent, such as polyethylene glycol, or a non-ionic detergent. An example of the effect of this is shown in Fig. 7.4 (39), where chromatograms of a mixture including polar components first on pure silicone oil, and second on silicone oil with added polyethylene glycol, are

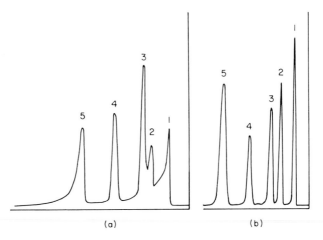

Fɪɢ. 7.4. Chromatograms on: (a) silicone 550 on 42 to 50 mesh firebrick, (b) the same, plus 2% w/w polyethylene glycol 600. Johns (*39*). 1, Ethanol; 2, methyl ethyl ketone; 3, carbon tetrachloride; 4, octane; 5, butyl acetate.

compared. The author of this example showed that any of several polar compounds, e.g., oleic acid or a long chain amine, had much the same effect.

Another example of the use of a polar component in the stationary liquid to inhibit adsorption is contained in the original paper on GC by James and Martin (*1*). Here, the authors show that the incorporation of 5% of stearic acid into their solvent removes tailing in the separation of mixtures of fatty acids (Section 12.6).

A volatile adsorption inhibitor can also be used; in this case, the chromatography is conducted in a carrier gas containing a constant small proportion of a polar material, which saturates the adsorption of the support (cf. Fig. 4.5). Water vapour and amines for alkanol and amine solutes (*49, 50*), ammonia for aminoacid esters (*51*), or formic acid for higher fatty acids (*52*), have all been used in this way. The obvious drawbacks are that there is a permanent contaminant in the carrier gas which may perturb the detection, and the reagent may affect the stationary liquid.

It is commonly observed that in the chromatography of a polar vapour on a non-polar stationary liquid on an adsorptive support, previous samples of the vapour can effectively condition the column against tailing, so that separations improve with use. Also, in routine analyses the first one or two analyses are often in error; a probable reason is that some components are almost irreversibly adsorbed, and only when such adsorption is saturated will successive runs become reproducible.

7.3. OPEN-TUBE COLUMNS; CAPILLARY COLUMNS

Capillary columns should more properly be called "Open-Tube Columns," since they are not necessarily restricted to columns so thin as to be hair-like. They are discussed in detail by Ettre (53). The preparation of efficient capillary columns probably requires a greater ratio of art to science than with packed columns.

(a) Tube Material

Capillary columns have been constructed of copper, stainless steel (54), glass (55, 56), and nylon (57); of these, copper is liable to deleterious oxidation if used at high temperatures (58), and nylon has a slight retention for some compounds, e.g., higher aromatic hydrocarbons, but not paraffins (57). Stainless steel is less frangible than glass, although coils of fine glass tube are remarkably resilient. Capillary columns are invariably used in coils; Desty et al. (59) have described a simple machine for constructing uniform coils of fine glass tube, in which 4- to 6-mm glass tubing is fed by rollers into a furnace from which it is drawn at 50 times the speed into a semicircular metal tube heated to the softening point of the glass. It emerges from this as the required helix. Glass or metal capillaries may be used up to at least 250°C. The maximum temperature of nylon columns is between 100° and 180°C, depending on the kind of nylon.

In current practice, stainless steel is the commonest tube material, probably followed by glass. Diameters are normally between about 1 mm and 0.25 mm (0.05 and 0.01 inches). In most analytical practice, column lengths are between about 15 and 60 metres (50 and 200 feet), though there is no special reason for these lengths; much longer columns may be necessary for the greatest resolution, and much shorter lengths may be used for greater speed.

It appears that the nature of the stainless steel can greatly affect the efficiency of a column that can be made from it, and many workers have found that different batches of apparently the same material have differed greatly in their ability to produce good columns. The exact criteria which give good columns can scarcely be specified, except that it is presumably necessary that the inside walls do not contain large or irregular fissures, and that they are not contaminated with any agent which prevents their being wetted by the stationary liquid.

(b) Coating Techniques

The coating of stationary liquids on the inside walls of capillary columns must be very thin and very uniform. Two main methods have been developed.

Method 1. The stationary liquid is dissolved to make a dilute solution in a volatile solvent, and the resulting solution is passed into one end of the empty capillary tube. This is usually done by connecting the open end of the tube to the lower part of a reservoir containing the solution, and applying slight pressure to the solution, e.g., from a gas cylinder. For short columns, the pressure of the domestic gas supply may be adequate. This procedure may be continued until either the tube is filled with solution, which then emerges from the far end, or there is a sufficiently long slug of solution in the column. After this, the reservoir of solvent is removed, and the solution is blown out of the column, leaving the inside walls wet.

In this method, the choice between completely filling the column and using a slug of sufficient volume to wet the whole length seems immaterial. In the slug method, it appears that the slug should be at least of the order of 5 or 10% of the column length. The critical part of the operation is the speed at which the solution is pushed out of the column; it is necessary that the speed of the rear of the solution zone moves slowly. Thus, a maximum figure of 10 cm/sec is given by Desty and Goldup (*60*), while other authors recommend speeds of about 2 cm/sec (*53, 61, 62*). If pressure is used to extrude the zone of solution from the column, it is liable to accelerate either continuously if the whole column was filled, or when the far end of a slug reaches the far end of the column, since the solution offers progressively less resistance. In order to avoid this, Kaiser (*61*) generated the gas to drive the solution electrolytically. It is, however, possible to control the flow adequately by controlling the pressure as the extrusion proceeds.

The thickness of film of stationary liquid increases with (a) the concentration of stationary liquid in the solvent, (b) the viscosity of the solution, and (c) the speed of extrusion of the zone. It may also increase with the polarity of the solvent for the stationary liquid. Most current practice uses concentrations of between 5 and 10% of stationary liquid in the solvent. Dichloromethane is a commonly used solvent.

Method 2. This method was originally used by Golay (*54*), and, though less common than Method 1 in current practice, has been successfully applied by Horvath (*63*) and Halasz and Horvath (*64, 65*) for the porous layer open tube columns described below. In the method, the column tube is completely filled with a solution of the stationary liquid, and one end is closed. The column is then fed through an oven open end first, thus evaporating the solvent and leaving the liquid. Since it is done from the open end first, no solution is displaced by boiling vapour and an even layer is obtained. The advantage of this method is that the quantity of stationary phase deposited is calculable from the volume of the tube and the concentration of the solution. Its drawback is that it requires a more elaborate apparatus consisting of a tubular oven together with apparatus for passing the column at a steady slow rate through the oven. In this technique, stationary liquid concentrations are smaller, since all the stationary liquid is deposited. Concentrations of about 1% are usual.

From Sections 6.3 and 6.14, it is seen that the thickness of the stationary liquid should not be greater than about 1/300th of the tube diameter, and, from Sections 5.7 and 6.14, the desirability of large values of k implies that the film thickness should not be unnecessarily small. With capillary columns of diameter about 0.01 inch, therefore, the film thickness should be neither very much greater nor very much less than 0.00003 inch, which is approximately 1μ. The above procedures secure approximately correct film thickness. Dijkstra and Goey (66) report a film thickness of 5μ, which is clearly too great and does not enable capillary columns to be used to their best advantage.

(c) Stationary Liquids

Capillary columns can be made using any of the common stationary liquids. Stainless steel columns can be made to accommodate either polar or non-polar liquids. However, extensive experience from many workers shows with little doubt that it is more difficult to produce an efficient column with stationary liquids which have large proportions of polar groups. In particular, it is difficult to produce efficient columns with polyester stationary liquids such as are commonly used for analysis of higher fatty acid esters or fatty alcohols. Glass columns appear to be unsatisfactory for non-polar solvents (67), since the liquid layer is stable only for limited periods. In many cases, capillary columns are found to be more efficient if a small proportion, e.g., 10%, of a surface-active agent, e.g., a non-ionic detergent, is added to the stationary liquid. In part, the effect of this appears to be to block adsorption sites (68). In part also, it probably acts by reducing the surface tension of the solvent, and promoting a smoother film (69). In cases where capillary columns have been used to analyse acidic or basic substances, the addition of acid detergent material or basic detergent material has been found to improve efficiency, just as described in the previous section for packed columns (70, 71).

(d) Porous Layer Open-Tube Columns

Soon after the introduction of capillary columns it was recognised that their capabilities could be improved if the inside tube surface were roughened so that it could contain more stationary liquid (72). The inside surface of an open tube can be roughened either by etching it chemically or by depositing a rough layer of coherent particles.

Columns made by etching glass tubes have been described by Mohnke et al. (73, 74), who used ammonia solution under pressure at 170°C, and by Liberti, and Bruner and Cartoni (67, 75), who used concentrated caustic soda solution at 100°C. Both methods cause a roughening of the inside surface. The surfaces so obtained can be used either as adsorbents in their own right, or they can alternatively be used as absorbents for a stationary liquid. Thus, Bruner and Cartoni illustrate the use of an alkali-etched glass tube coated with squalane for the separation of cyclohexane and perdeuterocyclohexane. An example of a rapid analysis on an etched glass column is shown in Fig. 12.3 (p. 429).

Columns in which a coherent porous layer is deposited on the inside have been described by Halasz and Horvath (63–65), by Grob (76), and by Ettre et al. (77–79). In the technique of Halasz et al. and Ettre et al., the powdered material to be deposited on the tube, which may be graphitised carbon black, ferric oxide, or alumina, is made into a stable emulsion with solvent and dispersants, and this mixture is then applied to the tube by either of the methods described above.

The advantage of the use of porous layer open tube columns, whether these be used as adsorption or as partition columns with subsequently added stationary liquid, is that they can be made so that they have larger partition ratios than ordinary capillary columns with very little loss of performance, since this is in any case almost completely determined by the C_g term (Section 6.11). Capillary columns tend to operate with small values of the partition ratio, k, with consequent loss of resolution, as described in Section 6.14. The use of porous layer columns largely corrects this defect, and enables open tube columns to employ their characteristic speed and large plate number without losing resolution through small partition ratios. The point is well illustrated in Fig. 7.5 (65), which compares a simple separation of some hydrocarbons, first on an ordinary liquid layer capillary column, and then on a porous layer column. Peaks 2 and 3, which are poorly resolved in the top chromatogram, are clearly resolved in the lower.

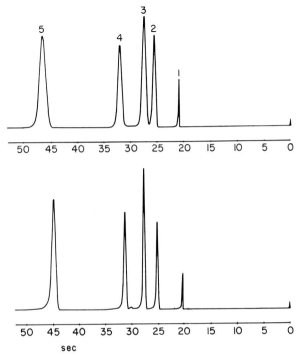

FIG. 7.5. Separations of simple hydrocarbons on an ordinary liquid layer capillary column (upper) and on a porous layer capillary column (lower). Operating conditions are virtually identical for both columns: length, 30 m; diam., 0.25 mm; flow rate, 140 cm/sec; carrier gas, H_2; temp., 80°C. Open tube column coated with squalane; porous layer tube with ferric oxide doped with triethylene glycol. Halasz and Horvath (65). 1, methane; 2, n-pentane; 3, 2,2-dimethylbutane; 4, n-hexane; 5, n-heptane.

(e) Packed Capillary Columns

Another scheme for producing a long, thin column of good efficiency without undue pressure drop is to make an ordinary packed column of ordinary dimensions, e.g., 4 mm internal diameter, containing an adsorbent in glass tubing, and then to pass the column so made through the apparatus used to make capillary tubes from glass tubes referred to in Section 7.3a. The result is a fine coiled tube in which the particles of the adsorbent are embedded in the walls of the glass capillary, and, with correct choice of the dimensions and packing for the original column, the resulting coiled capillary is reasonably robust and easily permeable by gas (80, 81). Granular alumina has most commonly been used as the adsorbent. The advantage possessed by these columns in rapid analysis is illustrated by the separation of light hydrocarbons shown in Fig. 12.4 (p. 431).

7.4. Use of Two Stationary Liquids

In a mixture of more than two substances, it often happens that one pair of components overlaps when chromatographed on one stationary liquid, and that a different pair of components overlaps when it is chromatographed on another stationary liquid. It is clear that all components could be resolved by running the mixture first on a column of one stationary liquid, and then on a column of the other. This is occasionally necessary, but it is time-consuming, and it is common practice where possible to combine the two stationary phases in such a way that all components are resolved. For example, in a mixture of ethane, ethene, propane, and propene (Section 12.3) the alkanes may be separated from the alkenes with a column of silver nitrate in glycol, and the C_2's may be separated from the C_3's with a column of tri-isobutylene. A column of tri-isobutylene and silver nitrate-glycol used together, however, can separate all four components, and, with careful choice of the proportions of each stationary phase, does not cause any other overlaps. Such a procedure is very common.

The use of two stationary liquids is generally most effective when they are of different chemical type. They may be used together in three different ways:

(1) Series columns each packed with material made with one stationary liquid.

(2) One column packed with an intimate mixture of separate packings each made with one stationary liquid.

(3) One column with a packing made from a mixture of the stationary liquids.

If no interaction occurs between the stationary liquids and if the pressure drop across columns in series is small, the retention volumes for vapours on a composite column may be presumed to be the sum of the retention volumes on each stationary liquid. Thus, if superscripts ‡ and † are used for each of two stationary liquids, the retention volume of a vapour is given by

$$V_R{}^0 = (V_R{}^0)^\dagger + (V_R{}^0)^\ddagger = V_M{}^\dagger + W^\dagger \beta^\dagger + V_M{}^\ddagger + W^\ddagger \beta^\ddagger, \quad (7.1)$$

using the symbols of Chapter 2. When both the stationary liquids are contained in the same column, $V_M{}^\dagger = V_M{}^\ddagger$. Note that relative retention times on a composite column cannot be calculated directly from relative retention times on each component stationary liquid of the column.

Using Eq. (2.12) and the adjusted retention volume, V_R' (Section 2.4), Eq. (7.1) becomes:

$$\frac{V_R'}{W^\dagger + W^\ddagger} = \frac{W^\dagger}{W^\dagger + W^\ddagger} (\beta^\dagger - \beta^\ddagger) + \beta^\ddagger. \qquad (7.2)$$

The right-hand side of this is a kind of specific retention volume for the composite column, without any correction for pressure drop (for which, see below), and the equation shows that it is a linear function of $W^\dagger/(W^\dagger + W^\ddagger)$, which is the proportion by weight of one of the stationary liquids. Thus, a plot of the modified specific retention volume defined above, or of the corresponding retention time obtained by dividing by the flow rate, against the proportion of one of the stationary liquids should

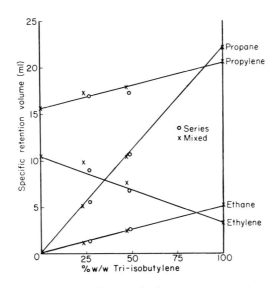

Fig. 7.6. Specific retention volumes of solutes on either series or mixed column materials as a function of the proportion of one column material. Primavesi (82). Solutes: ethylene, ethane, propylene, propane. Solvents: triisobutylene, ethylene glycol —silver nitrate.

give a straight line. This has been indicated specifically by Primavesi (82), using the case of ethane, ethene, propane, and propene quoted above (Fig. 7.6). Such a plot gives one straight line for each component of the vapour mixture, and the value of the abscissa for which there is adequate vertical distance between all pairs of lines gives the proportions of stationary liquids for which a good separation of all the components may be secured.

In a complex mixture of vapours for which there are different overlaps on each of two pure stationary phases, a random choice of proportions of the two stationary liquids for use in a composite column may lead to a column which gives further overlaps, as indeed has often been found. This suggests that the kind of plot given in Fig. 7.6 may be generally useful in choosing proportions of stationary liquids for a composite column.

If the pressure drop across the column is small, and if the mixture of the two stationary liquids is thermodynamically perfect, the three methods of combination listed above should give similar results. This has usually been assumed in the literature (82–86), and has been checked in one case by McFadden (87). If, however, the mixture of stationary liquids is not perfect, the retention volume of a solute in the mixture is not necessarily the sum of those in the separate stationary liquids, and Eq. (7.1) does not necessarily hold. Thus, method 3 may give a different result from methods 1 and 2. The author has shown that in many common cases, the retention volume of a solute in a mixture of stationary liquids is by no means a linear function of composition, and the plot may even contain maxima; this is implicit in Fig. 3.10.

It has frequently been observed that the order of elution of components from series columns is changed if the columns are reversed. No systematic study of this phenomenon has been published, but a simple theoretical argument shows that it will inevitably occur if the pressure drop across the columns is not small. The arrangement is illustrated in Fig. 7.7; let † refer to the first column, and let ‡ refer to the second; let symbols be as in Chapter 2. The retention time in the first column is:

$$t_{21}^{\dagger} = \{V_M{}^{\dagger} + W^{\dagger}\beta^{\dagger}\}j\left(\frac{P_2}{P_1}\right) \Big/ \dot{V}_1, \qquad (7.3)$$

where $j(P_2/P_1)$ is the pressure correction factor between P_2 and P_1. The unknown quantity $\dot{V}_1$ is related to the measurable quantity $\dot{V}_o$ by the equation:

$$\dot{V}_1 = \dot{V}_o \cdot \frac{P_o}{P_1}. \qquad (7.4)$$

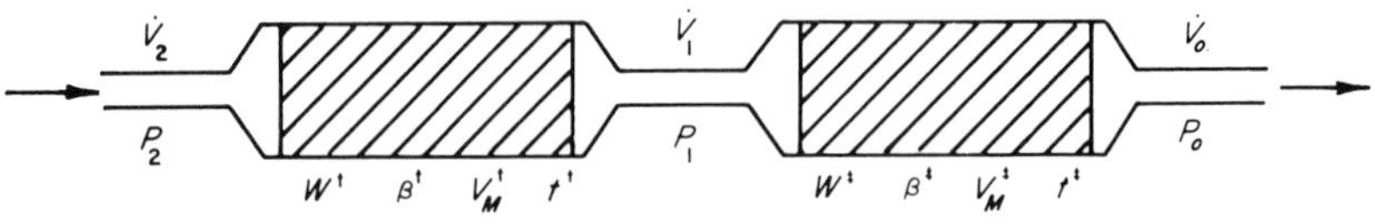

Fig. 7.7. Specification of symbols for the discussion of series columns with pressure drop.

The retention time in the second column is given by

$$t_{1o}^{\ddagger} = (V_M{}^{\ddagger} + W^{\ddagger}\beta^{\ddagger})j\left(\frac{P_1}{P_o}\right)\bigg/ \dot{V}_o.$$ (7.5)

The total retention time is given by the sum of Eq. (7.5) and the product of Eqs. (7.3) and (7.4):

$$\begin{aligned} t &= t_{21}^{\ddagger} + t_{1o}^{\ddagger} \\ &= \left\{ (V_M{}^{\dagger} + W^{\dagger}\beta^{\dagger})j\left(\frac{P_2}{P_1}\right) \cdot \frac{P_1}{P_o} + (V_M{}^{\dagger} + W^{\ddagger}\beta^{\ddagger})j\left(\frac{P_1}{P_o}\right) \right\} \frac{1}{\dot{V}_o}. \end{aligned}$$ (7.6)

If, for simplicity, it is assumed that the columns have similar permeabilities and dead volumes, interchanging the columns does not affect P_1, and the total retention time is:

$$\begin{aligned} t &= t_{21}^{\ddagger} + t_{1o}^{\ddagger} \\ &= \left\{ (V_M{}^{\ddagger} + W^{\ddagger}\beta^{\ddagger})j\left(\frac{P_2}{P_1}\right) \cdot \frac{P_1}{P_o} + (V_M{}^{\dagger} + W^{\dagger}\beta^{\dagger})j\left(\frac{P_1}{P_o}\right) \right\} \frac{1}{\dot{V}_o}. \end{aligned}$$ (7.7)

Equations (7.6) and (7.7) are *not* identical except when $W^{\dagger}\beta^{\dagger} = W^{\ddagger}\beta^{\ddagger}$, and in practice this is most unlikely, since the columns have almost certainly been chosen so that $\beta^{\dagger} \neq \beta^{\ddagger}$. What has happened is that everything in the first column is P_1/P_o times slower than in the second column, so that a large retention in the first column has a greater effect on the over-all retention time than a similarly large retention in the second. Hence vapours that are largely retained by the first column and not by the second will come through faster when the columns are interchanged, and vapours that are largely retained by the second column and not by the first will come through more slowly on interchange.

7.5. Programmed Temperature Operation

When chromatographing a mixture of large boiling range on a column at constant temperature, the first peaks to be eluted are very high and narrow, and the last peaks are eluted as long and shallow zones after an inconveniently long retention time. The first and last peaks are also liable to give erroneous quantitative analyses; the first on account of the difficulty in measuring the area inside such a long boundary and the possibility of the concentration being such that the detector is non-linear; the last because of the incorporation of much noise into the peak. These drawbacks may all be overcome by increasing the temperature of the column in the course of the run, so that the initial temperature is low enough to produce reasonable shapes for the initial peaks, and the final temperature is high enough to allow the elution of the last peaks at reasonable speed. The contrast between a constant temperature run and a run with continuously increasing temperature is shown clearly in Fig. 7.8, from dal Nogare and Bennett (88).

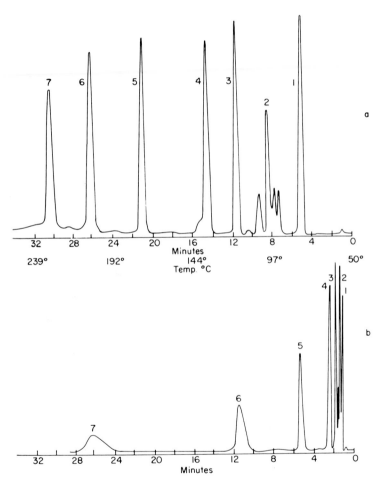

FIG. 7.8. To illustrate the effect of temperature programming. (a) Chromatogram of a hydrocarbon mixture on a temperature programmed column. (b) The same mixture chromatographed at 168°C. From dal Nogare and Bennett (88). 1, Pentane; 2, hexane; 3, heptane; 4, 1-octene; 5, decane; 6, 1-dodecene; 7, 1-tetradecene.

The column temperature may be increased during a run in any of three ways:

(1) discontinuously either with or without interruption of the gas flow during the heating periods,

(2) continuously in an uncontrolled manner (*87, 89–95*),

(3) continuously with a linear relation between temperature and time (*88, 96–99*).

The method of heating is referred to as the "Programme," even though such a title is rather pretentious in some applications, and the technique is called "Programmed Temperature" operation.

(1) *Discontinuous heating.* The column is heated between the appearance of the more volatile and the less volatile components of interest. This simple method has been used regularly in applications of gas chromatography since its early days.

(2) *Uncontrolled continuous heating.* In this technique, the detector is run in a separate thermostat at a temperature greater than that of the column as its hottest, and the column is heated continuously from the time the sample is introduced. In most examples of this technique, the column is contained in a furnace which is heated electrically with a constant voltage input. As the temperature rises, the rate of heat loss and also the resistance of the heating elements increase, so that the rate of increase of temperature falls. This is shown by Harrison *et al.* (*96*). If, however, the furnace is well lagged, and the range of the temperature programme is not too great, the rate of rise in temperature may well be nearly linear, as was found by Griffiths *et al.* (*89*). Much of the utility of programmed temperature operation is lost if as much time is taken by the furnace in cooling down for a new run as is saved in operation by its use. Thus, in practice it is necessary to use a furnace of small heat capacity, as for example is described by Roper (*100*).

(3) *Linear temperature programming.* Temperature programmed operation is most useful when the column is heated linearly at a reproducible rate. This may be done by controlling the temperature of the furnace with a standard commercial temperature controller in which the thermostatted temperature is continuously adjustable, and by linearly varying the latter, for example by driving the control with a geared-down servo-motor (*88*).

Ideas on retention volumes, retention times, and column performances all need modification in considering chromatograms from programmed temperature columns. The most noticeable feature of chromatograms of homologous series is that, so long as the partition coefficient at the emergence temperature is large, the retention time is approximately proportional to the carbon number. This is clearly seen from Fig. 7.8; it is illustrated for a number of heating rates in Fig. 7.9 (97), which shows a plot of the retention time against homologue number for a homologous

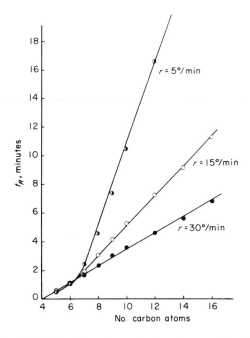

FIG. 7.9. Plots of retention time, t_R, against carbon number for various heating rates, r. From dal Nogare and Langlois (97).

series. Two interpretations follow, each leading to a comparison of performances in programmed temperature operation with those in isothermal operation.

(1) If the number of theoretical plates is defined phenomenologically by any of the methods given in Section 5.5, then the chromatogram of Fig. 7.8a shows that the number of plates so defined rises rapidly with retention time. If it is assumed that all peaks are equally wide, then

$$\mathcal{N} \propto t^2; \qquad \sqrt{\mathcal{N}} \propto t. \qquad (7.8)$$

The other factor in determining separation is the relative retention, which again, if regarded phenomenologically, is the ratio of retention times. It is observed that substances of which the retentions are in a constant time *ratio* on isothermal columns produce peaks with an approximately constant time *difference* on linear programmed temperature columns. Thus, if $1 + x_{23}$ is the phenomenological relative retention of two close components, then

$$x_{23} = \frac{t_3 - t_2}{t_2} = \frac{\text{const}}{t_2}, \qquad (7.9)$$

i.e., the phenomenological relative retention is inversely proportional to the retention time. If we now multiply Eqs. (7.8) and (7.9), then the resolution, given by $x\sqrt{\mathcal{N}}$ [Eq. (5.36)], is seen to be independent of t, and therefore unaffected by the increase of the phenomenological plate-number with retention time. The conclusion is that the resolution of a column is not appreciably affected by temperature programming.

(2) Habgood and Harris (*98*) argue that since a peak moves through most of the column when the column temperature is close to the emergence temperature (see below), the number of plates in the column is virtually given by:

$$\mathcal{N} = 16\left(\frac{(t)_{T_R}}{M_{(t)}}\right)^2, \qquad (7.10)$$

where $(t)_{T_R}$ is the retention time for the vapour in the same column used isothermally at the temperature at which the vapour emerges, T_R (emergence temperature), and $M_{(t)}$ is as defined in Eq. (5.23), expressed in time units. The quantity $(t)_{T_R}$ may be calculated from the emergence temperature, and from $\log(t) - 1/T$ plots, as described in Section 3.10. It appears that $(t)_{T_R}$ is virtually independent of T_R, so that the number of plates calculated on this basis is more or less constant. Since in this case retention volumes of different close vapours are compared isothermally, the temperature programme does not affect the calculated relative retention, and so has little effect on the resolution of two vapours.

Both these arguments neglect the relatively small changes in plate-height with temperature and retention volume. The conclusion is that temperature programming does not grossly affect the resolution, and this is illustrated in Table 7.3, which shows plate-heights in programmed runs compared with plate-heights run isothermally at the emergence temperature (*98*).

The calculation of retention times in programmed temperature operation involves the integration of the continuously changing speed of the

TABLE 7.3

PLATE-HEIGHTS IN A COLUMN RUN WITH A LINEAR TEMPERATURE PROGRAMME
COMPARED WITH THOSE IN THE SAME COLUMN RUN ISOTHERMALLY AT THE EMERGENCE
TEMPERATURE[a]

Vapour: hexane
Parameters: heating rate and flow rate

Flow rate (ml/minute)	Heating rate (°C/minute)	T_R (°C)	Plate-height (cm) Programmed	Isothermal
125	1.66	40	0.45	0.49
118	3.7	49	0.48	0.40
44	1.58	52	0.27	0.19
45	3.6	66	0.21	0.21
17	1.65	71	0.22	0.27
17	3.7	92	0.22	0.28
24	9.1	111	0.26	0.27
17	13.4	158	0.56	0.47
17	20	166	0.42	0.51

[a] See Habgood and Harris (98).

zone of a vapour during its elution. In linear programmed operation, the temperature T at time t is given by

$$T = T_0 + rt, \tag{7.11}$$

where T_0 is the temperature at the start of the run and r is the heating rate. The change in temperature can cause alteration of several column parameters:

(1) the partition coefficient,
(2) the gas flow rate in the column,
(3) the pressure ratio,

of which the first is by far the largest. All three factors have been taken into account by dal Nogare and Langlois (97) in the calculation of the retention time. The result is a complicated integral with a large number of parameters which can only be integrated numerically, for which purpose the authors use a digital computer.

Since the effect of temperature on the partition coefficient greatly exceeds the effect on the flow or the pressure drop, no great error is introduced into the calculations if the effects of (2) and (3) above are neglected. In this case, retention times in temperature programmed runs can be treated either graphically, by a method of Habgood and Harris (*98*), or analytically, as has been done by Giddings (*101*).

Habgood and Harris use the equation:

$$\int_{T_0}^{T_R} \frac{dT}{(V)_T} = \frac{r}{\dot{V}},$$
(7.12)

where T_R is the emergence temperature, related with the retention, t_R, by Eq. (7.11), and $(V)_T$ is the retention volume at a temperature T; this equation is easily derived from equations given below. The authors plot $1/(V)_T$ against T, either empirically, or by replotting known $\log(V)_T$ versus $1/T$ plots, and by measuring the areas of these plots between T_0 and T, the integral of Eq. (7.12) may be plotted as a function of T_R. The value of T_R for a given vapour is then given by the abscissa on such a plot corresponding to an ordinate of the known value of $r/\dot{V}$. Finally, the retention time is obtained from Eq. (7.11).

The essential difficulty in deriving an analytical expression for t_R lies in the fact that the integral involved can only be expressed exactly as a power series. However, a simple approximate formula may be derived as follows.

The partition coefficient, β, may be expressed as a function of temperature by Eq. (3.81), which on integration becomes:

$$\beta = CTe^{\Delta H/RT},$$
(7.13)

where C is an integration constant. The basic approximation is that $\Delta H/RT$ is always sufficiently large that $d\beta/dT$ is dominated by the exponential term, so that in Eq. (7.13), the T outside the exponential may be replaced by a constant. In this case, C may be replaced by $e^{\Delta S/R}$, where ΔS is the entropy of solution, and is treated as if independent of temperature.

From Eq. (2.17) and the definition of R_F, the speed of a zone through the column, u_v, is:

$$u_v = \frac{u}{1+k} = \frac{u}{1+k'e^X},$$
(7.14)

where $k' = (WTe^{\Delta S/R})/V_M$ and $X = \Delta H/RT$. The distance travelled along the column by a zone is $\int u_v \, dt$, so that, if the length of the column is l, then the retention time, t_R, is given by:

$$l = \int_0^{t_R} u_v \, dt.$$
(7.15)

Substituting Eq. (7.14), and changing the variable of integration from t to T by Eq. (7.11),

$$l = \frac{u}{r} \int_{T_0}^{T_R} \frac{dT}{1 + k'e^X}. \tag{7.16}$$

In most application of programmed temperature chromatography, $k \gg 1$, so that $1 + k \approx k$, and this becomes

$$\frac{lrk'}{u} = \int_{T_0}^{T_R} e^{-X} \, dT. \tag{7.17}$$

This may be integrating using the approximation mentioned above, by dividing the right-hand side of Eq. (7.17) inside the integral by a function of T which makes it immediately integrable, and multiplying the right-hand side by the constant value of the same function at a temperature intermediate between T_0 and T_R. By the nature of the approximation, the choice of the intermediate temperature is not critical. Giddings (*101*) chooses such a value that, on performing the integration, the result is:

$$\frac{Rrlk'}{u \, \Delta H} = \frac{e^{-X_R}}{(X_R - 1)^2} - \frac{e^{-X_0}}{(X_0 - 1)^2}. \tag{7.18}$$

If T_R is considerably greater than T_0, the second term may be neglected, and

$$\frac{Rrlk'}{u \, \Delta H} = \frac{e^{-X_R}}{(X_R + 1)^2}. \tag{7.19}$$

In this equation, $T_R = \Delta H / R X_R$, and all the quantities on the left-hand side are known or knowable. Thus, T_R may be computed numerically.

The significance of Eq. (7.19) may be demonstrated by using the rather gross approximation that unity may be neglected in comparison with X_R, so that the equation becomes, after rearrangement:

$$T_R = \frac{-\Delta H / R}{\ln \left\{ \dfrac{rlk' \, \Delta H}{RuT_R^2} \right\}}. \tag{7.20}$$

Let z equal the argument of the logarithm. The behaviour of Eq. (7.20) is apparent when it is recalled that $d(\ln z)/dz = 1/z$, so that the larger z is, the smaller the variation of the logarithm with change of any of the quantities composing z. Thus, when z is large,

$$T_R \propto -\Delta H. \tag{7.21}$$

Hence, when z is large, a plot of retention time or emergence temperature against heat of solution should be linear. Successive homologues have constant increments to ΔH, as described in Section 3.10, so that the linear plot of emergence temperature against carbon number shown in Fig. 7.9 is explained. If z is to be large, the column length, heating rate, retention volume, and heat of solution must be adequately large, and the flow rate must not be too large. The specific effect of ΔH is seen from Fig. 7.9; when this falls below a certain value, its linear relation with emergence temperature fails. Increase in flow rate, reduction in heating rate and in retention volume, and decrease in column length all contribute to performing the whole elution in conditions that there is insufficient temperature rise between introduction and emergence. It is clear that in this case Eq. (7.20) must inevitably fail, for the elution approaches isothermal elution, in which case the usual logarithmic relation between retention time and heat of solution must inevitably supervene.

The linear relation between T_R or t_R and homologue number is approximate even though z is large, partly because of the approximations involved in calculating Eq. (7.20), partly because successive increments in ΔH for homologues are a function of temperature, and partly because of the temperature dependence of flow rate and pressure ratio. In particular, especially with constant mass-flow rate, the time between successive homologues declines with increase in homologue number.

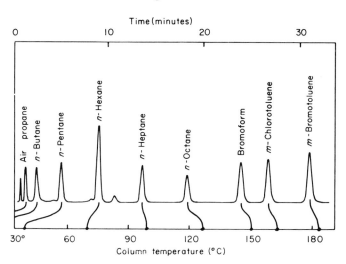

Fig. 7.10. Linear temperature programmed chromatogram illustrating that vapours may emerge at temperatures close to their normal boiling points. From Habgood and Harris (98).

The approximate proportionality of ΔH and T_R may be interpreted in a manner which shows the nature of programmed temperature chromatography. The approximate constancy of $\Delta H/T_R$ recalls Trouton's law [Eq. (3.29)] for boiling points. In programmed temperature chromatography in conditions that z is large, vapours spend the great majority of their residence time in the first few per cent of the column, and only when the temperature comes within a few degrees of T_R do they begin to move appreciably through the column, which they do at a rapidly increasing rate on account of the large value of $d\beta/dT$. Vapours may, therefore, be described as evaporating out of the column at a temperature T_R in the same way that vapours in a distillation column boil out at their boiling point; and both processes obey Trouton's law. The analogy between programmed temperature chromatography and boiling is shown clearly in a chromatogram given by Habgood and Harris (98) (Fig. 7.10) in which vapours chromatographed on a column in which differences in activity coefficients are small all emerge at temperatures close to their boiling points.

7.6. PREPARATIVE COLUMNS

Many workers have scaled up analytical gas chromatography for the preparation of small pure samples. The scaling up introduces a number of new problems. The general effect is that, as the quantity increases, the column performance declines; this may be analysed under three headings:

(a) Change in performance with diameter (Section 6.17).
(b) Change in performance with sample size (Section 6.19).
(c) Change in input distribution with sample size (Section 6.7).

(a) Change in Performance with Diameter

As described in Section 6.17, no problem arises for columns of up to about $\frac{1}{2}$ inch diameter, but above that, most workers find that the plate-height increases rapidly. This is probably due to unevenness of packing, and the results of Huyten et al. (102) suggest that the unevenness usually takes the form of tighter packing at the centre than at the outside. These authors have found that the mode of packing is critical, as is shown in Table 7.4, but there is no obvious logic behind the results. Since the result which gives the smallest plate-height also gives the largest velocity gradient across the column (102), it seems that none of the packing methods listed is ideal.

TABLE 7.4

EFFECT OF PACKING METHOD AND MESH SIZE ON COLUMN PERFORMANCE[a]

Column length: 1 metre   Temperature: 22°C
Column diameter: 3 inches   Packing: 30/100 w/w silicone oil MC 200/200
Carrier gas: 385 litres/hour   on Sil-O-Cel
Sample: 1 ml n-pentane

Mode of packing	Mesh size (B.S.S.)	Mean plate-number
Pouring	30–40	250
Pouring followed by gentle beating	30–40	120
Vibration	30–40	220
Beating	30–40	330
Beating together with a filling speed of 20 g/minute	30–40	500
Vibration plus beating	30–40	400
Vibration plus beating	50–80	315
Vibration plus beating	20–70	300

[a] See Huyten et al. (102).

(b) *Change in Performance with Sample Size*

As described in Section 6.19, the larger the sample, the worse the performance. The steepness of the decline in performance with increase in samples is greater when the proportion of stationary phase is smaller, and if it is assumed that a preparative column is to be designed so as to have as large a throughput as possible, the proportion of stationary phase should be large. A large proportion of stationary phase implies a long retention time, so a further conclusion is that the larger the sample, the longer the separation time for a given resolution.

The effect of temperature on the maximum sample size for a given resolution is complicated. Lowering the temperature increases resolution on account of increase in relative retentions (Section 3.10) and on account of decrease in plate-height (Section 6.15), and, with small samples, this is decisive. With large samples, furthermore, the lower the temperature, the longer the retention volume, and, according to Section 6.19, the smaller the effect of quantity. All these arguments, however, may well be upset by the fact that the lower the temperature, the smaller the concentration of vapour at which non-linearity becomes important. The result is that there is an optimum temperature above which decreases in retention volume, retention ratio, and plate-number are predominant, and below which broadening due to non-linearity is predominant.

(c) Change in Input Distribution with Sample Size

A considerable amount of heat is required to volatilise a liquid sample. Sample injectors of the type used in analytical work (Section 11.2) cannot usually supply this, and sample injectors designed for preparative work usually consist of a cavity in front of the column packed with metal beads (45, 103). This may be heated to such a temperature that its heat capacity is sufficient to volatilise all the sample. The sudden creation of vapour produces a large increase in pressure at the head of the column, which may easily cause a reverse flow of carrier gas and vapour into the carrier gas feed line. This may be cured either by heating a region of the feed line (45), or by incorporating a non-return valve in the gas line immediately behind the introducer (104).

(d) Effect of Stationary Phase

As is indicated above and in Section 6.19, the partition coefficient should be large in preparative work. This may be achieved by choosing a station- ary phase in which components of interest have small activity coefficients; in such circumstances, partition coefficients are large, and furthermore, non-linearity does not occur until fairly large vapour concentrations are reached, so that large samples may be used without peak broadening. There is, however, another consideration working against this. Preparative gas chromatography is presumably only undertaken in cases where there is some good reason against using simpler means, e.g., distillation, and in most applications, it is likely that use is to be made of differences in activity coefficients. Now, when activity coefficients are all small, so that partition coefficients are large, the differences in activity coefficients of different vapours are also small, since activity coefficients less than unity rarely fall below 0.5 except as a result of molecular size effects. Differences in activity coefficients provide the greatest advantage in separating different substances when the activity coefficients are greater than unity, in which case they may span a range from unity to infinity; in these circumstances, however, partition coefficients are small, with consequent peak broadening when quantities are increased. It is, in fact, impossible to make the best of both sets of circumstances. Given that a large sample is to be used in a preparative column, one may either use a stationary phase giving small activity coefficients, with no peak-broadening, but no possibility of using large differences in activity coefficients, *or* one may use a stationary phase giving large activity coefficients, with the advantage of large differences in activity coefficients, but with so much peak broadening that the advantage may well be nullified.

(e) Detector

In preparative work, the conditions for the detector are very much simpler than for analysis, for the detector is only required to record the presence of components and not to measure them. In most apparatuses, an analytical detector of no special sensitivity is run on a small monitoring stream of carrier gas taken off from the main stream, which passes to the fraction collectors. It is possible, however, to put a detector probe, e.g., a catharometer element, directly in the main gas stream (*105*) with satisfactory results.

(f) Collecting Traps

It is difficult to trap out vapour completely from a large volume of fast flowing carrier gas. The usual technique is to pass the column effluent into a trap cooled in a suitable coolant, e.g., liquid air, solid carbon dioxide, or ice, according to the volatility of the components. Several workers have found that the efficiency of a simple U- or concentric-tube trap is poor; partly because it requires the rapid transfer of much heat in order to cool the carrier gas sufficiently to condense the vapours, and partly because vapours condense as a fog which is carried through the trap.

Some workers have improved the heat transfer between the coolant and the gas by passing the latter through some sufficiently long tube contained in the coolant. Thus, Kirkland (*45*) passes the gas through a trap, consisting of a central indented tube, where most of the sample collects, and a long helical outlet, where the remainder is condensed. Atkinson and Tuey (*103*) find that condensation efficiency as a function of gas flow rate possesses a minimum; below the minimum, there is sufficient time for the gas to be cooled sufficiently below the dew point, and, above the minimum, the gas flow becomes turbulent, thus producing better heat transfer. All designs using relatively narrow tubes are inapplicable if the vapour is frozen out as a solid which would block the tubes.

The problem of fog formation has been solved by Atkinson and Tuey with an electrostatic precipitator consisting of two electrodes between which a potential of about 8 kV is applied from a commercial E.H.T. unit. Simpler solutions involve packing the trap with glass wool, or adsorbing the product on alumina, from which it is removed later by heating.

(g) Carrier Gas and Column Material

The solid supports and liquids used in analytical gas chromatography are frequently expensive, and preparative columns using these materials would be unduly expensive. Most of the cost of the supports is due not to the raw material, but to the preparation, particularly the size-grading. In analytical gas chromatography size-grading is desirable for reducing the plate-height, but, since plate-heights in preparative columns are large for other reasons, elaborate size-grading is unnecessary. This is illustrated, for example, in the last three entries of Table 7.4, where the size-range has negligible effect on the efficiency. Thus, in preparative gas chromatography, cruder supports may be used satisfactorily.

A preparative apparatus passes a large volume of carrier gas, which may be expensive and troublesome if obtained from tanks of compressed gas. Some workers have incorporated apparatus for recycling carrier gas (104). Another solution is to use dried and filtered air, which is satisfactory in any circumstances where oxidation does not occur.

(h) Automatic Batchwise Operation

The amount of material produced in a preparative apparatus may be multiplied by continuous repetition of the same run. Several authors have contrived apparatus to perform such repetitions automatically (*103, 106, 107*). The apparatus consists of the usual units required for preparative chromatography, together with servo-mechanisms capable of putting a reproducible sample into the column and of switching from one collector to another as zones of product come through. The servo-units are controlled by a programming unit, which may be actuated either by time-cycles or by the chromatographic peaks as they appear in the output of the detector. In the latter scheme, the cycles are upset if the programmer responds to any spurious electrical impulse given by the detector. In the former scheme, the flow rate in the columns is set constant, and the programme is such that the apparatus puts on a sample, switches from one fraction collector to another at times pre-set between each required peak, and repeats the cycle after a given time in which all components have appeared. This first scheme is used by all the workers referred to above.

(i) Continuous Gas Chromatography

Preparative gas chromatography can be carried out continuously in various ways, but as the method resembles extractive distillation, it is doubtful whether it finds a place in this book. In the technique, column packing is moved down a tube in the opposite direction to a stream of carrier gas by some vibrating device, and the vapour to be separated is fed into the middle. In an arrangement described by Scott (*108*) (Fig. 7.11),

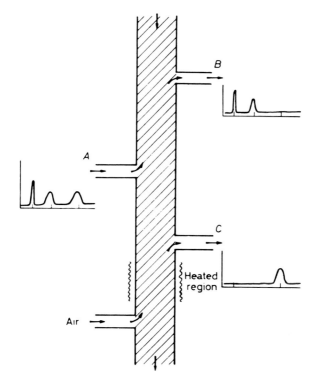

FIG. 7.11. Scheme for continuous chromatography. Scott (*108*). The mixture enters at *A*, and is divided into the more volatile components, which emerge at *B*, and the less volatile components, which emerge at *C*.

the relative speeds of the carrier gas upwards and the column packing downwards are adjusted so that zones of more volatile components move upwards, and are extracted from the emerging carrier gas, while zones of less volatile components move downwards, and are extracted from the column packing by heat, as illustrated. See also Benedek *et al.* (*109*).

Another technique for continuous chromatography is to use a circular column which rotates relative to various inlets and outlets conveying gas and samples to and from the column (*110–113*). An example of such a system is shown in Fig. 7.12 (*113*). In essence, such a system is like that of Fig. 7.11 with the bottom of the column bent round to join the top. All such systems enable a single continuous stream of components to be separated into two streams each containing components faster or slower than a given threshold. Their technology is rendered difficult by the need to produce gas-tight valves between the ports and the moving column.

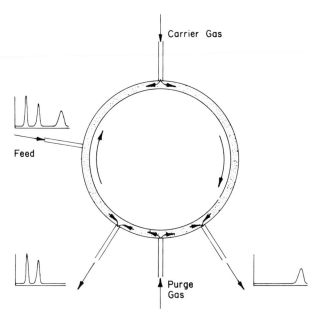

FIG. 7.12. Circular chromatography machine. From Glasser (*113*). The column moves clockwise as shown, with the inlets and outlets stationary. The purge gas serves to strip vapour from the column.

(*j*) *Summary*

It is apparent that there are many factors preventing the limitless scaling-up of gas chromatography. The technique is commonly used for quantities of the order of 100 mg to 100 g, and commercial apparatus is available for operation on this scale. Probably the commonest application of such apparatus is for the isolation of quantities of sample sufficient for further study by other means, e.g., various forms of spectroscopy; see Chapter 11.

7.7. FRONTAL AND DISPLACEMENT ANALYSIS

(a) *The Formation of Sharp Fronts*

Frontal and displacement analyses operate on stationary phases with Langmuir-type isotherms. Consider a column packed with such a stationary phase through which a stream of carrier gas passes, and at a given instant the entering carrier gas picks up a constant concentration of vapour which thereafter passes into the column continuously. The stationary phase at the start of the column adsorbs vapour until it is in equilibrium with the vapour; further vapour entering passes through the equilibrated region to clean stationary phase further along the column. This process continues until the vapour breaks through the column at the far end, and the whole column is in equilibrium with the entering vapour stream. This is the basis of the technique for determining adsorption isotherms described in Section 4.4a. The above process operates whether the isotherm is Langmuir or linear, but in the case of a Langmuir isotherm the mechanism described in Section 6.6 operates, and excessive diffuseness in the advancing front is nullified by the tendency of regions of greater vapour concentration to move faster through the column. The result is that, with Langmuir isotherms, the front that breaks through the far end of the column is sharp, however long the column. Also, any vapour in a region behind the front in which the concentration is greater than that in surrounding regions tends to move towards the front, thus levelling out any concentration gradients behind the front. The result is that the concentration of vapour behind the front is constant.

(b) *Frontal Analysis*

In frontal analysis, the technique is as above, except that the vapour introduced continuously into the carrier gas stream is the vapour of the mixture to be analysed. In this case, the least adsorbed of the components breaks through first, and appears as a step on the recorder of the detector. Some time later, a further step appears due to the next component, and so on, so that the observed chromatogram appears as a series of steps, as shown by the full line in Fig. 7.13. The first step contains pure vapour of the first species, but the second zone contains vapour both of the second species and the first species, and in general the nth zone contains n species, since vapour of every species is continuously entering the column, and vapours of species in equilibrium with the whole column must necessarily emerge from it. The concentration of a species coming through first in a

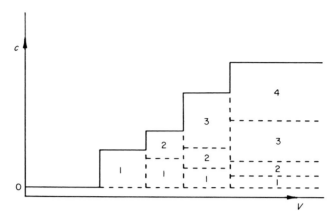

FIG. 7.13. Chromatogram obtained in frontal analysis.

given step is smaller in all subsequent steps, as indicated by the dotted lines shown in Fig. 7.13, because of the characteristics of the Langmuir isotherm for mixed vapours. The result is that the height of successive steps cannot be used directly as a measure of the concentration of the nth species in the mixture. A study of the theory of the process, however, can yield simple equations for the heights of both dotted and full lines of all steps in Fig. 7.13 [Claesson (114–116)], so that the frontal technique can be used if required for quantitative analysis. The retention volumes of the fronts in frontal analysis are functions of all the vapour concentrations and are not significant in identifying vapours qualitatively, as in linear elution chromatography.

Frontal analysis can be performed on partition columns with a gas stream of mixed dilute vapours interacting linearly with the stationary phase. In this case, the self-sharpening feature of the fronts is absent; nevertheless a column used in this way gives phenomenological plate-heights considerably smaller than if it were used in the usual elution technique. For example, Boeke (117) reports plate-heights of 0.15 mm from an ordinary packed column used in frontal analysis.

It should be emphasised that though frontal analysis indicates the existence of components in a mixture, it does not separate them.

(c) *Displacement Analysis*

In displacement analysis a discrete sample of the mixture to be analysed is placed at the beginning of a column packed with an adsorbent, and a carrier gas stream containing a constant concentration of a vapour called

the "Displacer," more strongly adsorbed than any of the components of
the mixture, is passed through the column. An approximate explanation
of what happens is given below.

The components of the mixture start to be eluted through the column,
and would normally form a series of unsymmetrical elution zones in the
usual way. However, the conditions are chosen so that the front of the
displacer moves faster than any of the elution zones. The displacer first
reaches the rear profile of the slowest of the zones, and displaces the vapour
contained in the profile from the adsorbent. This material is thus pushed
forward ahead of the advancing front of displacer, and the zone of vapour
is compressed into a step, which is pushed along by the front of displacer
at the displacer's speed. By the same argument as used in Subsection (a),
the step consists of a region of column with a constant concentration of
vapour in each phase. The step next to the displacer then encounters the
rear profile of the next slowest zone, and acts towards that as the displacer
did towards it. This process continues, so that the chromatogram obtained
at the far end of the column is a series of flat steps each containing one
pure component, followed by a continuous zone of pure displacer, as
illustrated in Fig. 7.14.

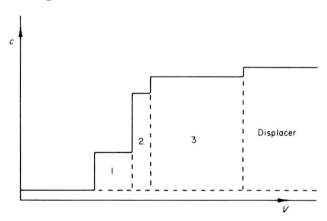

FIG. 7.14. Chromatogram obtained in displacement analysis.

The conditions for displacement chromatography and the concentrations
of the successive steps may be obtained by a construction originally due to
Tiselius (118). The speed of a zone or a front through a column is determined
by the effective value of the ratio q/c, whether this is dependent on or
independent of concentration. Thus, on an isotherm, or plot of q against c,
the slope of a straight line through the origin defines a speed. The heavy

line in Fig. 7.15 shows the isotherm of the displacer. If the concentration of displacer is c_d, then the slope of the line OA determines the speed of the displacer front and therefore the speed of all the zones of displaced vapours, so that the concentrations of the vapours in the zones are given by the points at which the isotherms of the vapours intersect the line OA, i.e., at c_1, c_2, etc. The less strongly the vapour is adsorbed, the shallower is its isotherm and the smaller the concentration at which the speed of the zone equals the speed of the displacer front. Hence, if the units of the abscissa of Fig. 7.15 are the same as those of the ordinate, all the steps of Fig. 7.14 are upwards, as shown.

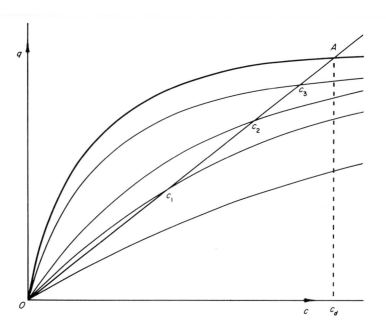

FIG. 7.15. Construction for calculating the conditions for displacement chromatography, and the concentrations of vapours within the steps.

The explanation is incomplete so far, since no relation is given between the units of concentration for different vapour species, without which any argument involving comparison of isotherms is meaningless. In gas chromatography, such a relation is given by the general properties of physical adsorption given in Section 4.1. Usually, if a number of isotherms are plotted together with c and q expressed in molar units, the initial slopes are inversely proportional to the vapour pressure of the pure liquids, and change in saturation levels between different vapours is very much smaller than change in initial slope. The result is that the order of elution is at least approximately the order of boiling point, as is seen from the example of displacement chromatogram [James and Phillips (*30*)] given in Fig. 7.16. Some adsorbents, however, are slightly selective, as discussed in Section 4.2.

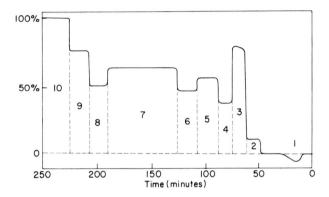

FIG. 7.16. A displacement chromatogram. James and Phillips (*30*). 1, Water; 2, diethyl ether; 3, chloroform; 4, ethyl acetate; 5, thiophen; 6, dioxan; 7, pyridine; 8, butyl acetate; 9, chlorobenzene; 10, bromobenzene (displacer).

It is apparent that the chromatogram of Fig. 7.16 does not show a series of ascending steps as predicted for Fig. 7.14. The reason is that the mixture contains some volatile compounds of relatively large molecular weight, and, since the detector gives a response proportional to weight concentration and not mole concentration, the relatively small mole concentration appears magnified for these components. Note also in Fig. 7.16 that water appears as an elution peak, since the initial slope of the isotherm was less than that of the line *OA* in the conditions used.

Displacement analysis cannot be used for qualitative identification, but quantitative identification of components is particularly simple, for the zones of vapour appear as rectangles the area of which is proportional to the weight of vapour.

(d) Use of Thermal Gradients

Several techniques have been described employing a thermal gradient in the chromatographic column (*119–121*). In the technique described by Zhukhovitski (*119*) and by Kaiser (*121*), the column is fitted with a ring-oven which covers a short length of the column, and the oven is moved along the column in the direction of the gas flow from inlet to outlet. A moving hot zone thus produced has the effect on vapours in the column as illustrated in Fig. 7.17. If there is a zone of vapour ("peak") in the stationary phase in front of the hot zone whose speed of elution by the carrier gas is slower than that of the hot zone, the hot zone will catch up to it, and the peak becomes progressively warmer as it is engulfed by the hot zone. This causes reduction in the partition coefficient of the vapour in the peak with

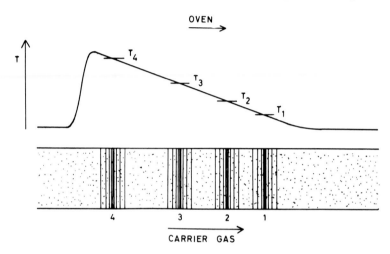

FIG. 7.17. Illustration of the effect of a moving temperature gradient, after Kaiser (*121*).

its consequent acceleration, till, at a particular point on the front profile of the temperature gradient of the hot zone, the speed of the peak equals the speed of the hot zone as a whole. Any solute in front of this point is thus engulfed. If any part of the vapour in the front temperature profile lags, it encounters a still higher temperature, which further accelerates it till it catches up. The result is that the peak moves along with the hot zone at a given point in the front profile.

The above mechanism operates not only when a vapour is initially present in the column as a peak, but also when it is uniformly or irregularly distributed throughout the column. The effect of the moving hot zone in either case is to engulf vapours in the manner described, so that they form a set of peaks distributed along the front temperature profile of the hot zone at positions at which their temperature is such that their speed of elution equals that of the oven. The only vapours to escape this process are those which are either eluted too fast and race the hot zone, or those which are adsorbed too strongly, and are not desorbed, even at the highest temperature of the front profile.

The effect of the above process in concentrating substances in a column makes it particularly suitable for trace analysis. In the technique described by Kaiser (*121*) ("Reversions-Gas-Chromatographie") a gas containing traces in the ppb range is passed through a column continuously, so that the traces collect along the length of the column during the course of a period the duration of which depends on the concentration of the traces. When enough have collected, an oven is moved along the column, and the contents of the thermal gradient are studied as they are eluted out when the gradient reaches the far end. In this way, concentrations down to 1 ppb or less in gases, e.g., city air, can be determined.

REFERENCES

1. James, A. T., and Martin, A. J. P., *Biochem. J.* **50**, 679 (1952).
2. Hull, W. Q., Keel, H., Kenney, J., and Gamson, B. W., *Ind. Eng. Chem.* **45**, 256 (1953).
3. Cummins, A. B., *Ind. Eng. Chem.* **34**, 403 (1942).
4. Keulemans, A. I. M., and Kwantes, A., *in* "Vapour Phase Chromatography," Proceedings of the First Symposium, London, May, 1956 (D. H. Desty, ed.), p. 15, Academic Press, New York, 1957.
5. Callear, A. B., and Cvetanovic, R. J., *Can. J. Chem.* **33**, 1256 (1955).
6. Littlewood, A. B., *in* "Gas Chromatography 1958," Proceedings of the Second Symposium, Amsterdam, May, 1958 (D. H. Desty, ed.), p. 23. Academic Press, New York, 1958.
7. Hishta, C., Messerly, J. P., and Reschke, R. F., *137th Am. Chem. Soc. Meeting, April, 1960.*
8. Liberti, A., Cartoni, G. P., and Pallotta, U., *Ann. chim. (Rome)* **48**, 40 (1958).
9. Naves, Y.-R., *J. Soc. Cosmetic Chemists* **9**, 101 (1958).
10. Naves, Y.-R., *Am. Perfumer Aromat.* **71**, 38 (1958).
11. Kwantes, A., and Rijnders, G. W. A., *in* "Gas Chromatography 1958," Proceedings of the Second Symposium, Amsterdam, May, 1958 (D. H. Desty, ed.), p. 125. Academic Press, New York, 1958.
12. Sorensen, I., and Soltoft, P., *Acta Chem. Scand.* **10**, 1673 (1956).
13. Cropper, F. R., and Heywood, A., *Nature* **174**, 1063 (1954).
14. Cropper, F. R., and Heywood, A., *in* "Vapour Phase Chromatography," Proceedings of the First Symposium, London, May, 1956 (D. H. Desty, ed.), p. 316. Academic Press, New York, 1957.
15. Desty, D. H. and Harbourn, C. L. A., *Am. Chem. Soc. Symposium, New York, September, 1967*, p. D157.
16. Desty, D. H., and Harbourn, C. L. A., *Anal. Chem.* **31**, 1965 (1959).
17. Decora, A. W., and Dineen, C. U., *Anal. Chem.* **32**, 164 (1960).
18. Villalobos, R., *I.S.A. Symposium on Instrumental Methods, Montreal*, 1960.

19. Ellis, J. F., and Iveson, G., *in* "Gas Chromatography 1958," Proceedings of the Second Symposium, Amsterdam, May, 1958 (D. H. Desty, ed.), p. 300. Academic Press, New York, 1958.
20. Sunner, S., Karrman, K. J., and Sunden, V., *Mikrochim. Acta* p. 1144 (1956).
21. Robinson, C. F., U. S. Patent 2,845,136 (1958).
22. Lukes, V., Komers, R., and Herout, V., *J. Chromatog.* **3**, 303 (1960).
23. Ottenstein, D. M., French Patent 1,456,205 (1966).
24. Kirkland, J. J., "Gas Chromatography 1964," Proceedings of the Fourth International Symposium (A. Goldup, ed.), p. 285. Institute of Petroleum, 1965.
25. Kirkland, J. J., *Anal. Chem.* **37**, 1458 (1965).
26. Halasz, I., and Horvath, C., *Anal. Chem.* **36**, 2226 (1964).
27. Horvath, C., Thesis, Frankfurt/Main, 1963.
28. Ohline, R. W., and Jojola, R., *Anal. Chem.* **36**, 1681 (1964).
29. Ottenstein, D. M., *Advan. Chromatog.* **3**, 137 (1966).
30. James, D. H., and Phillips, C. S. G., *J. Chem. Soc.* p. 1600 (1953).
31. Smith, E. D., *Anal. Chem.* **32**, 1049 (1960).
32. Baker, W. J., Lee, E. H., and Wall, R. F., *I.S.A. Second International Symposium, Lansing, Michigan, 1959.*
33. Macrae, J. C., Finlayson, P. C., and Gray, W. A., *Nature* **179**, 1365 (1957).
34. Cooper, J. A., Canter, R., Estes, F. L., and Cast, J. H., *J. Chromatog.* **3**, 87 (1960).
35. Hesse, G., *Z. Anal. Chem.* **211**, 5 (1965).
36. Blandenet, G., and Robin, J. P., *J. Gas Chromatog.* **2**, 225 (1964).
37. Eggertsen, F. T., and Knight, H. S., *Anal. Chem.* **30**, 15 (1958).
38. Bens, E. M., *Pittsburgh Conf. Anal. Chem. and Appl. Spectroscopy, March*, 1960.
39. Johns, T., *in* "Gas Chromatography," I.S.A. Symposium, August 1957 (V. J. Coates, H. J. Noebels, and I. S. Fagerson, eds.), p. 31. Academic Press, New York, 1958.
40. Evans, M. B., and Smith, J. F., *J. Chromatog.* **30**, 325 (1967).
41. Ormerod, E. C., and Scott, R. P. W., *J. Chromatog.* **2**, 65 (1959).
42. Holmgren, *in* "Gas Chromatography," I.S.A. Symposium, August, 1957 (V. J. Coates, H. J. Noebels, and I. S. Fagerson, eds.), p. 39. Academic Press, New York, 1958.
43. Tornquist, J., *Acta Chem. Scand.* **19**, 777 (1965).
44. Mitzner, B. M., and Jacobs, M. H., *137th Am. Chem. Soc. Meeting, Cleveland, Ohio, April*, 1960.
45. Kirkland, J. J., *in* "Gas Chromatography," I.S.A. Symposium, August, 1957 (V. J. Coates, H. J. Noebels, and I. S. Fagerson, eds.), p. 203. Academic Press, New York, 1958.
46. Zlatkis, A., Ling, S., and Kaufman, H. R., *Anal. Chem.* **31**, 945 (1959).
47. Horning, E. C., Moscatelli, E. A., and Sweeley, C. G., *Chem. Ind. (London)*, p. 751 (1959).
48. Perrett, R. H., and Purnell, J. H., *J. Chromatog.* **7**, 455 (1962).
49. Knight, H. S., *Anal. Chem.* **30**, 2030 (1958).
50. Davis, A., Roaldi, A., and Tufts, L. E., *J. Gas Chromatog.* **2**, 306 (1964).
51. Saroff, H. A., Karmen, A., and Healy, J. W., *J. Chromatog.* **9**, 122 (1962).
52. Ackman, R. G., and Burgher, R. D., *Anal. Chem.* **35**, 647 (1963).
53. Ettre, L. S., "Open Tubular Columns in Gas Chromatography." Plenum Press, New York, 1965.

54. Golay, M. J. E., *in* "Gas Chromatography," I.S.A. Symposium, August 1957 (V. J. Coates, H. J. Noebels, and I. S. Fagerson, eds.), p. 1. Academic Press, New York, 1958.
55. Desty, D. H., Goldup, A., and Swanton, W. T., *Nature* **183**, 107 (1959).
56. Desty, D. H., Goldup, and Whyman, B. H. F., *J. Inst. Petrol.* **45**, 287 (1959).
57. Scott, R. P. W., *Nature* **183**, 1753 (1959).
58. Condon, R. D., *Anal. Chem.* **31**, 1717 (1959).
59. Desty, D. H., Haresnape, J. H., and Whyman, B. H. F., *Anal. Chem.* **32**, 302 (1960).
60. Desty, D. H., and Goldup, A., "Gas Chromatography 1960," Proceedings of the Third International Symposium (R. P. W. Scott, ed.), p. 162. Academic Press, New York, 1960.
61. Kaiser, R., "Capillary Gas Chromatography," Vol. II of "Chromatography in the Gas Phase," English Translation, Butterworth, New York, 1963.
62. Scott, R. P. W., and Hazeldean, G. S. F., "Gas Chromatography 1960," Proceedings of the Third International Symposium (R. P. W. Scott, ed.), p. 144. Academic Press, New York, 1960.
63. Horvath, C., "Separation Columns with Thin Porous Layers for Gas Chromatography," Thesis, Frankfurt/Main, 1963.
64. Halasz, I., and Horvath, C., *Nature*, **197**, 71 (1963).
65. Halasz, I., and Horvath, C., *Anal. Chem.* **35**, 499 (1963).
66. Dijkstra, G., and Goey, J. de, "Gas Chromatography 1958," Proceedings of the Second International Symposium (D. H. Desty, ed.), p. 56. Academic Press, New York, 1968.
67. Bruner, F., and Cartoni, G. P., *Anal. Chem.* **36**, 1522 (1964).
68. Averill, W., "Gas Chromatography," Proceedings of the ISA Symposium (N. Brenner, J. E. Callen, and M. D. Weiss, eds.), p. 1. Academic Press, New York, 1962.
69. Farre-Rius, F. J., Henniker, J., and Guiochon, G., *Nature* **196**, 63 (1962).
70. Butler, J. N., and McAlpine, R. D., *Can. J. Chem.* **41**, 2487 (1963).
71. Averill, W., *J. Gas Chromatog.* **1**, 22 (1963).
72. Golay, M. J. E., "Gas Chromatography 1960," Proceedings of the Third International Symposium (R. P. W. Scott, ed.), p. 139. Academic Press, New York, 1960.
73. Mohnke, M., and Saffert, W., "Gas Chromatography 1962," Proceedings of the Fourth, International Symposium (van M. Swaay, ed.), p. 216. Academic Press, New York, 1962.
74. Leibnitz, W., and Mohnke, M., *Chem. Tech. (Berlin)* **14**, 753 (1962).
75. Liberti, A., "Gas Chromatography 1966," Proceedings of the Sixth International Symposium (A. B. Littlewood, ed.), p. 95. Institute of Petroleum, London, 1967.
76. Grob, K., "Gas Chromatography 1966," Proceedings of the Sixth International Symposium (A. B. Littlewood, ed.), p. 113. Institute of Petroleum, London, 1967.
77. Ettre, L. S., Purcell, J. E., and Norem, S. D., *J. Gas Chromatog.* **3**, 181 (1965).
78. Purcell, J. E., and Ettre, L. S., *J. Gas Chromatog.* **4**, 23 (1966).
79. Ettre, L. S., "Gas Chromatography 1966," Proceedings of the Sixth International Symposium (A. B. Littlewood, ed.), p. 115. Institute of Petroleum, 1967.
80. Halasz, I., and Heine, E., *Anal. Chem.* **37**, 495 (1965).

81. Heine, E., Thesis, Frankfurt/Main, 1963.
82. Primavesi, G. R., *Nature* **184**, 2010 (1959).
83. Barnard, J. A., and Hughes, H. W. D., *Nature* **183**, 250 (1959).
84. Maier, H. J., and Karpathy, O. C., *J. Chromatog.* **8**, 308 (1962).
85. Rohrschneider, L., *Z. Anal. Chem.* **170**, 256 (1959).
86. Singliar, M., Bobak, A., Brida, Q., and Lukacovic, L., *Z. Anal. Chem.* **177**, 161 (1960).
87. McFadden, W. H., *Anal. Chem.* **30**, 479 (1958).
88. dal Nogare, S. D., and Bennett, C. E., *Anal. Chem.* **30**, 1157 (1958).
89. Griffiths, J. H., James, D. H., and Phillips, C. S. G., *Analyst* **77**, 897 (1952).
90. Guild, L. V., Bingham, S., and Aul, F., *in* "Gas Chromatography 1958," Proceedings of the Second Symposium, Amsterdam, May, 1958 (D. H. Desty, ed.), p. 241. Academic Press, New York, 1958.
91. Kogler, H., *Chem. Tech. (Berlin)* **9**, 400 (1957).
92. Greene, S. A., Moberg, M. L., and Wilson, E. M., *Anal. Chem.* **28**, 1369 (1956).
93. Drew, C. M., and McNesby, J. R., *in* "Vapour Phase Chromatography," Proceedings of the First Symposium, London, May, 1956 (D. H. Desty, ed.), p. 213. Academic Press, New York, 1957.
94. Ryce, S. A., and Bryce, W. A., *Anal. Chem.* **29**, 925 (1957).
95. Eggertsen, F. T., Groennings, S., and Holst, J. J., *Anal. Chem.* **32**, 904 (1960).
96. Harrison, G. F., Knight, P., Kelly, R. P., and Heath, M. T., *in* "Gas Chromatography 1958," Proceedings of the Second Symposium, Amsterdam, May, 1958 (D. H. Desty, ed.), p. 216. Academic Press, New York, 1958.
97. dal Nogare, S., and Langlois, W. E., *Anal. Chem.* **32**, 767 (1960).
98. Habgood, H. W., and Harris, W. E., *Anal. Chem.* **32**, 450 (1960).
99. Habgood, H. W., and Harris, W. E., "Programmed Temperature Gas Chromatography," Wiley (Interscience), New York, 1966.
100. Roper, J. N., Jr., *Anal. Chem.* **32**, 447 (1960).
101. Giddings, J. C., *J. Chromatog.* **4**, 11 (1960).
102. Huyten, F. H., Beersum, W. van, and Rijnders, G. W. A., "Gas Chromatography 1960," Proceedings of the Third International Symposium (R. P. W. Scott, ed.), p. 224. Academic Press, New York, 1960.
103. Atkinson, E. P., and Tuey, G. P., *in* "Gas Chromatography 1958," Proceedings of the Second Symposium, Amsterdam, May, 1958 (D. H. Desty, ed.), p. 270. Academic Press, New York, 1958.
104. Johns, T., "Gas Chromatography 1960," Proceedings of the Third International Symposium (R. P. W. Scott, ed.), p. 242. Academic Press, New York, 1960.
105. Patrick, C. R., Informal Symposium on Gas Chromatography (Gas Chromatography Discussion Group), Bristol, September, 1959.
106. Heilbronner, E., Kovats, E., and Simon, W., *Helv. Chim. Acta* **40**, 2410 (1957).
107. Ambrose, D., and Collerson, R. R., *Nature* **177**, 84 (1956).
108. Scott, R. P. W., "Gas Chromatography 1958," Proceedings of the Second Symposium, Amsterdam, May, 1958 (D. H. Desty, ed.), p. 287. Academic Press, New York, 1958.
109. Benedek, P., Szepesy, L., and Szepe, S., "Gas Chromatography," I.S.A. Symposium, August, 1957 (V. J. Coates, H. J. Noebels, and I. S. Fagerson, eds.), p. 225. Academic Press, New York, 1958.

110. Barker, P. E., and Huntington, D. H., "Gas Chromatography 1966," Proceedings of the Sixth International Symposium (A. B. Littlewood, ed.), p. 135. Institute of Petroleum, London, 1967.

111. Barker, P. E., and Huntington, D. H., *J. Gas Chromatog.* **4**, 59 (1966).

112. Luft, L., U.S.P., 3, 016, 106 (1962).

113. Glasser, D., "Gas Chromatography 1966," Proceedings of the Sixth International Symposium (A. B. Littlewood, ed.), p. 119. Institute of Petroleum, London, 1967.

114. Claesson, S., *Arkiv Kemi, Mineral Geol.* **23A**, 1 (1946).

115. Claesson, S., *Ann. N.Y. Acad. Sci.* **49**, 183 (1948).

116. Claesson, S., *Discussions Faraday Soc.* **7**, 34 (1949).

117. Boeke, J., "Gas Chromatography 1960," Proceedings of the Third International Symposium (R. P. W. Scott, ed.), p. 88. Academic Press, New York, 1960.

118. Tiselius, A., *Arkiv Kemi, Mineral Geol.* **16A**, No. 18 (1943).

119. Zhukhovitski, A. A., and Turkeltaub, N. M., *Dokl. Akad. Nauk.* **116**, 986 (1957).

120. Zhukhovitski, A. A., "Gas Chromatography 1960," Proceedings of the Third International Symposium (R. P. W. Scott, ed.), p. 293. Academic Press, New York, 1960.

121. Kaiser, R., *Chromatographia* **1**, 199 (1968).

Chapter 8

The Use of Detectors for Quantitative Analysis

8.1. Principles of Quantitative Analysis by Gas Chromatography

(a) *Classification of Detectors*

In virtually every practical detector in current use, the output by which the vapour is measured consists of either a change of voltage or a change in current. In detectors where the response is essentially one involving current, the current is frequently converted to a voltage through a load resistor before actual display, so that detector response can be specified by a voltage, E_g. As nearly all practical detectors are of the differentiating class (Section 1.2), we shall therefore restrict our discussion to these.

It is useful to divide quantitatively viable detectors into two classes, following Halasz (*1*):

(1) *Concentration-Sensitive Detectors.* In these, the electrical response is proportional to the concentration of vapour within the detector cavity. Generally, these detectors are those in which the detector measures some physical property, usually a transport property, of the gas, e.g., the thermal conductivity detector (Chapter 10), or the ionisation cross-section detector (Section 9.5). In such detectors, the sample does not usually undergo chemical reaction, and is unchanged by the act of detection.

(2) *Mass-Flow Sensitive Detectors.* In these, the response is proportional to the rate at which vapour enters the detector. The response usually results from some definite irreversible change occurring to the vapour molecules. Thus, it includes the Flame Ionisation Detector (Section 9.2) where the vapour is burned, and any coulometric system where the vapour undergoes stoichiometric reaction. This class also includes some types of ionisation detector, e.g., the "micro-argon" detector.

Let c be vapour concentration (weight/volume) for consideration of concentration-sensitive detectors, and let $\dot{w}$ be mass flow (weight/time) for mass-flow sensitive detectors. The *sensitivities* of the detectors of either class can be defined by the quantities S_c and S_w as follows:

$$E_g = S_c \cdot c, \qquad (8.1)$$

$$E_g = S_w \cdot \dot{w}. \qquad (8.2)$$

A detector is said to be *linear* within a given range of c or $\dot{w}$ if the constants S_c or S_w are invariant within the range. Only detectors which are at least approximately linear are used for quantitative analysis. A convenient unit for S_c is that of a detector which gives a response of 1 mV for a concentration of 1 mg/ml. The sensitivity of concentration-sensitive detectors can thus be expressed in units of:

$$mV/(mg/ml), \qquad i.e., \qquad (mV\ ml)/mg.$$

For example, the sensitivities of ordinary catharometers are often of the order of 1000 (mV ml)/mg. (see Section 10.3). The sensitivity of a mass-flow sensitive detector can similarly be expressed in units of:

$$mV/(\mu g/sec), \qquad i.e., \qquad (mV\ sec)/\mu g.$$

This unit is less familiar in general use than the corresponding unit for concentration-sensitive detectors. Since mass-flow sensitive detectors are generally those whose essential response is a change in current, a more appropriate unit for detailed discussion of these detectors is in fact:

$$(mA\ sec)/\mu g \equiv mcoulomb/\mu g.$$

For coulometric detectors this quantity is accurately calculable for any vapour (see Section 11.3c). For example, for benzene in a combustion coulometer, the sensitivity is 37.1 mcoulomb/μg. For detectors which are not absolute, no such precise figure can be given; a typical figure for a flame ionisation detector would be 0.01 mcoulomb/μg.

In practical GC, quantities are measured by peak areas. Fundamentally, the area of a peak is given by:

$$A = \int E_g\ dt. \qquad (8.3)$$

The area is thus expressed as a product of voltage and time. It can be related with the weight of sample producing the peak, w, through the sensitivities S_c or S_w as follows.

In case of concentration-sensitive detectors,

$$w = \int c \, dV, \tag{8.4}$$

where the integration is over all the gas, volume V, in which c is significant. If the flow-rate of gas through the detector is $\dot{V}$, $dV = \dot{V} \, dt$. Substitution of this and Eq. 8.1 into Eq. 8.4 yields:

$$w = \frac{\dot{V}}{S_c} \int E_g \, dt, \quad \text{i.e.,} \quad \frac{A}{w} = \frac{S_c}{\dot{V}}. \tag{8.5}$$

In the case of mass-flow sensitive detectors,

$$w = \int \dot{w} \, dt. \tag{8.6}$$

Substitution of Eq. (8.2) and (8.3) into this yields:

$$w = \frac{1}{S_w} \int E_g \, dt, \quad \text{i.e.,} \quad \frac{A}{w} = S_w. \tag{8.7}$$

In practice, it may be more convenient to measure the area of a peak on a strip chart in actual area units, e.g., cm². In that case, Eqs. (8.5) and (8.7) can be easily transformed, using C_1, the chart speed in cm/sec, and C_2, the recorder sensitivity in cm/mV. With these,

$$\frac{A}{w} = \frac{S_c C_1 C_2}{\dot{V}}, \tag{8.5a}$$

$$\frac{A}{w} = S_w C_1 C_2. \tag{8.7a}$$

Equation (8.5a) was first described by Dimbat et al. (2).

(b) Choice of Detector Class

The quantities S_c and S_w discussed above are invariants, and can thus be used to give a proper characterisation of a particular detector. However, their numerical values alone are not sufficient to enable one to choose a suitable detector for a given purpose. Consideration of carrier gas flow rate, noise, detector volume, etc., are also relevant, as discussed below.

The essential practical difference between concentration–sensitive and mass-flow sensitive detectors is that the first involves the flow-rate, while the second does not; c.f., Eqs. (8.5) and (8.7). In the case of mass-flow sensitive detectors, the peak area per unit weight of vapour is independent of flow rate, which can alter during a chromatogram without perturbing a quantitative analysis. In the case of concentration-sensitive detectors, however, the peak area per unit weight of sample is inversely proportional to the flow rate, so that for accurate analysis the flow rate must be constant throughout the chromatogram; see Section 8.1d.

In most practice, the lower limit on the quantity which can be used for GC analysis is provided by the detector noise. In a case where detector noise can be specified simply by a voltage or current, and the consideration of noise areas given in Section 8.3 are not relevant, the utility of each of the two classes of detector can be compared, following Halasz's argument (1). Figure 8.1 shows a plot of the response, E_g, against mass-flow rate,

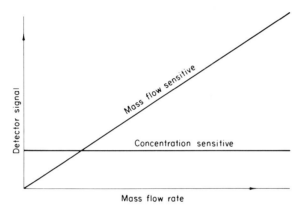

FIG. 8.1. To illustrate the difference between concentration-sensitive and mass-flow-sensitive detectors. Halasz (1).

$\dot{w}$, for each class of detector. Let us compare the use of each on vapour streams in which the concentrations of vapour are comparable, but may vary in flow rate over a wide range. We thus have the relation $\dot{w} = c\dot{V}$, where in comparisons c is assumed to be roughly constant. It is seen that when $\dot{V}$ is large, mass-flow-sensitive detectors give the larger signal, but when it is small, concentration-sensitive detectors are preferable. In practice, the numerical values which would be attached to Fig. 8.1 are such that with packed columns, where $\dot{V}$ is comparatively large, mass-sensitive detectors such as the FID almost invariably give better signals and signal-to-noise ratios than concentration-sensitive detectors. With capillary columns, however, where $\dot{V}$ is small, concentrations are no smaller than with packed columns, but emergent mass-flows are small, with the result that concentration-sensitive detectors may well have an advantage.

A further relevant factor in assessing a detector's performance, especially for accurate analysis of rapid peaks, is the detector volume. As pointed out above, a concentration-sensitive detector may be used to measure small masses at slow mass flows so long as the concentration of the peaks is adequate. In analysis, however, slow mass flows, e.g., from capillary columns, often also imply slow carrier flows, so that the total volume of gas occupied by a peak may be small. The volume of the detector cavity must, therefore, also be small, so that sensitivity is not lost because the vapour from the column, in entering the large cavity, becomes diluted. Furthermore, a large detector volume causes loss of resolution of close peaks, as described in Section 6.11d. The factor of volume is relevant especially with concentration-sensitive detectors, but not normally with mass-flow–sensitive detectors, where either the volume in which reaction takes place is sufficiently small, or the flow is augmented by scavenging gases; see below and Sections 9.8d and 11.3.

(c) *Inter-Relation of Detector Classes*

Several detectors only belong to one or other of the above classes of detector either approximately, or in an ideal case.

In some detection systems, e.g., the micro-argon detector, the carrier gas is mixed with a stream of scavenging gas either just before or in the cavity wherein detection occurs. If the flow rate of scavenging gas greatly exceeds that of the carrier gas, the concentration of vapour in the combined gas stream is nearly proportional to the mass-flow rate of vapour into the combined stream and is virtually independent of the concentration of vapour in the carrier, since the carrier flow rate contributes little to the combined flow. If the detection system using a scavenging gas in this fashion employs a detector which is essentially concentration-sensitive, then the response of the system as a whole will be mass-flow sensitive. The micro-argon detector and probably also the FID are mass-flow sensitive only for this reason.

In addition to the above case in which a concentration-sensitive detector is constrained to become mass-flow sensitive, there is a common case of the converse. There are mass-flow-sensitive detection systems in which a substance undergoes stoichiometric reaction at a particular location, e.g., a surface. An example is an electrochemical cell such as the Hersch cell (3, 4). If in such a system the flow-rate of carrier is increased, the transfer of vapour to the reacting surface becomes limited by slow diffusion, with the result that the reaction is less than stoichiometric, and some of the vapour passes through the detector unchanged. In the limit, when only a small proportion of the vapour reacts and most passes through, the response is proportional to the rate of diffusion between the bulk of the gas and the reactive sites, and this rate is proportional to the concentration of vapour in the gas. Thus, an electrochemical cell used as a detector can be used either as a mass-flow-sensitive detector (*3*), or, with different geometry, as a concentration-sensitive detector (*4*).

(d) Basic Equations for Quantitative Analysis

In the great majority of applications of gas chromatography, quantitative analysis consists of the determination of relative proportions by weight of components in a mixture, and not the determination of absolute weights of vapour. The relative weight of two components i and j is given by:

$$\frac{w_i}{w_j} = \frac{A_i/S_i}{A_j/S_j}, \tag{8.8}$$

where S stands either for S_w, or for S_c so long as $\dot{V}$ is constant, and the proportion by weight of a component i in a mixture is

$$w_i = \frac{A_i/S_i}{\sum\limits_{k} (A_k/S_k)}, \tag{8.9}$$

in which the summation includes the peaks due to every component of the mixture. These equations form the basis of quantitative analysis by gas chromatography. Similar equations apply in many other analytical techniques, and are commonplace.

Since quantitative analysis normally consists of the determination of relative weights, it is apparent that it is only necessary to make measurements of relative areas and relative sensitivities; Eq. (8.9) may equally well be written:

$$w_i = \frac{A_i/S_i}{\sum\limits_{k} (A_k/S_k)} \times \frac{S_n/A_m}{S_n/A_m} = \frac{A_{im}/S_{in}}{\sum\limits_{k} (A_{km}/S_{kn})}, \tag{8.10}$$

in which A_{im} is the area of the peak due to the component i relative to that due to the component m, and S_{in} is the sensitivity of the vapour i relative to that of the vapour n. The operations necessary in performing an analysis for weight proportions are, therefore:

(1) Determine the sensitivities relative to a single standard of each vapour passing through the detector.

(2) Chromatograph the sample, and measure the relative areas of all the peaks.

(3) Use Eq. (8.10).

In connection with (1), it will be appreciated that the standard need not be a component of the mixture being analysed, and in connection with (2), the areas of peaks may be measured in arbitrary units. Details of the above operations, and of useful variants, are given in the following section.

In the case of concentration-sensitive detectors, the use of Eqs. (8.8), (8.9), and (8.10) requires that $\dot{V}$ is constant throughout the run. The flow-rate through the column can be controlled with a flow control at the column inlet, and this is usually done. However, in spite of this, there are two fundamental respects by which the vapours themselves perturb the flow rate through the detector:

(i) As soon as the vapour leaves the column it is added to the gas volume, thus augmenting the flow rate. This factor was studied first by van der Craats (5), who showed that the increase in flow rate on this account is given by:

$$70x_{\max} \frac{k}{1+k} \%,\tag{8.11}$$

where $x_{\max}$ is the mole fraction of vapour in the peak maximum, and k is as in Chapter 2.

(ii) The viscosity of the gas-mixture composed of vapour and carrier gas differs from that of pure carrier gas. Since most flow controls are actually pressure controls maintaining a constant inlet pressure to the column, the flow rate is determined either wholly or at least partly by the resistance of the column, which thus depends on the vapours within it. This factor has been studied by Dyson and Littlewood (6), who also included the surge effect described above. They conclude that the perturbation of flow rate due to a vapour retained in the column on account of both effects is given by:

$$\frac{\Delta \dot{V}}{\dot{V}} = -\frac{(\beta + 22.4M)w}{V_R},\tag{8.12}$$

where w is the weight of vapour retained in the column (grams), V_R is its retention volume (litres), M is its molecular weight, and

$$\beta = \frac{1}{\mu} \frac{\partial \mu}{\partial c},\tag{8.13}$$

where μ is gas viscosity. The quantity β is the concentration coefficient of viscosity of the vapour in the carrier gas. It can have either sign; some values are given in (6).

The perturbations of flow rate can in practice cause definite errors of the order of 1% but the error becomes less the smaller the samples.

8.2. Technique of Quantitative Analysis

(a) The Determination of Relative Sensitivities

Ideally, the sensitivity of a detector should be a simply calculable function of the molecular structure of the molecule of the vapour, but this is only so with a few detectors, e.g., coulometric detectors. With other detectors, the relation between sensitivity and structure is complicated, and investigation of it is incomplete. A very approximate general rule which holds with all common designs of ionisation detector and with catharometers is that the weight sensitivities of organic compounds consisting mainly of carbon, hydrogen, and not too much oxygen are constant if the molecular weight of the compound is greater than a certain value (usually of the order of 100). For accurate analysis, relative sensitivities may occasionally be found in the literature but must usually be determined experimentally.

The simplest technique for experimental determination of relative sensitivities is to chromatograph a sample of a mixture of known composition. The relative sensitivity of any two components is then given by Eq. (8.8) rearranged:

$$\frac{S_i}{S_n} = S_{in} = \frac{A_i/w_i}{A_n/w_n}. \tag{8.8}$$

It is convenient to regard the sensitivity of one vapour, e.g., n, as standard, so that $S_{nn} = 1$, and to use Eq. (8.8) on every other vapour i $(i \neq n)$, so as to give a series of values of S_{in}.

The analysis of a particular mixture of interest requires that relative sensitivities be known, and the above procedure implies that the qualitative composition of the mixture is known, and that separate samples of its pure components are available. Both of these conditions restrict the quantitative use of gas chromatography, though there is not much indication in the literature that the restriction has so far proved onerous. In the case that only impure samples are available from which to determine relative sensitivities, it is possible to work out an iterative technique by which accurate relative sensitivities can be obtained. The details of this are a matter of general analytical procedure.

(b) Use of Internal Standards

A common technique, as in many other branches of analysis, is to add an accurately measured weight proportion of a known pure substance to the sample of interest; in gas chromatography, this must be chosen so as not to give a peak which overlaps with any other peak.

The principal advantage in the use of an internal standard in quantitative analysis lies in the implications of the word *every* in connection with the summation of Eq. (8.9). If no internal standard is used, it is necessary to measure the peak due to *every* component of the mixture and to know the relative sensitivity of every component of the mixture. This may be inconvenient, or even impossible, if, for example, the mixture contains involatile components. If, however, a known proportion of internal standard is added to the mixture, absolute weight proportions of individual components may be obtained using Eq. (8.8) and the known value of w for the internal standard.

Another advantage of the internal standard is that its weight proportion may be made approximately equal to that of a component of particular interest, and it may be chosen so that it has a comparatively close retention volume. In this way, errors due either to slight non-linearity of the detector or due to slow drift in the quantities C_1, C_2, or $\dot{V}$ can be minimised.

Lee and Oliver (7) have suggested the use of two or more internal standards in certain circumstances. Thus, if two components of interest are separated by a long time on the chromatogram, one internal standard appearing near each component of interest enables errors due to change in sensitivity with time to be eliminated. Also, if two components of interest are present in very unequal proportions, two internal standards in roughly the same proportions enable errors due to non-linearity to be eliminated.

(c) Analysis by Peak Height

In some cases, it is possible to obtain rapid but approximate analyses by assigning a height-sensitivity, defined as peak height per unit weight, to each component, and by using this in Eq. (8.9), heights replacing areas. If all the chromatographic conditions are sufficiently constant, there is no doubt that this method can give results within a few per cent, but the technique is very liable to error. Any process which alters the plate-number of the column alters the ratio of peak area to peak-height, and thus invalidates the analysis. Since changes in the plate-number are a function of nearly every possible variable, this is very liable to happen. In particular, one of the principal variables which alters the area-to-height ratio is the sample size itself (Section 6.19), so that the range of linearity of height measurements is likely to be small.

(d) The Measurement of Peak Areas

Areas of peaks may be measured by any of the following methods:

(1) Providing that the peaks are Gaussian, measure the height of the peak, h, and the width at the half-height, $\omega_{1/2}$ (see Fig. 5.4). The area is:

$$A = 1.064h\omega_{1/2} \qquad [1.064 = (\pi/\ln 2)^{1/2}/2]. \qquad (8.14)$$

In relative area measurements, the value of the constant is immaterial.

(2) Providing that the peaks are Gaussian, draw tangents at the points of inflection, and form a triangle with these and the base line (Fig. 5.5). The area of this triangle, i.e., half the base times its height (A') is related with the area of the peak by:

$$A = 1.032A' \qquad [1.032 = (2\pi e)^{1/2}/4]. \qquad (8.15)$$

Again, the value of the constant is superfluous in relative area measurements.

(3) By planimetry.

(4) By cutting out and weighing.

(5) By integrators or computers, which are discussed in Section 11.7.

(e) The Measurement of Absolute Sensitivities

Absolute sensitivities can be measured by an experiment in which all quantities other than S_c or S_w in Eqs. (8.5) or (8.7) are measured. With detectors which respond adequately to relatively large samples, such an experiment is straightforward. With sensitive ionisation detectors which cease to be linear at concentrations greater than, e.g., 1 in 10^4, however, any sample that is sufficiently small that its greatest concentration in the detector is less than the allowable maximum is too small to be accurately weighable and accurately introduced into the apparatus. Several convenient method have been suggested for introducing measurable and reproducible small concentrations into a sensitive detector, of which two are described below.

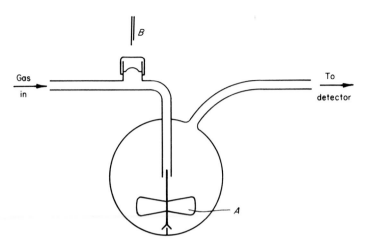

FIG. 8.2. Exponential dilution apparatus for securing a known concentration of dilute vapour. A is a magnetically operated paddle which ensures complete mixing within the flask. The sample is injected at B. After Lovelock (8).

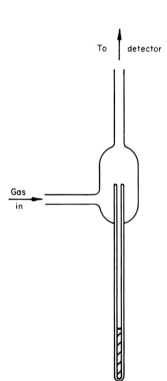

FIG. 8.3. Apparatus for securing a dilute vapour of calculable concentration. After Desty *et al.* (9).

Lovelock (8) uses an exponential decay technique (Fig. 8.2), in which the detector is connected directly to the effluent from a large flask through which carrier gas is passing. A sample of the substance of which the sensitivity is to be determined is injected into the flask; this sample is sufficiently large to be accurately measured. It is assumed that complete mixing occurs within the flask, and thus the concentration of vapour in the flask decreases exponentially with a time constant equal to the volume of the flask divided by the flow rate, both of which may be measured. Though the concentration of vapour is probably too large for the detector immediately after the sample is injected, it decreases continuously and calculably, and after a few time constants have passed, the concentration is within the region of linearity of the detector.

Desty et al. (9) use a technique in which carrier gas passes over the open end of a length of capillary tube closed at the other end containing the sample, as shown in Fig. 8.3. The vapour of the sample is delivered into the gas stream at a rate which is determined calculably by the diameter of the capillary, the length from the surface of the liquid to the open end of the capillary, and the diffusion coefficient of the vapour of the sample.

8.3. Properties of Detectors

The essential quality of a detector is the sum of a large number of individual properties; we recognise the following as principally relevant in any evaluation: (a) sensitivity, (b) signal-to-noise ratio, (c) drift, (d) linearity, (e) independence of extraneous variables, (f) ease of calibration in terms of known properties, (g) speed of response, (h) chemical inertness, (i) range of application. In addition to these, other considerations such as robustness, price, safety, and the extent to which a detector has already been studied are obviously relevant, but do not require any special discussion. Some general notes on the above qualities are given below, and with regard to each detector in the next three chapters. Reviews in English specifically on the general classification of detectors have been given by Janak et al. (10), Cremer (11), Gudzinowicz (12), and the author (13).

(a) Sensitivity

It is usually desirable that a detector should be sensitive. Even if a large sensitivity is not required for a particular application, it is comparatively easy to divide a large sensitivity by an accurately known fraction, but it is not possible to multiply a small sensitivity in like manner.

(b) Signal-to-Noise Ratio

After sufficient amplification, the output of a detector always shows random variations called "Noise." Since by suitable electronics, the electrical output of a detector can always be multiplied by almost any factor, the sensitivity as described above may be made as great as one pleases. This amplification also amplifies inherent noise in the detector, which can obscure peaks due to small quantities of vapour. Thus, the amplitude of the noise is a more important criterion of a detector's ultimate performance than its sensitivity.

The amplitude of the noise, or "Noise Level," is most simply expressed as its average electrical amplitude, e.g., in μV. Dividing the noise by the sensitivity, the result is the vapour concentration or the mass-flow which would give a signal equal to the noise. In cases that the noise is visible on the recorder, the figure makes a convenient though crude method of expressing the detector performance, since it does not contain any electrical units. The ratio of the response of the detector produced by a given concentration of vapour to the noise is called, by analogy with communications technology, the "Signal-to-Noise Ratio." Detector performances are sometimes specified by the vapour concentration which gives some stated signal-to-noise ratio other than unity, e.g., 2.

The specification of noise by a vaguely defined average value is sometimes inadequate, and in some circumstances gives an entirely false idea of the performance of a detector, for the noise may be such that signals in which the signal-to-noise ratio is much less than unity may be significant. This can be seen by the three examples given in Fig. 8.4. In Fig. 8.4a, a noisy base line has been drawn, and there are variations in the base line which may or may not be peaks. In these circumstances, which are unfortunately rather common in practice, no signal smaller than the maximum noise can be measured with any degree of confidence in a single run, and the crude specification of noise already given is adequate. In Figs. 8.4b and 8.4c, however, two extreme cases have been drawn in which peaks may by identified with confidence from a single run, even though the signal-to-noise ratio is less than unity. The characteristic of these examples is that the average period of the largest component of the noise is very different from the time occupied by a peak.

Of the two extreme cases shown in Figs. 8.4b and 8.4c, the case in Fig. 8.4c is always a result of instrumental imperfection, but the case in Fig. 8.4b arises in several detectors where there is a high-frequency noise inherent in the operation, for example, ionisation detectors using

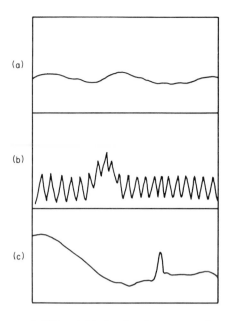

Fig. 8.4. Diagrams of different kinds of noise expressed as plots of amplitude against time.

α-radiation of small intensity such that the number of ionising particles emitted in unit time is small enough that there are significant statistical variations in their number in successive short periods. In these circumstances, the base line averaged over different short periods shows significant deviations from period to period, but if the base line is averaged over longer periods, the deviations become smaller and smaller as the periods over which the averages are taken become longer. If, therefore, the behaviour of the base line over short periods is not relevant in securing information on the chromatogram, nothing is lost by smoothing out the base line by increasing the time constant of the detector.

It should be emphasised that, though the use of a large time constant improves the signal-to-noise ratio, it does not improve the performance of the detector, which in such a case is determined not by the ratio of the signal to the *actual* variations in the base line, but to the *significant* variations in the base line, which are much smaller. If the peak becomes quicker, so that the period occupied by the peak becomes smaller, then the significant deviations in the base line averaged over the peak become greater and the ratio of signal to significant noise becomes smaller. Thus, the relevant factor in judging the detector performance is not the time constant of the detector, but the ratio of the time occupied by a peak to the average period between successive random events, e.g., the evolution of α-particles. In other words, increasing the time constant makes the chromatograms prettier, but not more informative.

The statistical theory of detector noise, including the above qualitative arguments, is given by Johnson and Stross (*14*), who describe a method of determining a "Limit of Detection" which takes into account the factors described above. In this, noise is defined in terms of a "Noise Area," which is a measure of the total error in area produced by noise in a given region of base line at least as great as that occupied by a peak. If the standard deviation of a number of such noise areas is N_s, and the sensitivity of the detector as described in the last subsection is S, then Johnson and Stross propose that the quantity:

$$W = (\text{const} \cdot N_s)/S, \qquad (8.16)$$

should be called the "Limit of Detection," which is such that, for each of 19 out of 20 similar detectors, W is the least amount of sample for which at least 19 out of 20 trials will produce sample peaks with areas which deviate no more than $\pm 50\%$ from the area they would have if the detector were noiseless. The value of the constant depends on the number of noise areas used in the determination of N_s, e.g., for 24 noise areas it is 5.29. The fact that in most cases N_s is less than individual noise areas corresponds to the fact that significant variations in base line are generally smaller than the actual noise.

(c) Drift

A feature of imperfect detectors is that their base line slowly drifts in the course of time. In principle, drift is a type of very low-frequency noise, and the treatment of Johnson and Stross can include both drift and noise. In practice, however, drift and noise can generally be distinguished, drift being regarded as base line changes the average period of which is greater than that of the time occupied by a chromatogram, whereas noise has an average period less than that occupied by a chromatogram. Commonly, drift and noise are caused differently. No exact means of specifying drift has been given; statistical methods of expression could easily be produced, but to do so would normally be more trouble than the matter is worth. It is, however, very desirable to quote drift in terms of average voltage drift per unit time, e.g., millivolt/hour, and this has occasionally been done.

(*d*) *Linearity*

In order for quantitative analysis to be possible by the methods described in the previous sections, the detector must be linear, and in practice, such linearity is usually assumed in quantitative analysis. Perfect linearity is an ideal attained by few real detectors, but there appears to be no accepted way of specifying non-linearity. In principle, the response of a detector could be expressed by a polynomial, e.g., $E_g = \sum_{i=0}^{\infty} a_i c^i$ for a concentration-sensitive detector, in which departures from non-linearity would be specifiable in terms of non-zero values of coefficients other than a_1, which is S_c. In practice, however, detectors have rarely been studied in such detail. Some workers have investigated detector linearity over the large dynamic ranges required in GC using the exponential dilution apparatus described above, in which, for a given flow rate through the mixing chamber, the logarithm of the concentration at the outlet is proportional to time, and they have plotted $\log \log E_g$ against $\log t$. In such a case, the detector is linear if the plot is straight *and* if it has a slope of unity. Rectilinearity but non-unit slope of the log plot implies non-linearity of the detector. In practice, detectors may give lines with slopes between about 0.95 and 1.05; this figure provides some measure of the detector linearity.

(*e*) *Independence of Extraneous Variables*

Many detectors respond to variables other than a change in concentration of the vapour in the carrier gas; examples are change in flow rate, pressure, temperature, conditions of the electrical supply, etc. Such extraneous response can, of course, be eliminated by keeping all other variables constant, but this may be troublesome and expensive. Independence of extraneous variables, therefore, is a desirable feature of detectors. In practice, it is the lack of such independence on the part of many common detectors that is responsible for much of the noise and the drift, particularly the latter.

(*f*) *Ease of Calibration*

Detectors in which the relation between response and concentration is a calculable function of some known molecular property have an advantage over others in that relative sensitivities do not have to be determined experimentally, and that, therefore, it is not necessary to have samples of the components of a mixture of interest.

(*g*) *Speed of Response*

This factor is discussed in detail in Section 6.8.

(*h*) *Chemical Inertness*

Some detectors destroy the sample in the act of detecting; others preserve it so that separate fractions may be collected. In practice some of the most sensitive detectors destroy the sample, but if a sample is required it has often been found advantageous to make use of the sensitivity of the detector by detecting only a small fraction of the carrier gas stream, and passing the rest into collection apparatus.

(*i*) *Range of Application*

Some detectors will detect almost any vapour; others will only detect efficiently certain classes of chemical compound and are thus termed *specific*. For analytical purposes, systems in which a general detector is combined with a detector which is in some respects specific is particularly useful, since the general detector can provide quantitative analysis, while the response of the specific detector, when compared with that of the general detector, provides a measure of qualitative identification.

REFERENCES

1. Halasz, I., *Anal. Chem.* **36**, 1428 (1964).
2. Dimbat, M., Porter, P. E., and Stross, F. H., *Anal. Chem.* **28**, 290 (1956).
3. Phillips, T. R., Johnson, E. G., and Woodward, H., *Anal. Chem.* **36**, 450 (1964).
4. Burton, G., Littlewood, A. B., and Wiseman, W. A., "Gas Chromatography 1966," Proceedings of the Sixth International Symposium of the GC Discussion Group (A. B. Littlewood, ed.), p. 193. Institute of Petroleum, 1967.
5. van der Craats, F., *in* "Gas Chromatography 1958," Proceedings of the Second Symposium, Amsterdam, May 1958 (D. H. Desty, ed.), p. 241. Academic Press, New York, 1958.
6. Dyson, N., and Littlewood, A. B., *Anal. Chem.* **39**, 638 (1967).
7. Lee, E. H., and Oliver, G. D., *Anal. Chem.* **31**, 1925 (1959).
8. Lovelock, J. E., *Anal. Chem.* **52**, 162 (1961).
9. Desty, D. H., Goldup, A., and Geach, C. J., "Gas Chromatography 1960," Proceedings of the Third International Symposium (R. P. W. Scott, ed.), p. 46. Academic Press, New York, 1961.
10. Janak, J. *et al.*, *Chromatog. Rev.* **8**, 90 (1966).
11. Cremer, E., *J. Gas Chromatog.* **5**, 329 (1967).
12. Gudzinowicz, B. J., "The Practice of Gas Chromatography" (A. Zlatkis, and L. S. Ettre, eds.), p. 239. Wiley (Interscience), 1967.
13. Littlewood, A. B., "Gas Chromatography 1968," Proceedings of the Sixth Symposium of the Academy of Berlin, Akademie Verlag, Berlin, 1969.
14. Johnson, H. W., Jr., and Stross, F. H., *Anal. Chem.* **31**, 1206 (1959).

Chapter 9

Ionisation Detectors

9.1. INTRODUCTION

In normal conditions gases and vapours emerging from a column are virtually perfect electrical insulators, but if caused to ionise they will conduct. There are great differences, both in kind and degree, in the ease of ionisation of different substances and in the conductivity that ionisation gives to the gas. Thus, the conductivity of an ionised carrier gas almost invariably changes when the gas contains a vapour, and this change may be measured and made the basis of a gas-chromatographic detector. In particular, certain types of ionisation detector have a very small background conductivity for pure carrier gas and show a great rise in conductivity when a vapour enters, so that they give a positive response to a vapour rather than measuring a small change in an already large quantity. This is advantageous in producing little noise and great useful sensitivity.

Ionisation detectors may conveniently be classified by the manner in which the carrier gas is ionised:

(1) *Flame Ionisation Detector*, in which the carrier gas is burned in a flame, which causes ionisation.

(2) *Radiation (Radiological) Detectors*, in which ionisation is produced by ionising radiation, usually α- or β-rays. The following four are in use:

  (i) Ionisation Cross-Section Detector.
  (ii) Electron Capture Detector.
  (iii) Electron Mobility Detector.
  (iv) Argon Detector.

(3) *Ionisation Gauge Detector*, in which electrons are obtained by emission from a heated cathode, and these ionise the gas.

(4) *Discharge Detectors*, in which ionisation results from an electrical discharge between two electrodes.

The study of ionised gases has formed a branch of physics for many years, but it has impinged little on chemistry. Much of the principles and theory of ionisation in the following pages will be commonplace to a physicist, yet probably unfamiliar to the chemist. Useful books are those of Townsend (1) and von Engel (2). Of the different kinds of detector classified above, the Flame Ionisation Detector (FID) is currently the most commonly used. This detector and the catharometer described in the next chapter are used in the great majority of current gas-chromatographic applications.

9.2. Conduction of Electricity in Ionised Gases

The conductivity of an ionised gas can be measured by placing two electrodes in the gas, between which a potential may be applied. The current can then be measured. The reactions occurring in the gas may be very complicated; we consider briefly below only those mechanisms which have so far been recognised as being relevant in gas-chromatographic detectors.

(a) At Small Ion Concentrations

When the potential is small, positive ions drift in the electric field towards the cathode, and negative electrons towards the anode. When these arrive at their destinations, they discharge, and the result shows as a current. The magnitude of the current is determined by the concentration of charged particles and their speed of drift. Often the concentration is stationary, and the speed of drift is proportional to the field, so that, if the current is sufficiently small, it is proportional to the applied voltage, and the gas obeys Ohm's law (region A, Fig. 9.1). As the applied voltage, and therefore the ion current, increases, the removal of ions by drift to the electrodes augments the removal of ions by other processes, so that the steady-state concentration of ions begins to fall. This causes the current to lag behind the Ohm's law prediction (region B). With more intense fields, ion removal by conduction predominates, until eventually, at sufficiently intense fields, virtually every ion formed is removed by conduction, so that further increase in the applied voltage produces no further increase in the current (region C). Such a condition is called "saturation." Finally, at still greater voltages, electrons reach sufficient speeds in the course of their drift to ionise further molecules by collision, and there is a sharp increase in the current; the eventual result is a spark discharge (region D).

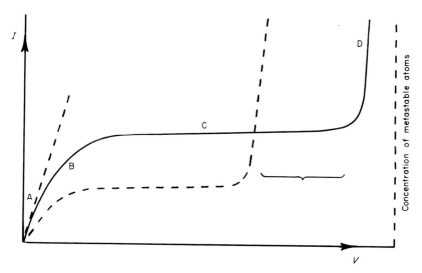

FIG. 9.1. *Full line*: Plot of current against applied voltage in an ionisation chamber. *Dashed line*: Plot of the concentration of metastable argon atoms against applied voltage in a simple argon detector; see Section 9.8b.

(b) At Large Ion Concentrations

If the concentration of ions is not small, a complication derives from the fact that positive ions move more slowly than electrons, so that, in the space near the cathode, there is a large concentration of relatively slow moving positive ions. These form a "space charge" close to the cathode. Inside the space charge, the gas is highly conducting, and therefore the field is small. The volume, the strength, and the effect of the space charge all increase with increase in the ion concentration. Space charge effects become appreciable at current densities greater than $\approx 10^{-8}$ amp/cm² (2).

(c) Non-Uniform Field

The discussion so far tacitly implies parallel plate electrodes. In practical detectors, either approximately coaxial cylindrical or concentric spherical electrodes are often used. This has the result that the field is non-uniform even in the absence of a space charge, and different parts of the gas between the electrodes operate on different parts of the curve of Fig. 9.1. If the ratio of the dimensions of the electrodes is not very large, the only effect at small ionisations is to reduce the range of voltage over which the cell exhibits saturation. At large ionisations, the effects become complicated, but significant observations are (1) that the breakdown potential, i.e., the voltage where the current becomes infinite, is greater when the small electrode is the anode; (2) when the small electrode is the anode, the space charge has a modifying influence on any increase in current produced by increased ionisation.

(d) Electron Capture

Free electrons, particularly those of fairly small energies, may be captured by neutral atoms or molecules, to give negative ions. The negative ions so formed recombine much more readily with positive ions than do free electrons, so that the result of adding a compound with large electron affinity to a gas is to decrease the ionisation current within it. The effectiveness of atoms and molecules in capturing electrons depends very much on molecular structure and composition. Complex molecules, particularly when they contain electronegative elements, or elements or groups with large electron affinity, e.g., the halogens, are much more effective electron capturers than the rare gases.

(e) Elastic and Inelastic Electron Collisions

In a gas containing unaccelerated electrons, i.e., with no electric field, the electrons and molecules and atoms of the gas are in thermal equilibrium. As soon as a field is applied, however, the electrons acquire further energy by acceleration in the field, whereas the neutral atoms or molecules retain the same energy. If the gas consists exclusively of rare gas atoms, the collisions between electrons and atoms not producing ionisation or excitation are necessarily elastic, since there is no way in which kinetic energy can be lost during the collision. The result is that since the electron and the atom have very different masses, very little energy is transferred, and the speed of the electron is scarcely changed. If, however, the gas consists of or contains molecules, which possess internal degrees of freedom, their collisions with electrons are inelastic, and much of the excess energy given to the electrons by acceleration in the field is transferred to the gas molecules. After such collisions, the electrons are slowed.

(f) Ionisation Efficiency

An important measure of the performance of ionisation detectors in general is their *ionisation efficiency*, which is the ratio of the number of ions or electrons collected by the electrodes to the number of molecules of vapour causing the electrons to be formed. This figure is easily obtained by dividing the total quantity of electricity (coulombs) passed by the cell as a result of the vapour by the product of the number of moles of vapour and the value of the faraday, which is 96,494 coulombs/mole.

9.3. FLAME IONISATION DETECTOR

Gases burning in a flame contain an appreciable concentration of free electrons resulting from ionisation, thus giving the flame an electrical conductivity. The conductivity of a hydrogen flame is exceptionally small, but when an organic vapour enters the flame the conductivity rises, and this increase can be measured and recorded. This is the basis of the flame ionisation detector (3–12).

The detailed mechanism of ion formation in flame is complex and not completely understood. The temperature of the flame is insufficient to produce the observed number of ions by any equilibrium process. Also, any explanation postulating ionisation from heated particles, e.g., of carbon (13), in the flame has proved inadequate (14). Most probably, the observed comparatively large concentration of electrons comes from chemi-ionisation reactions, in which pairs of species react together in the flame to give products at least one of which is an ion. These ions are not stable at equilibrium and possess energy considerably in excess of the thermal energy corresponding to the flame temperature. The degradation of their energy by collisions, however, is sufficiently slow that their concentration in the flame in the steady state is comparatively large (14–16). A further possibility is that electrons created by a primary process, be it chemi-ionisation or some other, are created with energies considerably above those of thermal equilibrium and thus cause further ionisation when they collide with neutral molecules (17). Sternberg et al. (16) list various possible chemi-ionisation reactions, and investigate their feasibility. The ionisation efficiency of the hydrogen flame detector is small; it has been quoted as 0.01 to 0.05% (5) and, in many cases, is even smaller than this.

In the detector (Fig. 9.2), the effluent from the column passes into a hydrogen flame, the conductivity of which is measured either between two electrodes (4), or, more commonly, between a metal jet and one electrode, as shown in the figure. The simplest arrangement is to use hydrogen as the carrier gas and to burn it at the jet at the column outlet. If, however, hydrogen is not to be used as carrier, the carrier gas may be mixed with sufficient hydrogen for the mixture to burn.

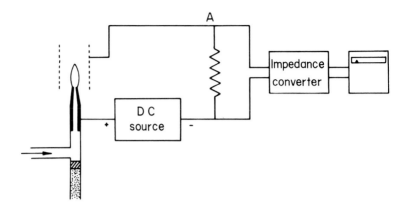

FIG. 9.2. Basic circuit of the flame ionisation detector. If hydrogen is not used as the carrier gas, it may be introduced by the tube indicated with the arrow.

(a) Design and Operation

The variation of current with voltage applied across the electrodes in general is as outlined in Section 9.2a. When the applied voltage is small (≈ 5 V/cm), the flame obeys Ohm's law, in that the current is determined by the rate of migration of ions, which is proportional to the field. When the applied voltage is greater, all available ions arrive at the electrodes, so that further increase in voltage does not increase the current; this region of saturation holds from about 10 V/cm up to at least several hundred V/cm (*3, 11, 18*). At still higher voltages, the result is a rapid increase in current followed by a discharge. Flame ionisation detectors are operated in the saturation region, and the voltage applied to the electrodes is usually 200–300 V.

A workable FID flame unit is easily constructed, and the general performance of the instrument is not particularly sensitive to small changes in the geometry of the flame jet or the electrodes (*12*). However, the detailed response, and especially the exact linearity, appear to depend critically on the geometry in a manner which cannot really be systematised. Some notes on specific design features are given below.

(*1*) *Number of Electrodes.* The conductivity of the flame can be measured either by having two similar electrodes in the flame, usually one each side, or by having one electrode in the flame and using the jet as the other. It has been found that the arrangement with two electrodes tends to give non-linear response at lower mass flow rates of vapour than the arrangement with one electrode and a jet (*19*), which is thus generally preferred.

(2) *Polarity of Electrodes*. Given that the jet is used to form one electrode, the FID works satisfactorily whether this be positive or negative. It has been found, however, that, if the jet is negative, any overheating of the jet leads to electron emission, which augments the noise; thus the jet is usually made positive.

(3) *Circuit Location of the Polarising Voltage*. Usually, one of the inlet leads to the impedance converter is grounded for all except DC. Almost invariably, this is the lead attached to the jet. In principle, the DC source providing the polarising voltage can be in either lead, but for electronic reasons it is best in the grounded lead. Thus, the arrangement of Fig. 9.2 is the most commonly adopted (*18*). Its only drawback is that the jet is at a DC potential to ground and thus must be isolated from other metal components.

(4) *Jet Material*. In order to prevent the jet becoming too hot, it should be fairly heavily constructed of metal so that heat is easily conducted away from the tip into a sizeable heat sink. Since it is liable to corrosion, it should be made of inert metal. Stainless steel is normally found adequate.

(5) *Flame Electrode*. The flame electrode can consist, for example, of a gauze above the flame, or a cylinder surrounding the flame. The flame electrode should not become too hot, and this condition is most easily satisfied by the cylindrical arrangement. The electrode should neither be too close to the flame, which would cause overheating, nor too far away, in which case ions would recombine before reaching it. In practice, a gauze about 1 cm above the flame, or a cylinder of diameter of the order of 1 cm around the flame, is found suitable. The flame electrode must be supported rigidly by a support which must be a good insulator. This support, therefore, should be located in a cool region of the instrument, e.g., below the flame (*20*), though this is not necessary.

(6) *Air or Oxygen Supply*. It is not normally adequate to allow the flame to burn in the open air. In most designs, air or oxygen for combustion is supplied separately to the base of the flame; this supply must necessarily be smooth and even, and evenly distributed round the flame. Different designs take considerable care to ensure this. One such system is illustrated in the design of Ongkiehong (*11*) shown in Fig. 9.3. The flow rate for air or oxygen must normally be at least ten times the flow rate of the hydrogen (*18*); smaller flows of air can produce either loss of sensitivity (*18*), or noisy and irregular response (*21*).

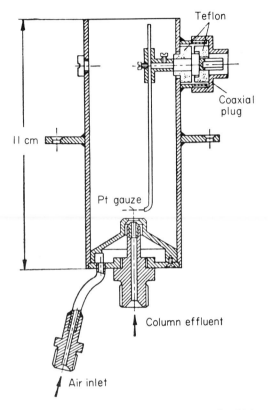

Fɪɢ. 9.3. Flame ionisation detector according to Ongkiehong (*11*).

(7) *Protection.* The flame must, of course, be protected from draughts and other disturbance by a suitable chimney.

The current corresponding to the saturation region of a pure hydrogen flame is of the order of 10^{-11} amp, and this may increase to a maximum of about 10^{-7} amp, in the presence of organic vapour. This current is measured by using it to develop a voltage across a load resistor (Fig. 9.2), and the voltage is applied to an "amplifier" which converts the input into form suitable for application to a display instrument, e.g., a strip-chart recorder. The actual voltage change at the point A produced by vapours is at least equal to, and usually much greater than, the span of a potentiometric recorder, so that the "amplifier" does not provide voltage amplification, but rather serves to match the very high impedance of the flame to the much lower impedance of the recorder or other display unit. It is thus more accurately called an "impedance converter." Impedance converters of this type are commonplace in scientific instrumentation.

(b) Sensitivity and Noise

The FID is a mass-flow sensitive detector (Section 8.1), so that its response is measured in terms of the current given for a given mass flow of vapour, e.g., in amperes per (gram per second), i.e., coulombs per gram.

The ultimate sensitivity is determined by the noise. The number of ions produced in the time of a time constant of the order of 1 sec is sufficiently large that statistical variations in this number do not contribute to the noise. The background current produced by the pure hydrogen flame, however, is proportional to the flow rate of hydrogen, and thus variations in the flow rate appear as background (11). The effect of this factor and the resultant sensitivity can be illustrated by the following approximate figures which typify the performance of an FID and are consistent with a large range of designs, since, as stated previously, performance of different designs usually differs only in detail. A typical steady-state current in the hydrogen flame is 10^{-11} amp. The hydrogen flow rate can be controlled with reasonable ease to within 0.1% (11), with the result that typical noise is about 10^{-14} amp (18). In converting the current noise to an equivalent mass noise, let us consider the detection of methane and assume that one molecule is ideally equivalent to one electron. Assuming a typical ionisation efficiency of 0.01%, therefore, a current of 10^{-14} amp is equivalent to:

$$\frac{16 \times 10^{-14}}{96494 \times 10^{-4}} \ \text{g/sec}, \quad \approx 10^{-14} \ \text{g/sec},$$

where the numerator contains the molecular weight of methane, and the denominator contains the number of coulombs given by 1 mole of methane at 0.01% ionisation efficiency. This typical figure is confirmed by Bruderreck et al. (18). At a typical flow rate of 1 ml/sec, a mass-flow of 10^{-14} g/sec of methane corresponds to a concentration of 10^{-9} molar. Several authors have confirmed that concentrations of the order of 10^{-9} molar give responses in the FID approximately equivalent to the noise (7, 11, 12).

In a given detector, the sensitivity can usually be increased several-fold [e.g., 6-fold (17)] by using oxygen in place of air to support the flame. However, the noise level rises by the same proportion, thus leading to an unchanged signal to noise ratio.

(c) Linearity

The FID is at least approximately linear over a large range; thus Mc-William and Dewar (6) show straightline plots of peak area against mass for a variety of compounds; Desty *et al.* (12) show a linear plot of the log of the current response against the log of the mass flow rate over a 100-fold range of the latter. Some other authors, however, have found significant departures from linearity (18), the size of which depends on detailed design. The detector is useable from the limit of detection at about 10^{-14} g/sec of organic material ($\approx 10^{-9}$ mole of methylene group per mole of carrier at 1 ml/sec) up to about 10^{-7} g/sec (10^{-2} molar, similarly), but the linearity over so large a range is inevitably suspect.

In addition to non-linearity of the current response of the flame itself, it should be remembered that the range of linearity of most impedance converters is limited and may only cover a restricted range, e.g., 10^4.

(d) Calibration

Among hydrocarbons, there is a general tendency for molar response (i.e., coulombs per mole) to increase linearly with carbon number, so that the weight response of hydrocarbons is approximately steady. Such a rule, however, is only good to within about 20%. Thus, Desty *et al.* (12) find that the molar response of 2,2,4-trimethylpentane is 30% greater than that for ethylbenzene, and 15% greater than that for *n*-octane, all C_8 molecules. Furthermore, the exact calibration coefficients vary within at least 10% with alteration of the geometry and operating conditions of the flame, as is shown clearly by Bruderreck *et al.* (18). Yet again, the way in which calibration coefficients vary with alteration in operating conditions such as hydrogen gas flow depends on the exact geometry of the flame unit.

Among oxygenated compounds, there is a qualitative rule that the greater the ratio of oxygen to carbon in the molecule, the smaller the weight response. An approximate rule formulated by Ongkiehong (11) is that the molar response is approximately proportional to a "carbon number" calculated as the number of carbon atoms left after as many CO_2 groups as possible have been split off.

Several workers have published tables of response factors for substances in the FID (22–27) and have tried to systematise them. As Bruderreck *et al.* have pointed out (18), such calibration coefficients inevitably apply accurately only in the specific conditions in which they were determined.

(e) Range of Application

The hydrogen flame detector responds to all compounds containing CH groups, but fails to respond to a number of common inorganic compounds. A list of such compounds is given by Condon *et al.* (3), and is reproduced below:

Rare gases	Silicon tetrachloride
Oxides of nitrogen	Silicon tetrafluoride
Hydrogen	Trichlorosilane
Oxygen	Hydrogen sulphide
Nitrogen	Sulphur dioxide
Oxides of carbon	Carbonyl sulphide
Ammonia	Carbon disulphide
Water	

The lack of response to water and the air gases is useful in that these need not be removed from the carrier gas or from samples when they are not components of interest. Thus, the detector can be used for the analysis of aqueous solutions or mixtures of organic substances (e.g., *28*).

Though water and other of the substances listed above do not give a positive response in the FID, they affect the response of other compounds. In particular, it has been found that water (*28, 29*) and silicon compounds (*30, 31*) inhibit the response of other substances. If the FID is used continuously to register a constant proportion of an organic vapour, e.g., methane, the presence of water or other such inhibiting agents appears as a negative peak. In this way, the FID can be rendered sensitive to substances on the above list (*32*).

(f) Alkali Metal Thermionic Detector

Karmen, Giuffrida, *et al.* observe that if there is a suitably volatile alkali halide present in the flame of a flame ionisation detector, the detector sensitivity to compounds containing halogens or phosphorus is enhanced (*33–36*). This effect has been used to produce a useful modification of the FID which can distinguish and determine compounds of these elements. In descriptions of such an instrument given by Karmen *et al.* (*33–35*), and by Janak and Svojanovsky (*37*), the gas from the column first enters an ordinary FID unit (Fig. 9.4), which responds, as already described, to organic compounds. At the top of the flame is a gauze, piece of ceramic, or platinum loop treated with alkali halide. Immediately above this is a second flame unit, with a second collector electrode. The second flame is

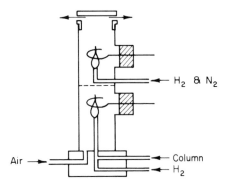

FIG. 9.4. Schematic diagram of coupled FID (lower flame) and alkali metal thermionic detector (upper unit). The alkali metal halide impregnates the gauze drawn
between the two flame units [Karmen (*34*)].

coloured in the usual way by alkali metal ions. The presence of phosphorus
or halogen compounds in the burned gases from the first flame stimulates
the production of alkali metal ions from the alkali halide, and these extra
ions cause an increase in conductivity of the upper flame.

The operation of this detector may be illustrated by the results shown
in Fig. 9.5 (*34*). The upper record shows the chromatogram from the FID
of small proportions of (1) carbon tetrachloride, (2) fluorobenzene, (3) toluene, and (4) chlorobenzene in diethyl ether. All give peaks except the
carbon tetrachloride, which does not burn. In the case of the response from
the upper flame, shown in the lower record, the carbon tetrachloride gives a
large response, but the toluene, being the only unhalogenated compound,
gives none.

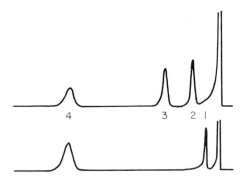

FIG. 9.5. Chromatograms taken by FID (upper record) and sodium thermionic
detector (lower record) of: 1, carbon tetrachloride; 2, fluorobenzene; 3, toluene; 4,
chlorobenzene; all dissolved in diethyl ether.

9.4. IONISATION BY RADIATION

Gases become ionised when traversed by "Ionising Radiation," which includes α- and β-rays, ultraviolet radiation, γ-rays and X-rays. In gas chromatography, only the first three are used, the first two being conveniently obtained from suitable sources of radioactive material. For purposes of rough explanation, one may regard α- or β-rays as streams of particles emanating from the source. These traverse the gas, and, after traversing a distance the average length of which is the mean free path, they collide with an atom or molecule of the gas. The rays are emitted from the radioactive material with a large energy, which we may assume to be kinetic; thus they collide so hard with the atom or molecule of gas that they are capable of providing sufficient energy to displace an electron. The reaction is therefore:

$$M \to M^+ + \varepsilon^-$$

The energies with which ionising particles are emitted from radioactive materials are of the order of 10^4 to 10^6 eV, whereas the energy required to ionise singly an atom or molecule is of the order of 10 eV. Thus, after one collision, the ionising particle has lost very little energy, and it can then go on to collide with another atom, produce another ion and electron, and so on until it is finally brought to equilibrium. The progress of an ionising particle in this way can be seen in Wilson Cloud Chamber photographs, which are generally familiar.

Knowledge of the range of ionising radiation is important in connection with health hazard and with the design of ionisation detectors. With α- and β-rays, the range is inversely proportional to the density of the medium and very approximately proportional to the energy of emission of the rays. Because of the first proportionality, the product of range and density is constant for a given energy, so that range is usually quoted in units of cm g/cc, i.e., g/cm². For β-rays, the range in these units is very approximately given by (*38*):

$$\text{Range} \quad (\text{g/cm}^2) \approx 0.5 \times \text{energy} \quad (\text{MeV}).$$

For example, the range of β-radiation from ^{90}Sr (0.54 MeV) in air (0.001 g/cc) is approximately 2.7 m. The range of α-radiation is much smaller and normally lies between 3 and 7 cm in air. The ranges of γ- and X-radiation cannot be quoted by formula, since the intensity of a beam declines exponentially with distance. Extinction coefficients are a function both of the wavelength of the radiation and the material through which it passes, but are all such that the distance through air required to halve the radiation intensity is many metres, so that the effective range is greater than those of α- and β-rays.

The greater the amount of ionisation produced in unit volume by the radiation, the greater the specific conductivity of the ionised gas. Of the types of radiation, α-rays produce the greatest density of ionisation, followed by β-rays, followed by γ-rays, which is the inverse order of their ranges; the more frequently the particles collide and produce ions, the shorter the range in which their energy is exhausted. The density of ionisation is also a function of the energy of the radiation. When the energies are less than the ionisation potential, clearly no ionisation occurs at all. At energies greater than this, ions are formed, and as the energy increases to a figure of the order of 100 eV, the ionisation rapidly increases to a maximum. At still greater energies, the ionisation density declines, and this trend continues into the MeV range.

Whereas ions are formed at a rate which depends only on the intensity of radiation, and is constant at a given pressure and temperature, ions are removed by any of a number of processes, e.g., collision with neutral molecules, at rates depending on and increasing with their concentration. Thus, on applying radiation to a gas, the concentration of ions will rise until the rate of removal of ions equals the rate of creation by the radiation, so that normally there is a stationary concentration of ions, a state which is reached almost instantaneously.

The sources of radiation which have been used in gas-chromatographic

TABLE 9.1

SOURCES OF RADIATION

Element	Effective radiation	Radiation energy (MeV)	Half-life (years)	Approximate quantity used in GC detectors
Tritium (^{3}H)	β	0.018	12.5	
^{63}Ni	β	0.067	85	10–100 mC
^{90}Sr	β	0.54	25	
^{85}Kr	β	0.72	9.4	
^{226}Ra	α^a	4.795	1620	
	α^a	5.3	—	20–100 μC
RaD = ^{210}Pb	α^a	5.3	25	

^{a} From daughter species, and not from the original element.

ionisation detectors are given in Table 9.1. Note that α-sources may be weaker than β-sources, since the ionisation intensity produced by α-rays is so much greater.

9.5. The β-Ray Ionisation Cross-Section Detector

The saturation current, i.e., the level of the plateau of Fig. 9.1, is determined by the number of ions produced per second. Among other things, this depends upon the composition of the gas, for the larger the gas molecules, the larger is the area which they present to the stream of ionising radiation, and the greater the chance that ionisation will occur. This fact is used in the "Cross-Section" detector, described by Boer (*39*) and by Deal *et al.* (*40, 41*). It has been used occasionally since, especially for the detection of permanent gases, but it has been rather overshadowed by the argon detector which was developed from it.

The detector is shown diagrammatically in Fig. 9.6. Essentially, it consists of a cavity through which the column effluent passes, and which is irradiated from a suitable radiation source contained within it. The cavity itself is made of metal, and forms one electrode; the other electrode consists of a metal rod, or other shape, well insulated from the cavity. A constant potential such as to maintain saturation current (region C,

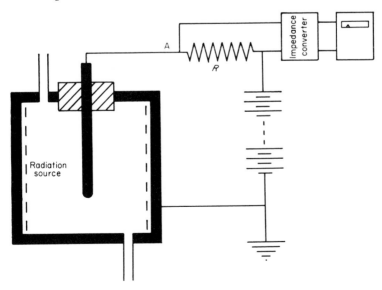

Fig. 9.6. Basic circuit associated with an ionisation cross-section detector.

Fig. 9.1) is applied across the electrodes. With dimensions of the order of centimetres, this is of the order of 300 V.

The currents and voltages involved in the cross-section detector are of the same order as those found in the FID, and thus the electronic circuitry associated with the ionisation unit is similar to that of the FID.

The sensitivity of the ionisation cross-section detectors is determined by the amplification provided by the electronics, and, since it is found in practice that the noise arises from the detector itself and not from the electronics, the useful sensitivity is determined by the signal-to-noise ratio and not by the amplification. A minimum to the noise is provided by the discontinuous nature of the evolution of β-rays from the radioactive source. If N ionising particles are emitted in a time equal to one time constant of the apparatus, the random fluctuations in the current are of the order of $N^{-1/2}$ of the total current. One curie represents 3.7×10^{10} disintegrations per second, so a 10 mC source and 1 sec time constant gives $N \approx 10^8$, whence $N^{-1/2} \approx 10^{-4}$. Deal et al. (41) claim that the noise found experimentally was of the order expected from the above source. In their detector, the signal equivalent to the noise was produced by a concentration of 0.005 mole % of heptane in nitrogen, so that the detector would give unit signal-to-noise ratio for a concentration change of 1 part in 2×10^4. The noise may be reduced by increasing the intensity of the source, or by increasing the time constant; the first, however, is restricted by practical considerations and by considerations mentioned in the previous section, and the second by whatever resolution is required from the apparatus. Such a sensitivity is small compared to that of many other detectors.

The current is proportional to the concentration of ions, and the latter is proportional to the cross section offered to the radiation by the molecules of gas contained in the cell. The cross section offered by the gas, assumed to be a mixture of carrier gas (g) and a vapour (v), is proportional to the sum of the products of the molar concentrations (c) of the components and their molecular ionisation cross sections (Q). Thus, the current I is given by:

$$I = k'(c_g Q_g + c_v Q_v) = \frac{k}{RT}(p_g Q_g + p_v Q_v), \qquad (9.1)$$

where k and k' are apparatus constants, and the second form of writing takes into account variation in temperature, p_g and p_v being partial pressures. Normally, $p_g + p_v$ is a constant, usually atmospheric pressure, P, so that

$$I = \frac{k}{RT}\{(P - p_v)Q_g + p_v Q_v\},$$

whence ΔI, the change in current produced by a partial pressure p_v of vapour, is given by:

$$\Delta I = \frac{k}{RT} \, p_v(Q_v - Q_g), \qquad (9.2)$$

and the proportional change in current is given by:

$$\frac{\Delta I}{I_0} = \frac{p_v}{P} \cdot \frac{Q_v - Q_g}{Q_g}. \qquad (9.3)$$

Hence the calibration factors connecting response with concentration are proportional to the difference between the ionisation cross sections of carrier and vapour. Ionisation cross sections relative to hydrogen of a number of common gases have been determined, and are given in Table 9.2. Not many ionisation cross sections of the individual organic molecules likely to be encountered in gas chromatography are available, but Otvos and Stevenson (42) have shown that they may be obtained by adding together ionisation cross sections of individual atoms in the molecule. Table 9.2 also shows relative ionisation cross sections of some common

TABLE 9.2

HIGH-ENERGY β-RAY IONISATION CROSS SECTIONS OF COMMON GASES RELATIVE TO HYDROGEN

Gas	Relative ionisation cross section for ^{90}Sr radiation	
	Observed	Calculated
H_2	1.23	—
He	1.64	—
Ar	10.9	—
N_2	7.04	—
O_2	8.55	—
CO_2	10.8	—
CH_4	7.04	7
C_2H_4	10.7	10.6
C_2H_6	12.7	12.6
C_3H_6	15.7	15.9
C_3H_8	17.8	17.9
C_4H_{10}	23.1	22.8

organic compounds, obtained from data given by Otvos and Stevenson (*42*), and for comparison gives ionisation cross sections calculated on the assumption that C = 3.2 and H = 1 (arbitrary units). The agreement suggests that use of Eq. (9.2) in conjunction with tables such as Table 9.2 would make a satisfactory method of calibrating ionisation cross-section detectors a priori. A few results given by Boer (*39*) and by Deal *et al.* (*41*) confirm this, but the relation has not been confirmed for many chemical types.

With regard to the other properties of interest given in Section 8.3, the *linearity* of the detector is adequate. Deal *et al.* (*41*) show that a plot of response against mole fraction may be made at least up to mole fractions of 0.06, and the plot is virtually linear up to 0.01 mole fraction, which is not normally exceeded in analytical gas chromatography. The linearity, together with other features of the performance, may be poor if the design of the cell is such that the space charge is appreciable, or if the field is locally very large, e.g., through using too small a central electrode or leaving sharp edges on any of the metal inside the chamber. Deal *et al.* (*41*) find that the single cell instrument does not produce significant *drift* in ordinary operating conditions; however, any drift due to excessive fluctuations in temperature or pressure, or drift produced through use of a more sensitive unit can be eliminated using the twin-cell arrangement described by Boer (*39*).

The *speed of response* of the cell is determined by its volume, and not by any lag in the change in conductivity. There is no theoretical lower limit on the size of cells, and models with volumes as small as $8\mu l$ have been described (*43, 44*). In these, the use of tritium, whose emission is weak and short range, enables a large intensity of ionisation to be used, with useful increase in sensitivity. Such cells can be used with capillary columns.

The cross-section detector is as versatile as the catharometer, and the few substances which fail to give a response in one carrier gas will respond in another gas. In spite of this versatility, the detector has not been extensively used; the reasons are probably the comparatively low sensitivity, which gives it no advantage over the catharometer, already well established in use and considerably cheaper; and the intensive development of the FID. On the other hand, the ancillary apparatus used with the cross-section detector is similar to that used with the FID, and furthermore, the cross-section detector can serve purposes that the FID cannot. The result is that the cross-section detector is very conveniently substituted for the FID or other ionisation detectors, and forms a simple complement to them.

9.6. The Electron Capture Detector

If the electric field in an irradiated ionisation chamber is small, the electrons have comparatively small energies and are therefore relatively easily captured by any vapour molecules with large electron affinities, as described in Section 9.2d. A detector selective for electron-capturing vapours operating in this manner was first described by Lovelock and Lipsky (45). It has been developed considerably since then (46–49) and is extensively used for detection of compounds containing halogens or phosphorus; its use in pesticide analysis is particularly notable. The sensitivity of the detector to suitable electron-capturing groups, e.g., iodides or polyaromatics, is so great, that, for the detection of extreme traces, it may prove worth while to introduce chemically an electron-capturing group into the molecule of the trace, so that this detector may be used (50).

(a) Construction and Principles

Since the electron capture (EC) detector operates at a low field, the electrodes of the ionisation chamber should be such as to generate a roughly homogeneous field and should therefore be of comparable size. In early designs, plane parallel electrodes were used (45), but designs with concentric cylinders are perfectly adequate, so long as the central electrode is not too small (47).

In most designs, the radiation source is a short-range β source, e.g. tritium (titanium tritide) or ^{63}Ni, which irradiates the volume of the cavity close to the cathode, but has insufficient range to reach the anode, as is illustrated in Fig. 9.7. A voltage of 10 to 50 V is applied across the electrodes, producing a current of electrons migrating from the irradiated zone across the unirradiated zone. In the absence of a compound which can capture the electrons, there is a steady current which in practice is of the order of 10^{-9} amp. As soon as an electron-capturing substance enters the gas, some of the electrons are captured, and since the ions thereby formed move more slowly, they cannot carry any appreciable current, and there is a drop in current. It should be emphasised that the response of an EC detector consists of a *drop* in current.

In the earliest usage of the EC detector, the field was applied continuously to the ionisation chamber, and a gas such as nitrogen was used as carrier. In this case, an electron-capturing molecule produces a drop in current by electron capture, but it can also produce other responses by other mechanisms (46). For example, the cell inevitably acts as a cross-

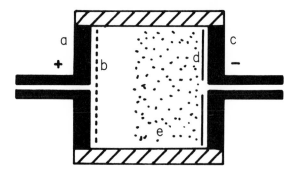

FIG. 9.7. Schematic diagram of an electron capture detector cell. (a) anode; (b) baffle to distribute the flow of gas; (c) cathode; (d) radioactive source; (e) irradiated region.

section detector whether or not there is electron capture and since vapour molecules are normally larger than carrier molecules they produce an increase in cell current due to the cross-section effect in opposition to the electron capture effect. Thus, though there are many cases of satisfactory operation with a continuously applied field, there are also many cases of anomalous response.

In order to overcome anomalies due to the cell operating in several modes simultaneously, and to produce a detector working as much as possible purely by electron capture, Lovelock (46, 51) modified the apparatus in two respects:

(1) By use of a carrier gas consisting of argon or other inert gas containing 5%-10% v/v of an alkane, e.g., methane or butane. This gas can be introduced between the column and the detector as a separate stream if it is not convenient to use it in the column.

(2) By applying the potential to the electrodes in the form of square-wave pulses of duration about 0.5 to 1 μsec at intervals of about 0.05 to 2 msec (see below).

Alkane molecules do not capture slow electrons, but undergo inelastic collisions with them. The effect, therefore, of the addition of the hydrocarbon to the carrier is to promote numerous inelastic collisions with the electrons in the irradiated gas, so that the electrons thereby lose energy till they are in effective equilibrium with the thermal motion of the gas as a whole. In this state, they are described as *thermal* electrons. It is thermal electrons, rather than their more energetic companions emitted from the source or accelerated by the field, which are primarily captured by electron-capturing molecules. A pulse of potential of the order of $0.5\mu\text{sec}$ is long enough to collect every thermal electron present in the irradiated gas. The current given by the pulse, therefore, is a measure of the concentration of thermal electrons in the irradiated gas at the beginning of the pulse. Since the pulse current measures the electron concentration in a state during which no field is applied, there are no perturbations on the electron concentration due to the field. The effect of electrons being captured by vapour molecules is to reduce the electron concentration, and thus any reduction in the current of a given pulse indicates the effect of electron capture and nothing else. The pulsed mode of operation is thus simpler and more reliable than the DC mode, and is now the most commonly used.

(b) Linearity

It is clear that a detector which responds by a drop in current cannot be linear over a large range, since the current cannot fall below zero. The detailed theory of operation of the EC detector has been studied by Wentworth et al. (48), who find that, in the conditions of their proposed mechanism, the response of the detector is given by:

$$\frac{I_a - I_b}{I_b} = Kc, \tag{9.4}$$

where I_a is the standing current due to pure carrier gas, I_b is the current in the presence of a concentration c of electron–capturing vapour, and K is a constant which expresses the sensitivity of the detector to the vapour. The constant K is studied in detail by Wentworth et al. (48, 52); see also below. By Eq. (9.4) the response is approximately linear only in the region that $I_a - I_b$ can be neglected in comparison with I_a. Simmonds et al. (47) have shown that Eq. (9.4) holds accurately over at least two orders of magnitude of concentration, including cases where $I_b \approx 0.1\,I_a$, i.e., cases where the current is reduced to only 10% of its standing value.

Because the process by which vapours capture electrons somewhat resembles the way in which substances absorb radiation, several authors (48, 49) have fitted Beer's law to the relation between current and concentration:

$$I_b = I_a e^{-Kc}. \tag{9.5}$$

There is, in fact, comparatively little difference in the shapes of the plots of Eqs. (9.4) and (9.5), and apparently either is adequate in practice for quantitative analysis.

(c) *Calibration*

The most striking property of the EC detector is that its response as given by K of Eq. (9.4) or (9.5) is critically dependent on the chemical nature of the vapour being detected. If operating correctly purely by electron capture, the response is a function of the electron affinity of the vapour molecule, and since these electron affinities vary very widely, so do the responses. In practice, values of K can span a range of 10^7 or more, the response of alkanes being negligible, while that of iodides or polyaromatics

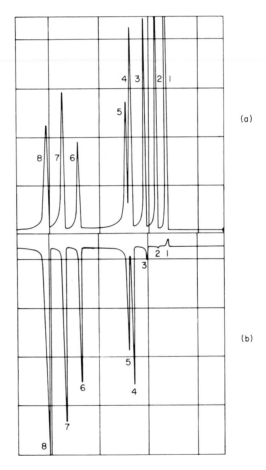

FIG. 9.8. Chromatograms of (1) cyclohexane, (2) fluorobenzene, (3) chlorobenzene, (4) *m*- and *p*-dichlorobenzene, (5) *o*-dichlorobenzene, (6) 1,3,5-trichlorobenzene, (7) 1,2,4-trichlorobenzene, and (8) 1,2,3-trichlorobenzene from an argon detector (a) and from an electron capture detector (b) [Lovelock and Lipsky (45)].

is very large indeed. As a result of this, the electron capture is extensively used as a detector selective for electron capturing molecules and as a qualitative tool for identifying them. A good example of this application is given in the original paper of Lovelock and Lipsky (45) (Fig. 9.8), where chromatograms taken on a EC detector and an argon detector (Section 9.8) are compared. The chlorinated compounds give large EC responses, but the alkane and the fluorinated compound give very small responses.

The response of the EC detector to a given compound is a steep function of temperature, because the process of electron capture depends critically on the electron temperature, and the electrons are thermal. Also, the responses of different compounds alter with temperature in very different

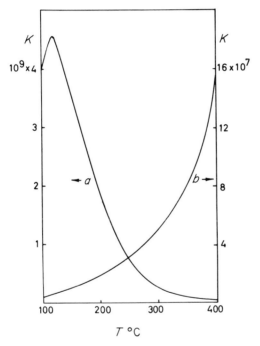

FIG. 9.9. Molar responses of azulene (a, left hand scale) and dodecyl bromide (b, right hand scale) as a function of temperature [Simmonds et al. (47)].

ways. As an example, Fig. 9.9 shows the molar responses of azulene and of dodecyl bromide, two substances of comparable molecular size, as a function of temperature. The result of this is that any quoted values of relative calibration coefficients are valid only at the exact temperature at which they were obtained.

Several authors have studied calibration coefficients of compounds of particular interest for the EC detector (e.g., 53–55), and have commented on the relation between calibration coefficient and molecular structure. Because of the dependence of the exact numerical values on exact conditions, we do not quote them. The order of magnitude of relative values of K can, however, be summarised, as in Table 9.3, in which the molar response of n-butyl chloride has been taken as unity and other classes of compounds compared with it, using results summarised by Devaux and Guiochon (49). A more detailed survey of typical response factors, drawn on a logarithmic ladder, is given by Clemons and Altshuller (54) and is shown in Fig. 9.10. It is apparent that halogenated and aromatic compounds give the biggest responses, but that the detector is also serviceable for many other com-

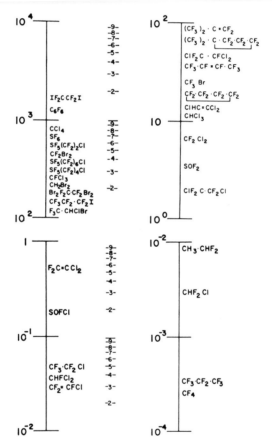

FIG. 9.10. Response factors of substances in an electron capture detector (room temperature) according to Clemons and Altshuller (54).

TABLE 9.3

ORDER-OF-MAGNITUDE RESPONSES OF SUBSTANCES IN AN ELECTRON CAPTURE
DETECTOR[a]

Substance	Response relative to n-butyl chloride
Alkyl chloride	1
Alkyl dichloride	100
Alkyl bromide	$100–10^3$
Alkyl dibromide	10^5
Chloroform	10^5
Carbon tetrachloride	10^6
Benzene	10^{-1}
Bromobenzene	10^3
Aliphatic alkanols, ethers, esters	1
2,3-Butane dione	10^5

[a] From Devaux and Guiochon (49).

pounds, so long as they contain oxygen atoms. The response of phosphorus compounds is also large. It is noteworthy that the addition of a second or third halogen multiplies the sensitivity many-fold; indeed the response is almost proportional to the exponential of the number of halogens. It appears also that conjugated double bonds in general, apart from aromatic compounds specifically, enhance the response.

(d) *Sensitivity and Noise*

As with the cross-section detector, the noise is determined by statistical fluctuations in the evolution of radioactive particles. Since source intensities are of the same order as those of the cross-section detector, the noise level is of the same order, i.e., about 10^{-4} of the standing current. Thus, with a standing current of 10^{-9} amp, the noise is of the order of 10^{-13} amp. In practical instruments, the minimum theoretical noise is fairly readily attained (49). In order to attain the theoretical noise level, however, cell conditions must be kept adequately constant, which requires stringent control of temperature and the parameters of height, width, and period of the pulses. In particular, the cell temperature must be controlled to within 0.01°C to give drift no greater than the statistical noise.

As is apparent from the previous subsection, the sensitivity attainable with the above noise depends greatly on the nature of the vapour and the temperature. The detector is essentially concentration-sensitive, and thus sensitivities can be expressed as the concentration equivalent to the noise. Typical figures for this are given by several authors (*44, 50*), and range from about 10^{-14} mole/cc, for substances such as chloroform and iodobutane, to figures at least seven orders of magnitude smaller, as implied by Table 9.3. The sensitivities for the heavily halogenated molecules are very great indeed.

Because of the great sensitivity and restricted linear range of the EC detector, it is often desirable to reduce its sensitivity. Since it is a concentration-sensitive detector, this is conveniently done by diluting a stream of vapour with a faster stream of purge gas before entering the detector cell.

The sensitivity of the EC detector as a whole in the pulsed mode increases with increase in the interval between the pulses, since with very short pulses there is no time for the steady-state electron concentration to be established. The longer the pulses, the closer is the electron concentration to its steady state before the succeeding pulse, and thus any effect on this concentration due to a capturing vapour is at its most apparent. In practice, the steady state is reached between 1 and 2 msec after a pulse, and ideally pulses should be thus spaced. However, the more widely spaced the pulses, the smaller the average current passed by the cell, and the better must be the specification of the auxiliary electronic apparatus; therefore, in practice, pulse periods of between 50 and 1000 μsec are used.

9.7. The Electron Mobility Detector

The apparatus used for the pulsed EC detector can also be used in a modification in which the primary mechanism is the effect on the mobility of super-thermal electrons in a rare gas produced by the introduction of any gas whose molecules possess internal degrees of freedom (*56, 57*). In this detector, the carrier gas is a heavy inert gas; in practice this restricts it to argon because of the cost. The cell is identical with an EC cell, and a pulsed potential of between 10 and 100 V is applied with pulses of about 1 μsec and pulse interval variable between about 1 and 100 μsec. When pure carrier gas is passing, the electrons produced by ionisation are moving at great speed, and the duration of the pulse is insufficient for them to be sufficiently deflected to arrive at the electrodes before the end of the pulse. Thus, the ionisation current is very small ($\approx 10^{-9}$ amp). When a molecular vapour enters, the electrons are slowed down as described in Section 9.2e, and after this, they may be deflected sufficiently during a pulse to be col-

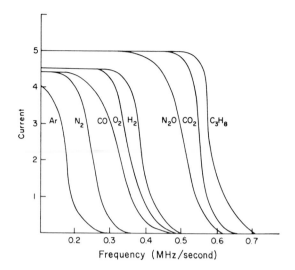

FIG. 9.11. Plot of current against pulse frequency for 0.1% by volume of various vapours in argon in an electron mobility detector. Lovelock (56).

lected. The result is an increase in the ionisation current which is recorded. When a proportion of hydrocarbon is included with the carrier gas for the pulsed EC detector, it is in effect a mobility detector working at saturation; the electrons are slowed down to the same temperature as the bulk gas.

The pulse frequency below which the pulse is long enough for electrons to be collected depends on the extent to which they are slowed by the inelastic collisions, and this appears to depend on the molecular complexity of the vapour. Thus, the more complex the vapour, the greater may be the frequency of the pulses without a fall in the current, as illustrated in Fig. 9.11, which shows a plot of current against frequency for the same concentration of various vapours. It is clear that this technique provides a limited means of qualitative identification of vapours.

The principal advantage of this form of detector is that it is the only ionisation detector which can be used for permanent molecular gases. Furthermore, it uses the same apparatus as the more commonly used EC detector.

9.8. THE ARGON DETECTOR

The apparatus for the Argon Ionisation detector, first introduced by Lovelock (58), consists of an ionisation chamber basically similar to that for the cross-section detector. The differences are in the details of design, that either argon, neon, or helium must be used as carrier gas, and that the potential applied across the electrodes is much greater, normally between 1000 and 2000 V. The principle of operation is completely different. Argon has been used most commonly as the carrier gas and has given its name to the detector, but it is not the only usable gas.

By slight alterations in the design and operating conditions of the ionisation chamber, different aspects of the complicated processes of ionisation and recombination such as are mentioned in Section 9.2 can be brought into prominence, and the detector can operate usefully in several entirely different ways, as Lovelock (*59*) has emphasised. Often, if the conditions are not correct, it operates in several ways at once, with consequent unreliability, non-linearity, etc., so that careful attention to design and conditions is necessary to obtain full advantage from any one mode of operation.

(a) *The Production of Excited Atoms*

In addition to producing ionisation, radiation can interact with atoms or molecules to raise them to an excited state in which the atoms or molecules have more energy than normal, but insufficient to cause them to ionise. The half-lives of the excited atoms of rare gases are very much longer than those of the molecules of other gases, in which the energy is rapidly distributed among internal degrees of freedom, so that their stationary concentration can be relatively large. At atmospheric pressure, half-lives of such states may be of the order of 10^{-4} sec, whereas those of the ions are of the order of 10^{-8} sec. For this reason, such excited atoms are called "metastable." Unlike ions, they do not contribute to the conductivity of the gas.

The excited atoms of the first three inert gases, He, Ne, and Ar, are of particular interest, for their energies of excitation are greater than the ionisation potentials of most organic compounds, so that a collision between an excited atom and an organic molecule is energetically capable of ionising the latter, and in fact it generally does so. Thus, using argon as an example, the reaction:

$$Ar^* + M \rightarrow Ar + M^+ + \varepsilon^-$$

occurs, and the consequent organic ion and the electron contribute to the gas conductivity. Table 9.4 gives excitation and ionisation potentials of the rare gases, and the ionisation potentials of a number of common compounds.

In an irradiated rare gas, the concentration of ions is small, so the electrical conductivity is small, and a comparatively small concentration of

TABLE 9.4

IONISATION AND EXCITATION POTENTIALS

Substance	Ionisation potential (volts)	Excitation potential (volts)
He	24.46	19.8
Ne	21.47	16.6
Ar	15.68	11.6
Kr	13.93	10
H	13.527	—
H_2	15.6	7.0
N_2	15.51	6.3
O_2	12.5	—
CO	14.1	—
CO_2	14.4	—
H_2O	12.56	—
H_2S	10.42	—
CH_4	14.5	—
C_2H_6	12.8	—
C_6H_6	9.6	—
Organic compounds	≈ 11	—

organic vapour capable of being ionised by collisions with excited molecules causes a large proportional increase in the conductivity. This has been shown for gases in helium irradiated with α-rays in a parallel-plate ionisation chamber by Jesse and Sadauskis (60), who plotted the proportional increase in ionisation against the concentration of added trace component (Fig. 9.12). At small concentrations, the increased response is determined by the concentration of the trace component causing it, so that the curve is roughly linear. At large concentrations, the response is determined by the concentration of excited atoms, which is a constant, and thus the curve exhibits saturation. The detailed kinetics of the reactions leading to curves such as those of Fig. 9.12 have been studied by several authors (60–63).

(b) Ion Multiplication by the Field

So far, the description applies to cases where the potential between the electrodes is relatively small, so that electrons are not accelerated appreciably by the field. When, however, the field is increased by application of a greater voltage, there comes a stage when the field is such that electrons are sufficiently accelerated between collisions to acquire the energy

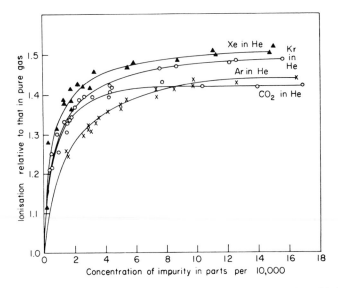

Fig. 9.12. Increase in ionisation produced by an impurity in irradiated helium as a function of the impurity concentration. Jesse and Sadauskis (*60*).

required to *excite* the rare gas atoms, but do not acquire the energy sufficient to *ionise* them. The reaction is thus:

$$Ar + \varepsilon^{-*} \rightarrow Ar^* + \varepsilon^-$$

where ε^{-*} is an electron which has been accelerated in the field sufficiently to cause excitation. At such voltages, the number of metastable atoms is much multiplied, but the number of ions remains steady. This is illustrated in Fig. 9.1, which shows, in addition to the curve already discussed, the concentration of metastables as a function of applied potential (dotted line). It is clear that in the region bracketed, where there is a large concentration of metastables but few ions, the effect of an organic vapour described above is very much enhanced, and it is in these circumstances that the simplest form of argon detector operates.

(c) *The Simple Argon Detector*

The simple argon detector (*58*) is designed to take advantage of electron multiplication by the field, but not to use other effects, such as space charge, electron capture, etc., described below. Ideally, the cell should employ parallel-plate electrodes so as to produce a uniform field, but, in practice, the cell normally consists of one electrode inserted in a metal cavity which forms the other electrode, and, so long as the central electrode is not too small, the field is not sufficiently inhomogeneous to cause complications. Satisfactory cells have been constructed using an automobile spark plug as the central electrode, soldering a small circular metal plate on the electrode in order to increase its size (64). Lovelock (65) has used a rod inside a metal cavity exactly as indicated in Fig. 9.6. Dimensions are conveniently such that the cell volume is of the order of 1 to 10 cc.

The percentage change in current as a function of proportion to a vapour, with applied voltage as a parameter, is shown in Fig. 9.13. At

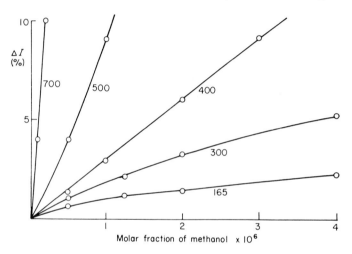

FIG. 9.13. Increase in ionisation current as a function of the concentration of an added vapour (methanol) in a simple argon detector with applied voltage as parameter. Lovelock (58).

low voltages, when there is no field-excitation, the increase in current is linear at very small concentrations, but reaches saturation at larger concentrations, as in Fig. 9.12. At large voltages where there is very considerable field excitation, every electron created by ionisation of an organic molecule with a metastable atom is subject to excitation by the field, thus creating more metastable atoms, and so on, in a chain reaction, with the result that the current increases extra-linearly with concentration of vapour. In the extreme case, further addition of vapour promotes a non-terminating chain, with a consequent spark discharge in the cell. At one specific voltage between the low values resulting in saturation and the high voltages resulting in chain reaction, the detector is approximately linear; this value is 400 V in the figure.

It is apparent from Fig. 9.13 that the sensitivity is enormously dependent on the applied voltage. When this is small, the sensitivity is small, but the detector may be used up to a large vapour concentration; when the applied voltage is large, the sensitivity becomes very great, but there is the possibility of breakdown and other effects if the vapour concentration is large. The chief virtue of the argon detector is that it is capable of very great sensitivity, and, for this, it is operated at such a voltage that every primary electron produced by the radiation creates as many as 10^4 more by acceleration in the field.

When there is considerable field-excitation, detector non-linearity can be largely corrected by a "Linearising Resistance" in series with the detector, usually of the order of 10^9 to 10^{10} ohms. When a vapour enters the cell, the current rises, and without the linearising resistance, would rise extra-linearly. However, with a suitable series resistance, as soon as the current increases, the voltage drop across the resistance increases, so that the voltage across the cell falls, causing a drop in amount of field excitation, whence the extra-linear part of the current increase may be prevented. The best value of the linearising resistance must be found empirically.

With the simple argon detector, the background current equivalent to the primary ionisation is usually about 10^{-8} amp, and the maximum current at which the response is approximately linear, using a linearising resistance, is about 10^{-7} amp. At currents greater than this, no single linearising resistance can maintain even approximate linearity at all vapour concentrations.

The ionisation efficiency of the simple argon detector is about 0.1%.

(d) Effects of Geometry and Space Charge; Micro-Argon Detector

In the case that the anode is small compared to the cathode, as in a cell which consists of a small anode placed in a large cavity forming the cathode, the field in the neighbourhood of the anode is intense, and the field in the neighbourhood of the cathode is small. Positive ions moving slowly towards the cathode soon leave the intense field around the anode, and enter a region of small field, which will augment their natural sluggishness described in Section 9.2c. The result is that in these circumstances a strong space charge is formed around the cathode.

When a detector is constructed in this way, the space charge and the inhomogeneity of the field cause it to behave very differently from the simple detector. The first difference is that the field is only sufficiently intense to produce metastable atoms by collision with accelerated electrons

in the immediate neighbourhood of the small electrode, and since metastable ions produced in this manner vastly outnumber those produced by
collision with primary ionising radiation, the detector will only respond
to vapour in this region. Hence, however large the cell cavity, the effective
detector volume is located within a few diameters of the small electrode.
Such a detector has been described by Lovelock (59, 65), and may be
called the micro-argon detector.

A diagram of a micro-argon detector is given in Fig. 9.14. The central
electrode is hollow, and carries the gas to be analysed, which is thus deliv-

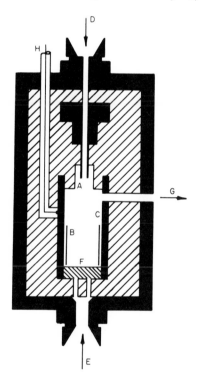

FIG. 9.14. Micro-argon detector. After Wiseman (68). A, Anode; B, radiation
source; C, cathode; D, inlet from column; E, inlet for scavenger gas; F, baffle for
scavenger gas; G, common outlet; H, insulated lead to cathode.

ered straight into the region of high field. In order to prevent back–diffusion
of vapour already recorded from the main volume of the cell into the
effective region around the small electrode, vapour leaving this region is
at once swept out of the cell by an auxiliary stream of carrier gas, conventionally referred to as the *scavenger* gas. It is found in practice that the

flow of scavenger gas must be laminar throughout the cell, and it is necessary to distribute the flow of incoming gas by means of some kind of baffle, e.g., of gauze, as shown in the figure.

The performance of the micro-argon detector is modified in other ways also. In the case that the central electrode is the anode, an increase in the current causes a change in the space charge, such that there is a decrease in the field immediately around the anode. This cause reduction in ion multiplication. Thus, the space charge fulfills the same purpose as a linearising resistance, and, if the geometry of the space charge is correct, then no such external resistance is required. Lovelock has found that the relation of the space charge to the anode can be easily controlled in a cell consisting of coaxial cylindrical electrodes by moving the central anode in and out of the cell along its axis. It is found in practice that the space charge is such as to give linearity if the end of the anode is several millimetres beyond the end of the cathode and well away from the source of radiation, as shown. Since the linearity depends on the space charge, the magnitude of which is a function of the primary ion concentration, it is necessary that the standing ion current be maintained at a sufficient value. In practice, with cells of the order of 1 to 10 cc total volume, a current of not less than 10^{-8} amp is necessary.

The small effective volume of the micro-argon detector recommends its use for capillary columns, where not only great sensitivity but also small detector volume is required. In another modification, the "Triode Detector" (65), a third electrode in the form of a ring coaxial with the other two inside the cavity serves to collect the positive ions produced from reaction of vapour molecules with excited argon atoms, but nothing else, so that there is little or no background current when there is no vapour present.

The ionisation efficiency of the micro-argon detector is larger than that of the simple argon detector, and may be as great as 1% (65).

(e) Sensitivity and Noise

The response is essentially change in the current through the cell, and we may consider sensitivity in terms of this. As with the cross-section detector, the minimum noise level is determined by random fluctuations in the current caused by the discontinuous nature of the radiation so that, for example, with sources of ≈ 10 mcoulombs and a time constant of 1 sec, the noise is $\approx 0.005\%$ of the total (see Section 9.5). The difference between the argon detector and the cross-section detector, however, is that the change in current produced by the same concentration of vapour is very much greater, so that, though the noise is the same, the signal-to-noise ratio is much greater. With the cross-section detector, a concentration of 1 part in 10,000 of, for example, n-butane in argon would cause a proportional increase of:

$$10^{-4} \times \frac{10.9 + 23.1}{10.9} = 0.031\%,$$

in the current (figures from Table 9.2). With the argon detector, the corresponding percentage increase would be of the order of 10 to 100%, depending on the applied voltage (see, for example, the percentage increases in current caused by methanol given in Fig. 9.13).

Simple argon detectors, the effective volume of which is that of the whole cavity, give a response proportional to concentration, and thus sensitivity is expressible as the minimum detectable concentration. Lovelock (65) quotes a figure of 4×10^{-11} g/ml, which, for a substance of molecular weight of 100 is a mole fraction of 10^{-8}. Condon et al. (3) quote a figure of 1.5×10^{-10} g/ml for a signal-to-noise ratio of 2 : 1 for propane. A very rough guide is that one molecule of vapour per million of argon produces $\approx 1\%$ increase in current in a normally operating detector.

With micro-argon detectors, in which the column effluent flows from a small anode (Fig. 9.14), the response is proportional to the mass flow rate. Lovelock (65) quotes a figure minimum detectable rate of vapour flow of 4×10^{-13} g/sec for a detector such as shown in Fig. 9.14, and 2×10^{-14} g/sec for the triode detector. These figures may be converted into the equivalent concentrations in grams per millilitre by dividing by the flow rate in millilitres per second. Using Lovelock's figures, this gives 1.2×10^{-12} and 6×10^{-14} g/ml for the cases quoted above.

It will be appreciated that these sensitivities are very great indeed.

(f) Linearity

The argon detector operating with considerable electron excitation is essentially a non-linear detector, even though its non–linearity can be inhibited by a linearising resistance. However, though the threshold of concentration or mass-flow above which it is appreciably non-linear may be small, the great sensitivity of the detector is such that there may be a considerable dynamic range between this threshold and the limit of detection.

When vapour concentrations become large, reactions not considered in Section 9.2c become significant. In particular, the added vapour causes electrons to lose energy by inelastic collision as described in Section 9.2e with the result that there are fewer electrons with sufficient energy to cause the excitation (66, 67).

The result is that at comparatively large vapour concentrations the current reaches a maximum and at still greater concentrations it declines. Clearly, in the limiting case of 100% vapour, the current is determined by the ionisation cross section of the vapour alone, and electron multiplication by the field is absent. The kinetics of processes at large vapour concentration

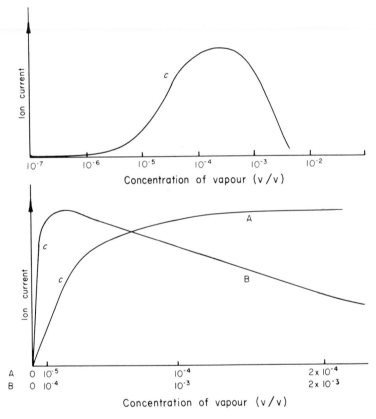

FIG. 9.15. Plot of ionisation current against concentration of butane in an argon detector, using large concentrations of butane. Wiseman (68). Point c indicates the upper concentration limit of approximate linearity. *Upper*: Traced from experimental record of response produced by vapour from an exponential dilution apparatus— logarithmic concentration scale. *Lower*: The same plotted on (A) large linear scale, (B) small linear scale.

is complicated, but the observation is commonplace. Figure 9.15 shows a plot of response against concentration of butane in argon, obtained by replotting the record obtained from an exponential dilution experiment on semi-log paper [Wiseman (*68*)].

In a detailed study of the detector at large vapour concentrations, Shahin and Lipsky (*63*) find that the mechanism described in Section 9.8c (Penning mechanism) is substantially correct up to vapour concentrations of about 3×10^{-4} M, but that other mechanisms become dominant at greater concentrations. This is consistent with Lovelock's finding (*65*) that linearity is adequate up to a concentration of about 5×10^{-4} M. With an ultimate limit of detection of about 10^{-8} mole fraction, this gives a useful dynamic range of between 10^4 and 10^5.

(g) *Effect of Contamination*

One of the most serious drawbacks to argon detectors is that their sensitivity may become very poor when the carrier gas is contaminated with traces of other gases. The commonest and most serious of these are water and carbon dioxide. Figure 9.16 shows the effect of various contaminants on the sensitivity as a function of mole fraction. It is seen that an increase in water concentration from about 30 ppm to 1000 ppm causes a ten-fold diminution in sensitivity. Similar figures are reported by Hill and Newell (*69*). The result is that water and other contaminants must be rigorously removed from gases feeding into argon detectors.

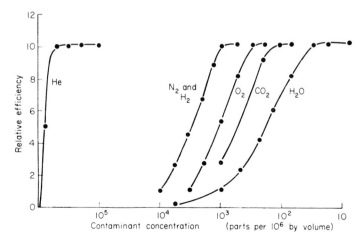

F<small>IG</small>. 9.16. Plot of the effect of contaminant gases in argon on the sensitivity of a simple argon detector [Lovelock (*59*)].

(h) Calibration

Since the effect of vapour molecules is exercised as the result of their collisions with excited atoms, it has been considered that the response given by a particular molecule is proportional to the frequency of collisions, which is a function of the sizes and relative velocity of excited argon atoms and vapour molecules (58). With vapours of molecular weight greater than about 100 whose molecules are largely paraffinic, it is found that molar sensitivities are proportional to molecular weight, so that weight sensitivities are more or less constant. With lighter molecules, this relation breaks down. Fair agreement has been obtained between practice and results derived by calculation of collision frequencies, but compounds such as aromatics completely fail to fit.

(i) Range of Application

The detector will give a sensitive response only to substances which can be ionised by excited molecules. When argon is the carrier gas, this includes nearly all organic compounds and many inorganic compounds, but excludes the following: H_2, N_2, O_2, CO_2, CO, $(CN)_2$, H_2O, CH_4, fluorocarbons, nitriles. These compounds give weak responses in an argon detector operating at least partially as a cross-section detector (66, 70, 71), but linearity and performance are unreliable. In addition to these, other compounds with large electron affinity may fail to give normal responses, but much depends on the exact design of the cell.

If helium is used as carrier gas, then all the above gases may be detected and measured with the characteristic great sensitivity, but the use of helium is restricted by the necessity for excessive purity, as described below.

Willis (72) has described a device by which argon detectors using argon may be used to detect permanent gases. In this, the argon is mixed with a constant trace quantity of an organic vapour, e.g., 1 in 10^6 part of ethylene, which causes a considerable increase in the cell current. When a trace quantity of permanent gas is introduced, the current produced by the ionisation of the ethylene falls, thus giving a measurable response to the inert gas. This device enables the argon detector to be used for as little as 0.5 ppm of hydrogen, oxygen, or methane. This adaptation of the argon detector probably operates largely on account of the mechanism mentioned in Section 9.3e. Addition of a permanent molecular gas causes a drop in the proportion of electrons sufficiently excited by the field to produce metastable argon atoms, with the result that fewer ionised ethylene molecules are produced, and hence the current is reduced.

(j) The Use of Helium in Argon Detectors

It is apparent from the figures of Table 9.4 that though excited argon atoms cannot ionise the molecules of permanent gases, those of helium can do so, and indeed, excited helium atoms have sufficient energy to ionise every other molecular species. This suggests the use of helium rather than argon in argon detectors. It is in fact possible to use helium, but its use involves much more difficulty. The basic reason for this is that the complications which cause argon detectors to fail at large vapour concentrations occur at much lower concentrations when helium is used as carrier gas. Thus, whereas the maximum allowable concentration of vapours in argon is about 100 to 500 ppm (see Sections 9.8c, 9.8f), the corresponding figures for helium are much smaller, probably of the order of 10 ppm or less. Furthermore, whereas the air gases do not have a very profound effect on the operation of the detector using argon except at rather large concentrations (Fig. 9.16), in helium, the air gases are ionised, and any appreciable concentration will cause the detector to become overloaded. The net result is that helium may only be used if *extremely* careful precautions are taken to purify it. If the necessary care is taken, helium can indeed be used in the detector to measure permanent gases, e.g., proportions of oxygen down to 0.03 ppm (73, 74).

9.9. OTHER IONISATION DETECTORS

Several other detectors depending on the modification of currents of ions by vapours have been described.

Ryce and Bryce (75, 76) showed that an ordinary triode ionisation gauge such as is used to measure vacuum can be used as a detector. In the apparatus, the column effluent leaks into the gauge through a fine constriction, and the far side of the gauge is pumped, preserving a pressure of about 1 mm in the gauge. The gauge has the three electrodes of the triode valve. In operation as a GC detector, the grid is set at about +18 V and the plate at about −20 V relative to the heated filament, and helium is used as the carrier gas. In this state, the potential on the grid is insufficient to ionise the helium, so no positive ions are attracted to the plate. As soon as a vapour appears, however, the potential fall of 18 V is sufficient to produce ions, which are thus attracted to the plate and produce a current. Some attention has been given to the improvement of the design (77), and the detector is capable of considerable sensitivity. However, its routine use is small, presumably because of the necessity to operate it at reduced pressure.

Several detectors have been described in which the current in a glow discharge is modified by the presence of vapour. Thus, the voltage across an ordinary discharge tube such as is used in voltage regulators operated at between 0.1 and 10 mm is altered by the presence of contaminant gases (78–81). By using a radiofrequency discharge, rather than a DC discharge, a discharge detector may be operated at atmospheric pressure (82).

REFERENCES

1. Townsend, J. S., "Electrons in Gases," Hutchinson, London, 1947.
2. von Engel, A., "Ionized Gases," Oxford Univ. Press, London and New York, 1955.
3. Condon R. D., Scholly, P. R., and Averill, W., "Gas Chromatography 1960," Proceedings of the Third International Symposium (R. P. W. Scott, ed.), p. 30. Academic Press, New York, 1960.
4. Harley, J., Nel, W., and Pretorius, V., Nature **181**, 177 (1958).
5. McWilliam, I. G., and Dewar, R. A., Nature **181**, 760 (1958).
6. McWilliam, I. G., and Dewar, R. A., in "Gas Chromatography 1958," Proceedings of the Second Symposium, Amsterdam, May, 1958 (D. H. Desty, ed.), p. 142 ff. Academic Press, New York, 1958.
7. Thompson, A. E., J. Chromatog. **2**, 148 (1959).
8. Ettre, L. S., and Claudy, H. N., Symposium on Gas Chromatography, Chemical Institute of Canada, Toronto, February, 1960.
9. Andreatch, A. G., and Feinland, R., Pittsburgh Conference on Analytical Chemistry, etc., March, 1960.
10. Arndt, R. R., Nel, W. J., and Pretorius, V., J. S. African Chem. Inst. **12**, 62 (1959).
11. Ongkiehong, L., "Gas Chromatography 1960," Proceedings of the Third International Symposium (R. P. W. Scott, ed.), p. 7. Academic Press, New York, 1961.
12. Desty, D. H., Geach, C. J., and Goldup, A., "Gas Chromatography 1960," Proceedings of the Third International Symposium (R. P. W. Scott, ed.), p. 46. Academic Press, New York, 1961.
13. Stern, O., see Levis, B., and von Elbe, G., "Combustion Flames and Explosions," 2nd ed., p. 558. Academic Press, New York 1961.
14. Calcote, H. F., Combust. Flame **1**, 385 (1957).
15. Calcote, H. F., and King, I. R., Fifth International Symposium, p. 423. Reinhold, New York, 1955.
16. Sternberg, J. C., Gallaway, W. S., and Jones, D. T. L., "Gas Chromatography," Proceedings of the Instrument Society of America Symposium, June 1961 (J. Brenner, J. E. Callen, and M. D. Weiss, eds.), p. 231. Academic Press, New York, 1962.
17. von Engel, A. and Cozens, J. R., Nature **202**, 480 (1964).
18. Bruderreck, H., Schneider, W., and Halasz, I., Anal. Chem. **36**, 461 (1964).
19. Novak, J., and Janak, J., J. Chromatog. **4**, 249 (1960).

20. Karmen, A., *J. Gas Chromatog.* **3**, 181 (1965).
21. Batt, L., and Cruickshank, F. R., *J. Chromatog.* **21**, 296 (1966).
22. Ettre, L. S., *J. Chromatog.* **8**, 525 (1962).
23. Perkins, G. *et al.*, "Gas Chromatography," Proceedings of the Instrument Society of America Symposium, June 1961. (N. Brenner, J. E. Callen, and M. D. Weiss, eds.), p. 269. Academic Press, New York, 1962.
24. Ettre, L. S., "Gas Chromatography," *ibid.* p. 307.
25. Ackman, R. G., and Sipos, J. C., *J. Chromatog.* **16**, 298 (1964).
26. Ackman, R. G., *J. Gas Chromatog.* **2**, 173 (1964).
27. Ackman, R. G., *J. Gas Chromatog.* **6**, 497 (1968).
28. Cincotta, J. J., and Feinland, R., *Anal. Chem.* **36**, 48 (1964).
29. Hill, D. W., and Newell, H. A., *Nature*, **206**, 708 (1965).
30. Garzo G., and Fritz, D., "Gas Chromatography 1966," Proceedings of the Sixth International Symposium (A. B. Littlewood, ed.), p. 150. Institute of Petroleum, London, 1967.
31. Lengyel, B., Garzo, G., Fritz, D., and Till, F., *J. Chromatog.* **24**, 8 (1966).
32. Somov, A. P., and Zhukhovitski, A. A., *Zavodsk. Lab.* **31**, 1442 (1965).
33. Karmen, A., and Giuffrida, L., *Nature*, **207**, 1204 (1964).
34. Karmen, A., *Anal. Chem.*, **36**, 1416 (1964).
35. Giuffrida, L., Ives, N. F., and Bostwick, D. C., *J. Assoc. Anal. Chemists*, **49**, 8 (1966).
36. Karmen, A., *J. Gas Chromatog.* **3**, 336 (1965).
37. Janak, J., and Svojanovsky, V., "Gas Chromatography 1966," Proceedings of the Sixth International Symposium, (A. B. Littlewood, ed.), p. 166. Institute of Petroleum, London, 1967.
38. Hine, G. J., and Brownell, G. L., "Radiation Dosimetry," p. 106. Academic Press, New York, 1956.
39. Boer, H., *in* "Vapour Phase Chromatography," Proceedings of the First Symposium, London, May, 1956 (D. H. Desty, ed.), p. 169 ff. Academic Press, New York, 1957.
40. Deal, C. H., Otvos, J. W., Smith, V. N., and Zucco, P. S., 129th Am. Chem. Soc. Meeting, Dallas, Texas, April, 1956.
41. Deal, C. H., Otvos, J. W., Smith, V. N., and Zucco, P. S., *Anal. Chem.* **28**, 1958 (1956).
42. Otvos, J. W., and Stevenson, D. P., *J. Am. Chem. Soc.* **78**, 546 (1956).
43. Simmons, P. G., and Lovelock, J. E., *Anal. Chem.* **35**, 1345 (1963).
44. Lovelock, J. E., Shoemake, G. R., and Zlatkis, A., *Anal. Chem.* **36**, 1410 (1964).
45. Lovelock, J. E., and Lipsky, S. R., *J. Am. Chem. Soc.* **82**, 431 (1960).
46. Lovelock, J. E., *Anal. Chem.* **35**, 474 (1963).
47. Simmonds, P. G., Fenimore, D. C., Pettitt, B. C., Lovelock, J. E., and Zlatkis, A., *Anal. Chem.* **39**, 1428 (1967).
48. Wentworth, W. E., Chen, E., and Lovelock, J. E., *J. Phys. Chem.* **70**, 445 (1966).
49. Devaux, P., and Guiochon, G., *J. Gas Chromatog.* **5**, 341 (1967).
50. Lovelock, J. E., "Gas Chromatography 1968," Proceedings of the Seventh International Symposium (C. L. A. Harboum, ed.), p. 95. Institute of Petroleum, London, 1969.

51. Lovelock, J. E., and Gregory, N. L., "Gas Chromatography," Proceedings of the Instrument Society of America Symposium, June 1961. (N. Brenner, J. E. Callen, and M. D. Weiss, eds.), p. 219. Academic Press, New York, 1962.

52. Wentworth, W. E., and Chen, E., *J. Gas Chromatog.* **5**, 170 (1967).

53. Zielinski, W. L., Fishbein, L., and Thomas, R. O., *J. Chromatog.* **30**, 77 (1967).

54. Clemons, C. A., and Altshuller, A. P., *Anal. Chem.* **38**, 133 (1966).

55. Zielinski, W. L., Fishbein, L., and Martin, L., *J. Gas Chromatog.* **5**, 553 (1967).

56. Lovelock, J. E., *Nature* **187**, 49 (1960).

57. Smith, V. N., and Fidiam, J. F., *Anal. Chem.* **36**, 1739 (1964).

58. Lovelock, J. E., *J. Chromatog.* **1**, 35 (1958).

59. Lovelock, J. E., *Nature* **182**, 1663 (1958).

60. Jesse, W. P., and Sadauskis, J., *Phys. Rev.* **100**, 1755 (1955).

61. Collinson, A. J. L., Bennett, J. R., and Hill, D. W., *Brit. J. Appl. Phys.* **16**, 631 (1965).

62. Knapp, J. Z., and Meyer, A. S., *Anal. Chem.* **36**, 1430 (1964).

63. Shahin, M. M., and Lipsky, S. R., *Anal. Chem.* **65**, 1562 (1963).

64. Lovelock, J. E., James, A. T., and Piper, E. A., *Ann. N. Y. Acad. Sci.* **72**, 720 (1959).

65. Lovelock, J. E., "Gas Chromatography 1960," Proceedings of the Third International Symposium (R. P. W. Scott, ed.), p. 16. Academic Press, New York, 1961.

66. Hill, D. W., and Newall, H. A., *J. Chromatog.* **32**, 737 (1968).

67. Collenson, E., Todd, J. F. J., and Wilkinson, F., *Nature* **206**, 394 (1965).

68. Wiseman, W. A., private communication, 1960.

69. Hill, D. W., and Newell, H. A., *Nature* **205**, 593 (1965).

70. Chmielowski, J., and Isaac, C. G., *Nature* **183**, 1120 (1959).

71. Graven, W. M., *Anal. Chem.* **31**, 1197 (1959).

72. Willis, V., *Nature* **184**, 894 (1959).

73. Bourke, P. J., and Dawson, R. W., *Nature* **211**, 409 (1966).

74. Bourke, P. J., Dawson, R. W., and Denton, W. H., *J. Chromatog.* **19**, 425 (1965).

75. Ryce, S. A., and Bryce, W. A., *Nature* **179**, 541 (1957).

76. Ryce, S. A., and Bryce, W. A., *Can. J. Chem.* **35**, 1293 (1957).

77. Hinkle, E. A., Tucker, H. C., Wall, R. F., and Combs, J. F., *in* "Gas Chromatography," 2nd International I.S.A. Symposium, June 1959 (H. J. Noebels, R. F. Wall, and N. Brenner, eds.), p. 55. Academic Press, New York, 1961.

78. Harley, J., and Pretorius, V., *Nature* **178**, 1244 (1957).

79. Pitkethly, R. C., 132 Am. Chem. Soc. Meeting, New York, September, 1957.

80. Pitkethly, R. C., *Anal. Chem.* **50**, 1309 (1958).

81. Basson, R. A., DeWet, C. R., Nel, W., and Pretorius, V., *J. S. African Chem. Inst.* **12**, 62 (1959).

82. Karmen, A., and Bowman, R. L., *Ann. N.Y. Acad. Sci.* **72**, 714 (1959).

Chapter 10

Thermal Conductivity Detectors

10.1. INTRODUCTION

The *Thermal Conductivity Detector,* or *Catharometer,** is designed to measure continuously the thermal conductivity of the column effluent. The catharometer and the flame ionisation detector are currently the most commonly used detectors in routine GC. The general advantages of the catharometer are simplicity, robustness, reliability, and generality of application. Its greatest drawback is that its concentration sensitivity is limited.

The instrument (Fig. 10.1) consists of a cavity, *A,* containing the gas of which the thermal conductivity is to be measured; in the continuous measurement of a flowing gas, the gas may go either through the cavity as shown, or past it, so that the cavity is fed by diffusion (Fig. 10.10). The walls of the cavity are held at a constant temperature, and the cavity contains an electrically heated *hot element, B,* of either metal or semi-conductor material. With a constant current in the hot element, the rate of production of heat is constant, and this heat must be dissipated, largely by conduction through the gas. The presence of a vapour changes the thermal conductivity of the gas, so that a different temperature gradient is necessary to maintain the required rate of dissipation, and therefore the hot element changes temperature. The temperature of the hot element is measured as if it were a resistance thermometer; change in temperature produces change in resistance, which is measured by including it as one arm of a Wheatstone's bridge circuit. It is almost universal practice to have two such cells forming adjacent arms of a Wheatstone's bridge, one

---

* The thermal conductivity cell was first introduced by Shakespear (*1*), who called it a "Katharometer," but in accord with modern practice in spelling words derived from the Greek κατα, it is spelt here with a "C."

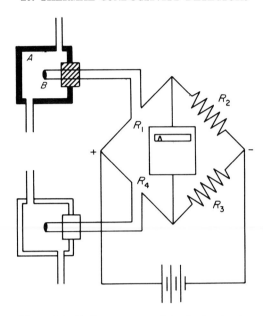

FIG. 10.1. Catharometer and its basic circuit.

carrying column effluent, and one carrying pure carrier gas; this procedure enables instrumental drift to be considerably reduced.

In most catharometers, the resistances of the hot elements and the other arms of the bridge are smaller than the maximum input impedance of potentiometric recorders, so that the galvanometer of the bridge may be replaced directly by such a recorder, and the continuous record of the out-of-balance emf of the bridge forms the chromatogram.

The catharometer was first used in gas chromatography by Claesson (2) in the early days of gas adsorption chromatography, and has been used regularly ever since. General accounts of catharometry are given in a book by Daynes (3) and in an article by Weaver (4).

10.2. THEORY OF CATHAROMETRY

The chain of events between the arrival of a vapour in the catharometer cell and the change in out-of-balance emf recorded on the meter may be regarded as a succession of four more or less independent relations:

(a) a relation between the concentration of vapour in the carrier gas and the change in thermal conductivity which it produces,

(b) a relation between the change in thermal conductivity and the change in temperature produced in the hot element,

(c) a relation between the change in temperature and the change in resistance of the hot element,

(d) a relation between the change in resistance of the hot element and the change in emf across the meter.

To a first approximation these may be considered independently, and the theory may be presented by giving equations for each and combining them. Of the four relations, (b), (c), and (d) may be worked out with complete accuracy; indeed, (c) is trivial. Relation (a), however, can be specified only approximately. We now consider the relations in turn.

(a) The Effect of a Vapour on the Thermal Conductivity of the Carrier Gas

This may be specified numerically by $\partial \lambda_{12}/\partial x_2$, where λ_{12} is the thermal conductivity of the mixture of carrier and vapour, and x_2 is mole fraction of vapour. In nearly all practical cases it is negative, so that presence of a vapour causes the hot element to become hotter. The study of the thermal conductivity of gases is a section of the study of gas transport properties, which also includes viscosity, diffusion, and thermal diffusion. This is part of the kinetic theory of gases and may be studied on two levels of sophistication, namely,

(1) elementary theory, using the concept of "Mean Free Path" of molecules between collisions and of fixed collision diameters, and ignoring all but head-on collisions,

(2) detailed theory based on the calculations of Chapman and of Enskog, for which the primary source is the book of Chapman and Cowling (5); other references include books by Hirschfelder et al. (6) and (as an introduction) Kennard (7).

Several formulae for $\partial \lambda_{12}/\partial x_2$ have been proposed, both as a result of experiment and by calculation. The simplest possible formula for the thermal conductivity of a binary mixture assumes a linear relation between thermal conductivity and mole fraction:

$$\lambda_{12} = x_1 \lambda_1 + x_2 \lambda_2 = \lambda_1 + x_2(\lambda_2 - \lambda_1), \qquad (10.1)$$

whence

$$\partial \lambda_{12}/\partial x_2 = \lambda_2 - \lambda_1, \qquad (10.2)$$

where

$\lambda_{12}, \lambda_1, \lambda_2$ are thermal conductivities of mixture, carrier, and vapour, respectively;

x_1, x_2 are mole fractions of carrier and vapour, respectively.

Such a relation has been assumed or implied by several authors on gas chromatographic catharometry, but it has no justification either in theory or in practice. It is possible to find binary mixtures for which it is approximately true, but this is coincidence. For mixtures of which the molecules have different weights, shapes, and sizes, as in gas chromatographic catharometry, Eq. (10.2) is not even approximately true.

An equation for the thermal conductivity of binary mixtures based on elementary kinetic theory has been given by Wassiljewa (8), and has been used by Lindsay and Bromley (9), Hoffmann (10), and others:

$$\lambda_{12} = \frac{\lambda_1}{1 + A(x_2/x_1)} + \frac{\lambda_2}{1 + B(x_1/x_2)}, \qquad (10.3)$$

where

$$A = \left(\frac{\sigma_1 + \sigma_2}{2\sigma_1}\right)^2 \left(\frac{M_1 + M_2}{2M_2}\right)^{1/2}, \qquad (10.3a)$$

$$B = \left(\frac{\sigma_1 + \sigma_2}{2\sigma_2}\right)^2 \left(\frac{M_1 + M_2}{2M_1}\right)^{1/2}, \qquad (10.3b)$$

where

σ_1, σ_2 are molecular diameters of carrier gas and vapour molecules, respectively;

M_1, M_2 are molecular weights of carrier gas and vapour, respectively.

These equations are moderately successful in satisfying experimental data; and at least they give the extreme points which are often observed in plots of experimental thermal conductivities against molar composition. If A and B in Eq. (10.3) are regarded as parameters and are fitted to experimental values, a good fit is obtained (i.e., small least-squares residues), but the values of A and B obtained are not in accord with Eqs. (10.3a) and (10.3b). Thus, it is legitimate to regard Eq. (10.3) as an adequate two-parameter equation to fit the facts; but the calculation of A and B by Eqs. (10.3a) and (10.3b) has little value except as a general guide.

As applied to gas-chromatographic catharometry, Eq. (10.3) can be simplified by assuming that x_2 is always small, and x_1 is approximately unity. In this case:

$$\lambda_{12} \approx \frac{\lambda_1}{1 + Ax_2} + \frac{\lambda_2}{1 + B/x_2} \approx \lambda_1(1 - Ax_2) + \frac{\lambda_2 x_2}{B}, \quad (10.4)$$

and

$$\frac{\partial \lambda_{12}}{\partial x_2} = \frac{\lambda_2}{B} - A\lambda_1, \quad (10.5)$$

where A and B are to be regarded as arbitrary constants of the order of unity. This equation has no quantitative use, but it is interesting in that it is consistent with the frequent observation that, when using heavy carrier gases, even though $\lambda_2 < \lambda_1$, $\partial \lambda_{12}/\partial x_2$ is positive, resulting in cooling of the hot element and thus producing a reversed peak. In such a case, B is sufficiently small that the first term of Eq. (10.5) exceeds the second.

In the case of heavy carrier gases, elementary theory can go no further without becoming grossly inaccurate, and, to date, detailed theory can provide no manageable equations for the thermal conductivity of mixtures of complex molecules. In the case of vapours in nitrogen or in cases in which the mixture consists of vapours the molecules of which have comparable masses, e.g., helium and hydrogen, the plot of thermal conductivity against molar fraction of vapour often shows a maximum, and van der Craats (11) has shown that in at least one case, acetylene in nitrogen, the maximum occurs at the remarkably small vapour concentration of 4%.

In the case of light carrier gases, Littlewood (12), Luy (13) and Mecke and Zirker (14) have proposed an application of the equations of the detailed theory which illustrates in a particularly simple way the mechanism of heat conduction in the type of binary mixture treated in gas-chromatographic catharometry. If, in the equations given by Chapman and Cowling (5) for the thermal conductivity of binary mixtures of gases not possessing internal degrees of freedom, it is assumed:

(1) that x_2 is small,
(2) that $M_2 \gg M_1$,
(3) that the molecules may be regarded as hard spheres,
(4) that the internal structure of vapour molecules has no effect on the validity of the equations other than possibly modifying the collision diameter,

then it can be shown that:

$$\frac{1}{\lambda_1} \frac{\partial \lambda_{12}}{\partial x_2} = -K \frac{\sigma_{12}^2}{\sigma_1^2}, \quad (10.6)$$

where K is a constant and $\sigma_{12} = (\sigma_1 + \sigma_2)/2$. This equation should be true to within a few per cent so long as $M_2 > 20M_1$, and the approximations are valid when helium is used as carrier gas. It illustrates how the vapour acts in changing the thermal conductivity of the carrier. The vapour molecules are large, heavy, and slow, whereas those of the carrier gas are small, light, and fast. Virtually all the heat is carried by the carrier molecules, and the vapour molecules act merely by getting in the way. The fact that they obstruct and thus reduce the thermal conductivity is expressed by the minus sign; the extent of their obstruction is proportional to their effective cross-sectional area, which is $x_2 \sigma_{12}^2$.

For hard sphere molecules, Littlewood finds that $K = 2.30$. Hoffmann (10) has obtained an equation of form similar to that of Eq. (10.6) by applying assumptions (1) and (2), together with the necessary result that $\lambda_1 > \lambda_2$, to Eq. (10.5); the difference is that the constant comes to $1/\sqrt{2}$ rather than 2.30. Similar equations are also given by Kebbekus et al. (15).

(b) The Effect of Thermal Conductivity on the Temperature of the Hot Element

The temperature distribution of the gas in the cell cavity satisfies the steady-state equation for the conduction of heat,

$$\text{div}(\lambda \text{ grad } T) = 0. \tag{10.7}$$

In catharometry, it is probably adequate to assume that λ is independent of temperature if the hot element is not too hot, in which case Eq. (10.7) becomes Laplace's equation:

$$\nabla^2 T = 0. \tag{10.8}$$

In catharometry, the surfaces of the hot element and of the walls of the cavity should each be isothermal. Thus, if T_1 and T_2 are the temperatures of, and $T'(\tau) = 0$ and $T''(\tau) = 0$ are the equations of the surfaces of the walls and hot element, respectively, where τ represents spatial coordinates, the boundary conditions are:

$$\begin{aligned} T &= T_1 &&\text{for} && T'(\tau) = 0 \\ T &= T_2 &&\text{for} && T''(\tau) = 0. \end{aligned} \tag{10.9}$$

Solutions of Eqs. (10.8) and (10.9) have been extensively studied for many sets of boundary conditions in connection with many kinds of problem.

General methods of solution may be found in texts on partial differential equations, e.g., (*16*), or in texts on any subject in which Laplace's equation is relevant, e.g., electrostatics.

We observe below a general consequence of Eqs. (10.8) and (10.9). If T satisfies Eq. (10.8), then

$$\varphi \equiv (T - T_1)/(T_2 - T_1) \tag{10.10}$$

also satisfies Eq. (10.8), since T_1 and $T_2 - T_1$ are both constants. In terms of φ, the boundary conditions (10.9) become $\varphi = 0$ and $\varphi = 1$, which are independent of T_1 and T_2. Hence, Eqs. (10.8) and (10.9) may be solved to give $(T - T_1)/(T_2 - T_1)$ as a function of the spatial coordinates only, so that at every point in the cavity, $(T - T_1) \propto (T_2 - T_1)$.

In catharometry, the quantity of interest is T_2, and there is the additional condition that the total heat flux through any surface surrounding the hot element is determined by the electrical input. If the resistance of, and the current in, the hot element are R and I, respectively, the total heat flux is I^2R/J, where J is Joule's constant. One may now derive a significant general equation [Eq. (10.15)] for T_2 in terms of the heat flux and the thermal conductivity. If the heat flux at any point in the cavity is $\mathbf{H}$, then, by definition of thermal conductivity,

$$-\lambda \operatorname{grad} T = \mathbf{H}. \tag{10.11}$$

Also

$$\int_s \mathbf{H} \cdot d\mathbf{s} = \frac{I^2R}{J}, \tag{10.12}$$

where the integration is over a surface including the hot element. Hence

$$-\int_s \operatorname{grad} T \cdot d\mathbf{s} = \frac{I^2R}{J\lambda}. \tag{10.13}$$

But,

$$\operatorname{grad} T = \operatorname{grad}(T - T_1)$$
$$= (T_2 - T_1) \operatorname{grad} \frac{T - T_1}{T_2 - T_1} = (T_2 - T_1) \operatorname{grad} \varphi. \tag{10.14}$$

Hence,

$$T_2 - T_1 = I^2R/J\lambda G, \tag{10.15}$$

where

$$G = -\int_s \operatorname{grad} \varphi \cdot d\mathbf{s}, \tag{10.16}$$

and is a function of the geometry of the cavity and hot element only.

The function G may be calculated from the geometry of the cell, though the calculation is complex except for simple geometries. Its form for two particularly common cases is given below:

(1) The hot element is a wire of radius r_2 and length l situated coaxially in a tube of radius r_1:

$$G = 2\pi l / \ln \frac{r_1}{r_2}.$$ (10.17)

(2) The hot element is a sphere of radius r_2 situated concentrically in a spherical cavity of radius r_1:

$$G = \frac{4\pi r_1 r_2}{r_1 - r_2}.$$ (10.18)

A significant approximate generalisation may be made from case (2). When $r_1 \gg r_2$, Eq. (10.18) becomes $G \approx 4\pi r_2$, which is independent of r_1. Thus, if a roughly spherical hot element is small compared with the cavity, the exact shape of the cavity does not much affect the sensitivity of the cell. The physical explanation of this is that, if the heat source is small, the temperature gradient is large only in its immediate neighbourhood.

The required effect of change in λ on T_2 is obtained by differentiation of Eq. (10.15) with respect to λ:

$$\frac{\partial T_2}{\partial \lambda} = -\frac{I^2 R}{J G \lambda^2}.$$ (10.19)

This equation was given (in effect) by Ray (17).

The above discussion is sometimes complicated in practice by the dissipation of heat other than by conduction. Other possible sources of heat loss are, in approximate order of magnitude:

(1) loss through mass-transfer, in which hot gas in the neighbourhood of the hot element is swept out in the gas stream (18),

(2) loss through thermal conduction in the support of the hot element (3, 19, 20),

(3) loss through convection,

(4) loss through radiation.

To discuss these quantitatively, a heat balance equation may be set up, with the heat input, $I^2 R / J$, on one side, and the sum of all sources of heat loss on the other. Application of Stefan's law shows that at temperatures at least as high as 200°C, radiation contributes less than 0.1% to the total heat dissipation. According to Daynes (3), convection is negligible in cavities smaller than about 1 cm linear dimensions. Snowden and Eanes (20) report that there is no difference in the power input required to maintain a given temperature in a wire axially placed in a tube of 5 mm diameter whether the tube is vertical or horizontal, thus showing that no appreciable heat is lost by convection. There is the possibility, however, that very slight convection may produce significant noise.

Losses from the first two factors given above may be serious, and have been considered in detail.

Bohemen and Purnell (18) have considered the effect of heat loss through mass-transfer in the case of a cell consisting of a heated wire situated axially in a glass tube carrying the column effluent, so that a certain proportion of the heat from the wire is carried out of the cell, and thus is not conducted to the walls of the tube. The heat balance equation in this case is:

$$I^2R/J = G\lambda(T_2 - T_1) + \dot{V}'C_p\varDelta T' + S, \qquad (10.20)$$

where

G is given by Eq. (10.16), and in addition to symbols already used,

$\dot{V}'$ is molar flow rate (moles/second) $= 237\dot{V}/22{,}400T$ cc/sec,

C_p is molar specific heat of carrier gas,

$\varDelta T'$ is average temperature difference between entering and departing gas,

S is other sources of heat loss not depending on V', including end effects, free convection, and radiation.

The importance of this equation is that when a vapour enters the cell, not only does λ change, but also C_p changes, so that in cases where the second term of the equation is comparable with the first, the final expression for the response will include the term $\partial C_p/\partial x_2$ in addition to $\partial\lambda_{12}/\partial x_2$. With cells in which the hot element is not in the gas path, there is no doubt that the second term in Eq. (10.20) is negligible, but Bohemen and Purnell conclude that, in the case they consider, the second term may be of the same order of magnitude as the first.

We now derive an equation [Eq. (10.23)] which will demonstrate the effect of heat losses other than thermal conduction on the response of the above design of cell. The response is proportional to the quantity dT_2/dx_2; in the absence of terms other than those due to thermal conduction in the heat balance equation, and assuming the independence of relations (a) and (b) given at the beginning of this section, this is given by the simple product $(dT_2/d\lambda_{12}) \cdot (d\lambda_{12}/dx_2)$. In this case, however, T_2 is a function of both λ_{12} and C_p, so that:

$$\frac{dT_2}{dx_2} = \frac{\partial T_2}{\partial \lambda_{12}} \frac{d\lambda_{12}}{dx_2} + \frac{\partial T_2}{\partial C_p} \frac{dC_p}{dx_2}. \tag{10.21}$$

The quantity $\Delta T'$ is also a function of T_2; Bohemen and Purnell assume that $\Delta T'$ is the difference between the temperature, T_1, of the entering gas and the average temperature of the distribution across the tube as given by Eqs. (10.8) and (10.9), from which:

$$\Delta T' = (T_2 - T_1)/2\ln(r_2/r_1). \tag{10.22}$$

Assuming this, substitution of Eq. (10.20) into Eq. (10.21) yields:

$$\frac{dT_2}{dx_2} = \frac{-1}{G\left(\lambda_{12} + \dfrac{\dot{V}'C_p}{4\pi l}\right)^2} \left[\frac{I^2R}{J} - S\right]\left[\frac{d\lambda_{12}}{dx_2} + \frac{\dot{V}'}{4\pi l} \frac{dC_p}{dx_2}\right]. \tag{10.23}$$

This equation largely summarises the effect of the important forms of heat loss other than thermal conduction. The first square bracket shows that the end losses S have no other effect than to subtract from the effective power input to the cell. The relative importance of thermal conduction and mass-transfer in producing the response is given by the comparative size of the terms in the second square bracket. The greater $\dot{V}'$, or the smaller l, the larger the effect of mass-transfer. In practice, $d\lambda_{12}/dx_2$ is normally negative, as already discussed, but dC_p/dx_2 is normally positive, so that the two terms tend to cancel rather than to reinforce. The effect of the mass-transfer terms on linearity will be considered in Section 10.7.

The relative contributions of thermal conduction through the gas, thermal conduction through the supports, and radiation have been determined by Snowden and Eanes (20) for a diffusion-fed cell, in which the mass-transfer effect is absent (Fig. 10.2). They have plotted the temperature of the hot element against power input, both in the presence of a carrier gas (curve A) and in a vacuum so that the gas conductivity is zero (curve B). In the former case, heat is lost by gas conduction, end losses, and radiation; in the latter case, by end losses and radiation only. At low temperatures, the loss by radiation is negligible, so the initial slope of the plot obtained in vacuo gives the end losses, which are assumed to be a linear function of the power input (curve C). The method of plotting results in four lines including the vertical axis, the horizontal distances between

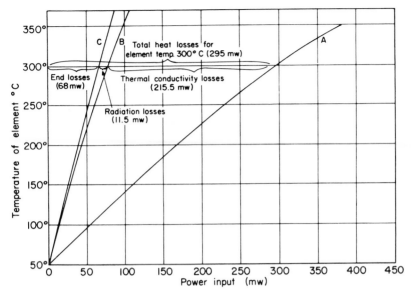

FIG. 10.2. Diagram by Snowden and Eanes (20) illustrating relative sizes of heat losses due to conduction through the supports of the hot element (end losses), radiation, and thermal conduction. Cell envelope maintained at 50°C ± 0.02° in oil bath. Curve A, total heat losses expressed in terms of power input (mw) required to maintain the cell element at a given temperature; air flowing through cell at atmospheric pressure at the rate of 200 ml/minute. Curve B, heat losses with cell evacuated to 10^{-4} Torr represents sum of radiation and end losses. Curve C, tangent to curve B at element temperature of 50°C represents end losses.

adjacent pairs of which represent the proportions of heat lost by each of the three causes at any temperature of the hot element.

(c) Effect of the Temperature of the Hot Element on Its Resistance

The resistance of the hot element and its temperature are approximately connected by the familiar relation:

$$R = R_0(1 + \alpha T), \qquad (10.24)$$

where α is the temperature coefficient of resistance, and is tabulated for many substances in many sources (21). On differentiation, this gives:

$$\frac{1}{R_0} \frac{\partial R}{\partial T} = \alpha. \qquad (10.25)$$

The above equation may be used provided that the temperature difference of the hot element produced by a vapour is small. If this is not so, account should be taken of the fact that α is not independent of temperature over a large range; it usually changes of the order of 1% per °C, and, over large ranges, the change of resistance with temperature is normally expressed as a power series in T. It is not normal to operate catharometers in such a manner that this source of non-linearity is significant.

Thermistors have negative temperature coefficients of resistance in which the resistance falls exponentially with increase in temperature.

(d) Effect of the Resistance of the Hot Element on the Out-of-Balance EMF of the Wheatstone's Bridge

If the resistances of a Wheatstone's bridge are numbered as in Fig. 10.1, and, in addition, we specify the general scheme of symbols in the following manner:

E, I are emf across the bridge and the total current in it,

E_n, I_n, R_n ($n = 1, 2, 3, 4$, or g) are voltage across, current in, and resistance of R_1, R_2, R_3, R_4, or the galvanometer,

then application of Kirchhoff's laws gives the equation:

$$I_g = \frac{E(R_2R_4 - R_1R_3)}{R_1R_2R_3 + R_2R_3R_4 + R_3R_4R_1 + R_4R_1R_2 + R_g(R_1+R_2)(R_3+R_4)}. \quad (10.26)$$

In the usual case that the resistance of the meter is great compared with that of any of the arms, and that the meter responds to E_g rather than to I_g, then E_g is given by:

$$E_g = \frac{E(R_2R_4 - R_1R_3)}{(R_1 + R_2)(R_3 + R_4)}, \quad (10.27)$$

if R_g is assumed to be infinite.

In the latter case, the effect on E_g of a change in resistance of the hot element, which we assume to be R_1, is found by differentiating Eq. (10.27) with respect to R_1:

$$\frac{\partial E_g}{\partial R_1} = -\frac{ER_2}{(R_1 + R_2)^2}. \quad (10.28)$$

Of greater practical significance is the change in E_g for a given proportional change in R_1, i.e., $R_1 \, \partial E_g / \partial R_1$:

$$R_1 \frac{\partial E_g}{\partial R_1} = -\frac{ER_1R_2}{(R_1 + R_2)^2}. \quad (10.29)$$

Note that this equation is independent of R_3 and R_4, which merely serve to fix the potential of one side of the galvanometer. Thus Eq. (10.28) is true whether or not the bridge is in balance, and thus the sensitivity of a catharometer is not affected if, for example, the base-line is moved from zero to the other side of the galvanometer or recorder scale by adjustment of the "zero set." Bridges are normally run near their balance point for convenience.

In the special case that $R_1 = R_2 = R$, Eq. (10.28) becomes:

$$\frac{\partial E_g}{\partial R_1} = -\frac{E}{4R}. \tag{10.30}$$

If the sum $R_1 + R_2$ is constrained to be constant, so that the current through the hot element is constant, the ratio of R_1 to R_2 for which $R_1 \partial E_g/\partial R_1$ is a maximum is easily calculated by differentiation of Eq. (10.28), and the result is that the maximum in the response occurs when $R_1 = R_2$. The special case of Eq. (10.30), therefore, is commonly employed in practice.

(e) *Combination of the Four Relations (a) to (d) Discussed Above*

The preceding four subsections have provided a set of equations, (10.6), (10.19), (10.25), and (10.29), giving in turn:

$$\frac{\partial \lambda_{12}}{\partial x_2}, \quad \frac{\partial T_2}{\partial \lambda_{12}}, \quad \frac{\partial R_1}{\partial T_2}, \quad \frac{\partial E_g}{\partial R_1}.$$

If all these differentials are independent, all four may be multiplied together to give dE_g/dx_2, which is the reading of the recorder for a given vapour concentration in the cell. Hence, an equation for dE_g/dx_2 may be obtained by multiplying together the above four equations, giving:

$$\frac{dE_g}{dx_2} = -K \frac{\sigma_{12}^2}{\sigma_1^2} \cdot \frac{I^2 R_1}{J\lambda_1 G} \cdot \alpha \cdot \frac{ER_1 R_2}{(R_1 + R_2)^2}, \tag{10.31}$$

the symbols of which are all defined in the previous subsections, and the sign of which applies for the polarities given in Fig. 10.1. The units of this equation are *volts/mole-fraction*. By the transformation

$$E_g{}' = 1000 E_g, \qquad c_2 = (M_2/22.4)x_2,$$

where M_2 is the molecular weight of the vapour, they may be turned into mv cc/mg, which are the sensitivity units used by Dimbat et al. (22)

(Section 8.1). In this case, the sensitivity, S, is given by:

$$S = \frac{dE_g{'}}{dc_2} = -\frac{K'}{M_2} \cdot \frac{\sigma_{12}^2}{\sigma_1^2} \cdot \frac{I^2R}{J\lambda_1 G} \cdot \alpha \cdot \frac{ER_1R_2}{(R_1 + R_2)^2}, \qquad (10.32)$$

where K' is a composite constant. If $K = 2.30$ as described in Section 10.2b, $K' = 5.1 \times 10^4$.

All the quantities on the right-hand side of Eq. (10.32) are known and knowable, and thus, in principle, this equation provides for the *a priori* calibration of catharometers. All the arguments leading to the derivation of this equation have been given in the literature, and it is presented here as a convenient summary of the theory of catharometers. It is consistent with the behaviour of the sensitivity of catharometers with change of any of the variables contained in it, as is shown in later sections, and the value of the constant K', is reasonable, as may be shown by substituting typical figures.

There are several cross-terms resulting in the mutual dependence of the four relations considered at the beginning of this section. Such terms are given by:

(1) the temperature dependence of $\partial \lambda_{12}/\partial x_2$,

(2) the temperature dependence of α,

(3) the change in I_1 on account of the change in R_1,

(4) the change in R_1, which enters as constant in Eq. (10.19).

All such terms are small and may be neglected if the temperature change in the hot element is sufficiently small. In the case that they are not small, as when $T_2 - T_1$ is large, the catharometer becomes non-linear. The effect of such terms has not been considered in detail.

The temperature of the hot element, T_2, may be determined from Eq. (10.19), but in practice, T_2 is usually a more significant quantity than G, so that it is desirable to be able to measure T_2 without knowledge of G. This may be done by placing an ammeter in series with and a voltmeter in parallel with the hot element, R_1, and plotting E_1/I_1 against I_1, so as to give R_1 as a function of I_1. By extrapolating to $I_1 = 0$, R_1^0, the resistance of R_1 at $T_2 = T_1$ is obtained; at any given current I_1, T_2 is then given by:

$$T_2 - T_1 = (R_1 - R_1^0)/\alpha. \qquad (10.33)$$

From Eq. (10.15), $(T_2 - T_1)$ is proportional to I_1^2; this relation has been confirmed with considerable accuracy in experiments by Bohemen and Purnell (*18*), and by Harvey and Morgan (*23*). As described in the next section, Eq. (10.32) implies that the sensitivity of a catharometer is proportional to $I_1{}^3$. Hence the sensitivity is given by:

$$S \propto (T_2 - T_1)^{3/2}. \tag{10.34}$$

This relation was given by Wiseman (*24*), who has confirmed it in practice, using tungsten and platinum hot elements (*19*).

10.3. SENSITIVITY

According to the theory given in the last section, the sensitivity of a catharometer is given in mv cc/mg by Eq. (10.32), which may be made the basis for discussion. Until fairly recently, values of S of the order of 100 were considered average, but in fact values of the order of 10^4 may easily be attained (*25*). The sensitivity is determined by the quantities appearing in Eq. (10.32), which will be discussed in turn.

(a) Applied Voltage

According to Eq. (10.32), the sensitivity is proportional to E and to $I_1{}^2 R_1$. If the change in R_1 is small, $I_1{}^2 \propto E^2$, so that the sensitivity is proportional to E^3. This rule would be expected to apply if all other conditions remain constant. In particular, it should apply in the range of values of E within which the temperature of the hot element is only slightly greater than that of the walls, so that R_1 changes but little and no appreciable change occurs in the relation connecting thermal conductivity with composition. It does not apply with thermistors, for which R_1 changes very rapidly with I_1, except at extremely small currents.

Most experimental studies of the effect of applied voltage on sensitivity use conditions such that the temperature elevation of the hot wire is not small. This has two results; first, the resistance of the hot element changes appreciably, so that in the case of metal elements, for which α is positive, the wattage dissipation is less than proportional to E^2; second, the change in temperature on raising E is sufficient to cause a fall in the value of α. Both these factors operate to reduce the increase in sensitivity with applied voltage, so that in these conditions it is found that $S \propto E^x$, where x is less than 3. Mellor (*26*) presents graphs showing the rapid rise in sensitivity with increase in catharometer current. Harvey and Morgan (*23*) present results which show that, on doubling the current supplied to the bridge, the sensitivity increases by a factor of between 5.5 and 6.5, i.e., $2^{2.46}$ to $2^{2.70}$. In some extreme conditions, the sensitivity varies in a more complex manner with applied voltage, but these conditions are such that for other reasons they should not be used in quantitative gas chromatography. In cases where a heavy carrier gas, e.g., nitrogen, is used as a carrier, a large increase in applied voltage may even produce a reduction of sensitivity, as is shown by Mellor (26) and by Bohemen and Purnell (18).

The variation of the sensitivity of thermistor cells with applied voltage is complicated, and depends sharply on other variables, especially the carrier gas and the cell temperature. In general, at small applied voltages,

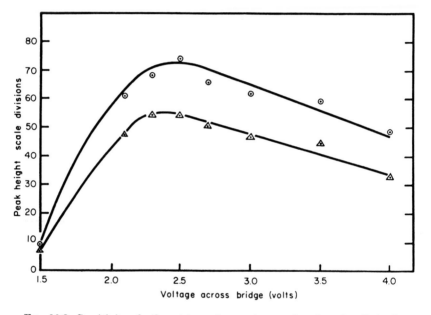

FIG. 10.3. Sensitivity of a thermistor catharometer as a function of applied voltage. Cowan and Stirling (27). Curves are for two different vapours in nitrogen as carrier gas.

the sensitivity rises sharply with increase in applied voltage, as it does for metal wires, but at a certain applied voltage the loss in sensitivity through reduction in R_1 balances the gain from increase in E, so that the sensitivity reaches a maximum; at greater applied voltages the sensitivity declines. This in shown by the results of Cowan and Stirling (27) (Fig. 10.3). The voltage of maximum sensitivity increases with increase in the thermal conductivity of the carrier gas.

(b) *Temperature Coefficient of Resistance*

The sensitivity of a catharometer is simply proportional to this quantity. Table 10.1 shows values of the temperature coefficients of resistance of a few common metals at room temperature. When other factors do not interfere, greatest sensitivity is provided by metals with large temperature coefficients, but the table shows that there is little to choose between

TABLE 10.1

TEMPERATURE COEFFICIENTS OF RESISTANCE OF COMMON METALS

Metal	Temperature (°C)	α (°C^{-1})
Copper	20	0.0039
Iron	20	0.0050
Nickel	20	0.006
Platinum	20	0.004
Tungsten	18	0.0045
Brass	18	0.001
Bronze	18	0.0005

several common metals. Platinum, tungsten, and nickel are all commonly used. Table 10.1 also shows that the temperature coefficients of resistance of alloys—not ones especially designed for the purpose—are much smaller than those of pure metals. This draws attention to the fact that the temperature coefficient of resistance of a metal may be considerably reduced by even a small proportion of impurity.

The temperature coefficients of thermistors may be as large as -0.1°C^{-1}. These coefficients are an order of magnitude larger than those for metals, and thus cells made with thermistors should be an order of magnitude more sensitive than those made with metal wires; as a result, a large number of designs of thermistor cells have been produced. In practice, however, thermistor cells do not always exhibit the expected advantage in sensitivity over cells with metal elements; the reason probably lies in the difference in the values of G as discussed in the next subsection. A further drawback is that the resistance of the hot element is halved for every 10 or 15°C rise in temperature. This causes a drop in the power dissipation with increase in temperature (see Section 10.3e), and also, since the resistance changes grossly with temperature, the Wheatstone's bridge can only operate efficiently over a very limited range of temperature. The result is that a cell which is sensitive at one temperature becomes much less sensitive at a higher temperature; furthermore, at a lower temperature its resistance becomes greater than the input impedance of the recorder, so that the latter may become sluggish. The conclusion is that the value of the temperature coefficient of resistance cannot be considered in isolation in the design of a sensitive catharometer.

(c) The Apparatus Constant, G

From Eq. (10.32), the sensitivity is inversely proportional to G, which is a positive function of the size of the hot element. Wiseman (19), for example, has shown that in the case of an axial wire, the sensitivity is proportional to the inverse fourth power of the wire radius. The above consideration, however, is generally insufficient, since for a given power dissipation, decrease in G causes an increase in the temperature of the hot element, which is undesirable. If the temperature of the hot element is constrained to be constant, Eq. (10.15) shows that $I_1 \propto G^{1/2}$. Under correct operating conditions, $S \propto I_1^3$. Thus, in the case that G is varied and I is adjusted so as to keep the hot element at a constant temperature,

$$S \propto I^3/G \propto G^{3/2}/G = G^{1/2}. \tag{10.35}$$

Hence, subject to the above constraint, the sensitivity increases with an increase in G, and thus increases the larger the hot element. The thermistors used in catharometry are usually very small so as not to be sluggish (Section 10.9a), and this above factor is probably partly responsible for the fact that their sensitivity is not as great as their large temperature coefficient would suggest. Equation (10.35) is implicit in the work of Cowan and Stirling (27), where it is considered in greater detail.

(d) Carrier Gas

The carrier gas can affect the catharometer sensitivity on account of the molecular quantities contributing to $\partial \lambda_{12}/\partial x_2$, and on account of the λ_1^2 of Eq. (10.19). Also, if the temperature of the hot element is constrained to be constant, the carrier gas affects the sensitivity on account of the changes in E and I necessitated by the constraint. We consider first the case of a cell in which all the quantities in Eq. (10.32) are constant other than the parameters of the carrier gas. As the thermal conductivity of the carrier gas *falls*, (1) the sensitivity rises on account of the λ_1^2 on the denominator of Eq. (10.32), (2) the sensitivity changes on account of change in

$\partial\lambda_{12}/\partial x_2$. The expression given in Eq. (10.6) holds only in the case of light carrier gases, and cannot be used in this discussion. In the catharometry of organic materials, the molecules of vapour are usually heavier and larger than those of the carrier. In general, therefore, the heavier the carrier gas, the more its molecules behave like the vapour molecules, and the smaller is $\partial\lambda_{12}/\partial x_2$. On this account, the heavier the carrier, the smaller the sensitivity.

Ray (17) has suggested that whereas according to (1) the sensitivity rises proportionally to $\lambda_1{}^2$ on decreasing the thermal conductivity of the carrier gas, it cannot fall faster than directly proportionally to λ_1 according to (2), so that the net sensitivity should rise with increasing molecular weight of carrier gas. This is confirmed with some vapours in helium and in argon. Ray's argument applies only to vapours which are considerably larger and heavier than the heaviest carrier gas considered. For vapours the molecular weight of which is close to that of the carrier, $\partial\lambda_{12}/\partial x_2$ may be quite small or even zero, and may change rapidly, with possible reversal of sign, as the concentration of vapour increases. In such cases, considerable variation of $\partial\lambda_{12}/\partial x_2$ may occur at mole fractions of vapour not much greater than 0.01.

In the case that the temperature of the hot element is constrained to be constant, considered by Schmauch and Dinerstein (28), Eden et al. (29), and Fredericks et al. (30), Eq. (10.15) requires that $I_1{}^2 R_1/J \propto \lambda_1$, so that, in place of the proportionality $\partial T_2/\partial\lambda_{12} \propto 1/\lambda_1{}^2$ considered above, Eq. (10.15) and the above condition yields $\partial T_2/\partial\lambda_{12} \propto 1/\lambda_1$. The above authors then find that on decreasing the value of λ_1, the sensitivity falls

TABLE 10.2

RELATIVE SENSITIVITIES OF A CATHAROMETER IN HELIUM AND NITROGEN, USING CONSTANT T_2

T_2	T_1	Solute	Response (mV) for $x_2 = 0.01$	
			Helium	Nitrogen
100	25	n-Hexane	21.2	2.20
100	25	Methanol	11.0	0.45
200	150	Benzene	9.9	0.29
200	150	Cyclohexane	10.8	0.20
200	150	n-Hexane	11.5	0.23

faster on account of changes in $\partial \lambda_{12}/\partial x_2$ than it rises on account of change in $\partial T_2/\partial \lambda_1$. The result is that decrease in the thermal conductivity of the carrier gas causes a large reduction in sensitivity. This is illustrated in Table 10.2 by values from Schmauch and Dinerstein (28).

The thermal conductivity of a pure gas is given approximately by the equation (6):

$$\lambda = K\left(C_v + \frac{9R}{4}\right)\left(\frac{T}{M}\right)^{1/2} \cdot \frac{1}{\sigma^2}, \qquad (10.36)$$

where

M is molecular weight,

C_v is molar specific heat at constant volume (cal mole^{-1} °C^{-1}),

T is temperature (°K),

R is gas constant (cal mole^{-1} °C^{-1}),

σ is collision diameter of molecule (Å),

λ is thermal conductivity (cal cm^{-1} sec^{-1} °C^{-1}),

K is 2.67×10^{-5} for the above units.

More detailed equations are given in the source for the above (6). It is apparent from the equation that the larger the molecule, the smaller its thermal conductivity; a short table of thermal conductivities is given in Table 10.3.

TABLE 10.3

THERMAL CONDUCTIVITIES OF COMMON GASES

Gas	$\lambda \times 10^5$ at 0°C (cal cm^{-1} sec^{-1} °C^{-1})
Helium	34.8
Hydrogen	41.6
Neon	11.1
Air	5.83
Nitrogen	5.81
Argon	3.98
Carbon dioxide	3.52

In general, heavy carrier gases of small thermal conductivity should not be used for catharometry; a summary of reasons, including those discussed above, is:

(1) Sensitivity comparable with that in light carrier gases can only be obtained by raising $T_2 - T_1$, which is undesirable, and, furthermore, may be ineffective on account of (5) below.

(2) $\partial \lambda_{12}/\partial x_2$ cannot be estimated *a priori*.

(3) $\partial \lambda_{12}/\partial x_2$ becomes small or even zero for vapours which are not very different from the carrier gas in molecular size or shape.

(4) The range of linearity is smaller with heavy carrier gases.

(5) The change in sensitivity with temperature is more rapid with heavy carrier gases (see below).

(6) The time constant of the hot element is greater the smaller the thermal conductivity of the carrier gas.

(e) Temperature

Increase in catharometer temperature almost invariably causes a decline in the sensitivity. The effect with metal wires is very much less than with thermistors, with which it is so great as to provide a serious drawback in their use. The effect may be analysed as follows.

Effect on α. With metal wires, α decreases slowly with rise in temperature, and this causes a small decrease in sensitivity.

Effect on R_1. In the case of wires, R_1 increases with increase in temperature; if the current I_1 were steady, this would cause an increase in the power dissipation, but generally, catharometers are run with E constant, so that as R_1 increases, I_1 decreases. The effect of temperature on the product $I_1^2 R_1$ for constant E clearly depends on the ratio R_1/R_2; if this is small, the power dissipated will increase with increasing temperature, and if it is large, it will decrease. Over limited temperature ranges, the effect is small. In the case of thermistors, the large decrease in R with increase in temperature produces a large drop in the power dissipation. This can be eliminated by making $R_1 > R_2$, so that I_1 increases fast enough to compensate for the drop in R_1, but this has drawbacks; two obvious ones are that the bridge is operating inefficiently, and that a catastrophe may occur if E rises above a certain threshold value, or even if a large concentration of vapour comes through.

Effect of $d\lambda_{12}/dx_2$. In general, this appears to decrease somewhat with increase in temperature, though there are few data. This conclusion is reasonable on the basis of the collision diameter theory, for collision diameters of the complex vapour molecules decrease rapidly with increase in temperature.

10.4. Noise

There is no theoretical lower limit to the noise from catharometers except that resulting from statistical fluctuations in current flow, which is very small, and actual noise results from instrumental imperfections. In current good designs, noise is smaller than about 5 μV.

Sources of noise may be subdivided into electrical and thermal.

(a) Electrical Noise

Thermoelectric. The Wheatstone's bridge circuit normally contains several intermetallic junctions, unequal heating of which leads to thermo-electric voltages. The most serious of these are at the leads into the cells, where the temperature may be high, where there may be convection draughts, and where intermetallic connections are likely. Thus, cell leads should be well protected, and preferably, intermetallic junctions should be bunched together in pairs arranged so that thermoelectric voltages cancel.

Temperature Variation in the Fixed Arms of the Bridge. All resistances other than the hot elements should be composed of resistance wire of negligible temperature coefficient, e.g., constantan or manganin. Thermo-electric voltages may also be eliminated by using wire which has both negligible temperature coefficient and small thermoelectric voltages with copper; such wire is commercially available.

Bad Contacts. It is obvious that these produce noise, but it is worth emphasising how good the contacts must be. For example, in a cell with $R_1 = 100$ ohms, $E = 20$ V, a noise of 5 μV is given by a change in resistance of 0.0001 ohm [Eq. (10.30)].

(b) Thermal Noise

Apart from electrical noise, thermal noise results from random variations in the temperature of the hot elements in adjacent arms of the bridge. If again we consider two cells, $R_1 = R_4 = 100$ ohms, $E = 20$ V, $\alpha = 0.004$ °C^{-1}, a noise of 5 μV is provided by random temperature differences of 2.5×10^{-4} °C. Thus, sensitive catharometers should be contained in a thermostat, and should be designed so that there is as good a temperature equality between the two cells as possible. This is normally done by building them into the same metal block.

10.5. DRIFT

Long-term drift is generally more troublesome than noise in catharometry. Apart from the extraneous causes of drift mentioned in Chapter 8, the most common serious causes of drift in catharometers are slow changes in the temperature of the metal block containing the cells and slow changes in the potential applied to the bridge.

In an "ideal" bridge, in balance, a change in E or T for two cells contained in the same metal block should not change the balance, for if R_1 and R_4 are properly matched, their resistances should each change in the same proportion. In practice, however, this is not quite true, for it is impossible to match two hot elements with sufficient accuracy, and the result is that slight changes in E and T cause drift. This drift may be eliminated using a Wheatstone's bridge circuit $R_1 - R_2 - R_3 - R_4$ modified by one or two of the resistances R_5, R_{5a}, R_6, or R_{6a} shown in Fig. 10.4. The operation of these may be explained qualitatively as follows. As T

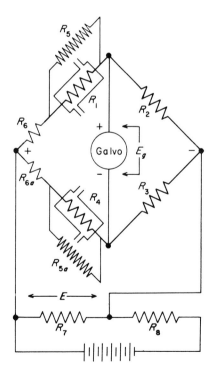

FIG. 10.4. Wheatstone's bridge circuit modified by resistances designed to reduce drift. Littlewood (31).

changes, R_1 and R_4 also change. Ideally, the temperature coefficients of resistance of R_1 and R_4 are identical, but in practice, the effect is that the temperature coefficient of one is slightly greater than that of the other. A fixed resistance is therefore placed either in series or in parallel with the hot element which effectively has the greater temperature coefficient, and its value is adjusted until the temperature coefficient of the two together equals that of the other hot element. After this, the net temperature coefficients of each arm of the bridge are identical, and change of temperature does not alter the balance. The same explanation serves for the correction of drift due to changes in E, but the value of the compensating resistance required is not necessarily the same. It is also possible to choose one series and one shunt resistance such that the catharometer does not drift for simultaneous changes in E and T.

Compensating resistances are used in many commercial catharometers. Methods for calculating those of the type illustrated in Fig. 10.4 are given by the author (*31*).

10.6. Linearity

If the concentration of vapour is such that Eq. (10.32) holds, and if the cross-terms mentioned in connection with it are negligible, then the catharometer is linear. The causes of non-linearity are complex, however, and it is not possible from existing theory or practice to give a value of x_2 for which the non-linearity at greater values of x_2 is greater than a given amount. General experience is that catharometers are linear within a few per cent up to the greatest mole fractions usually encountered in gas chromatography.

(a) Carrier Gas and Vapour

When the carrier gas and the vapour have comparable molecular dimensions and weights, non-linearity is likely to occur at relatively small vapour concentrations, as is indicated in Section 10.2a. Thus, for vapours in the C_2 to C_6 region, of which the molecular weight is less than 50 to 100, heavy carrier gases such as nitrogen or argon are likely to cause the vapours to give non-linear responses, and a light carrier gas should be used. This is illustrated in Fig. 10.5, which shows plots of response against molar concentration of butane in nitrogen, helium, and hydrogen (*32*). The linearity is clearly poorest in nitrogen.

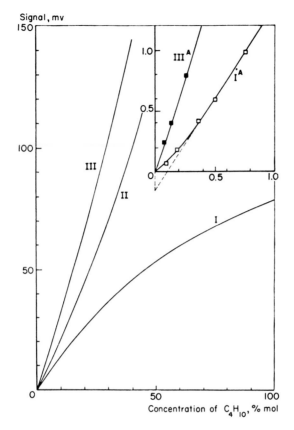

Fig. 10.5. Response of butane in various carrier gases as a function of its concentration. Curve I, n-butane in nitrogen; curve II, n-butane in hydrogen; curve III, n-butane in helium. Cell with Pt wires (diam 20 μ); bridge current, 200 ma. Curves I and III near the origin are magnified in the inset. From van der Craats (*32*).

(b) Temperature

In general, especially with heavy carrier gases, the higher the temperature, whether of the cell or the hot element, the smaller the range of linearity. When nitrogen is used as a carrier gas with vapours of up to about seven carbon atoms, there is often at high temperatures an extreme form of non-linearity in which the response changes sign at low concentrations, but maintains the same sign at large concentrations, so that a single peak appears as a "W." This is shown very well by Keppler *et al.* (*33*) (Fig. 10.6), who have put side by side a number of chromatograms of a similar sample of methanol in nitrogen taken at a succession of hot element temperatures. Schmauch and Dinerstein (*34*) illustrate the same behaviour by plotting

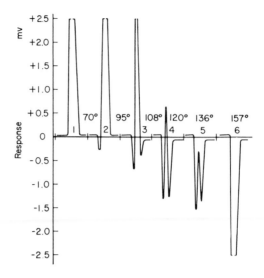

FIG. 10.6. Peaks due to methanol in nitrogen at various temperatures of the hot element. Keppler *et al.* (*33*).

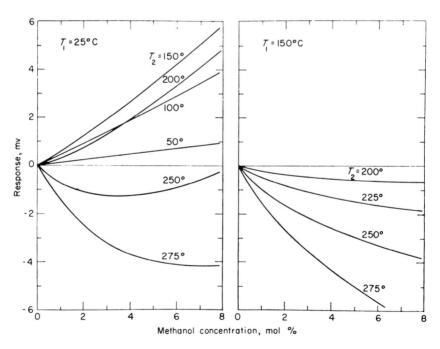

FIG. 10.7. Plots of response against concentration for methanol in nitrogen. Schmauch and Dinerstein (*34*).

response against concentration of methanol in nitrogen using both T_1 and T_2 as parameters (Fig. 10.7). From this plot it is seen that the response is reasonably linear if both T_1 and T_2 are small, but, as either of these temperatures becomes high, the detector becomes very non-linear, and the peak inversion of Fig. 10.6 is represented as negative response in Fig. 10.7. This result may be interpreted with a plot of λ_{12} for the system against molar composition with temperature as a parameter (Fig. 10.8) (23). At

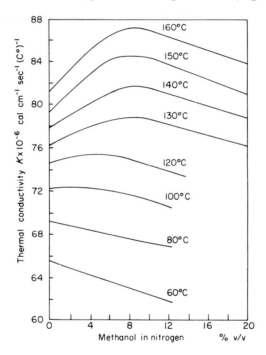

FIG. 10.8. Thermal conductivity of methanol in nitrogen as a function of methanol concentration, with temperature as parameter. Harvey and Morgan (23).

low temperatures, the thermal conductivity of the mixture drops monotonically with increase in x_2; at high temperatures, the value of $\partial\lambda_{12}/\partial x_2$ is positive at low concentrations and attains a maximum at a comparatively small value of x_2, after which it changes sign. Thus, at high temperatures the small concentration regions of the peak are inverted.

(c) Catharometer Design

Bohemen and Purnell (18) find that in heavy carrier gases loss of heat by mass-transfer rather than by conduction (see Section 10.2b, and 10.7) may cause non-linearity. In cases where this is true, therefore, a diffusion–fed cell, through which no gas passes, will not suffer from this source of non-linearity.

10.7. INDEPENDENCE OF EXTRANEOUS VARIABLES

The effect of changes in temperature and applied voltage on a catharometer has been considered in Section 10.5.

The effect of pressure on the base line in the case that the pressures of reference and measuring cell are not the same has been studied by Guild *et al.* (*35*); they find that a pressure differential between the two cells produces a small drift in the base line, e.g., a change of 20 cm Hg in one cell produces a deflection of 200 μV. Elementary theory predicts that at large pressures the thermal conductivity is independent of pressure; more detailed theory (*6*), and also experiment (*36, 37*), finds that thermal conductivity is a very shallow function of pressure. This, and the fact that the contribution to heat dissipation from mass-transfer is greater at the greater pressure, accounts for the small but noticeable dependence of the base line of catharometers on pressure differentials.

In catharometers in which the gas passes over the hot element, a change in the flow rate generally has a large effect on the base line. As discussed in Section 10.10b, this should ideally be cancelled out by a similar change in flow rate in the adjacent cell if the two cells are connected in series in the gas flow. In practice, however, the matching of the cells is not perfect, and changes in flow rate cause a residual change in the base line.

Bohemen and Purnell (*18*) have studied in detail the effect of flow rate in cells consisting of a heated wire in a glass tube carrying the column effluent. From their equation (10.23) for sensitivity including a mass-transfer term, the greater the flow rate, the greater the loss of heat through mass-transfer. Since the thermal conductivity term is generally of opposite sign to the mass-transfer term, the sensitivity should decline with increasing flow rate, and this is confirmed by results given by the authors.

Bohemen and Purnell also consider that mass-transfer is largely responsible for the increase in non-linearity, with eventual peak inversion, at high temperatures. The quantity $\partial \lambda_{12}/\partial x_2$ generally becomes less negative with increase in temperature, whereas $\partial C_p/\partial x_2$ remains relatively steady. The result is that the contribution of the mass-transfer increases with increase in temperature, until at a particular temperature the two terms are equal, and at small vapour concentrations, the response is zero. At still higher temperatures, the mass-transfer term exceeds the thermal conduction term at small concentrations, but at larger concentrations $\partial \lambda_{12}/\partial x_2$ is more negative, as shown in Fig. 10.8, so that the thermal conduction term exceeds the mass-transfer term. This leads to a W-shaped peak. Bohemen and Purnell deduce the importance of the mass-transfer from the fact that W-formation occurs at lower temperatures the greater the flow rate.

Bohemen and Purnell (*38*) also point out that one result of peaks for which there is little or no response at small concentrations is that they appear to be much sharper than they are, so that spuriously large plate-numbers are obtained.

10.8. CALIBRATION OF CATHAROMETERS

An approximate general rule is that with hydrocarbons or with molecules most of which consist of hydrocarbon chain in a light carrier gas, e.g., helium, the response of a catharometer is proportional to the concentration by weight of vapour. Thus, the weight fraction, w_i, of a component of a mixture is given by:

$$w_i = \frac{A_i}{\sum\limits_{j} A_j}, \tag{10.37}$$

where A is peak area. The accuracy of this rule has been studied by many authors (*39–41*) in the course of analyses of hydrocarbon mixtures, and the conclusion drawn from the results is that it is accurate to within 1% for unbranched alkanes, and to within about 4% for any non-aromatic hydrocarbon mixtures. It is accurate to within about 1% for mixtures of aromatic hydrocarbons only, but in mixtures containing aromatics and other hydrocarbons there are large errors in the proportions of aromatic and non–aromatic compounds. It is reasonable to suppose that similar errors will arise in analysis of mixtures of hydrocarbons the molecules of which contain aromatic nuclei associated with alkane chains of different lengths.

The above rule may not in general be extended to molecules not containing hydrocarbon chains, and it becomes totally inapplicable in mixtures of components containing elements other than carbon, hydrogen, and oxygen. For example, in mixtures containing halogenated compounds, Eq. (10.37) can lead to errors as great as 40% (*42*).

When nitrogen or other heavy gas is used as carrier gas, Eq. (10.37) may still hold, but in a much restricted set of circumstances. It is probably necessary for the cell temperature to be low, and the rule is probably not even approximately true for molecules lighter than C_6. Hinkle and Johnsen (43) have analysed the same mixture in the same conditions using nitrogen, hydrogen, and helium as carrier gases, to give the results shown in Table 10.4. It is apparent that with hydrogen or helium, the catharometer gives

TABLE 10.4

ANALYSES IN NITROGEN, HYDROGEN, AND HELIUM

Component	Analysis in:			Actual composition
	N_2	He	H_2	
Propane	3.8	5.6	5.4	5.2
i-Butane	19.0	20.1	19.6	19.9
n-Butane	43.0	43.5	44.0	44.0
1-Butene	21.2	20.1	19.8	19.8
2-Butene	5.6	5.0	5.1	5.1
n-Pentane	5.0	3.8	4.1	4.1
1-Pentene	2.4	1.8	2.0	1.9
Mean square error	1.005	0.093	0.020	0

a correct analysis, but that with nitrogen there are errors of up to 25%. The conclusion is that heavy carrier gases should not be used for quantitative analysis by catharometry unless unavoidable, in which case calibration coefficients (Section 8.2) should be determined.

Rosie and Grob (44), and Messner et al. (45) have determined a large number of calibration coefficients for vapours in helium by the analysis of known mixtures, and find that in any homologous series, the molar response is given by the equation:

$$\partial \lambda_{12}/\partial x_2 = A + BM_2, \tag{10.38}$$

where M_2 is the molecular weight of the vapour, and A and B are constants, the relative values of which are significant, but the absolute values of which are determined by setting the sensitivity of benzene arbitrarily at 100 units. Values of A and B for various series are given in Table 10.5, and Fig. 10.9 shows the accuracy of such a relation for the n-alkanes heavier than propane. Note that the small contribution of A when the carbon number is large is consistent with the approximate truth of the general rule of Eq. (10.37).

TABLE 10.5

CONSTANTS FOR THE GENERAL EQUATION: RELATIVE RESPONSE $= A + BM_2$

Homologous series	Range of experimental points	B (slope)	A (intercept)
n-Paraffins	C_1–C_3	1.015	19.8
	C_3–C_{10}	1.330	7.9
Methyl paraffins	C_4–C_7	1.270	9.3
Dimethyl paraffins	C_5–C_7	1.188	13.5
a-Olefins	C_2–C_4	1.188	13.5
Trimethyl paraffins	C_7–C_8	1.176	12.7
Methyl benzene	C_7–C_9	1.169	8.8
Mono n-alkyl benzenes	C_7–C_9	1.070	16.5
Mono sec-alkyl benzenes	C_9–C_{10}	1.042	18.7
n-Ketones	C_3–C_8	0.843	37.1
Primary alcohols	C_2–C_7	0.809	35.3
Tertiary alcohols	C_4–C_5	0.809	35.3
Secondary alcohols	C_3–C_5	0.839	35.1
n-Acetates	C_2–C_7	0.831	38.3
n-Ethers	C_4–C_{10}	0.874	44.2

The observations of Rosie *et al.* can be correlated with the theory of Section 10.2a relating $d\lambda_{12}/dx_2$ with the collision cross section of the vapour molecules in the carrier gas. Collision cross sections for transport properties are additive functions of the molecular groupings in the molecule. The addition, for example, of a methylene group to a molecule in order to

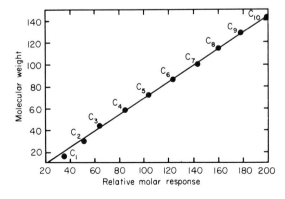

FIG. 10.9. Molar response of n-alkanes as a function of molecular weight, relative to benzene = 100. Messner *et al.* (*45*).

convert it into its next homologue adds a characteristic increment both to the molecular weight and to the collision cross-section, and this, together with Eq. (10.6), leads to Eq. (10.38). Also, frequently molecules which form dense liquids, e.g., halogenates or aromatics, have dense molecules in the gas phase, so that their cross-sections are relatively small. The rule found by Takayama (46), that the area of a peak produced by a component of a liquid mixture is proportional to the *volume* of the component rather than its *weight*, is therefore consistent with the application of Eq. (10.6).

10.9. OTHER CRITERIA

(a) Speed of Response

The speed of response is determined by the ratio of the detector volume to the flow rate and by the time constant of the hot element. The majority of catharometers in current use have volumes of the order of 0.1 to 1 ml and are thus suitable for use with packed columns, but not for capillary columns. Catharometers suitable for capillary columns with volumes of the order of microlitres have been described by several authors (47–50). The principles of this chapter show that concentration sensitivity is not necessarily lost merely by reducing the size of the catharometer, while the discussion of Section 8.1 shows that mass-sensitivity at slow flow rates is enhanced by such reduction.

The time constant of the hot element is given by the equation:*

$$k = C/\lambda G, \qquad (10.39)$$

where C is the heat capacity of the hot element and G is as defined in Eq. (10.16). For most hot elements, whether wire or thermistor, this is

---

* This equation is derived as follows: At T_2, the rate of loss of heat from the hot element is I^2R/J, so, if free cooling were to take place at temperature T_2, e.g., if the electricity were turned off, the rate of cooling would be I^2R/JC. We assume that C is constant, and that the rate of cooling at temperature T is proportional to $T - T_1$, whence:

$$\frac{dT}{dt} = -\frac{(T - T_1)}{(T_2 - T_1)} \cdot \frac{I^2R}{JC},$$

which gives:

$$T - T_1 = \exp\left\{\frac{-t}{[JC(T_2 - T_1)/I^2R]}\right\} = \exp\left\{\frac{-t}{C/\lambda G}\right\}.$$

The time constant is the denominator of the exponent.

usually small, but not so small that it can be dismissed without consideration. Below are three examples of hot elements together with conditions,
and rough calculation of their time constants.

Example 1. Thermistor; $\frac{1}{2}$ mm diameter; weight, 0.2 mg; specific heat
assumed to be that of copper oxide, 0.1 cal/(g °C); carrier gas, helium.

$$C = 2 \times 10^{-5} \quad \text{cal/°C}$$
$$G = 4\pi r_2 = 0.3 \quad \text{cm}$$
$$\lambda = 34 \times 10^{-5} \quad \text{cal cm}^{-1} \text{sec}^{-1} \text{°C}^{-1},$$

whence
$$k = \frac{2 \times 10^{-5}}{34 \times 10^{-5} \times 0.3} = 0.2 \quad \text{sec.}$$

Example 2. Platinum wire, 44 British standard wire gauge (diameter
0.008 cm), along the axis of a 1 cm tube. Carrier gas, helium; specific
heat of platinum, 0.03 cal/(g °C); density 21 g/cc.

$$C = 3.2 \times 10^{-5} \quad \text{cal/°C per unit length}$$
$$G = 2\pi/(\ln 1/0.004) = 1 \quad \text{cm per unit length of wire}$$
$$\lambda = 34 \times 10^{-5} \quad \text{cal cm}^{-1} \text{sec}^{-1} \text{°C}^{-1},$$

whence
$$k = \frac{3.2 \times 10^{-5}}{34 \times 10^{-5} \times 1} = 0.1 \quad \text{sec.}$$

Example 3. As Example 2, but nitrogen as carrier gas.

$$\lambda = 5.8 \times 10^{-5} \quad \text{cal cm}^{-1} \text{sec}^{-1} \text{°C}^{-1},$$

whence
$$k = \frac{3.2 \times 10^{-5}}{5.8 \times 10^{-5} \times 1} = 0.6 \quad \text{sec.}$$

Cowan and Stirling (27) quote experimental time constants of 6 to 8
sec in nitrogen and 1 to 2 sec in hydrogen for thermistors rather larger
than those used in the above examples ($D = 0.5$ mW/°C, see Section
10.10d); Snowden and Eanes (20) show curves of response against time
for an instantaneous change in vapour composition for wire elements
wound on mandrels (Section 10.10) which show time constants in air
of between $\frac{1}{2}$ and 1 sec.

For packed columns, a time constant of about 1 sec is usually adequate,
and for capillary columns, 0.1 sec. Thus, catharometers as described in the

example are adequate for use with capillary columns if helium or hydrogen is the carrier, but not if the carrier is a heavier gas. Also, they would become deleteriously sluggish if the hot elements were much bigger.

(b) Chemical Inertness

A catharometer is normally inert to any vapour passing through, but the hot element may pyrolyse relatively thermo-labile components if it is hot enough. In particular, it should be remembered that metal wire hot elements may act as catalysts.

(c) Range of Application

When helium is used as the carrier gas, the catharometer will respond adequately to every other gas or vapour. The catharometer is one of the most versatile of detectors, and in this respect is comparable with the ionisation cross-section detector described in Section 9.5.

10.10. DESIGN OF CATHAROMETERS

A catharometer is the sum of a number of separate components and features of design, and each of these is considered separately.

(a) Position of the Hot Element

Catharometer cells may have their hot element: (1) in the stream of carrier gas; these may be called directly fed (*18, 25, 32, 51–59*); (2) in a side arm; these may be called diffusion-fed (*20, 27, 58–62*). These arrangements are illustrated in Fig. 10.10. Each design has one specific drawback.

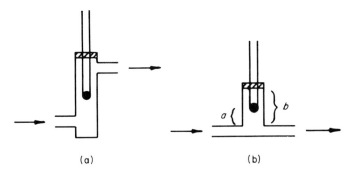

(a)   (b)

FIG. 10.10. (a) Directly fed and (b) diffusion-fed hot elements.

The drawback of directly fed cells is that heat may be removed by the gas flow as considered in detail by Bohemen and Purnell (*18*). As shown in previous sections, the effect of flow in directly fed cells can be deleterious since it can render the cell sensitive to flow rate, can reduce sensitivity, can cause the calibration to depend on flow rate, and can promote non-linearity. The flow sensitivity can effectively be removed by passing the same flow through opposed cells, as described in Subsection (*b*). The other effects may be minimised by correct selection of the geometry of the hot element. As shown in Section 10.2b for axial wires in tubes, the specific heat effect is relatively less the longer the wire and the slower the linear flow rate, and so for a relatively long straight wire in a tube with a small linear flow rate, the specific heat effect is small. When the hot element is short in the direction of the gas flow, e.g., in the case of a coiled wire axially in a tube, or a wire situated in a cavity at right angles to the gas flow, or in the case of a thermistor bead, the specific heat effect is likely to be great; indeed, such an arrangement may be used to measure specific heats.

The drawback of diffusion-fed cells is that they have a longer time constant than directly fed cells, but they do not suffer from the specific heat effect. The effect of the time constant on resolution has been illustrated by Baker *et al.* (*59*), who have used a cell as in Fig. 10.10b, in which thermistor hot element could be moved inside the side arm to any desired position. Table 10.6 shows the way in which the resolution of the two peaks deteriorates as the thermistor is moved further into the side arm. It should be noted in this connection that the time constant increases not only with

TABLE 10.6

Effect of Thermistor Position in a Diffusion-Fed Cell on Peak Resolution[a]

Position of thermistor	Resolution, expressed as ratio of peak-height to the height of the col between two close peaks
Centre of flow path	15
Edge of flow path, i.e., just at the entrance to the side arm	10.4
$\frac{1}{8}$ inch inside the side arm	8.2
$\frac{1}{4}$ inch inside the side arm	6

[a] Baker *et al.* (*59*).

increase in the distance a of Fig. 10.10b, but also with increase in b, so that it is important to keep the total depth of the side arm as small as possible.

(b) *Methods of Connecting Catharometer Cells in the Gas Flow*

In the normal case that two cells are used, they may be connected in any of the five ways illustrated in Fig. 10.11.

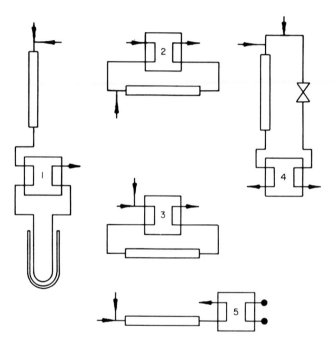

Fɪɢ. 10.11. Ways in which catharometer and column may be connected.

(1) In this arrangement, gas first passes from the column through the measuring cell, after which it is stripped out by a cold trap or by an adsorbent or by both, and it then passes through the reference cell. When used with flow-sensitive catharometer cells, this arrangement has the advantage that flow variations are balanced between the cells, and thus do not appear in the output. It has the additional advantage that both cells work at the same pressure and that any changes in the composition of the carrier gas are also cancelled out. A drawback is that, when a large sample is coming through, the flow rate in the reference cell is temporarily reduced while the sample is being condensed. This may produce a spurious response

if the cell is excessively flow sensitive. If, in this arrangement, the trap is replaced by a small length of tubing, so that the column effluent is not condensed, the record given by the detector is the differential with respect to volume of the vapour concentration.

(2) This arrangement is very common in practice. Gas first enters the reference cell, whence it goes to the sample injector and the column, after which it goes through the measuring cell. A minor drawback to this is that the pressure is greater in the reference cell than in the measuring cell, and, as pointed out in Section 10.7, the pressure difference causes a slight change in the base line, which must therefore be adjusted for each flow rate. Flow compensation is poor with this arrangement, and changes in flow produce drift in the response of flow-sensitive cells.

(3) In this arrangement, the sample injector comes before the reference cell, so that the whole sample passes through it on its way to the column and produces an inverted peak. This is often useful in providing an unambiguous mark for the beginning of a run. It should be noted that the area of the input peak will probably not equal the sum of the areas of the output peaks, since at the column inlet the volume flow rate is smaller, $\partial \lambda_{12}/\partial x_2$ may be appreciably different, and the total concentration of vapour may be beyond the region of linearity; indeed if the sample injector is efficient, it should be so.

A further advantage of arrangements (2) and (3) is that if the reference cell is of similar design to the measuring cell, chromatograms may be run with reversed flow. There are applications in which this is useful, e.g., in the analysis for proportions of volatile components of interest in the presence of less volatile components the relative proportions of which are not of interest.

(4) In this arrangement, the reference cell is separately fed.

(5) In this arrangement, there is a reference hot element situated in the same block as the measuring cell, but it is not fed by any gas flow. Such an arrangement has been used occasionally (62), and should be satisfactory with a flow-insensitive measuring cell, but it is probably not capable of great sensitivity, and its principal advantage is simplicity.

(c) *Design of the Cell Block*

The paramount consideration is that the two opposing cells of the catharometer should be at exactly the same temperature, as is shown in Section 10.4b. In current designs, the required temperature equality is almost invariably achieved by building the cells into the same metal block, for which purpose copper, brass, stainless steel, monel metal, etc., have all been used. Many individual designs exist, and most of the references given at the beginning of this sections include diagrams showing details of construction. Cell blocks are usually contained in a thermostat, and for this purpose vapour baths, circulating air baths, and conventional liquid thermostats have all been frequently used. Circulating air baths are commonest in commercial instruments.

(d) Design of the Hot Element

When a straight wire is used as a hot element, it is almost invariably stretched along the axis of a tube carrying the column effluent, and is held rigidly by supports at either end of the tube, which may be sprung in order to keep the wire taut (51, 52). Frequently also, wire hot elements are wound in a helix. Though such a helix is liable to produce noise from vibration (20, 55), careful construction can reduce the effect of vibration to negligible proportions. The use of the helical filament from an ordinary lamp-bulb as a hot element has been described (63). Extremely rugged hot elements can be prepared by winding wire onto mandrels (20), at the cost of some increase in time constant. Such units have been developed for process control applications.

The selection of thermistors for use in catharometers has been considered in detail by Cowan and Stirling (27). A quantitative approach to thermistor sensitivity is assisted by the fact that manufacturers of thermistors generally quote their resistance at a specified temperature and their "Dissipation Constant," defined as the power input in milliwatts required to produce a temperature elevation of 1°C in a given gas, usually dry air. If W is the power dissipated by the thermistor, and θ is its excess temperature, the dissipation constant D is shown by Eq. (10.15) to satisfy the equation:

$$D = W/\theta = J\lambda G. \qquad (10.40)$$

The dissipation constant is thus proportional to G.

If fixed resistors R_2 and R_3 are adjusted so that all arms of the Wheatstone's bridge are equal, then a simple equation may be derived giving the sensitivity in terms of the known quantities R and D. From Eq. (10.32),

$$S = KEW/G, \qquad (10.41)$$

where K includes all quantities not dependent on E or W, and is assumed to be independent of T. From the condition that $R_1 = R_2 = R_3 = R_4 = R$,

$E = 2(WR)^{1/2}$. If this and Eq. (10.40) are substituted in Eq. (10.41),

$$S = K'\lambda\theta^{3/2}(RD)^{1/2}, \tag{10.42}$$

where $K' = 2KJ$. Note that this equation and Eq. (10.40) include Eqs. (10.34) and (10.35). When θ is constrained to be constant, $S \propto (RD)^{1/2}$, as has been confirmed by Cowan and Stirling (27) (Fig. 10.12) for many thermistors in which R and D have many different values.

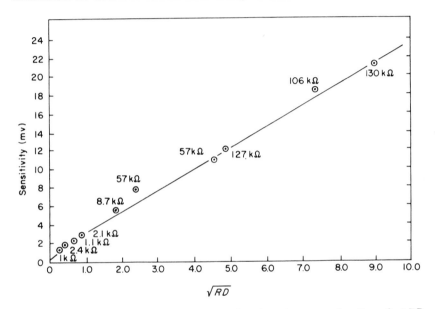

FIG. 10.12. Sensitivity of catharometers using thermistors as a function of $\sqrt{RD}$, for many values of R and D. Values of R are given against each point. Temperature difference, $\theta = 50^\circ C$. Cowan and Stirling (27).

From Eq. (10.42), the larger the product RD, the greater the sensitivity, and by design of the shape and size of the thermistor, R and D may be varied more or less independently. The dissipation constant D increases with increase in thermistor size, since the larger the thermistor, the greater the area over which heat may be conducted; the exact relation for wires and for spheres is contained in Eqs. (10.40), (10.17), and (10.18), assuming r_1 to be large in the latter two equations. In practice, the maximum size of a thermistor is limited by its time constant, as described in Section 10.9a. The value of R may be adjusted by altering the composition of the thermistor.

Cowan and Stirling (27) have found that thermistors produce considerably more electrical noise than hot wires. This noise is found to vary as I^n, where n lies between 1.2 and 1.8, and increases somewhat with increase in temperature. The noise is generally reduced by ageing the thermistors by heating them either in an oven or electrically.

The mixture of oxides of which thermistors are composed is liable to be reduced by hydrogen at temperatures greater than about 100°C, so that bare thermistors should not be used if hydrogen is the carrier gas, unless the temperature is always low. Thermistors manufactured for catharometry are coated with glass; this increases their thermal capacity a little, but overcomes their sensitivity to their medium.

(e) Wheatstone's Bridge Circuit

The Wheatstone's bridge circuit may be connected in either of the basic ways shown in Fig. 10.13, but, of the two, (a) is universally used, and it will be noted that this is implicit in all previous discussion of Wheatstone's

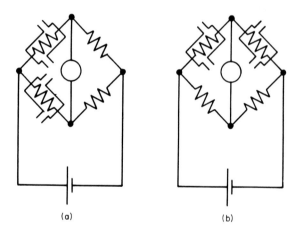

(a)   (b)

Fig. 10.13. Ways of connecting two catharometer cells in a Wheatstone's bridge.

bridges. Drawbacks to (b) are that the current in the measuring cell is subject to any fluctuations in the reference cell, that the current through the cells may not be controlled in any way other than by altering E, and that the appearance of a peak in the measuring cell alters the current in the reference cell in such a manner as to increase the non-linearity. In the case that thermistors are used, a special drawback of circuit (b) is that an accidental increase in E, or use of a carrier gas with small thermal conductivity, or even the presence of a large concentration of a vapour, may promote the infinite catastrophe in which an increase in temperature reduces the resistance of without reducing the voltage across the thermistor, so that the power dissipation increases, causing a further rise in temperature, *ad inf.*, until the thermistor burns out.

The exact balance of a catharometer circuit is usually achieved by large variable resistors used as shunts across the reference arms of the bridge, or by small variable resistors in series with them. The use of balancing resistors in association with either of the arms of the bridge containing the hot elements is undesirable, since it causes the sensitivity of the catharometer to temperature or applied voltage to alter as described in Section 10.5. The use of series rather than shunt resistors causes noise if the slide connection is imperfect.

As described in Section 10.2d, the sensitivity for a given bridge resistance is greatest when $R_1 = R_2$. It has been pointed out (24), however, that though such an arrangement is very commonly employed, it is subject to drawbacks. The principal drawback lies in the fact that the smaller the ratio R_2/R_1, the greater the dependence of I_1 upon R_1, thus producing non–linearity as mentioned in the restrictions on the application of Eq. (10.32), Section 10.2e. For hot elements of given resistance and for a given power dissipation, therefore, the non-linearity due to this can be reduced in comparison with the equal arm circuit by making $R_{2,3} \gg R_{1,4}$, and increasing E to compensate. Manipulation of the equations of Section 10.2d will show that this procedure also produces a small increase in sensitivity.

REFERENCES

1. Shakespear, G. A., *Proc. Phys. Soc. (London)* **33**, 163 (1921).
2. Claesson, S., *Arkiv Kemi, Mineral Geol.* **23A** (1), 1 (1946).
3. Daynes, H. A., "Gas Analysis by Measurement of Thermal Conductivity." Cambridge Univ. Press, London and New York, 1933.
4. Weaver, E. R., *in* "Physical Methods in Chemical Analysis" (W. G. Berl, ed.), Vol. 2, Academic Press, New York, 1951.
5. Chapman, S., and Cowling, T. G., "The Mathematical Theory of Non-Uniform Gases," 2nd ed. Cambridge Univ. Press, London and New York, 1952.
6. Hirschfelder, G. O., Curtiss, C. F., and Bird, R. B., "Molecular Theory of Gases and Liquids." Wiley, New York, 1954.
7. Kennard, A. E., "Kinetic Theory of Gases." McGraw-Hill, New York, 1938.
8. Wassiljewa, A., *Physik. Z.* **5**, 737 (1904).
9. Lindsay, A. L., and Bromley, L. A., *Ind. Eng. Chem.* **42**, 1508 (1950).
10. Hoffmann, E. G., *Anal. Chem.* **34**, 1216 (1962).
11. van der Craats, F., quoted in Keulemans, A.I.M., Kwantes, A., and Rijnders, G.W.A., *Anal. Chim. Acta* **16**, 29 (1957).
12. Littlewood, A. B., *Nature* **184**, 1631 (1959).

13. Luy, H., *Z. Anal. Chem.* **194**, 241 (1963).
14. Mecke, R., and Zirker, K., *J. Chromatog.* **7**, 1 (1962).
15. Kebbekus, B. B., Barsby, M. H., Rossi, R. T., and Jordan, J., *J. Am. Chem. Soc.* **88**, 2398 (1966).
16. Sneddon, I., "Elements of Partial Equations." McGraw-Hill, New York, 1957.
17. Ray, N. H., *Nature* **182**, 1663 (1958).
18. Bohemen, J., and Purnell, J. H., *J. Appl. Chem. (London)* **8**, 433 (1958).
19. Wiseman, W. A., *Ann. N.Y. Acad. Sci.* **72**, 685 (1959).
20. Snowden, F. C., and Eanes, R. D., *Ann. N.Y. Acad. Sci.* **72**, 764 (1959).
21. For example, "Handbook of Chemistry and Physics." Chemical Rubber Publishing Co., Cleveland, Ohio, published annually.
22. Dimbat, M., Porter, P. E., and Stross, F. H., *Anal. Chem.* **28**, 290 (1956).
23. Harvey, D., and Morgan, G. O., *in* "Vapour Phase Chromatography," Proceedings of the First Symposium, London, May, 1956 (D. H. Desty, ed.) p. 74. Academic Press, New York, 1957.
24. Wiseman, W. A., *Chem. Ind. (London)*, p. 1356 (1957).
25. Burg, S. P., and Stolwijk, J. A. J., *J. Biochem. Microbiol. Technol. Eng.* **1**, 245 (1959).
26. Mellor, N., *in* "Vapour Phase Chromatography," Proceedings of the First Symposium, London, May, 1956 (D. H. Desty, ed.), p. 63. Academic Press, New York, 1957.
27. Cowan, C. B., and Stirling, P. H., *in* "Gas Chromatography," I.S.A. Symposium, August, 1957 (V. J. Coates, H. J. Noebels, and I. S. Fagerson, eds.), p. 165. Academic Press, New York, 1958.
28. Schmauch, L. J., and Dinerstein, R. A., and Ray, N. H., *Nature* **183**, 673 (1959).
29. Eden, M., Karmen, A., and Stephenson, J. L., *Nature* **183**, 1322 (1959).
30. Fredericks, E. M., Dimbat, M., and Stross, F. H., *Nature* **184** *BA* 54 (1959).
31. Littlewood, A. B., *J. Sci. Instr.* **37**, 185 (1960).
32. van der Craats, F., *in* "Gas Chromatography 1958," Proceedings of the Second Symposium, Amsterdam, May, 1958 (D. H. Desty, ed.), p. 248. Academic Press, New York, 1958.
33. Keppler, J. G., Dijkstra, G., and Schols, J. A., *in* "Vapour Phase Chromatography," Proceedings of the First Symposium, London, May, 1956 (D. H. Desty, ed.), p. 222. Academic Press, New York, 1957.
34. Schmauch, L. J., and Dinerstein, R. A., *Anal. Chem.* **32**, 343 (1960).
35. Guild, L. V., Bingham, S., and Aul, F., *in* "Gas Chromatography 1958," Proceedings of the Second Symposium, Amsterdam, May, 1958 (D. H. Desty, ed.), p. 226. Academic Press, New York, 1958.
36. Kannaluick, W. G., and Martin, L. H., *Proc. Roy. Soc.* **A144**, 496 (1934).
37. Lambert, J. D., Staines, E. N., and Woods, S. D., *Proc. Roy. Soc.* **A200**, 262 (1950).
38. Bohemen, J., and Purnell, J. H., *Chem. Ind. (London)* 815 (1957).
39. Fredericks, E. M., and Brooks, F. R., *Anal. Chem.* **28**, 297 (1956).
40. Nunez, L. J., Armstrong, W. H., and Cogswell, H. W., *Anal. Chem.* **29**, 1164 (1957).
41. Browning, L. C., and Watts, J. O., *Anal. Chem.* **29**, 24 (1957).
42. Schomburg, G., *Z. Anal. Chem.* **164**, 147 (1958).
43. Hinkle, E. A., and Johnsen, S. E. J., *in* "Gas Chromatography," I.S.A. Symposium, August, 1957 (V. J. Coates, H. J. Noebels, and I. S. Fagerson, eds.), p. 165. Academic Press, New York, 1958.

44. Rosie, D. M., and Grob, R. L., *Anal. Chem.* **29**, 1263 (1957).
45. Messner, A. E., Rosie, D. M., and Argabright, P. A., *Anal. Chem.* **31**, 230 (1959).
46. Takayama, Y., *J. Chem. Soc. Japan, Ind. Chem. Sect.* **61**, 685 (1958).
47. Sasaki, N., Tominaga, K., and Aoyagi, M., *Nature* **186**, 309 (1960).
48. Petrocelli, J. A., *Anal. Chem.* **35**, 2220 (1963).
49. Camin, D. L., King, R. W., and Shawhan, S. D., *Anal. Chem.* **36**, 1175 (1964).
50. Clark, A. J., *SIRA Review* **7**, 17 (1966).
51. Ashbury, G. K., Davies, A. J., and Drinkwater, J. W., *Anal. Chem.* **29**, 918 (1957).
52. Davies, A. J., and Johnson, J. K., *in* "Vapour Phase Chromatography," Proceedings of the First Symposium, London, May, 1956 (D. H. Desty, ed.), p. 185. Academic Press, New York, 1957.
53. dal Nogare, S., and Safranski, L. W., *Anal. Chem.* **30**, 894 (1958).
54. Ogilvie, J. L., Simmons, M. C., and Hinds, G. P., *Anal. Chem.* **30**, 25 (1958).
55. Ryce, S. A., Kebarle, P., and Bryce, W. A., *Anal. Chem.* **29**, 1386 (1957).
56. Davies, A. D., and Howard, G. A., *J. Appl. Chem. (London)* **8**, 183 (1958).
57. Bayer, E., *in* "Gas Chromatography 1958," Proceedings of the Second Symposium, Amsterdam, May, 1958 (D. H. Desty, ed.), p. 333. Academic Press, New York, 1958.
58. Felton, H. R., and Buehler, A. A., *Anal. Chem.* **30**, 1163 (1958).
59. Baker, W. J., Norlin, H. L., Zinn, T. L., and Wall, R. F., *Am. Chem. Soc. Symposium, New York, Sept. 1957*, p. 43 (1957).
60. Ambrose, D., and Collerson, R. R., *J. Sci. Instr.* **32**, 323 (1955).
61. Walker, R. E., and Westenberg, A. A., *Rev. Sci. Instr.* **32**, 323 (1955).
62. Musgrave, W. K. R., *Chem. Ind. (London)*, p. 46 (1959).
63. Stuve, W., *in* "Gas Chromatography, 1958," Proceedings of the Second Symposium, Amsterdam, May, 1958 (D. H. Desty, ed.), p. 178. Academic Press, New York, 1958.

Chapter 11

Ancillary Apparatus and Techniques

11.1. INTRODUCTION

In addition to the column and detector, a complete GC apparatus requires a flow control or pressure control for the carrier gas, a sample injector, and possibly a flowmeter and devices for the collection of samples. There may also be other items, such as thermostats, apparatus for providing constant electrical supply, etc. Furthermore, the handling of GC data can be automated in several ways of varying sophistication. The result is that in a complete system the basic gas chromatograph may be associated with considerable ancillary apparatus.

Though GC is effective at separating the components of mixtures, the discussion of Chapter 3 makes it clear that its ability at qualitative identification of separated components is far from unambiguous. Thus, there are several systems in extensive use in which components separated by GC are studied by spectrometric methods, e.g., mass-spectrometry or infrared spectroscopy, these being well equipped to identify single components, but ill able to analyse mixtures. In such systems, each instrument is used to its best advantage, the chromatography doing the separating which the spectroscopy cannot do, and the spectroscopy doing the identification which the chromatography cannot do.

In this chapter, we describe sample injectors, data handling equipment in GC, and the use of GC in conjunction with other techniques. We refer the reader to standard texts on scientific apparatus for ancillary components which are common scientific hardware (*1*). We also include a section on detectors in common use not described in Chapters 9 or 10.

11.2. Sample Injectors

Since most analyses by gas chromatography aim to determine not absolute weights but relative weight proportions of the components of a sample of interest, most sample injectors aim to inject a representative sample of a mixture of interest and not an accurately known weight. The sample injector remains one of the least satisfactory items of gas chromatographic equipment; possibly for this reason, many designs for it have been produced.

Sample injectors must satisfy the general conditions that their volume should be small (Section 6.7), and that the temperature of devices designed to handle liquids or solids should be sufficiently high (Section 6.15). Many of the devices described below are fitted with facilities for heating separate from those provided for the column, so that the sample injector may be hotter than the column. Such heaters are referred to as "Flash Heaters."

(a) Designs Involving Use of Hypodermic Syringes and Their Modifications

The commonest kind of sample injector consists of a rubber cap attached to a very short side arm in the gas flow immediately before the column. The sample is contained in a hypodermic syringe, and is injected through the cap into the gas stream immediately above the column. In many early apparatuses, e.g., Ray (2), the cap is a "serum cap" of the kind used to seal bottles of serum, as used for medical injections. In most later designs, the cap is a compressed rubber or silicone rubber disc. Such a device is currently used on many commercial apparatuses, as it is inexpensive and moderately satisfactory for most applications.

The quantities of liquid required for injection into GC apparatus are usually much smaller than those used in medicine, and also they are usually required to be able to deliver their charge to the column against the column inlet pressure, which may be considerable. The system using hypodermic syringes is suitable only for moderate column inlet pressures, e.g., 1 to 5 atm, and many types of syringe designed explicitly for use in GC have been produced. For delivery of samples between about 1 and 50 μl, syringes in which the plunger is a stainless steel wire can be used. Alternatively, the plunger can consist of an elongation of the needle, so that in operation, the barrel of the syringe is pushed down over the needle, thus forcing liquid out through the hole through the needle. In either design, Teflon gaskets may be used. For delivery of samples less than 1 μl, and down to a minimum of about 0.01 μl (the latter figure only with luck and skill), there are various ingenious systems, e.g., one in which a stainless steel wire moves through a Teflon seal at one end of the barrel, and the needle moves through a similar seal at the other end. The needle and the wire have slightly different cross sections, so that if the wire and needle are butted together inside the barrel, and both are moved together, the volume inside the barrel decreases the greater the length of the thicker element entering the barrel. An alternative scheme is one in which the plunger to the syringe is a very fine wire operating down the hole through the hypodermic needle. The accuracy of the volume introduced by such devices is inevitably often poor.

Though the injector cavity is usually situated directly at the column inlet, it is possible to have an injection cavity so that it can be isolated from the column and the carrier gas stream, e.g., as illustrated in Figure 11.1. In this way, injection can be made at atmospheric pressure, and the

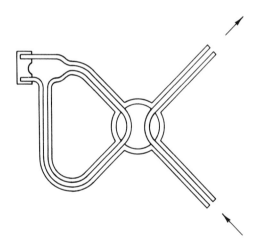

Fig. 11.1. Sample injector isolable from the gas stream. By turning the central stopcock barrel through $\frac{1}{4}$ turn, the carrier gas is diverted through the sample cavity (3).

column pressure is applied by turning the tap through $\frac{1}{4}$ turn only when injection has been completed (3). The drawback of such a system is that it is more difficult to keep heated. In the case that a sample for analysis contains non-volatile components, a small auxiliary cavity of column containing glass wool or other inert material can be inserted between injector and column, thus absorbing the solid material before it contaminates the column (4–6).

(b) *Methods Involving Sealed Ampoules*

Several designs of sample injector have been described in which the sample is sealed into some kind of frangible ampoule which is then inserted into the carrier gas stream, preferably without disturbing the gas flow, after which it is broken by some external control (7–12). As an example, Fig. 11.2 shows the device of Bowman and Karmen (12). The piston slides in the pressure-tight seal. With the piston pulled up, a sealed glass capillary containing the sample is placed in the slot. The piston is then pushed down, taking the capillary through the seal. Since the diameter of the tube inside the seal is relatively large, the capillary falls out on to the metal grid. The piston is then lifted up, and pushed down on to the capillary, which is thereby crushed.

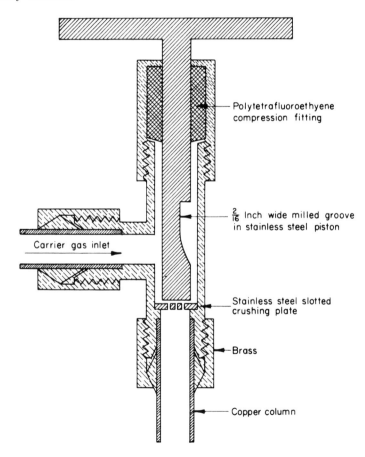

Polytetrafluoroethyene compression fitting

$\frac{2}{16}$ Inch wide milled groove in stainless steel piston

Carrier gas inlet

Stainless steel slotted crushing plate

Brass

Copper column

FIG. 11.2. Sample injector according to Bowman and Karmen (12).

An adaptation of the above technique used by Dubsky and Janak (*13*) for introducing solid samples at a high temperature is to seal the sample in a capillary of Wood's metal, and by means of an ingenious device to introduce the capillary into a small heated saddle in the carrier gas stream. The metal melts, and the sample volatilises. The saddle is made sufficiently large to contain the metal from several capillaries, and thus the device need not be cleaned after every use. A device working on a similar principle, but using indium in place of Wood's metal, has been patented by Nerheim (*14*).

(c) Sample Injection into Capillary Columns

The methods hitherto described fail or are very inaccurate for the very small samples required by capillary columns. Sample injectors for capillary columns, therefore, usually consist of one or other of the introduction devices described above, followed by a "stream splitter," in which the great majority of the sample is vented and goes to waste, and only a small proportion goes to the capillary column (*15–25*). Essentially, the stream splitter consists simply of a junction. One arm carries the incoming carrier gas, into which the sample has been homogeneously vaporised. One of the other arms leads to the capillary column, and the other arm leads to the atmosphere through an adjustable choke. The choke and the capillary thus form two resistances to the flow of gas, which is distributed between them. By adjusting the choke, the distribution can be adjusted, and in normal practice 99 to 99.9% of the gas is vented, and about 0.1 to 1% of the gas goes through the column.

It appears that the geometry of the stream splitter requires careful design in order to avoid some degree of fractionation of the sample, by which the composition of the vapour going to the column is neither the same as that vented nor the same as that entering the splitter. A simple

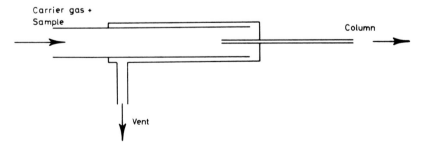

FIG. 11.3. Stream splitter designed to prevent sample fractionation (*25*).

Y-junction with unequal arms is inadequate. More satisfactory appear to be arrangements in which there are two concentric tubes, e.g., as shown in Fig. 11.3 (25).

(d) Gas Sampling Valves

The basis for most schemes for the injection of gases or samples of gases into chromatographic apparatuses is the circuit shown in Fig. 11.4. A sample cavity may be filled from the gas to be analysed, after which the gas may be isolated, and then swept into the column. Many apparatuses have been described in which this scheme or some obvious variant is used (26). Glass or metal stopcocks may be used, or the system of stopcocks may be made up into a "flat face valve," a valve in which flat discs of either metal or plastic carrying holes and cavities and sprung together are caused to rotate axially relative to one another. The tubes and cavities are arranged to provide sample cavities of suitable volume and the correct

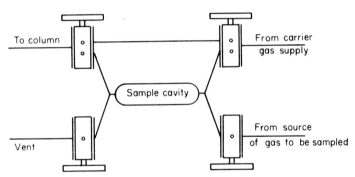

Fig. 11.4. Basic circuit for gas-sampling valves for gas chromatographic apparatuses.

switching of gas streams when the discs are turned (27, 28). Pratt and Purnell (29) describe a system in which there are two concentric cylinders, the outside diameter of the inner one being smaller than the inside diameter of the larger. The small cylinder is fitted with suitably arranged O-rings which divide the annular space between the cylinders into cavities; the cavities are fed by suitably bored holes in the cylinders.

(e) Sampling of Solids

Since liquids are more easily sampled than solids, it is preferable, if possible, to dissolve solid samples in a solvent which will not interfere in the chromatogram or in the detector, and to sample the solution. If samples must be introduced in the solid form, any of the techniques involving ampoules are satisfactory. In addition, several devices have been described for direct introduction of solids, e.g., ones in which solid samples are introduced on wires inserted down the inside of hypodermic needle tubing (*30, 31*), or ones in which small spoons carrying the samples are manipulated from the outside by magnets through suitably arranged air-locks (*32, 33*).

11.3. OTHER DETECTORS

The detectors described in Chapters 9 and 10 are the most frequently used for routine purposes. Numerous other detectors have been described, some of which find considerable application for non-routine or for special purposes. Frequently, these detectors are specific to particular types of compound, and can be used in conjunction with the general detectors described previously. A selection is described below.

(a) Absolute Integrating Detectors

A simple method for measuring gaseous solutes by the volume they occupy is to use carbon dioxide as carrier gas, and to collect the effluent

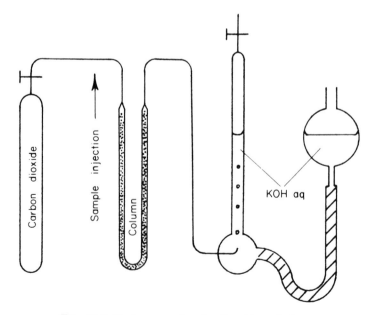

FIG. 11.5. Basic apparatus for Janak's technique.

from the column in a gas buret over potassium hydroxide solution (Fig. 11.5). This system was first introduced by Janak (*34*) and was subsequently elaborated (*35, 36*). At its simplest, the elution of each successive vapour is followed manually, the operator plotting the volume of gas collected against time, thus giving an integral chromatogram. The method can be used for any substance which is gaseous and does not dissolve in or react with the alkaline adsorbent or the carbon dioxide. It has been used especially for analysis of light hydrocarbons. The virtue of the system is its extreme simplicity and its independence of ordinary laboratory services e.g., dry ice can be used as the source of carbon dioxide (*35*). It is therefore suitable for incorporation into portable apparatus for field use. Various systems for automating the volume measurement have been described (*37–41*), but with these the simplicity is lost, and as a laboratory detector it compares unfavorably with other methods.

A method similar in principle to Janak's, but suitable for condensible or adsorbable material is that introduced by Bevan and Thorburn (*42, 43*). In this, the effluent from the column is led through a tube into an adsorption cell on one side of a balance (Fig. 11.6). As a solute appears from the tube, it is adsorbed in the cell, and the weight of solute is registered by the

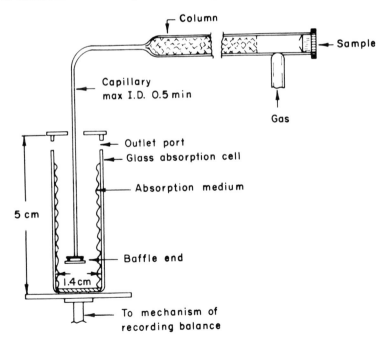

FIG. 11.6. Absolute mass detector of Bevan and Thorburn (*42*).

balance. Most conveniently, the balance is a recording electrobalance (43). The chromatogram appears in integral form.

The sensitivity of the detector depends on the sensitivity of the balance; Bevan *et al.* have used a balance which can weigh to 10^{-7} g. Since the detector measures mass directly, it requires no calibration of any sort, and its response is absolute, not relative.

(b) The Use of Servomechanisms

Measuring instruments as a whole can be classified into two classes: open- and closed-loop.

In open-loop instruments, the property to be measured is converted into a measurement in a series of stages involving a set of causal relations. For example, in the catharometer as described in Chapter 10, the vapour *causes* a change in thermal conductivity, which *causes* a change in the temperature of the hot element, which *causes* a change in its resistance, etc., till finally, the result of the presence of vapour shows as a deflection of a meter. If the response of an open-loop system is to be linear, every separate stage must be linear, which, as is apparent from Chapters 9 and 10, is not always easy to attain.

In a closed-loop instrument, the property to be measured is compared in a transducer with an equivalent property which can so react with the property that at perfect equivalence there is no output. With conditions other than perfect balance, there is an output from the transducer, called the "error signal," which is applied via further transducers to the transducer producing the equivalent property in such a way as to cause the error signal to converge to zero. The great advantage of the use of closed-loop systems, is that, of the various transductions, only one need be linear, i.e., that in which the property to be measured is balanced with its equivalent. The others need usually only be monotonic. For this and other reasons, there is a universal tendency in modern technology for closed-loop systems to replace open-loop systems where the two are otherwise comparable. Closed loop systems are used ubiquitously for control purposes, and their theory is well worked out, mainly in the context of electrical engineering, under the title of "Control Theory." In this context, closed loop control systems are usually called "Servomechanisms."

There are several GC servodetectors, in most of which the property of the vapour by which it is detected is a chemical property, and the equivalent property used to balance it is a chemical reagent which will react stoichiometrically with it. The general scheme, therefore, is as shown in

Fig. 11.7. Vapour from the column enters a *reactor*, and either in the reactor or beyond it, there is a *sensor* which is sensitive to the vapour. An error signal in the sensor promotes, via an *amplifier*, production of reagent in the *generator*, which is fed to the reactor till the sensor no longer gives an output.

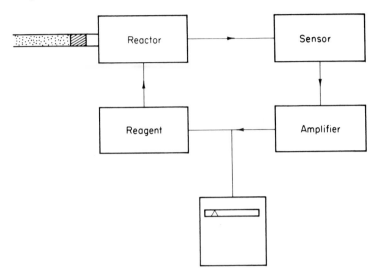

FIG. 11.7. Basic components of a servo-detector.

(c) Servodetectors

The first detector ever used for GLC, by James and Martin, was an automatic titrator for acid vapours, in which vapour from the column entered a titration cell; change in colour of the indicator was noted by a photocell, which thus formed the sensor. The error signal from the photocell operated a servo-amplifier which operated a motor-driven syringe buret filled with alkali (*44–46*). This apparatus has occasionally been used since (*47–51*), and a commercial automatic titrator has also been applied successfully to GC effluents (*52*).

More suitable for the small samples produced by GC are systems in which the reagent required to react with the vapours is produced coulometrically. Coulometric methods in GC were first used extensively by Liberti *et al.* (*53–57*) and by Juranek (*58*). Coulometric methods can be applied to any type of compound for which a suitable coulometric reaction exists. The standard method for solution coulometry of GC effluents can be illustrated by the method for the determination of halogens, using coulometrically generated silver (*59–62*). The titration cell (Fig. 11.8) contains four electrodes; two for the generation of reagent silver ions, and two for sensing whether or not there is still excess halide. The sensor electrodes consist of a silver/silver chloride electrode, together with a calomel electrode for reference. The generator electrodes consist of a silver cathode and a silver-plated platinum anode. The circuit is as shown in Fig. 11.8 (62). The output of the sensor cell is amplified and applied to a servomotor,

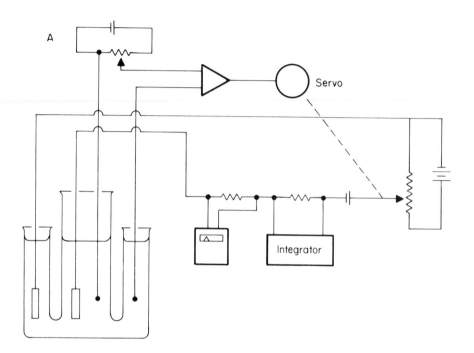

Fig. 11.8. Schematic diagram of a coulometer suitable for use as a gas-chromatographic detector.

which operates a potentiometer that supplies current to the generator electrodes. When the potential of the sensor cell falls to a value set by the backing-off circuit A, the generation of current ceases. In the steady state, therefore, there is no current, and current only flows when halogen halide is entering the cell from the column. The current is monitored by a strip-chart recorder, which thus shows an ordinary differential chromatogram.

In the majority of applications of solution coulometry to GC effluents, the effluent passes first through a reactor in which the vapours are converted into compounds which the coulometer can handle, and then directly into the coulometer cell. Thus, compounds containing only C, H, and O are converted to carbon dioxide, and it is this which is coulometrically estimated. The method is at its best for halogen and sulphur compounds, which are estimated as halogen halides, free halogens, or sulphur dioxide. For analysis of halogens, a silver cell is used, as described above. Sulphur dioxide from sulphur compounds is determined by coulometrically generated iodine (63, 64), or via silver (65) or bromine (66). For these substances, redox electrodes can be used as sensors. If carbon dioxide is titrated directly as a weak acid, it appears that the small pH changes resulting from solution of the carbon dioxide provide insufficient error signal to produce a viable servo-system. Carbon dioxide can, however, be titrated satisfactorily against coulometrically generated barium hydroxide, the barium carbonate being precipitated from solution. Coulometric titration of volatile strong acids or bases, e.g., amines or even ammonia, is feasible using potentiometric sensors (67, 68).

The servo-coulometer has been made the basis of a commercial instrument specially for GC purposes.

Littlewood, Wiseman et al. have described a type of coulometric servo-detector working entirely in the gas phase, the Reaction Coulometer (69). In this (Fig. 11.9), carrier gas from the column joins an auxiliary stream

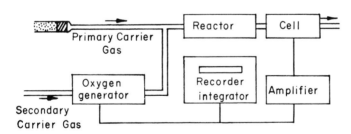

FIG. 11.9. Schematic diagram of reaction coulometer (69).

of gas which picks up a steady concentration of oxygen produced in the electrolytic generator by passage of a steady current. The two streams enter a reactor containing heated platinum, and thence to a cell sensitive to oxygen. The output of this cell is fed to an amplifier which supplies the current to the oxygen generator. In the absence of a vapour, a stable control loop is set up and the constant oxygen concentration provides a steady base-line. When a vapour appears, it burns with the oxygen in the reactor, causing a fall in the cell output, and thus an increase in the oxygen generation. The vapour, in fact, acts as a perturbation to the control of the oxygen concentration, and the system, if properly designed, acts as a perfect control in completely removing the perturbation. The extra oxygen required to do this is exactly equivalent to the perturbing vapour, and by monitoring the oxygen generation, a chromatogram is obtained.

The above scheme provides a general purpose detector for any combustible organic compound. The detector becomes specific to hydrogenatable material if the connections to the electrolytic generator are reversed so that it generates hydrogen, if a hydrogenation catalyst is employed in the reactor, and if a cell sensitive to hydrogen is used (70).

Coulometric methods have the great advantage that they are absolute; for every molecule of vapour entering the detector, an integral number of electrons is transferred in a stoichiometric reaction. Thus, the response is measured as a current which may be related exactly with the mass flow of vapour into the detector, and the area of a peak may be calculated in coulombs, which may be related with the mass of vapour in a peak. For example, a compound $C_aH_bO_c$ being analysed by combustion in a reaction coulometer will react:

$$C_aH_bO_c + zO_2 = aCO_2 + b/2 \ H_2O,$$

where $z = a + \frac{1}{4}b - \frac{1}{2}c$. Application of Faraday's law then shows that the number of coulombs in a peak is related with the mass of vapour of molecular weight M by the relation:

$$1 \ \text{coulomb} \equiv \frac{2.591}{10^6} \cdot \frac{M}{z} \ \text{g.}$$

The effective sensitivity of coulometric detectors is determined by the noise in current generation which, both for liquid phase and gas phase systems, appears to be in the range of microamperes. Quantities of electricity of the order of microcoulombs are significant, and calculation as exemplified above shows that this usually corresponds to masses of the order of 10^{-9} g.

The linearity of coulometric detectors depends solely on the stoichiometry of the reaction, and linearity in the production of reagent and in the read-out. Of these, error in linearity in read-out is easily avoided, and there is no evidence for non-linear production of reagent. Though there are regimens in which the stoichiometry of the reaction can err, e.g., formation of SO_3 rather than SO_2 during coulometric determination of sulphur (63) such cases are few.

11.4. Gas Chromatography and Mass Spectrometry

(a) *Mass Spectra*

The mass spectrum of a pure compound separated from a mixture by GC gives much evidence on its structure, and in many cases can enable one to identify it unambiguously. Analytical information is obtained from a mass spectrum from the *parent ion*, i.e., the ion formed simply by loss of one electron from the sample molecule, which at once gives the molecular weight; and from the *fragmentation pattern*, which is the pattern formed by the differing intensities of all ions of lower molecular weight made by fragmentation of the molecule during ionisation. Fragmentation patterns for most of the better-known classes of organic compounds have been extensively studied, and general rules relating pattern to structure are available (*71–76*). Also, mass spectra for large numbers of compounds are published (*77–79*).

Mass-spectrometers can be classified into "low-resolution" and "high resolution" instruments. The former are those which will resolve individual mass-numbers up to about 1000, and thus will give a separate peak for each unit mass number likely to be encountered in any molecule volatile enough to be introduced into the vapour phase. "High-resolution" is considered to be of the order of 1 in 10,000 or more. An instrument with this resolution not only resolves all mass-numbers likely to be found, but is also capable of distinguishing between different ions, e.g., CH_2^+ and N^+, which have the same unit mass number, but whose masses differ slightly because of the precise isotopic weights. The use of high-resolution techniques is somewhat more elaborate and expensive than low-resolution, but is particularly useful if samples may contain elements other than C, H, and O (*80*). Most current applications use low-resolution instruments. In addition to those using magnetic resolution, time-of-flight and quadrupole spectrometers can be used. The combination of GC with MS has been reviewed by Henneberg and Schomburg (*81*), by Vollmin *et al.* (*82*), and by Littlewood (*83*).

(b) *GC–MS Instrumentation*

The most straightforward ways of coupling MS and GC is to trap out a sample from the GC effluent, and apply this to the spectrometer through its normal inlet system. This system is commonly used, but of greater interest are systems whereby the GC outlet is coupled intimately with the MS inlet, so that emerging GC zones can enter the spectrometer directly, and mass spectra may be taken during the elution: a method often referred to as "on the fly." In coupling the GC to the MS, the principal requirement is that the pressure must be reduced from about atmospheric on the GC side to about 10^{-4} or 10^{-5} Torr at the MS inlet. If a capillary column of not more than 0.01 in. diameter is used for the GC, it has been found adequate simply to use the latter part of the column as the required choke, the column outlet being connected straight into the MS ion chamber. As is apparent from the discussion of Section 2.5, most of the pressure drop occurs at the end of the column, and the column efficiency is not materially affected (84).

A drawback to the use of a simple restrictive leak between GC column and MS inlet, whether this is part of a capillary column or a separate leak, is that the whole of the carrier gas enters the spectrometer. The carrier gas thus contributes the great majority to the pressure in the ion source, and since this pressure is subject to a maximum, the concentration of sample is severely limited. It is thus desirable to feed the column effluent to the spectrometer via a device which separates the carrier from the sample as far as this is possible. Such devices are called "molecular separators" and use the fact that the carrier molecules are lighter than those of the samples likely to be of interest. Ryhage (85, 86) uses a method described by Becker (87) in which, when the gas has been reduced to a pressure low enough for molecular flow by a preliminary choke, it is allowed to pass through two orifices in line with one another, the space between them being pumped (Fig. 11.10). In these circumstances, the heavy molecules passing through one orifice continue in a straight line to pass into the second orifice, while the light molecules are deflected to a greater extent by molecular collisions, so that they miss the second orifice, and eventually migrate to the pumps. By using two such separators, concentration factors of 50 : 1 can be achieved if helium is used as carrier (85, 88).

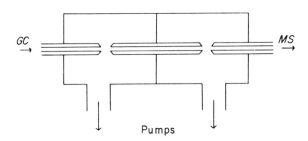

FIG. 11.10. Molecular separator operating by molecular momentum. Ryhage (85) and Becker (87).

An alternate type of molecular separator is illustrated in Figure 11.11. In this, the gas from the column first passes a restriction A, which reduces the pressure to give molecular flow within the porous tube B; the pressure in this tube should depend on the pore diameter, e.g., for 10 micron pore, the pressure should be of the order of 1 Torr. The far side of the porous tube is pumped, so that gas passes through the tube by effusion, which is faster for the carrier gas and slower for the sample. The gas inside the tube thus becomes enriched in sample. A second restriction at C lowers from that required for effusion to that required by the MS. Such a system has been used by several workers, using sintered glass as the porous medium (*89*). Yet another scheme is to use apparatus as in Fig. 11.11, but to use a material such as Teflon at about 250°C in place of the porous material for the tube (*80, 90, 91*).

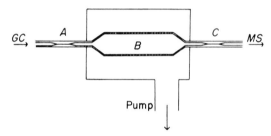

FIG. 11.11. Molecular separator working by effusion (*80, 89*).

The effluent from a GC column attached to a mass spectrometer can be monitored in any ordinary detector fed through a stream splitter (Section 11.2c); alternatively, the spectrometer itself can be used as the detector. Many spectrometers employ a "Total Ion Current Monitor," which collects a small proportion, e.g., 10% of all the ions, and records their current. This device can form as sensitive a detector as ordinary GC ionisation detectors. An alternative method is to use the advantage of the MS that a given mass peak in the mass spectrum is characteristic not only of the amount of a component, but also of its chemical nature. Thus, if in a chromatogram two substances overlap, and each substance has a characteristic mass peak not given by the other, separate resolved chromatographic peaks of each component can be obtained from each characteristic mass peak (*92, 93*). Sweeley *et al.* (*94*) describe an elaboration of this technique in which the spectrometer is caused to switch frequently from one pre-set characteristic peak to the other during the elution; the envelopes of the two repeating alternating peaks display the two chromatographic peaks (Fig. 11.12).

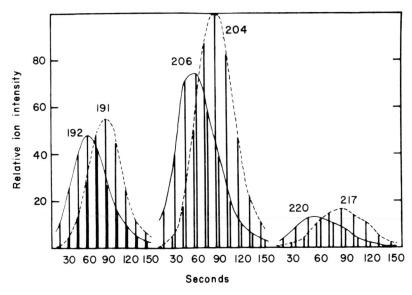

Fig. 11.12. Chromatographic peaks appearing as the envelopes of fragmentation ion intensities of successive mass-spectrometric measurements on a sample of mixed glucose and glucose-d$_7$ chromatographed on silicone SE30. Sweeley *et al.*, (*94*).

(c) *Operation of GC-MS*

The quantities required by a mass spectrometer are determined in part by its resolution, and in part by the requirements that, in general, ion currents should not exceed about 10^{-13} amp in order to avoid pressure broadening, and pressures in the ion source should not exceed about 10^{-5} to 10^{-4} Torr. With high resolution instruments, the sensitivity tends to be poor because of the narrowness of the slits, so that samples of the order of 10 μg are required (*80*). For lower resolution, however, smaller quantities are adequate. Thus, Ryhage *et al.* (*86*) report mass spectra from samples of 1 μg, and recognisable spectra in favourable cases from 20 ng. The total ion detector can work on a quantity considerably smaller than is required to give a spectrum suitable for qualitative identification; for example, a factor 100 smaller (*84*). Thus, it is possible to use the total ion monitor to detect as little as 0.5 ng (*86*).

From the above figures, it is apparent that the quantities handled by liquid layer capillary columns, which are of the order of micrograms, are adequate for use on relatively slow, low resolution, spectrometers. For fast, high resolution operation, however, there is a strong case for the use of porous layer open tube columns (Section 7.3d) which can handle larger samples (*80*), though, apparently, liquid layer capillary columns can also be used.

Packed columns are satisfactory for use with MS, in which case only a small proportion of the effluent is probably necessary for the spectrometer. In any column used with MS, it is more than usually important that there is no "bleed" of stationary liquid, since any such relatively involatile material is likely to produce memory effects in the spectrometer, or even a permanent background spectrum which may only be removed with difficulty.

If a mass spectrometer is to study each chromatographic peak separately during on-the-fly operation, it must be able to scan a mass-spectrum in less time than is occupied by the elution of a peak. The minimum scan time of the spectrometer is determined by the fact that each mass number must be scanned for long enough by the ion collector that statistical fluctuation in the number of ions is as small as is desired. The effect of fluctuations is best illustrated by the figures given by McFadden and Day (*95*), who point out that a peak with a typical ion current of 10^{-14} amp scanned for 1 msec gives a count of 100 ions; fluctuations in this may be as much as 10%. In practice, assuming 10^{-13} amp as an upper limit for ion current, peaks cannot, therefore, be scanned in less than about 10^{-4} sec. Thus, a typical low-resolution scan from 20 through 200 m/e would take not less than about 100 msec, and a high-resolution scan from 200 to 2000 could not take less than 1 sec. In practice, scan rates of this order are attainable, but usually scanning is somewhat slower, e.g., 0.5 sec for low resolution and 5 to 10 sec for high resolution. Scan rates may also be determined by the nature of the recording equipment; see Section 11.7.

(d) Applications

Combined GC–MS techniques have been extensively applied, mainly to large-scale analytical projects designed to elucidate the compositions of mixtures of complex organic compounds. The technique has found particular favour in the field of flavour research. Summaries of published applications are given in (*82*) and (*83*).

11.5. Gas Chromatography and Infrared Spectrophotometry

The analytical technique whereby IR spectrophotometry is used to study the separate components emerging from a GC column is probably the commonest of the combined techniques involving GC. A recent review has been given by the author (*96*).

There are several ways in which GC and IR may be coupled:

(1) The vapour emerging from the column is trapped, and simply transferred to an IR spectrophotometer.

(2) The vapour from the column is condensed so that it can be transferred to the IR cell without external handling, e.g., by washing through with a solvent.

(3) The vapour is condensed into a trap which also forms the IR cell.

(4) The vapour is passed into an IR gas cell, the spectrum being taken in the gas phase.

(5) IR spectra are taken of vapours "on the fly," as they are eluted.

Of these five methods, the majority of applications still use the simplest technique, i.e., (1). As technology improves, however, the more sophisticated methods are gaining favour.

(a) Sample Quantities

The average size of sample handled in analytical GC is considerably smaller than that normally used in IR spectrophotometry. Thus, for the combination, each technique must strain to meet the requirements of the other. The minimum samples required by the IR spectrometer can be assessed with reference to Beer's law:

$$A = \varepsilon c l,$$

where A is the absorbance, c is the sample concentration in moles/litre, l is the path length of the cell in centimeters, and ε is the molar extinction coefficient of the sample. The molar extinction coefficient is a function of the nature of the sample and the wavelength; a spectrum is essentially a plot of ε against wavelength. Practical IR spectrophotometers cannot conveniently handle values of A less than about 0.005. In IR spectra, a value of $\varepsilon \approx 1$ litre/mole/cm is regarded as a weak band, $\varepsilon \approx 10$ is considered as medium, and $\varepsilon \approx 100$ is considered strong. On this basis, one can construct a table (Table 11.1) showing minimum acceptable samples in different circumstances. All figures in Table 11.1 pertain to $A \not< 0.005$. The first row shows the minimum acceptable sample concentrations in mole/liter for which it is possible to obtain satisfactory spectra. This quantity is a function of path length, l.

The units of cl are mole/area. Thus, a criterion independent of cell length can be expressed in terms of a threshold in cl, expressed most suitably in micromoles per square centimeter, which gives the number of

TABLE 11.1

Approximate Minimum Samples for Infrared Spectrophotometry
of GC Effluents[a]

		Weak Band[b]	Medium Band[c]	Strong Band[d]
Concentration, moles/litre	≮	0.005/1	0.0005/1	0.00005/1
cl, μ moles/cm²	≮	5	0.5	0.05
Sample for 0.1 cm² cell cross section:				
μ moles	≮	0.5	0.05	0.005
μg of substance of M.W. = 200	≮	100	10	1
Sample for 1 cm² cell cross section:				
μ moles	≮	5	0.5	0.05
μg of substance of M.W. = 200	≮	1000	100	10

[a] For $A \nless 0.005$ (96).
[b] $\varepsilon \approx 1$ litre/mole/centimeter.
[c] $\varepsilon \approx 10$ litre/mole/centimeter.
[d] $\varepsilon \approx 100$ litre/mole/centimeter.

micromoles there must be in each square centimeter of cross-section of the sample through which the IR light passes in order to get a satisfactory spectrum. These figures are given in the second row of the Table. Practical IR spectrophotometers usually require cells whose cross-section is between 0.1 and 1 cm². In the following rows of the Table, therefore, we give the minimum sample, both in micromoles and in micrograms for a typical substance of molecular weight of 200, first for a cell of cross-section 1 cm², and then for a cell of cross-section 0.1 cm². It is seen that in the specially favourable case of a strong band in a spectrophotometer of cross-section 0.1 cm², a sample of 1 μg can be handled. In the least favourable case, 1 mg is necessary. General experience bears out the figures of the Table; samples of 50 μg and more can usually be made to give usable spectra with relative ease, but the difficulties increase with smaller samples.

The sensitivities of IR spectrophotometers can be increased to a limited degree either by a beam condenser, thus focussing more light through a cell of small cross-section, or by electronic expansion of the ordinate scale. By these means, a small decrease in the minimum usable adsorbance can be secured (97).

(b) *Liquid Samples*

The principal advantage of the use of liquid samples for IR is that the spectra of liquids are very much more familiar than those of gases, and thus there is a greater likelihood that a given sample will give a spectrum which can be identified either from general compilations of spectra, or from the general principles assigning different bands to given molecular structural features (*98*).

Many workers have devoted attention to the problem of condensing samples from GC streams without formation of fog, or other loss of sample (See Section 7.5). Many different designs of traps have been produced (*96*). Of most relevance to IR are those in which the trap also consists of the IR cell. In such devices, the GC effluent usually emerges through a heated hypodermic needle into a suitably cooled cell. In order to avoid deleterious effects from condensation of water vapour, materials other than alkali halides are used for the cell, e.g., polythene (*99*) or silver chloride (*100*). Cells working on multiple internal reflection rather than simple transmission have also been used for direct GC/IR application (*97, 101*). Liquid samples, as well as solid samples, can also be condensed into cooled potassium bromide crystals, which are subsequently made into IR windows in the usual way (*102–107*).

(c) *Gaseous Samples*

The principal advantage of using gas samples is that there is no need for condensation. A drawback is that the IR spectra of vapours are not so widely studied as those of liquids. Though the general pattern of gas spectra resembles that of the corresponding liquid, absorption bands in gases tend to be shallower and broader. With polar or hydrogen-bonded substances in particular, bands of the vapours are shifted from those of the liquids.

Because of the great dilution of vapour emerging from GC columns, the gas cells used for IR work must necessarily have long path lengths. Long gas cells consisting of straight "light pipes" can be accommodated on normal IR spectrophotometers if the base-plate is lengthened, and these can also be heated (*101*). This method seems to be preferred to the more compact gas cells which achieve long path length by internal mirrors (*108*).

The use of IR spectrophotometers for analysing GC peaks as they are eluted is complicated by the fact that, in general, spectrophotometers take their spectra more slowly than gas chromatographs produce their peaks (*97*). A further factor is that the volume occupied by a peak will in general not be the volume of the gas cell. The most desirable situation is that of Fig. 11.13a, in which virtually the whole of a peak just fits into the gas cell. If the peak is broader, however, the cell will accommodate at most only a fraction of the material of peak, thus losing sensitivity (Fig. 11.13b). If the peak is narrower, as shown in Fig. 11.13c, the whole of the material is contained in the cell, but there would be overlap in the measurement of two closely eluted peaks, thus effectively reducing the resolution of the

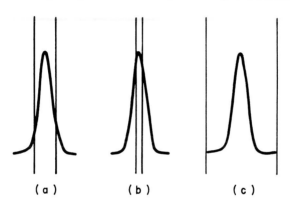

(a)   (b)   (c)

FIG. 11.13. To illustrate the effect of the relative volumes of a gas IR absorption cell and the volume of gas occupied by a peak. The abscissa represents volume and the distance between the vertical lines is the volume of the cell. (a) is optimum; in (b) sensitivity is lost; in (c) resolution is lost.

column. In order to overcome the incompatibility of times, several workers have tried to produce spectrophotometers with small scan times, yet without loss of IR resolution, e.g., by the use of spectrophotometers which scan simultaneously in two different regions of the spectrum, 2.5–7 μ and 6.5–16 μ (*101, 109*), or by the use of wedge spectrometers (*110*). Another solution is that of Scott *et al.* (*111*) who have described a technique in which the elution is interrupted as soon as a vapour is present in the IR cell, and the spectrum is run at leisure during the interruption. When the spectrum is complete, the elution is recommenced.

11.6. CHEMICAL METHODS USED WITH GAS CHROMATOGRAPHY

Chemical reactions used explicitly in connection with gas chromatographic analysis are frequently useful, especially for identification purposes, or in simplifying the analysis of complex mixtures. They may be classified into those which occur before separation, in a reactor placed before the column, and those which occur on separate components, in reactors after the column (*112*).

(*a*) *Pre-Columns for Selective Removal of Components*

In the analysis of a complex mixture, it is frequently advantageous to be able to remove groups of components belonging to specific classes. Reagents which react selectively with given groups of compounds, converting them into completely non-volatile products, can be packed into a short column which may be placed before the chromatographic column. Such a pre-column can be used in several ways:

(1) It is common to chromatograph a mixture on the same column twice, once with the subtractive column and once without it. By comparing the two chromatograms, the peaks in the second due to the components which react with the pre-column are absent in the first, and can thus be identified.

(2) If two components for which quantitative analysis is required cannot be resolved, a sample is chromatographed both with and without a pre-

TABLE 11.2

REAGENTS FOR SELECTIVE REMOVAL OF VAPOURS AT A GC COLUMN INLET[a]

Vapours removed	Reagent
Ethylene	Bromine/charcoal
Olefins	Cuprous chloride, mercuric perchlorate
Alkenes	Sulphuric acid/silica gel
Butadiene	Maleic anhydride
Aldehydes	Sodium bisulphite/ethylene glycol
Carbonyl compounds	Sodium bisulphite
Sulphur compounds	Mercuric chloride
Amines	Phosphoric acid
Secondary and tertiary alkyl bromides	Silver nitrate
Alkanols	Boric acid/Carbowax
Acids	Potassium hydroxide
Water	Calcium carbide, diglycerol, potassium carbonate, Drierite/PEG 400
n-Paraffins	Molecular sieve
Oxygen	Hydrogen/catalyst, ammoniacal palladium complex

[a] See Littlewood (*112*).

column which removes one component. From the difference in the peaks, the amount of the component removed may be computed. This system has application, e.g., in the analysis of argon and oxygen; see Section 12.1.

(3) In the analysis of very complex chromatograms, in which the removal of one or more classes of compounds enables the pattern of peaks among those remaining to be seen more clearly. For example, in the analysis of waxes, the removal of the n-alkanes reveals the pattern of branched components.

Table 11.2 gives a list of selective reagents the use of which has been published, together with the classes of compounds they remove. In general, conditions for preparing the pre-column appear not to be critical. Liquid or solid reagents may be suspended on Celite or silica gel, and pre-columns are prepared very much as for separating columns, but they are shorter. A reagent which is itself volatile may be rendered involatile by adsorption on a strong adsorbent (113, 114). The reactivity of a solid reagent may be increased if it is used in the presence of a solvent in which the substance to be removed has a large partition coefficient (115, 116).

(b) Catalytic Hydrogenation

For analysis of complex mixtures containing hydrogenatable material, it has often been found useful to hydrogenate the components in a pre-column, the hydrogenated products continuing to the separating column. Catalytic hydrogenations can normally be achieved so rapidly that there is negligible broadening of any peaks due to slow reaction in the hydrogenator. In this way, complicated mixtures of alkenes can be hydrogenated to give a much simpler mixture of alkanes, and the carbon skeletons of individual alkenes can be determined from the structure of the alkane they produce (117, 118), the latter being easily identifiable, e.g., by retention or MS. In another technique, the catalytic hydrogenator pre-column is provided with a by-pass, so that part of the sample escapes hydrogenation, the hydrogenated sample and the unhydrogenated sample both appearing on the same chromatogram (119, 120). In this way, the change in retention caused by hydrogenation can be observed directly and accurately, and hence the number and sometimes the positions of the double bonds can be identified using known retention relations.

In catalytic hydrogenation runs, hydrogen is necessarily used as the carrier gas, and the most suitable catalysts are the metals platinum, palladium, and nickel, of which the first two act very much more rapidly and effectively than the third. For hydrocarbons, a small pre-column of the metal packed on kieselguhr, with diameter similar to that of the separating column, and 5 to 10 cm long, is adequate (*121–124*). The preparation of hydrogenation catalysts for GC has been studied particularly by Beroza *et al.* (*125–130*), who have correlated catalytic activity with the acidity of the surface on which the metal is deposited. On the whole, neutral or alkaline catalysts are the more active, and, by controlling the amount of catalyst and the temperature, either double bonds alone, or double bonds together with various polar groups, can be reduced. By altering the conditions, therefore, different degrees of selectivity can be introduced.

(c) Reagent Pre-Columns

There are several useful techniques in which a pre-column contains a reagent which reacts on a sample, usually so as to produce compounds characteristic of the sample which are easily separated and estimated. In many cases, such a technique may be used to convert an involatile species directly introduced into the apparatus into a volatile derivative which may be analysed and separated from its fellows.

One of the first of such applications was that of "Flash Exchange" analysis, introduced by Ralls *et al.* (*131–133*). In this, mixtures of aldehydes were isolated in the form of their 2,4-dinitrophenylhydrazones, and these derivatives were injected into a pre-column containing α-ketoglutaric acid at 200 to 300°C. The involatile ketonic acid displaces the aldehydes from their derivatives, so that they enter the column to be chromatographed. The method can also be used for the analysis of mixtures of salts of fatty acids, in which case the potassium salts are introduced into a pre-column containing potassium hydrogen sulphate (*131*).

Since esters are easier to analyse by GC than their parent acids or alcohols, considerable effort has been applied to developing pre-columns for esterification. Alcohols are most easily esterified to their nitrites (*134, 135*). The use of acetic anhydride has also been reported (*136*). The preparation of methyl esters of fatty acids is considered separately in Section 12.6.

A very general method for microanalysis using GC and prior chemical reaction is described by Hoff and Feit (*137, 138*). In this, vapours for analysis are drawn into ordinary hypodermic syringes which contain the reagent. After reaction, the vapours may be injected directly into the gas chromatograph. The authors give a list of reagents and reactions which may be employed (Table 11.3). It is clear that any of the involatile reagents listed could also be used in pre-columns.

TABLE 11.3

Reagents Suitable for Use with Vaporised GC Samples[a]

Reagent	Function
Sodium metal	Removes all but ethers and hydrocarbons
Sulphuric acid	Removes most substances but leaves aromatics and paraffins
Hydrogen/platinum oxide	Saturates olefins
Hydrogen iodide	Cleaves ethers
Bromine water	Brominates; removes unsaturates
Hydroxylamine	Removes carbonyl compounds
Sodium borohydride	Converts carbonyl compounds to alcohols
Potassium permanganate soln. in water	Oxidises aldehydes, but leaves ketones; forms ketones from secondary alkanols
Sodium nitrite	Forms nitrites from alkanols
Acetic anhydride	Forms acetic esters from alcohols
Sodium hydroxide	Hydrolysis
Ozone	Removes unsaturates
Hydrochloric acid	Removes amines and other bases
Sodium bicarbonate	Removes acidic substances
Sodium arsenite	Reduces ozonides

[a] See Hoff and Feit (*137*).

(d) *Carbon-Hydrogen-Nitrogen Analysis*

The elemental analysis of organic compounds is one of the commonest of all analyses. Classically, the sample is burned in oxygen at about 900°C to give carbon dioxide, water, and nitrogen; any oxides of nitrogen also formed are reduced to nitrogen and water in a secondary reactor. The classical method can be combined with GC, if GC is used to determine the products. Several techniques have been described. In one, the mixture of nitrogen, carbon dioxide, and water are separated on a column using helium as carrier gas, and the peaks are measured catharometrically (*139*). Triethanolamine forms a particularly suitable stationary liquid for this separation (*140*). In another technique, the mixture of reaction products passes successively through three catharometers between each of which is a subtractive agent, water being removed between the first and second, and carbon dioxide between second and third. From the responses of the catharometers, the quantities can be determined (*141*).

(e) Reactions after Gas-Chromatographic Separation

There are two main reasons for causing vapours eluted from a column to pass through a reactor at the outlet:

(1) To convert the vapour to a form more suitable for detection. In particular, for accurate quantitative analysis, substances may all be converted stoichiometrically to a single species, e.g., carbon dioxide, thus avoiding the doubt inherent in attributing different calibration coefficients to each substance in the detector.

(2) For qualitative identification of eluted components, using specific spot tests.

The conversion of organic vapours to carbon dioxide has frequently been used, almost invariably with a reactor filled with granular copper oxide at about 700°C. In earlier work, the purpose was to stimulate sensitivity of catharometers, since in the oxidation, the mass of organic material to which the catharometer could respond was tripled (*142–146*). In more recent applications, however, the reason has been to secure accurate quantitative

TABLE 11.4

SPOT REAGENTS FOR GAS-CHROMATOGRAPHIC EFFLUENTS[a]

Class of Compound	Reagent	Colour
Alcohols	Potassium dichromate/nitric acid	Blue
Aldehydes	2,4-Dinitrophenylhydrazine	Yellow precipitate
Ketones	Schiff's	Pink
	2,4-Dinitrophenyl-hydrazine	Yellow precipitate
Esters	Ferrous hydroxamate	Red
Mercaptans	Sodium nitroprusside	Red
	Isatin	Green
	Lead acetate	Yellow precipitate
Sulphides, Disulphides	Sodium nitroprusside	Red
Amines	Hinsberg	Orange
	Sodium nitroprusside	Red (primary)
		Blue (secondary)
Nitriles	Ferrous hydroxamate/propylene glycol	
Aromatics, Aliphatic unsaturated	Formaldehyde/sulphuric acid	Red
Aliphatic unsaturated, Alkyl halide	Alcoholic silver nitrate	White precipitate

[a] See Walsh and Merritt (*153*).

analysis. For this, estimation of the carbon dioxide by titration (*147, 148*), by colorimetry (*149–152*) or by coulometry as described in Section 11.3c has been favoured.

Oxidation reactors oxidise sulphur compounds to sulphur dioxide, and nitrogen compounds to the element. The oxidation of halogens depends on exact conditions. Chlorine is converted to hydrogen chloride if there is also enough hydrogen in the molecule; otherwise, $COCl_2$ may be formed, and possibly some elementary chlorine. Bromine and iodine are oxidised to the elements.

Methods for spot testing of GC effluents have been developed by Walsh and Merritt (*153*), by Casu and Cavallotti (*154*), and by Janak (*155*). Walsh and Merritt divide the effluent into many different streams each of which passes through a suitable colour reagent. Casu and Cavallotti use a technique in which spot reagents are absorbed on filter paper. Table 11.4, from Walsh and Merritt, lists spot reagents suitable for GC effluents.

11.7. DATA HANDLING EQUIPMENT

By far the commonest vehicle for display of GC data is the strip-chart recorder, and analytical measurements of retention, peak area, or peak height are conveniently made from the chromatograms it produces. The exclusive use of strip-chart recorders for routine analytical operation requires, however, considerable man-power, and it is usually economical to use more sophisticated data handling equipment. Items in current use are integrators for measurement of peak areas, and digitisers so that chromatograms can be digitised for handling in digital computers.

(a) *Integrators*

Integrators for determining areas in GC can be classified into three main classes, digital integrators, mechanical integrators, and integrating amplifiers, of which the first attract the most attention.

In a digital integrator, the signal from the chromatograph is caused to generate electrical pulses via a voltage-to-frequency converter, at a rate accurately proportional to the voltage or current from the peak. The total number of pulses produced during the peak is thus proportional to its area. This number is counted and displayed visually or on a printing counter, or both. With mechanical counters, the maximum count rate is about 10,000 per minute. For much gas chromatography this is adequate, since the majority of peaks do not occupy less than about 10 sec. If the maximum of such a peak were set to give maximum rate, it would register about 800 counts, the statistical fluctuation in which would normally be considered negligible. For faster peaks, or for analyses of pairs of peaks of very different areas, a faster count rate can be provided by apparatus using electronic counters, which can count up to 10^6 per minute or faster.

In all digital integrators, counting is initiated only after the peak has started, since the signal to start counting can only be given by peak itself. Similarly, at the end of peak, counting is terminated only by the act of the peak fading into the base-line. Initiation and termination occur either on the departure of the record from the baseline and its return (difference initiation), or on the slope of the record as the peak starts and finishes (slope initiation).

It is clearly desirable that the thresholds of difference or slope above which counting is initiated be as small as possible, so that as little as possible of the ends of the peaks is not counted. It is easy to adjust the electronics to make very small initiation thresholds, but in practice they must be made large enough that initiation is not caused by noise or any slight base-line drift. Thus frequently, errors due to non-negligible initiation thresholds are appreciable. Fig. 11.14 illustrates a Gaussian peak of height

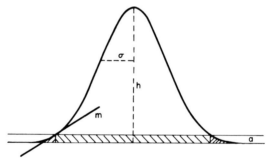

FIG. 11.14. Illustration of the errors inherent in the use of a digital integrator.

h and standard deviation σ where initiation and termination of integration are assumed to occur at points a above the base-line, or at slopes $\pm m$. The proportional error in measurement of area due to initiation and termination at $a > 0$ is a function of a/h. It is shown as the heavily shaded area in Fig. 11.14 and is tabulated as a percentage in the first column of Table 11.5. The significance of a in relation to h is immediately obvious; for example, if initiation occurs more than 5% of the way up a peak, the error exceeds 1.4%. Another serious error in digital integration occurs if

TABLE 11.5

PERCENTAGE ERRORS IN INTEGRATION OF GAUSSIAN PEAKS[a]

a/h	A[b] $200 \, \text{erfc}\left(2 \ln \dfrac{h}{a}\right)^{1/2}$	B[c] $A + 200 \, \dfrac{a}{h}\left(\dfrac{1}{\pi} \ln \dfrac{h}{a}\right)^{1/2}$
0.005	0.12	1.42
0.01	0.24	2.66
0.02	0.52	4.98
0.03	0.76	7.10
0.05	1.42	11.2
0.07	2.10	15.0
0.10	3.2	20.2
0.15	5.1	28.4
0.20	7.2	36.0
0.50	23.8	70.8

[a] See Littlewood (*156*).

[b] Peak of height h; integrator base-line coincident with true base-line; initiation and conclusion of counting at height a above base-line.

[c] Peak of height h; integrator base-line at a point a above true base-line; counting for all positive signals to integrator.

the zero count rate of the integrator does not exactly coincide with the chromatographic base-line. If the zero of the integrator lies above the chromatographic base-line, the whole of the shaded area of Fig. 11.14 remains uncounted; the corresponding error is again a function of a/h, with a representing the ordinate distance between the two zeros. The percentage error is tabulated in the second column of Table 11.5. It is apparent from the table that even very small deviations can cause large errors; for example, a misplacement of the integrator zero by only 0.5% of the peak height causes an error of 1.42% in analysis.

In the case of slope initiation, the error is a function of $m\sigma/h$, and a table of errors similar to that of Table 11.5 can be constructed (*156*).

Among mechanical integrators, the "Ball and Disc" system is the most familiar. This device can be attached to a strip chart recorder; a ball moves with the recorder pen, at the same time being in contact with a disc revolving at a constant rate, the centre of the disc corresponding to the recorder zero. The disc causes the ball to rotate at a speed which is proportional to its distance from the disc centre, which is also proportional to the pen reading. A count of the number of ball rotations thus gives the area of a peak.

The integrating amplifier is a device which provides an output which is the time integral of the input; it thus converts an ordinary differential chromatogram into its integral form, from which peak areas can be measured as the distance between steps. Though integrating amplifiers are commonplace, and indeed form a component in digital integrators, their use for direct integration in this manner appears to be small.

(b) Digitisation of Chromatograms

In order for continuously generated data, e.g., chromatograms, to be handled by digital computers, it must first be converted into digital form. In the case of GC, this is done by sampling the electrical output of the detector at regular intervals so that the chromatogram is represented by a set of numbers. The sampling must occur fast enough that no significant information is lost between samples; sampling rates between about 30 (157) and 5 (158) samples per peak have been used satisfactorily, but the exact rate of sampling depends exactly on how the digitised chromatogram is to be processed; see below.

The digitised samples representing the chromatogram can either be written onto a transfer medium, e.g., punched or magnetic tape, or can be introduced directly to a computer; the latter case is known as *on line* operation. A typical example of the essential apparatus for digitisation in the former case is illustrated in Fig. 11.15. The signal from the detector is put into an *analog-digital converter* (A/D converter), which converts the

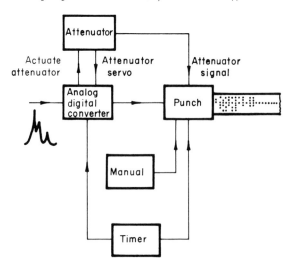

FIG. 11.15. Block diagram of apparatus for digitising a chromatogram.

analog value of voltage or current at a given instant or averaged over a given short period into a set of electrical pulses representing its digital value. A suitable A/D converter for GC use is an integrating digital voltmeter, many varieties of which are commercially available. The set of pulses is then transferred to paper tape, as shown, by a tape punch, or to magnetic tape in a suitable recorder. A timer is used to trigger the instants or periods at which the A/D converter takes its readings. For GC purposes in which of the order of 10 samples are required per peak, the timer will normally operate at a frequency between 10 times per second and once every 10 seconds, depending on the speeds of appearance of peaks. In addition, an attenuator is usually necessary to be able to cover the large dynamic range covered by GC, and attenuation information is also printed onto the transfer medium. Finally, the operator may wish to introduce manual instructions or labels on to a given chromatogram; the normal technique for this is to have a typewriter keyboard by which letters and/or numbers can be typed straight onto the tape. The literature contains a growing number of papers with details of the many variants of digitisation systems suitable for different experimental circumstances (*157–169*).

In the case of on-line operation, there is the choice between the use of a small computer which reads and handles the output of just one chromatograph, or the use of a larger machine which can handle the output of many chromatographs simultaneously. The latter system, which is suitable for the larger analytical installations, uses "multiplexing" apparatus, by which the outputs from each of many chromatographs are sampled in rotation. Both types of system are produced commercially.

(c) *Computer Programs for GC*

Any arithmetical operation required on data from a chromatogram of resolved or almost resolved peaks to produce analytical data is feasible with ease on any computer large enough to contain the data itself. Thus, programs to perform the following operations on a digitised chromatogram are simply prepared:

(1) Allow for base-line noise and drift;

(2) Record peak retentions either absolutely or relatively, either linearly or logarithmically;

(3) Calculate and display peak areas, either relatively or absolutely, and apply calibration factors if required. This calculation is usually done by simple addition of all digital readings in a peak, less base-line values;

(4) Handle incompletely resolved peaks. The simplest way is to treat

overlapping peaks of comparable size by calculating areas either side of a perpendicular drawn at the bottom of a valley. Overlapping peaks where one component is present in large excess can be treated by constructing a straight line tangential to the parts of the curve at the feet of the minor component, and considering this line as the division between the two peaks.

In the programs designed to do operations such as the above, the analytical information is obtained by performing arithmetical operations directly on the data itself. An alternative system is to store the data chromatogram, and to program the computer to construct a chromatogram from parameters corresponding to the retentions, heights, and widths of peaks till the chromatogram constructed by the computer is as close as it can get to the data chromatogram. The parameters of the peaks which the computer has used in order to get this fit are the best representations that the computer can find of the parameters of the data chromatogram, and these parameters, which can be printed, given the required analytical information (*169, 170*). This procedure, which uses well-established mathematical methods of "Curve-Fitting," has the advantages first that it uses to the full the computer's ability to perform extensive routine arithmetic by giving it a substantial mathematical problem, and secondly, that the curve-fitting can be performed almost as quickly on unresolved peaks as on resolved ones. There is thus no necessity to waste time in pursuing chromatographic analysis to the extent of complete separation. Mathematical resolution on a partly-resolved chromatogram can in this way substitute for the chromatographic resolution, which may be slower (*169*).

REFERENCES

1. Weissberger, A., (ed.), "Technique of Organic Chemistry," Vol. 1. *of* "Physical Methods of Organic Chemistry," 2nd ed., Sections in Part 1. Wiley (Interscience), New York, 1949; Reilly, F., and Rae, W. N., "Physico-Chemical Methods," Methuen, London, 1943, 1948. Berl, W. J., (ed.), "Physical Methods in Chemical Analysis" (4 Vols.). Academic Press New York, 1952–1961. Zlatkis, A., and Ettre, L. S., (eds.), "The Practice of Gas Chromatography." Wiley, New York, 1967.
2. Ray, N. H., *J. Appl. Chem.* **4**, 82 (1954).
3. Jeffrey, P. G., and Kipping, P. J., "Sample Transfer Systems," pp. 8–22. Macmillan, New York, 1964.
4. Brealey, L., Elvidge, D. A., and Proctor, K. A., *Analyst* **84**, 221 (1959).
5. Porter, R. S., and Johnson, J. F., *Anal. Chem.* **31**, 866 (1959).
6. Ciepelinski, E. W., and Ettre, L. S., *J. Chromatog.* **4**, 169 (1960).
7. McReadie, S. W. S., and Williams, A. F., *J. Appl. Chem.* **7**, 47 (1957).
8. Sorensen, I., and Soltoft, P., *Acta Chem. Scand.* **12**, 814 (1958).
9. Franc, J., and Jokl, J., *Collection Czech. Chem. Commun.* **24**, 144 (1959).

10. Joklik, J., and Bazant, V., *Chem. Listy* **53**, 277 (1959).
11. Singliar, M., and Brida, J., *Chem. Prumysl* **8**, 588 (1958).
12. Bowman, R. L., and Karmen, A., *Nature* **182**, 1233 (1958).
13. Dubsky, H. E., and Janak, J., *J. Chromatog.* **4**, 1 (1960).
14. Nerheim, A. G., *Anal. Chem.* **66**, 1686 (1964). U.S.P. 3, 063, 286 (1962).
15. Lipsky, S. R., Landowne, R. A., and Lovelock, J. E., *Anal. Chem.* **31**, 852 (1959).
16. Desty, D. H., Goldup, A., and Whyman, B. H. F., *J. Inst. Petrol.* **45**, 287 (1959).
17. Condon, R. D., *Anal. Chem.* **31**, 1717 (1959).
18. Halasz, I., and Schneider W., *in* "Gas Chromatography" (N. Brenner, J. E. Callen, and M. D. Weiss, eds.), p. 287. Academic Press, New York. 1962.
19. Halasz, I., and Schreyer, G., *Chem. Ingr. Tech.* **32**, 695 (1960).
20. Brenner, N., and Ettre, L. S., *Acta Chim. Acad. Sci. Hung.* **27**, 205 (1961).
21. Ettre, L. S., "Open Tubular Columns in Gas Chromatography." Plenum Press, New York, 1965.
22. Ettre L. S., and Averill, W., *Anal. Chem.* **38**, 680 (1961).
23. Ettre, L. S., and Kabot, F. J., *Anal. Chem.* **34**, 1431 (1962).
24. Ettre, L. S., Ciepelinski, E. W., and Brenner, N., *ISA Trans.* **2**, 134 (1963).
25. Clarke, D. R., *Nature* **198**, 681 (1963).
26. Cavagnol, J. C., and Betker, W. R., "The Practice of Gas Chromatography," see ref. 1, p. 71 *et seq.*
27. Hausdorff, H. H., *in* "Vapour Phase Chromatography," Proceedings of the First Symposium, London, May 1956 (D. H. Desty, ed.), p. 377. Academic Press, New York, 1957.
28. Hill, D. W., and Hook, J. R., *J. Sci. Instr.* **37**, 253 (1960).
29. Pratt, G. L., and Purnell, J. H., *Anal. Chem.* **32**, 1213 (1960).
30. Parker, K. D., Fontan, C. R., and Kirk, P. L., *Anal. Chem.* **35**, 356 (1963).
31. McComas, D. B., and Goldfien, A., *Anal. Chem.* **55**, 263 (1963).
32. Cagnazzo, G., Ros, A., and Bignardi, G., *J. Chromatog.* **19**, 185 (1965).
33. Renshaw, A., and Biran, L. A., *J. Chromatog.* **8**, 343 (1962).
34. Janak, J., *Chem. Listy* **47**, 464, 817, 828, 837, 1184, 1348 (1953); *Collection Czech. Chem. Commun.* **18**, 798 (1953), **19**, 684, 917 (1954).
35. Rouit, C., *in* "Vapour Phase Chromatography," Proceedings of the First Symposium, London, May 1956 (D. H. Desty, ed.), p. 291. Academic Press, New York, 1957.
36. Ray, N. H., *Analyst* **80**, 853 (1955).
37. Leibnitz, E., Hrapia, H., and Konnecke, H. G., *Brennstoff-Chem.* **38**, 14 (1957).
38. Janak, J., and Tesarik, K., *Chem. Listy* **51**, 2048 (1957); *Z. Anal. Chem.* **164**, 62 (1958).
39. Sevenster, P. G., *S. African Ind. Chemist* **12**, 75 (1958).
40. Janak, J., and Tesarik, K., *Collection Czech. Chem. Commun.* **24**, 536 (1959).
41. Velut, M., and Jourda, J., *Rev. Inst. Franc. Petrole Ann. Combust. Liquides* **13**, 1635 (1958).
42. Bevan, S. C., and Thorburn, S., *J. Chromatog.* **11**, 301 (1963).
43. Bevan, S. C., and Thorburn, S., *Chem. Brit.* **2**, 206 (1965).
44. Insull, W., and James, A. T., *Advan. Gas Chromatog.* (ACS Symp., New York, 1957) p. D 111.
45. James, A. T., and Martin, A. J. P., *Analyst* **77**, 915 (1952).
46. James, A. T., and Martin, A. J. P., *Biochem. J.* **50**, 679 (1952).

47. Heines, V., JuHasz, R., O'Leary, M. A., and Schramm, G., *Trans. Kentucky Acad. Sci.* **18**, 1 (1957).
48. Hughes, R. B., *J. Sci. Food Agr.* **11**, 47 (1960).
49. Kamer, J. H., Gerritsma, K. W., and Wansink, E. J., *Biochem. J.* **61**, 174 (1955).
50. McInnes, A. G., "Vapour Phase Chromatography," Proceedings of the First International Symposium of the GC Discussion Group, London, 1956 (O. H. Desty, ed.), p. 304. Butterworth, 1957.
51. Tilley, J. M. A., Canaway, R. J., and Terry, R. A., *Analyst* **89**, 363 (1964).
52. Aunstrup, K., and Djiertoft, R., *Brymesteren* **17**, 137 (1960).
53. Liberti, A., *Anal. Chim. Acta* **17**, 247 (1957).
54. Liberti, A., and Cartoni, G. P., *Atti Accad. Naz. Lincei, Rend. Classe Sci. Fis. Mat. Nat.* **20**, 787 (1956).
55. Liberti, A., and Cartoni, G. P., "Gas Chromatography 1958," Proceedings of the Second International Symposium of the GC Discussion Group, Amsterdam, 1958 (O. H. Desty, ed.), p. 321. Butterworth, 1958.
56. Liberti, A., Cartoni, G. P., and Pallotta, U., *Il Latte* **30**, 581 (1956).
57. Liberti, A., and Cartoni, G. P., *Chim. Ind. (Milan)*, **39**, 821 (1957).
58. Juranek, J., *Tech. Dig.* **11**, 14 (1960).
59. Cipriano, C., and Hayes, W. J., *J. Agr. Food Chem.* **19**, 366 (1962).
60. Coulson, D. M., Cavanagh, L. A., DeVries, J. E., and Wlather, B., *J. Agr. Food Chem.* **6**, 399 (1960).
61. Hayes, W. J., Dale, W. E., and LeBreton, R., *Nature* **199**, 1189 (1963).
62. Coulson, D. M., and Cavanagh, L. A., *Anal. Chem.* **32**, 1245 (1960).
63. Martin, R. L., and Grant, J. A., *Anal. Chem.* **37**, 644 (1965).
64. Bosin, W. A., *Anal. Chem.* **35**, 833 (1963).
65. Fredericks, E. M., and Harlow, G. A., *Anal. Chem.* **36**, 263 (1964).
66. Klaas, P. J., *Anal. Chem.* **33**, 1851 (1961).
67. Martin, R. L., *Anal. Chem.* **38**, 1209 (1966).
68. Thielemann, H., Behrens, V., and Leibnitz, E., *Chem. Tech. (Berlin)* **14**, 162 (1962).
69. Burton, G., Littlewood, A. B., and Wiseman, W. A., "Gas Chromatography 1966," Proceedings of the Sixth International Symposium of the GC Discussion Group (A. B. Littlewood, ed.), p. 193. Institute of Petroleum, 1967.
70. Littlewood, A. B., and Wiseman, W. A., *J. Gas Chromatog.* **5**, 334 (1967).
71. Beynon, J. H., *et al.*, "The Mass Spectrometry of Organic Molecules." Elsevier, Amsterdam, 1968.
72. Beynon, J. H., "Mass Spectrometry." Elsevier, Amsterdam, 1960.
73. Biemann, K., "Mass Spectrometry-Organic Chemical Applications," McGraw-Hill, 1962.
74. McLafferty, F. W., "Mass Spectrometry of Organic Ions." Academic Press, 1963.
75. McLafferty, F. W., "Interpretation of Mass Spectra; an Introduction." Benjamin, 1966.
76. White, F. O., "Mass Spectrometry in Science and Technology." Wiley, New York, 1968.
77. American Petroleum Institute Project 44. A and M University, College Station, Texas, U.S.A.
78. Mass Spectrometry Bulletin. Mass Spectrometry Data Center, AWRE, Aldermarston, Berks, U.K.

79. Mass Spectrometry Data Center, National Bureau of Standards Institute for Basic Standards, Washington, D.C. 20234.

80. Lipsky, S. R., McMurray, W., and Horvath, C., "Gas Chromatography 1966," proceedings of the Sixth International Symposium (A. B. Littlewood, ed.), p. 229. Institute of Petroleum, 1967.

81. Henneberg, D., and Schomburg, G., *Z. Anal. Chem.* **211**, 55 (1965).

82. Vollmin, J. A., Simon, W., and Kaiser, R., *Z. Anal. Chem.* **229**, 1 (1967).

83. Littlewood, A. B., *Chromatographia* **1**, 37 (1968).

84. Teranishi, R., Buttery, R. G., McFadden, W. H., Mon, T. R., and Wassermann, J., *Anal. Chem.* **36**, 1509 (1964).

85. Ryhage, R., *Anal. Chem.* **36**, 759 (1964).

86. Ryhage, R., Wikstrom, S., and Waller, G. R., *Anal. Chem.* **37**, 435 (1965).

87. Becker, E. W., "Separation of Isotopes" (H. London, ed.). Newnes, London, 1961.

88. Ten Noewer De Braun, M. C., and Brunnee, C., *Z. Anal. Chem.* **229**, 321 (1967).

89. Watson, J. T., and Biemann, K., *Anal. Chem.* **37**, 844 (1965).

90. Lipsky, S. R., Horvath, C., and McMurray, W., *Anal. Chem.* **38**, 1585 (1966).

91. McMurray, W. J., Greene, B. N., and Lipsky, S. R., *Anal. Chem.* **38**, 1194 (1966).

92. Banner, A. E., Elliott, R. M., and Kelly, W., "Gas Chromatography 1964," Proceedings of the Fifth International Symposium (A. Goldup, ed.), p. 181. Institute of Petroleum, 1965.

93. Lindemann, J. P., and Annis, J. L., *Anal. Chem.* **32**, 1742 (1960).

94. Sweeley, C., Elliott, W. H., Fries and Ryhage, R., *Anal. Chem.* **38**, 1549 (1966).

95. McFadden, W. H., and Day, E. A., *Anal. Chem.* **36**, 2362 (1964).

96. Littlewood, A. B., *Chromatographia*, **1**, 223 (1968).

97. "The Combination of Gas Chromatography and Infrared Spectrophotometry," Symposium of the GC Discussion Group and IR Discussion Group, Sept. 1967. *see* Littlewood, A. B., *J. Gas Chromatog.* **6**, 65 (1968).

98. Bellamy, L. J., "The Infrared Spectra of Complex Molecules." Methuen, London, 1961.

99. Chang, S. S., Brobst, K. M., Ireland, C. E., Tai, H., *Appl. Spectry.* **16**, 106 (1962).

100. Tadayon, J., Informal Symposium of the G. C. Discussion Group, Sept. 1967; *see* Littlewood, A. B., *J. Gas Chromatog.* **6**, 65 (1968).

101. Wilks, P. A., and Brown, R. A., *Anal. Chem.* **36**, 1896 (1964).

102. Allen, R. R., *Chem. Ind.* (*London*), **1965**, 1560.

103. Copier, H., and van der Maas, J. H., *Spectrochim. Acta* **23A**, 2699 (1967).

104. Gray, L. S., Metcalfe, L. D., and Leslie, L. D., Fourth International Gas Chromatography Symposium. Michigan State University, June 1963.

105. Hansen, R. P., Shorland, F. B., and Morrison, J. D., *J. Dairy Res.* **32**, 21 (1965).

106. Hoffman, R. L., and Silveira, A., Jr., *J. Gas Chromatog.* **2**, 107 (1964).

107. Paulig, G., *Deutsche Lebensm. Rundschau* **57**, 42 (1961).

108. Flett, M. St. C., and Hughes, J., *J. Chromatog.* **11**, 434 (1963).

109. Bartz, A. M., and Ruhl, H. D., *Anal. Chem.* **36**, 1892 (1964).

110. Low, M. J. D., and Freeman, S. K., *Anal. Chem.* **39**, 194 (1967).

111. Scott, R. P. W., Fowlis, I. A., Welti, D. and Wilkins, T., "Gas Chromatography 1966," Proceedings of the Sixth International Symposium (A. B. Littlewood, ed.), p. 318. Institute of Petroleum, 1967.

112. Littlewood, A. B., *Chromatographia* **1**, 133 (1968).

113. Martin, R. L., *Anal. Chem.* **32**, 436 (1960).
114. Ray, N. H., *Analyst* **80**, 853 (1955).
115. Ikeda, R. M., Simmons, D. E., and Grossman, J. D., *Anal. Chem.* **36**, 2188 (1964).
116. Kerr, J. A., and Trotman-Dickenson, A. F., *Trans. Faraday Soc.* **55**, 572 (1959).
117. Nelson, K. H., Hines, W. J., Grimes, M. D., and Smith, D. E., *Anal. Chem.* **32**, 1110 (1960).
118. Schomburg, G., and Henneberg, D., "Gas Chromatography 1968," Proceedings of the 7th International Symposium (C. L. A. Harbourn, ed.), p. 45. Institute of Petroleum, 1969.
119. Beroza, M., and Sarmiento, R., *Anal. Chem.* **38**, 1042 (1966).
120. Franc. J., and Kolouskova, V., *J. Chromatog.* **17**, 221 (1965).
121. Drawert, F., Felgenhauer, R., and Kupfer, G., *Angew. Chem.* **72**, 555 (1960).
122. Drawert, F., and Reuther, K. H., *Chem. Ber.* **93**, 3066 (1960).
123. Mounts, T. L., and Dutton, H. J., *Anal. Chem.* **37**, 641 (1965).
124. Thompson, C. J., Coleman, H. J., Hopkins, R. L., and Rall, H. T., *Anal. Chem.* **37**, 1042 (1965).
125. Beroza, M., *Nature* **196**, 768 (1962).
126. Beroza, M., *Anal. Chem.* **34**, 1801 (1962).
127. Beroza, M., *J. Org. Chem.* **28**, 3562 (1963).
128. Beroza, M., and Sarmiento, R., *Anal. Chem.* **35**, 1353 (1965).
129. Beroza, M., and Sarmiento, R., *Anal. Chem.* **36**, 1744 (1964).
130. Beroza, M., and Sarmiento, R., *Anal. Chem.* **38**, 1042 (1966).
131. Ralls, J. W., *J. Agr. Food. Chem.* **8**, 141 (1960).
132. Ralls, J. W., *Anal. Chem.* **32**, 332 (1960).
133. Stephens, R. L., and Teszler, A. P., *Anal. Chem.* **32**, 1047 (1960).
134. Drawert, F., *Angew. Chem.* **72**, 33 (1960).
135. Drawert, F., Felgenhauer, R., and Kupfer, G., *Angew. Chem.* **72**, 555 (1960).
136. Haken, J. K., *J. Gas Chromatog.* **1**, 30 (10) (1963).
137. Hoff, J. E., and Feit, E. D., *Anal. Chem.* **36**, 1002 (1964).
138. Hoff, J. E., and Feit, E. D., *Anal. Chem.* **35**, 1298 (1963).
139. Anon., *Chem. Eng. News* **41**, 62 (1963).
140. Huyten, F. H., and Rijnders, G. W. A., *Z. Anal. Chem.* **205**, 460 (1964).
141. Clerc, J. T., Dohner R., Sauter, W., and Simon, W., *Helv. Chim. Acta* **46**, 2369 (1963).
142. Hunter, I. R., Ortegren, V. H., and Pence, J. W., *Anal. Chem.* **32**, 682 (1960).
143. Jamieson, G. R., *Analyst* **84**, 75 (1959).
144. Nel. W., Mortimer, J., and Pretorius, V., *S. African Ind. Chemist* **13**, 68 (1959).
145. Simmons, M. C., Taylor, L. M., and Nager, M., *Anal. Chem.* **32**, 701 (1960).
146. Wurst, M., and Dusek, R., *Coll. Czech. Chem. Commun.* **25**, 2022 (1961).
147. Blom, L., and Edelhausen, L., *Anal. Chim. Acta* **15**, 559 (1956).
148. Blom, L., Edelhausen, L., and Smeets, T., *Z. Anal. Chem.* **189**, 91 (1962).
149. Juranek, J., *Chem. Listy* **51**, 2280 (1957).
150. Juranek, M., *Chem. Listy* **52**, 1289 (1958).
151. Juranek, J., *Coll. Czech. Chem. Commun.* **24**, 2306 (1959).
152. Juranek, J., *Coll. Czech. Chem. Commun.* **24**, 135 (1959).
153. Walsh, J. T., and Merritt, C., *Anal. Chem.* **32**, 1378 (1960).
154. Casu, B. and Cavallotti, L., *Anal. Chem.* **34**, 1514 (1962).
155. Janak, J., *J. Chromatog.* **16**, 543 (1964).

156. Littlewood, A. B., *Z. Anal. Chem.* **236**, 39 (1968).
157. Dymond, H. F., and Kilburn, K. D., "Gas Chromatography 1966," Proceedings of the 6th International Symposium (A. B. Littlewood, ed.), p. 353. Institute of Petroleum, 1967.
158. Jones, K., McDougall, A. O., and Marshall, R. C., "Gas Chromatography 1966," Proceedings of the 6th International Symposium (A. B. Littlewood, ed.), p. 376. Institute of Petroleum, 1967.
159. Flynn, T., Greunke, O., and Savitzky, A., Gas Chromatography application Leaflet GC-AP-006. Perkin Elmer Corp. 1965; presented at the 16th Pittsburgh Conference on Analytical Chemistry 1965.
160. Littlewood, A. B., *Z. Anal. Chem.* **236**, 39 (1968).
161. Fraser, R. D. B., and E. Suzuki, *Anal. Chem.* **38**, 1770 (1966).
162. Johnson, H. W., Jr., *Anal. Chem.* **35**, 521 (1963).
163. Savitzky, A., and M. J. E. Golay, *Anal. Chem.* **36**, 1627 (1964).
164. Vollers, Y., Schuringa, A., and Homs, C. C., "Gas Chromatography 1968," Proceedings of the 7th International Symposium (C. L. A. Harbourn, ed.), p. 319. Institute of Petroleum, 1969.
165. Merritt, C., Jr., Walsh, J. T., and Robertson, D. H., "Gas Chromatography 1968," Proceedings of the 7th International Symposium (C. L. A. Harbourn, ed.), p. 338. Institute of Petroleum, 1969.
166. Baumann, F., Wallace, D., Herlicska, E., Katzive, R., and Blesch, J., "Gas Chromatography 1968," Proceedings of the 7th International Symposium (C. L. A. Harbourn, ed.), p. 346. Institute of Petroleum, 1969.
167. Karohl, J. G., "Gas Chromatography 1968," Proceedings of the 7th International Symposium (C. L. A. Harbourn, ed.), p. 359. Institute of Petroleum, 1969.
168. Levy, E. J., Radvany, I., Goland, D., Chant, L., and Malatesta, T. M., "Gas Chromatography 1968," Proceedings of the 7th International Symposium (C. L. A. Harbourn, ed.), p. 367. Institute of Petroleum, 1969.
169. Littlewood, A. B., Gibb, T. C., and Anderson, A. H., "Gas Chromatography 1968," Proceedings of the 7th International Symposium (C. L. A. Harbourn, ed.), p. 297. Institute of Petroleum, 1969.
170. Levy, E. J., and Martin, A. J., Pittsburgh Conference on Analytical Chemistry Pittsburgh, Pennsylvania, March, 1968.

Chapter 12

Applications of Gas Chromatography

12.1. BIBLIOGRAPHY OF APPLICATIONS OF GC

The number of published papers containing descriptions of applications of gas chromatography is well over 10,000, and in many of these the part of the paper dealing with GC is incidental and not referred to in the title. The process of tracing a report of a particular application, therefore, from general sources such as *Chemical Abstracts* may be unrewarding. There are several more specific sources which are more easily searched for specific applications of GC:

(*a*) *Gas Chromatography Abstracts*, Institute of Petroleum, London. The Gas Chromatography Discussion Group of the Institute of Petroleum, London, prepares abstracts of all papers dealing with GC, which are circulated quarterly to members of the Group. Annual volumes prepared from the quarterly issues are published by the Institute of Petroleum (UK) and by Elsevier (Amsterdam). These abstracts are particularly well indexed, and all substances the GC of which has been reported are listed in detail. In addition, there is a cumulative index published as a separate volume covering the years up to 1963.

(*b*) *Journal of Gas Chromatography*, Preston Technical Abstracts Co., Evanston, Illinois. This journal is obviously of general relevance, and its pages contain much of the original literature, particularly in the field of new applications. In addition, one of its issues generally contains an indexed annual bibliography.

(*c*) *Journal of Chromatography*, Elsevier, Amsterdam and New York. As with the *Journal of Gas Chromatography*, this contains much of the original literature and bibliographical indexes. It embraces all forms of chromatography.

(d) *Analytical Chemistry*, American Chemical Society, Washington. This journal probably contains the largest proportion of significant original literature. Gas Chromatography is generally reviewed in the annual review issue of the journal.

(e) *A Comprehensive Bibliography and Index to the Literature on Gas Chromatography*, Preston Technical Abstracts Co., Evanston, Illinois. This is a book which covers all the literature of GC from 1952 to 1962.

(f) *Guide to the Gas Chromatography Literature*, by A. V. Signeur, Plenum Press, New York, 1964, 1967. A general indexed bibliography of GC.

Compilations of retention data, which give the user the basic information necessary to plan a given separation, are also published:

(a) *Compilation of Gas Chromatographic Retention Data* by J. S. Lewis, A.S.T.M., Philadelphia, 2nd ed., 1967.

(b) *Gas Chromatographic Retention Data*, by W. O. McReynolds, Preston Technical Abstracts, Evanston, Illinois, 1965.

There are also various textbooks dealing with specific applications:

(a) Burchfield, H. P., and Storrs, E. E., "Biochemical Applications of Gas Chromatography." Academic Press, New York, 1962.

(b) Jeffery, P. G., and Kipping, P. J., "Gas Analysis by Gas Chromatography." Pergamon Press, Oxford, 1964.

(c) Moshier, R. W., and Sievers, R. E., "Gas Chromatography of Metal Chelates." Pergamon Press, Oxford, 1965.

(d) Wotiz, H. H., and Clark, S. J., "Gas Chromatography in the Analysis of Steroid Hormones." Plenum Press, New York, 1966.

Of the total number of reported applications of GC, there are some which are very much more commonly encountered than others. The remainder of this chapter summarises some of the commonest applications.

12.2. PERMANENT GASES AND METHANE

Permanent gases are usually analysed on adsorbents, of which charcoal, molecular sieves, silica gel, porous polymers, and alumina are the commonest.

It should be emphasised that the retaining power of inorganic adsorbents is not reproducible in ordinary practice, and depends sharply on pre-treatment and on the amount of material such as water already adsorbed; it is not uncommon for retention volumes to increase by a factor of 10 or more on removal of water from charcoal or silica gel, and thus it is impossible to quote reproducible retention data (see Section 4.3).

(a) Inert Gases

Mixtures of all the inert gases are easily separated (1, 2). Janák has listed the relative retention volumes given in Table 12.1, column (a), for the gases on charcoal at 20°C, from which it is apparent that helium and neon do not separate, but the other gases separate easily, though the

TABLE 12.1

SEPARATION OF INERT GASES[a]

| Gas | Retention volumes | | | |
	(a)[b]	(b)[c]	(c)[d]	(d)[e]
Helium	1	180	—	—
Neon	1	360	—	—
Argon	2.1	—	150	160
Krypton	6.4	—	240	540
Methane	—	—	240	660
Xenon	38	—	840	960[f]

[a] See Janák and Greene (1) and (2).

[b] (a) Charcoal at 20°C, hydrogen carrier; relative to helium and neon.

[c] (b) Charcoal at —196°C, hydrogen carrier. Note. For columns (b), (c), and (d), 10-foot × ¾-inch columns of 20 to 40 mesh material, flow rate 60 ml/minute.

[d] (c) Silica gel at 23°C, oxygen carrier.

[e] (d) Molecular sieve at 23°C, oxygen carrier.

[f] Accelerated by heating to 100 after CH_4.

retention of xenon is likely to be long. Oxygen and nitrogen do not separate from argon. Greene has analysed the rare gases in mixtures also containing oxygen, nitrogen, and methane on three columns as specified in Table 12.1, columns (b), (c), and (d). The retention volumes show that helium and neon, which are not resolved on charcoal at 20°C, are easily resolved at 77°K (—196°C, i.e., liquid nitrogen bath). Argon, krypton, and xenon are easily resolved at room temperature on silica gel, but if methane is present, it interferes with the krypton. In the latter case, the separation of argon, krypton, methane, and xenon may be achieved on a molecular sieve column at room temperature. With this, the xenon is retained excessively long, so, after the other three gases are eluted, it may be removed by heating the column to 100°C. Krypton, nitrogen, and methane may be separated at room temperature with a mixture of one part of charcoal and 10 parts of molecular sieve 5A (3). It is apparent that relative retentions are greater on molecular sieve than on charcoal or silica gel.

Hydrogen cannot be separated from helium and neon on charcoal at room temperature (1), but it may be with molecular sieve 5A (3). Using molecular sieve, helium and neon may be separated at −78°C (3).

The separation of krypton and xenon has been studied separately by Gluekauf and Kitt (4) and by Koch and Grandy (5, 6), in each case using convenient radioactive isotopes of the gases for following the separation. Gluekauf has studied in detail the case of the separation of krypton and xenon which are sufficiently radioactive to heat the column in the course of their elution (7, 8).

(b) Atmospheric Gases O, N, and Ar

Oxygen and nitrogen are most easily separated on molecular sieve 5A (2, 9–11), on which oxygen comes through with about half the retention volume of nitrogen. The separation can be conveniently done in a few minutes using hydrogen or helium as carrier gas at a column temperature of about 100°C (9, 10) with columns of about 1 metre or longer. With less active adsorbent, it can also be done at room temperature. These gases can also be separated on other adsorbents, but the retention ratio is smaller; thus on charcoal at 20°C the retention ratio is 1.18 (12), so that a longer column is required. Alumina, silica gel and porous polymers can also be used for the O/N separation, but their retention of permanent gases is rather small, so that the value of k is small and separations are poor on that account; they are not recommended unless there is some other good reason for using them.

In all cases that oxygen and nitrogen are appreciably retained, e.g., on molecular sieves up to about 100°C or on charcoal, hydrogen is easily separated, for it is scarcely retained by any adsorbent.

Hydrogen, oxygen, and nitrogen are all easily separated from the common air contaminants, carbon monoxide, carbon dioxide, and methane, all of which come through considerably later; see below.

Argon has a similar retention to oxygen on all adsorbents, and its separation from oxygen is relatively difficult (*13*). The two gases may be separated at room temperature on columns of the order of 10 m length packed with molecular sieve 5A or 13X which have been pre-heated to 400–500°C (*14, 15*). A chromatogram is shown in Fig. 12.1. Lord and Horn (*16*) have performed the same analysis on a 6 ft. column of the same material used in two runs; a run at room temperature serves to separate O_2 and Ar from N_2, after which a run at −72°C serves to separate O_2 from Ar, the nitrogen not being eluted. This procedure is quicker.

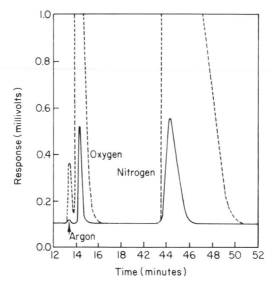

Fig. 12.1. Separation of argon, oxygen, and nitrogen on a 10-metre column of molecular sieve 5A operated at room temperature. Vizard and Wynne (*14*); (a) 9.831 ml of sample (- - -), (b) 0.768 ml of sample (—).

(c) Carbon Monoxide and Carbon Dioxide from Other Gases

Carbon monoxide is separable from oxygen, nitrogen, and methane with ease either on a molecular sieve 5A (*10, 17*) at about 100°C, on charcoal at room temperature (*12, 18–22*), or on any grade of porous polystyrene type copolymer at −78°C (*23*). In any of these cases, separation is achieved in a few minutes on a column of the order of 1 m length. Carbon monoxide and methane may be separated easily from the air gases on silica gel or alumina (*11*), but, as described above, the air gases do not themselves separate easily (*17*). Approximate relative retention data for the four gases are given in Table 12.2; note the remarkable inversion of elution order on

TABLE 12.2

SEPARATION OF CARBON MONOXIDE AND METHANE FROM AIR GASES

Substance	Relative retention times			
	(a)[a]	(b)[b]	(c)[c]	(d)[d]
Oxygen	0.85	3.5	0.4	1.12
Nitrogen	1.0	4.8	1.0	1.0
Carbon monoxide	1.6	13.2	3.4	1.55
Methane	5	—	1.8	7.8

[a] (a) 25-ft charcoal column at room temperature (11).
[b] (b) 6-ft silica gel column at −78°C (24).
[c] (c) 16-ft molecular sieve column 5A at 100°C (10).
[d] (d) 12-ft "Porapak T" column at −78°C (23).

molecular sieve 5A for carbon monoxide and methane. Alumina gives the same elution order as charcoal and silica gel (11).

Analyses of mixtures containing carbon dioxide are restricted by the fact that carbon dioxide is almost irreversibly adsorbed on molecular sieve 5A and on alumina. Graven (21), however, has succeeded in analysing a mixture of O_2, N_2, CO, C_2H_6, N_2O, and CO_2 in the order given with a 10 ft. column of 40–60 mesh molecular sieve 5A temperature-programmed from room temperature to 400°C in 25 minutes. If the air gases need not be resolved, mixtures containing these together with CO, CH_4, CO_2, and hydrocarbons may be analysed on silica gel (11). If, in addition, the air gases are to be resolved, a charcoal column of at least 2 metres may be used, but the elution time of carbon dioxide is long without temperature programming. Porous polymer columns are particularly suitable for analysis of mixtures containing carbon dioxide, for which room temperature is suitable. In all cases, the separation of carbon dioxide from nitrous oxide is somewhat difficult, since the molecules of these two are very similar. Columns of "Porapak" porous polymer, however, give relative retentions of about 1.2 or 1.3 according to grade.

(d) Oxides of Nitrogen

Szulczewski and Higuchi (24) have separated N_2, O_2, NO, CO, N_2O, and CO_2 on 40–60 mesh silica gel. At room temperature, the first four gases appear together, followed by N_2O and CO_2, which are well separated on a 6-foot column. At −78°C, the first four gases are resolved in the order given, but the last two are retained unduly long. All six gases may be satisfactorily resolved by running the chromatogram at $-78°C$ until CO is through, and by warming the column to room temperature for the last two, which separate in the order given above. Similar results are obtained by Marvillet and Tranchant (*25*), who show that if resolution of NO and CO is not required the whole analysis may be run at an intermediate temperature, e.g., $-20°C$, or $0°C$.

Porous polymers are probably the most suitable material for separation of NO and N_2O from other gases likely to accompany them. This is exemplified by Fig. 12.2 (*23*), which also illustrates the characteristic near-symmetry of the peaks obtained on this material.

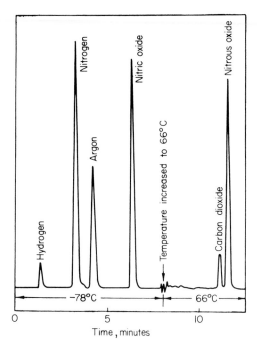

Fig. 12.2. Chromatogram of oxides of nitrogen and other gases; 12-foot column of "Porapak Q" (*23*).

Adlard and Hill (*26*) find that mixtures containing air gases, nitrous oxide, and carbon dioxide, such as are encountered in respired anaesthetic mixtures, can be analysed more rapidly on polar partition columns than on adsorbents such as described above. Thus, a mixture of these gases can be resolved (without resolution of the air gases) on a 24-foot column of

28% propylene carbonate on firebrick in $2\frac{1}{2}$ minutes, or on a 20-foot 20% dimethyl sulfoxide column in 1 minute, both columns at room temperature.

NO_2 cannot be analysed as such, for it is too reactive; in the presence of moisture it reacts to give NO and nitric acid; furthermore, if nitric oxides is present, it reacts reversibly to form N_2O_3 which causes very broad peaks (27). It may be analysed satisfactorily by the method of Greene and Pust (28), in which it is caused to react to completion with water by the reaction:

$$6NO_2 + 3H_2O \rightarrow 4HNO_3 + 2NO + H_2O,$$

after which the nitric oxide is passed through a molecular sieve 5A column. The technique of Greene and Pust is obviously inapplicable if oxygen is also present. In such a case, Smith et al. (29) remove NO_2 in a cold trap, and analyse the uncondensed fraction which contains the oxygen. The NO_2 is then separately determined by chromatographing it by Greene and Pust's technique in an inert carrier gas.

(e) Isotopes and Isomers of Hydrogen

Molecular hydrogen can occur as H_2, D_2, T_2, HD, HT, DT, $o\text{-}H_2$, $p\text{-}H_2$, $o\text{-}D_2$, or $p\text{-}D_2$, where D stands for ^2H and T stands for ^3H. The separation of hydrogen isotopes is generally easy, for their physical properties differ considerably.

H_2, HD, and D_2 can be easily separated at $-196°C$ on either molecular sieve 5A (30–32), or chromia-alumina catalyst material (33). Ohkoshi et al. (30–32) use an 80 cm column of molecular sieve 5A with hydrogen as carrier gas, so that hydrogen is not detected, but peaks are produced for the other two isotopes, the chromatogram taking about 8 minutes. Smith and Hunt (33) use a 12 ft. column of chromia-alumina, with neon as carrier gas, so that three peaks are obtained. With freshly activated column material, the separations are good, but the chromatogram is slow. It may be accelerated by treating the column with water. In all the cases the order of elution is the order of volatility, with H_2 first and D_2 last.

Gant and Yang (34) have analysed mixtures of H_2, HT, and T_2 on a 6.1-metre molecular sieve column operating at $-160°C$, using helium as carrier gas.

In analyses for hydrogen isotopes, particularly for analysis of traces of D and T in H, or H and T in D, it is convenient to use the major component as carrier gas, so that peaks are obtained only from minor components. In such a case, accurate quantitative analyses require the introduction of reproducible samples, but with permanent gases this is relatively easy. Riedel and Uhlmann (35), and Arnett (36) describe a special case of this technique; the deuterium content of a substance (not necessarily volatile) is converted to HD, e.g., by means of calcium hydride, and the HD is estimated in a gas-chromatography apparatus, using hydrogen as carrier gas. In this case, the column is not really necessary, for HD is the only species measured. A column, however, serves to retain any other impurities which may be present in the gas.

When ordinary adsorbents are used for hydrogen isotope analyses, no equilibration occurs between mixed and simple molecular species, e.g., between H_2, HD, and D_2. On any substrate which adsorbs atoms rather than molecules, however, this equilibration occurs, and the result is that, if such a substrate is used as a column, HD is changed to H_2 and D_2 in the course of the analysis. Gluekauf and Kitt (37) and Thomas and Smith (58) have used this fact for the preparation of pure deuterium. The column material is palladium, which adsorbs hydrogen readily, and deuterium rather less readily. Since the adsorption occurs as atoms, the Law of Mass Action implies that the adsorption isotherm has the form:

$$q \propto \sqrt{c},$$

so that the chromatography is not linear; thus frontal and displacement techniques were used. With a column of 44×0.8 cm of a mixture of Pd black and purified asbestos operating at temperatures between $0°$ and $100°C$, with the column initially filled with helium, using a sample of mixed H_2-HD-D_2, and with pure hydrogen as the displacer, Gluekauf and Kitt produced a zone of pure deuterium. Similar experiments have been made by Thomas and Smith (38), using a 43 ft column containing 7 g of palladium suspended on quartz. Thomas and Smith also partially separated D_2 and H_2 by elution on this column using helium as carrier gas. Unlike the separation on adsorbents, the deuterium appears first. For practical analysis, palladium is inferior to adsorbents.

Ortho- and para-hydrogen may easily be separated on columns of activated alumina at $-196°C$ pre-treated in nitrogen at $200°C$ (39, 40), or molecular sieve at $-160°C$ (54), or carbon (41). In all cases, the p-form appears before the o-form. Ortho- and para-deuterium are not so easily separated. Moore and Ward (39) obtain a partial separation, with o–appearing first, but van Hook and Emmett (40) fail to get any separation. A complete separation of o- and p-deuterium requires the efficiency given by a capillary column; this was first shown by Mohnke and Saffert (42), using

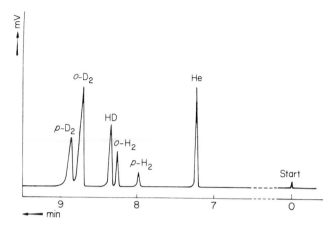

Fig. 12.3. Chromatogram of hydrogen isotopes and nuclear spin isomers. Etched glass column of 80 m length at −196°C. Mohnke and Saffert (42).

an adsorption column made by suitably etching the inside of a glass capillary (Section 7.3d). Their chromatogram of both o-/p- pairs and HD taken on this column at −196°C is shown in Fig. 12.3.

12.3. LIGHT HYDROCARBONS, C_1–C_5

All the light hydrocarbons may be separated from each other on various kinds of column, and the problem has been studied widely. A column designed to separate every member from every other is necessarily long, since a large number of components must be included in the chromatogram; such an analysis takes a long time. If few members of the group are to be separated, shorter and simpler columns may be used, thus speeding the analysis. The compounds normally encountered in light hydrocarbon analysis are listed in Table 12.3. Other compounds in the group are not normally found in conditions where they need be separated from many other light hydrocarbons. Every separation of any member from every other member of the group, except the separation of hydrogen and permanent gases from methane, may be achieved on a partition column. The partition coefficients at room temperature of the C_1 to C_4 hydrocarbons are rather small, so that they are only slightly retained, and, even though their relative retentions are great, the ratio of their retention volumes is small (Section 5.8). This means that rather long columns are necessary, and packed columns with a large proportion of stationary phase should be used. The retention times,

TABLE 12.3

LIGHT HYDROCARBONS AND THEIR BOILING POINTS

Hydrocarbon	bp (°C)	Hydrocarbon	bp (°C)
Methane	−161.5	1-Butyne	8.7
Ethylene	−103.7	Neopentane	9.5
Ethane	−88.6	1,2-Butadiene	10.85
Acetylene	−84.0	3-Methyl-1-butene	20.1
Propene	−47.7	1,4-Pentadiene	26.1
Propane	−42.1	Isopentane	27.8
Propadiene	−35.0	1-Pentene	30.1
Cyclopropane	−33.5	2-Methyl-1-Butene	31.1
Propyne	−23.3	Isoprene	32.6
Isobutane	−11.7	n-Pentane	36.1
Isobutene	−6.9	trans-2-Pentene	36.4
1-Butene	−6.3	cis-2-Pentene	37.4
1,3-Butadiene	−4.5	2-Methyl-2-butene	38.5
n-Butane	−0.5	Cyclopentadiene	41.0
trans-2-Butene	0.9	1-trans-3-Pentadiene	42.1
Cyclobutene	2.4	1-cis-3-Pentadiene	44.1
cis-2-Butene	3.7	Cyclopentene	44.2
Methylcyclopropane	4.5	Cyclopentane	49.3
Butenyne	5.3		

however, are short. The small retention of the C_1 to C_4's may be overcome by using reduced temperatures, but this is usually more of an inconvenience than the use of long columns.

Adsorbents are often used to advantage for light hydrocarbon separations. Since the more active adsorbents usually operate effectively at temperatures well above the boiling points of the solutes being chromatographed, they can often be used for gaseous hydrocarbons at room temperature or above. They have been extensively used in Russia (1).

Liquid-coated open tube capillary columns are not really suitable for light hydrocarbon analysis, and, even though they may be used at room temperature for the purpose (2, 3), their large separating potentialities are wasted on account of the small retentions. Capillary columns containing adsorbents, however, can perform very effective, very rapid analyses of light hydrocarbons. Figure 12.4 illustrates a rapid separation obtained on a glass capillary column packed with granular alumina; see (4) and Section 7.3e.

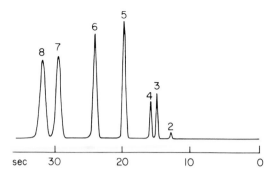

Fɪɢ. 12.4. Chromatogram of light hydrocarbons on a capillary column packed with granular alumina. Column length: 5 metres. 2, methane; 3, ethane; 4, ethylene; 5, propane; 6, propylene; 7, *i*-butane; 8, *n*-butane. After Heine (*4*).

Porous polymers at room temperature or above are also very effective for light hydrocarbons. Several examples are shown by Hollis *et al.* (*5–7*).

(a) *Methane,* C_2*, and* C_3 *from Each Other, from Higher Hydrocarbons, and from Permanent Gases*

Complete separations of mixtures of permanent gases and hydrocarbons to C_3 may be achieved on adsorbents. On charcoal, the separation follows the order of boiling points (*8*), so that the order of elution of gases and C_1 and C_2 is (*8–10*):

$$H_2, \ O_2, \ N_2, \ CO, \ CH_4, \ CO_2, \ C_2H_2, \ C_2H_4, \ C_2H_6.$$

These may be separated on a charcoal column at room temperature, though the analysis is rather long if the charcoal is too active.

A similar separation may be achieved on silica gel or alumina so long as the air gases do not need to be resolved, but in this case alkenes and alkynes are selectively retained relative to alkanes. The orders of elution on silica gel and alumina are (*11–13*):

Silica gel: H_2, air, CO, CH_4, C_2H_6, CO_2, C_2H_4, C_3H_8, C_2H_2

Alumina: H_2, air, CO, CH_4, C_2H_6, C_2H_4, C_3H_8, C_3H_6, C_2H_2.

If the resolution of methane and the permanent gases is not required, partition columns run at room temperature may be used. On paraffinic or only weakly polar stationary phases, separation is in order of boiling point, with the result that ethylene and ethane fail to separate. Polar stationary phases provide a specific retention of alkenes, and a very large

TABLE 12.4

RETENTIONS RELATIVE TO ETHENE OF C_1–C_3 HYDROCARBONS

				Stationary phase				
	Paraffin oil	Tri-isobutylene	Dionyl phthalate or didecyl phthalate	Alumina modified with silicone	Acetonyl-acetone	Dimethyl-formamide	Dimethyl-sulfolane	Ethylene glycol/$AgNO_3$
Temperature (°C):	40	20	0	70	20	0	0	20
Reference:	13	16	14, 15	13	10	13, 14	15	16
Methane	0	0	0	0.2	0	0	0	0
Ethene	1.0	1.0	1.0	1.0	1.0	1.0	1.0	1.0
Ethane	1.0	2.0	1.0	0.7	1.0	0.6	0.75	0
Ethyne	—	0.75	—	—	10.3	23	10.5	—
Propene	3.3	8.0	4.0	3.8	5.0	4.2	4.2	1.0
Propane	3.3	9.5	4.0	2.4	2.7	2.2	2.2	0
Propyne	—	10.2	34	—	36	56	—	—

specific retention of alkynes, and for separations up to C_3 the choice of such stationary phase is immaterial. Adjusted retention volumes relative to ethylene are given in Table 12.4.

If resolution of methane and the permanent gases is also required, temperature programming will probably be necessary to avoid undue spread of the chromatogram. Porous polymers provide good separation of air gases and methane at room temperature, and with these, therefore, it is not necessary to start the run below ambient temperature.

The alkenes may be separated from the alkanes by a column containing a saturated solution of silver nitrate in glycol or benzyl cyanide as a stationary phase. This does not retain the alkanes at all, but provides good retention for the alkenes, as is shown in the last column of Table 12.4 (the fact that the retentions of ethene and propene are given as the same is deceptive; the results derive from inaccurate measurements of rapid peaks, and the first place of decimals is not significant).

In the separation of ethane, ethene, propane, and propene, Table 12.4 shows that the best separation of alkane from alkane is given by $AgNO_3/$ glycol, that good separation of C_2 from C_3 is given by any other column, but that no column provides more than adequate separation of all four components. Though the separation is easily enough achieved with a sophisticated column design, as is shown by Fig. 12.4, a solution which may sometimes be simpler for this common analysis is to use either a combined column of two series columns (Section 7.4) containing in part $AgNO_3/$ glycol and in part any other substantially paraffinic material (17, 18).

On some polar stationary phases, e.g., acetonylacetone at 20°C (16) (but not at 0°C) (19), dimethylformamide, or dimethylsulfolane (20), isobutane may overlap with propene, the relative retention being about 1.1. A better separation of these two substances is secured with any non-polar stationary phase.

(b) C_4 Hydrocarbons

The saturated alkanes may be easily separated in almost any reasonable conditions, i.e., any column providing adequate retention for chromatography to occur.

The separation of the C_4 alkanes and alkenes present in a single mixture normally involves the two butanes, the four butenes, and 1,3-butadiene. The separation of these has been extensively studied. Adjusted retention volumes relative to n-butane are given in Table 12.5.

On non-polar stationary phases, separation is in order of boiling points,

TABLE 12.5

RELATIONS RELATIVE TO *n*-BUTANE OF C$_4$ HYDROCARBONS

	Stationary phase											
	Mineral oil	Tri-iso-butylene	Di-isodecyl phthalate	Dinonyl phthalate	Acetonyl-acetone	Acetonyl-acetone	Dimethyl-formamide	Dimethyl-formamide	Dimethyl-sulfolane	Dimethyl-sulfolane	Carbitol	Ethylene glycol/AgNO$_3$
Temperature (°C):	25	20	35	40	20	20	0	0	0	25	0	20
Reference:	23	16	15	14	16	19	14	13	15, 22	23	21, 22	16
Isobutane	0.63	0.72	0.66	0.68	0.65	0.64	0.65	0.62	0.61	0.61	0.64	0
Isobutene	0.80	0.88	1.0	1.0	1.74	1.90	2.14	2.09	1.84	1.71	1.32	2.5
1-Butene	0.81	0.88	1.0	1.0	1.74	1.72	1.89	1.87	1.68	1.61	1.32	5.5
1,3-Butadiene	0.83	0.88	—	1.53	4.05	4.21	5.55	—	4.1	3.58	—	9.25
n-Butane	1.0	1.0	1.0	1.0	1.0	1.0	1.0	1.0	1.0	1.0	1.0	0
trans-2-Butene	1.08	1.08	1.8	1.53	2.2	2.28	2.57	2.52	2.29	2.08	1.74	1.0
cis-2-Butene	1.25	1.21	1.8	1.74	2.65	2.73	3.06	3.00	2.74	2.44	2.10	4.7

which results in the overlaps: n-butane–trans-2-butene; isobutene–1-butene–1,3-butadiene; so that such stationary phases are unsuitable for this separation (24).

On weakly polar stationary phases, e.g., phthalate esters, olefins are somewhat retained; with dinonyl phthalate and didecyl phthalate, this selective retention is just sufficient to make the 1-butene and isobutene overlap with the n-butane, but with the slightly more polar dibutyl phthalate these two olefins appear on the slow side of n-butane, though they are not themselves resolved. With any of the phthalate esters, the cis- and trans-2-butenes are resolved (24), though poorly with didecyl phthalate (15).

With moderately polar phases, e.g., dimethylformamide, dimethylsulfolane, acetonylacetone, etc., all the seven compounds are resolved, but the relative retention of isobutene and 1-butene is always small. McKenna and Idleman (25) have studied a large number of moderately polar non-volatile liquids for their ability at this separation. Among the liquids tested, the order of value for those more familiar as stationary phases is:

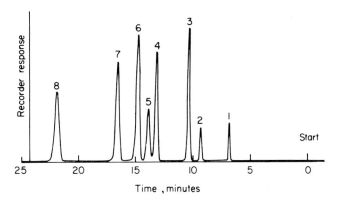

FIG. 12.5. Chromatogram of C_4 hydrocarbons on mixed glutaronitrile and propylene carbonate. McKenna and Idleman (25). 1, Air; 2, isobutane; 3, n-butane; 4, 1-butene; 5, isobutene; 6, trans-2-butene; 7, cis-2-butene; 8, 1,3-butadiene.

acetonylacetone, β,β'-oxydipropionitrile, dimethylsulfolane, γ-butyrolactone, propylene carbonate, the last giving the best separation. Propylene carbonate secures good separation of the other butenes, but belongs to those referred to in the preceding subsection which cause overlap between isobutane and propene. A mixture of glutaronitrile and propylene carbonate, however, produces as good a separation of the C_4's, with propene appearing between isobutane and n-butane. The separation of the C_4's on this mixture is shown in Fig. 12.5.

A saturated solution of silver nitrate in glycol gives zero retention for the alkanes, but retains the alkenes as shown in Table 12.5. The retention order bears no relation to volatility, since it is determined by the stability of the silver nitrate complex and not by vapour pressure.

With non-polar phases or weakly polar phases such as phthalic esters, no overlap occurs between C_4's and C_5's, except that the comparatively rarely encountered 1,2-butadiene is retained into the C_5's on dinonyl phthalate (14). On the more polar phases used for complete separation of the C_4's, however, cis- and trans-2-butenes may overlap with iso- and n-pentane. On acetonylacetone and dimethylsulfolane, trans-2-butene overlaps with isopentane, with n-pentane coming through after cis-2-butene. On dimethylformamide, isopentane comes through with isobutene, with n-pentane between the two 2-butenes (14). Fredericks and Brooks (15) have eliminated this overlap with series columns of 6 feet of didecyl phthalate and 16 feet of dimethylsulfolane, but in this case 1-butene and isobutene fail to resolve.

All the C_4's may be separated on polar adsorbents, especially silica gel and alumina. Molecular sieves may also be used, but it is reported that a certain amount of almost irreversible adsorption also occurs (26), causing a slow continuous elution of hydrocarbons after a period of use. The use of silica gel has been extensively reported by Russian workers (1). Scott (27) has shown that alumina acts as a polar stationary phase, with all the alkenes appearing after the alkanes. Of the alkenes, isobutene is separate from 1-butene, but overlaps with trans-2-butene.

The separation and analysis of the C_4 hydrocarbons is described in simple detail in (22).

(c) C_5 Hydrocarbons

Relative retention data is tabulated in Table 12.6.

The three C_5 alkanes may be separated by any column capable of providing adequate retention; this includes any column containing at least some alkyl groups operated at temperatures not higher than approximately 100°C. The relative retention of neopentane and isopentane is large; the relative retention of isopentane and n-pentane is between 1.2 and 1.3, so for complete separation of these two a column of not less than approximately 1000 plates is required.

On all columns, cyclopentane appears after and is well separated from n-pentane.

TABLE 12.6

RETENTIONS RELATIVE TO n-PENTANE OF C_5 HYDROCARBONS

Stationary phase

	Mineral oil	Dinonyl phthalate	Didecyl phthalate	Dimethyl-formamide	Dimethyl-formamide	Tricresyl phosphate	Carbitol	Hexamethylphosphoramide	Acetonyl acetone	Dimethyl-sulfolane	Dimethyl-sulfolane	β,β'-Oxydipropionitrile
Temperature (°C):	25	40	25	0	0	25	0	30	0	0	25	25
Reference:	23	14	23	14	21	23	21	28	19	15	23	23
Neopentane	0.35	—	0.35	—	—	0.34	—	—	0.35	—	0.36	0.41
3-Methyl-1-butene	0.56	0.71	0.66	1.17	1.15	0.78	0.81	0.83	1.08	1.05	1.03	1.35
1,4-Pentadiene	0.65	—	0.95	—	—	1.42	—	—	—	—	—	3.76
Isopentane	0.74	0.76	0.74	0.75	0.66	0.72	0.74	0.75	0.71	0.73	0.74	0.72
1-Pentene	0.81	1.0	0.98	1.79	1.78	1.20	1.28	1.29	1.67	1.60	1.54	1.90
2-Methyl-1-butene	0.89	—	1.07	2.18	2.19	1.35	1.46	1.39	2.03	1.95	1.81	—
Isoprene	0.99	1.48	1.54	—	5.55	2.32	2.65	2.75	4.85	4.06	3.93	6.2
n-Pentane	1.00	1.00	1.00	1.00	1.00	1.00	1.00	1.00	1.00	1.00	1.00	1.00
trans-2-Pentene	1.04	1.30	1.22	2.26	2.19	1.56	1.61	1.53	2.13	2.06	1.90	2.24
cis-2-Pentene	1.08	1.30	1.30	2.49	2.42	1.66	1.76	1.63	2.31	2.28	2.08	2.70
2-Methyl-2-butene	1.21	1.48	1.48	3.02	2.88	1.86	1.93	1.75	2.70	2.76	2.41	3.10
Cyclopentadiene	1.30	—	2.30	—	11.52	4.34	4.66	—	—	—	7.7	—
trans-Piperylene	1.24	—	2.04	—	7.69	3.22	3.51	3.34	6.60	—	5.3	8.1
cis-Piperylene	1.38	—	2.22	—	8.73	3.70	4.02	3.71	7.47	—	5.9	9.8
Cyclopentane	2.12	2.19	2.28	—	3.16	2.88	2.65	2.31	3.19	—	2.88	3.42
Cyclopentene	1.80	2.19	2.30	—	5.02	3.44	3.11	—	—	—	4.18	6.4

Mixtures containing all or some of the six C_5 monoalkenes appear to be separated easily on diethylene glycol monomethyl ether (carbitol, *21*), though this material has not been extensively used for this separation; it differs from more commonly reported stationary phases in that *n*-pentane appears after the most volatile olefin. The six monoalkenes alone may be easily separated on dimethylsulfolane at 0°C (*15*), and less completely at 25°C (*29*), but with this the separation factor of 3-methyl-1-butene and *n*-pentane is 1.05, so that complete separation requires an efficient column. Acetonylacetone behaves similarly to dimethylsulfolane (*19*), but the relative retention of the above pair is improved to 1.08. With dimethylformamide, the separation of 3-methyl-1-butene and *n*-pentane is adequate (relative retention 1.15), but the relative retention of 2-methyl-1-butene and *trans*-2-pentene is only 1.035, which produces overlap on all but the most efficient columns.

The separation of the C_5 hydrocarbons, C_5H_8, which comprise five pentadienes, two methylbutadienes, and cyclopentene, has been studied by Knight (*29*). All these compounds have approximately unit acitivity coefficients in nonpolar stationary phases, but have small activity coefficients in polar stationary phases. On moderately polar phases, such as dimethylformamide, dimethylsulfolane, β,β'-oxydipropionitrile, etc., the dienes are all well separated from the monoenes, probably including the most volatile diene, 1,4-pentadiene, though no sample of this has been tested. Knight does not give any stationary phase which will separate all the above eight compounds; his results show, however, that the important members isoprene and cyclopentene are separated on dimethylsulfolane; reference to Table 12.6 shows that these may also be separated on dimethylformamide and dinonyl phthalate. A complete separation would require either a capillary column of very great efficiency, or two stages, e.g., use of dinonyl phthalate to separate the cyclopentene, followed by a more polar stationary phase.

Cyclopentadiene, C_5H_6, is very strongly retained on a polar stationary phase, and its separation from any other C_5 hydrocarbon presents no difficulty. It is retained so long on polar phases that it is probably better in practice to use a weakly polar stationary phase, e.g., carbitol.

When C_5 hydrocarbons are separated as a class from a more complex mixture by means of a carbon-number selective stationary phase, the most volatile of the hexenes, 3,3-dimethyl-1-butene, may be associated with the pentenes. On dimethylsulfolane, this is adequately separated, appearing between 1-pentene and 2-methyl-1-butene (*29*), but on either more or less polar stationary liquids, there is possibility of overlap.

12.4. PETROLEUM ALKANES, ALKENES, AND NAPHTHENES

The components of petroleum mixtures have been studied very extensively. We outline here the chromatography of only the commonest compounds. Some references describing the chromatography of the whole spectrum of petroleum hydrocarbons are (1–6), and references contained therein.

(a) Alkanes in General

The chromatography of alkanes can be systematised more precisely than that of any other group of compounds, and the detailed principles and relations are described in Sections 3.5–3.7, and 3.10. The outline of these principles as they apply to alkane separations is as follows:

(1) On non-polar stationary liquids, alkanes separate approximately in order of boiling point. However, there are many systematic small differences in the proportionality between the logarithm of the retention and the boiling point. For example, branched alkanes tend to have smaller retentions than their boiling points suggest, particularly at low temperatures.

(2) The specific retention volumes of alkanes vary little with the molecular weight or the exact structure of a non-polar stationary liquid.

(3) The specific retention volume of an alkane is less in a polar stationary liquid than in a non-polar one. The larger the proportion of polar groups in the solvent structure, the smaller is the retention of an alkane. With dilute solvents, e.g., phthalic esters, the decrement in retention is between 1-fold and 10-fold, and these solvents are easily usable for analysis of hydrocarbons. With concentrated solvents, e.g., polyethylene glycols, glycerol, etc., the decrement in retention may be very great, e.g. 100-fold. Alkanes are very sparingly soluble in such solvents, and the chromatography of alkanes is either hard or impossible in them.

(4) The systematic small differences in activity coefficients which occur in polar solvents are often different from those in non-polar ones. Change of solvent, therefore, can very often resolve an overlap.

(b) Hexanes

Relative retention data for the five hexanes, together with n-pentane, cyclopentane, and cyclohexane for cross-reference, are given in Table 12.7.

Of the five hexanes, any non-polar or intermediate stationary phase produces adequate separation of all pairs other than the pair 2,3-dimethylbutane–2-methylpentane, which have a relative retention of less than 1.03.

TABLE 12.7

RETENTIONS OF HEXANES RELATIVE TO n-PENTANE

	Boiling point	Stationary phase												
		Mineral oil	Apiezon A oil	Paraffin wax	Squalane	Squalane	Didecyl phthalate	Dinonyl phthalate	Tetrahydrofurfuryl phthalate	Benzyl diphenyl	2,5-Hexanedione	Dimethylsulfolane	2,2'-Oxydipropionitrile	Polyethylene glycol
Temperature (°C):	—	45	65	78.6	80	105	20	118	20	78.6	0	25	25	78
Reference:	—	13	8	10	9	9	11	8	11	7	12	13	13	8
n-Pentane	36.1	1.00	1.00	1.00	1.00	1.00	1.00	1.00	1.00	1.00	1.00	1.00	1.00	1.00
2,2-Dimethylbutane	49.7	1.40	1.42	1.34	1.44	1.4	1.45	1.25	1.15	1.26	1.51	1.32	1.28	1.00
2,3-Dimethylbutane	58.0	1.93	1.91	1.90	—	—	2.10	1.65	1.65	1.74	2.10	1.88	1.73	1.72
2-Methylpentane	60.3	1.98	1.95	1.87	—	1.8	2.15	1.59	1.65	1.79	—	1.90	1.55	1.39
3-Methylpentane	63.3	2.27	2.22	2.17	—	—	2.60	1.78	2.30	2.05	—	2.26	1.97	1.62
n-Hexane	68.7	2.72	2.58	2.46	2.42	2.3	3.10	1.92	2.20	2.31	2.59	2.62	2.00	2.28
Cyclohexane	80.2	5	—	4.46	4.38	4.0	—	3.42	—	5.54	—	6.65	6.8	6.2
Cyclopentane	49.3	1.92	1.94	—	1.86	1.8	—	1.77	—	2.54	—	2.89	3.42	2.82

The separation of all five using a non-polar stationary phase may be achieved with a capillary column (14), but not otherwise. The above pair is resolved on polar stationary phases, e.g., polyethylene glycol or β,β'-oxy-dipropionitrile, in which case the 2-methylpentane appears before the 2,3-dimethylbutane (13, 15). In this case, however, the relative retention of 3-methylpentane and n-hexane is small, and a long column is necessary because of this and also because the activity coefficients are of the order of 10.

Zlatkis (16) has found that a mixture containing only the five hexanes may easily be resolved on a column of isoquinoline; a $2\frac{1}{2}$ m column used at room temperature performs the separation in about 20 minutes. The drawback to this is that cyclopentane has the same retention as n-hexane; this can be overcome by including in series a short column of some less polar stationary phase on which the naphthenes are not so selectively retained, e.g., squalane. Figure 12.6 shows the chromatogram of the hexanes and cyclopentane on squalane and isoquinoline columns in series.

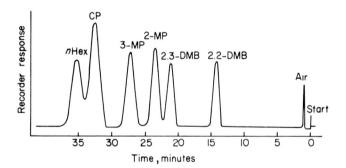

FIG. 12.6. Separation of the hexanes and cyclopentane on series columns of squalane and isoquinoline. Zlatkis (16).

The hexanes also separate on active charcoal modified with 1.5% by weight of squalane (17), though relative retentions are not large and a long column is required. There is no interference from C_5's or C_7's, for the principal characteristic of this column is that it separates compounds into their carbon numbers; see Subsection (d) and Section 4.3.

(c) *Heptanes*

Table 12.8 shows the retention volumes of the nine heptane alkanes on various stationary phases relative to n-heptane. It is seen that the only serious overlap is between 2,2-dimethylpentane and 2,4-dimethylpentane.

TABLE 12.8

RETENTION OF HEPTANE ALKANES RELATIVE TO n-HEPTANE

	Stationary phase				
	Hexatria-contane	Squalane	Benzyl-diphenyl	Poly-ethylene glycol	β,β'-Oxy-dipropio-nitrile
Temperature:	78	70	78	78	25
Reference:	7, 10	18	7	8	15
2,2-Dimethylpentane	0.523	0.514	0.49	—	0.55
2,4-Dimethylpentane	0.538	0.532	0.500	0.49	0.55
2,2,3-Trimethylbutane	0.610	0.593	0.560	—	0.69
3,3-Dimethylpentane	0.720	0.704	0.730	—	0.84
2,3-Dimethylpentane	0.795	0.784	0.765	—	0.90
2-Methylhexane	0.745	0.752	0.710	—	0.75
3-Methylhexane	0.815	0.813	0.789	0.745	0.85
3-Ethylpentane	0.905	0.889	0.880	—	1.00
n-Heptane	1.00	1.00	1.00	1.00	1.00

Desty *et al.* (*14*) have shown that the heptanes can be resolved using the paraffinic stationary phase squalane on a capillary column with not less than 100,000 theoretical plates. Their chromatogram is reproduced in Fig. 12.7.

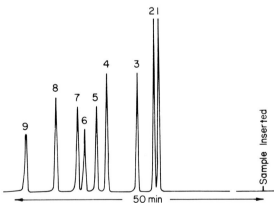

FIG. 12.7. Separation of the heptanes on a capillary column coated with squalane. Desty *et al.* (*14*). 1, 2,2-Dimethylpentane; 2, 2,4-dimethylpentane; 3, 2,2,3-trimethyl-butane; 4, 3,3-dimethylpentane; 5, 2-methylhexane; 6, 2,3-dimethylpentane; 7, 3-methylhexane; 8, 3-ethylpentane; 9, n-heptane.

(d) Naphthenes

On paraffinic columns, naphthenes have significantly smaller activity coefficients than the corresponding alkanes, so that they are retained for longer. This is illustrated in Table 12.9, which shows absolute activity coefficients of some naphthenes obtained by Kwantes and Rijnders (*9*) and also activity coefficients relative to *n*-pentane determined from retention data for a number of naphthenes. On benzyldiphenyl and probably on other intermediate stationary phases, the effect is intensified, so that the relative retention of the naphthene and its corresponding alkane is greater. On polar stationary phases such as polyethylene glycol (*8*) or β,β'-oxydipropionitrile (*16*), the relative effect is further magnified, though absolute activity coefficients are considerably increased. Remarkable exceptions are glycerol and diglycerol (*19*) which show the same alkane/naphthene relative retention as a paraffinic stationary phase. On these, however, absolute retentions are very small.

TABLE 12.9

ABSOLUTE AND RELATIVE ACTIVITY COEFFICIENTS FOR ALKANES AND NAPHTHENES
IN DIFFERENT STATIONARY PHASES COMPARED

	Stationary phase				
	Squalane	1,2,4-Tri-chloro-benzene	Hexatria-contane	Benzyl-diphenyl	Poly-ethylene glycol 1000
Coefficient:	γ_{abs}	γ_{abs}	γ_{rel}	γ_{rel}	γ_{rel}
Temperature (°C):	80	30	78	78	78
Reference:	*9*	*9*	*7*	*7*	*8*
n-Pentane	0.67	2.97	*1.00*	*1.00*	*1.00*
Cyclopentane	0.52	2.11	—	—	—
n-Hexane	0.66	2.93	1.09	1.15	1.52
Cyclohexane	0.52	2.32	0.83	0.675	0.60
Methylcyclopentane	0.55	2.37	0.89	0.77	0.64
n-Heptane	0.68	—	1.13	1.23	1.31
Methylcyclohexane	0.54	—	0.89	0.81	0.76

Within any one carbon number, the naphthenes are less volatile than the alkanes, and the effect of their small activity coefficients is to augment the difference in vapour pressures, so that naphthenes are retained longer than the corresponding alkanes on both counts. Thus, the relative retentions of cyclopentane and n-pentane, cyclohexane and n-hexane, cycloheptane and n-heptane, are all large (e.g., 2 to 3), and these separations are very easy. Branched naphthenes also have small activity coefficients, as is apparent from the entries on Table 12.9. The branching, however, produces the usual increase in vapour pressure, and thus, as in general, retentions of branched members are smaller than those of the unbranched naphthenes of the same carbon number. Whether or not branched naphthenes of a particular carbon number overlap into the corresponding alkanes of the same carbon number appears to depend on the amount of branching, on the carbon number, and on the stationary phase. With C_5 hydrocarbons, the most volatile dimethylcyclopropane, 1,$trans$-2-dimethylcyclopropane, appears in front of n-pentane on a paraffinic stationary phase and on di-n-decyl phthalate, but n-pentane appears first on tricresyl phosphate and more polar stationary phases (*13*). On polar stationary phases, therefore, there is complete separation of C_5 alkanes and naphthenes. With C_6 hydrocarbons, methylcyclopentane is eluted after n-hexane whatever the stationary phase. With C_7 hydrocarbons, the most volatile of the common naphthenes, 1,1-dimethylcyclopentane, is sufficiently branched to appear well before n-heptane on a paraffinic stationary phase (*7*) and just before n-heptane on an intermediate stationary phase (benzyldiphenyl) (*7*). It is probable that on a more polar stationary phase, complete separation of C_7 alkanes and naphthenes into two groups would occur.

Another result of the small activity coefficients of naphthenes is that the unbranched naphthene of one carbon number overlaps into the branched alkanes of the next carbon number, thus spoiling a group separation according to carbon number. In order to overcome this, Eggertsen *et al.* (*17*) make use of the observation that adsorbents such as charcoal adsorb naphthenes less readily than alkanes (Section 4.2a). On pure charcoal, peaks are too asymmetrical with solutes so involatile as petroleum fractions, and furthermore, the relative acceleration of naphthenes is too great. Both these drawbacks are overcome by modifying the adsorbent by mixing it with a small (1.5% w/w) proportion of a paraffinic stationary liquid, squalane. This has the effect of saturating all the more active sites in the charcoal, thus reducing peak asymmetry, and also superimposing a certain amount of the character of a paraffinic stationary phase, so that cyclohexane is retained longer than n-hexane, but not so long as the first of the heptanes,

2,2-dimethylpentane. This stationary phase acts as a group separator for carbon numbers in mixtures containing alkanes and naphthenes which is effective at least up to C_8.

(e) Olefins

In paraffinic stationary phases olefins, like alkanes, usually separate in order of boiling point. In many cases, however, small deviations in activity coefficient may be sufficient to cause overlap in pairs of solutes of slightly different boiling point or to cause resolution of pairs of solutes of very similar boiling point. In dilute polar stationary liquids, alkenes are slightly retained relative to alkanes. The effect is not very large, and is not enough to be able to separate completely the alkanes and alkenes of a particular carbon number into two discrete groups of peaks, but it is sufficient to be useful in individual separations. Thus, hexene-1, which is eluted just in front of n-hexane on a paraffinic column, is unresolved from n-hexane on di-isodecyl phthalate (11) and is eluted just after n-hexane on benzyl-diphenyl (7). Again, on dilute polar stationary phases, olefins separate among themselves roughly in order of boiling point, as may be seen from the results of Sullivan et al. (11). On concentrated polar stationary phases, olefins are further retained relative to alkanes, but the effect is still not large, so that, for example, on β,β'-oxydipropionitrile, hexene-1 appears on the middle of the heptanes (20). As with alkanes (Section 3.7), the spread of activity coefficients within a carbon number on a polar stationary phase may not be much larger than on a paraffinic stationary phase, but at least it is different, so there is a good chance that what is not separated on the one may be separated on the other.

For olefins, there is a useful specific stationary phase made by dissolving silver nitrate in some non-volatile polar substrate, of which ethylene glycol, propylene glycol, and benzyl cyanide are most common (21–23). The silver nitrate forms complexes with the olefins, with the effect that they are selectively retained. Non-olefinic compounds behave as if the silver nitrate were not there. Thus, when glycerol or ethylene glycol are used as solvents for the silver nitrate, the retention of alkanes is virtually nil, and such a stationary phase serves to separate olefins and acetylenes as a group from alkanes over several carbon numbers. If less silver nitrate is used, or if the solvent is not so polar (generally the one accompanies the other, since the more polar the solvent, the more soluble the silver nitrate), the properties of the solvent become more significant. If benzyl cyanide is used as solvent, the alkanes are considerably retained, and simple mixtures of alkanes and alkenes can be analysed in a single run, as is shown by the retention data of Table 12.10 (*21*). All solutions of silver nitrate are unstable when heated above about 50°C and should not be allowed to exceed this temperature. 1-Alkynes react with silver nitrate, and spoil columns containing it.

TABLE 12.10

RETENTION DATA RELATIVE TO ISOPRENE OF HYDROCARBONS AT 30°C ON BENZYL CYANIDE-SILVER NITRATE[a]

Substance	Relative retention	Substance	Relative retention
n-Butane	0.041	2-Methyl-1-butene	0.598
Ethylene	0.042	1-Pentene	0.597
Propylene	0.100	*n*-Heptane	0.649
n-Pentane	0.111	Cyclohexane	0.811
Propadiene	0.115	*cis*-2-Pentene	0.810
trans-2-Butene	0.154	Isoprene	*1.00*
Isobutylene	0.195	2-Methyl-1-pentene	1.122
n-Hexane	0.268	*trans*-1,3-Pentadiene	1.377
1-Butene	0.287	2-Butyne	1.619
cis-2-Butene	0.345	1,4-Pentadiene	1.571
Cyclopentane	0.367	*cis*-1,3-Pentadiene	1.825
1,3-Butadiene	0.366	Cyclopentadiene	2.464
trans-2-Pentene	0.371	Cyclopentene	2.461
2-Methyl-2-butene	0.393	2-Pentyne	3.236
3-Methyl-1-butene	0.452		

[a] See Armitage (*21*).

The general features of the separation of alkenes from naphthenes is deducible from comparison of Sections 12.4(d) and the above. On paraffinic stationary phases, alkenes behave like alkanes, but napthenes are retained both because of higher boiling point and because of smaller activity coefficients; the result is that naphthenes separate easily from alkenes of the same empirical formula, but that there is no marked separation into groups over more than one carbon number. The magnitude of the activity effects can be shown by the relative retention of methylcyclohexane (b.p. 100.9°C) and 2,4,4-trimethylpentene-1 (b.p. 101.4°C), which is 1.28, or of cycloheptane (b.p. 118.9°C) and octene-1 (b.p. 121.3°C) which is 1.20, with the octene being eluted first.

On polar stationary phases, both alkenes and naphthenes are retarded somewhat relative to alkanes, so their relations to one another are little changed. A survey of published data does not reveal any simple stationary phase on which there is any effective group separation of the two classes.

(f) Ancillary Techniques

The analysis of complex hydrocarbon mixtures with the aid of gas chromatography is frequently assisted when other techniques are also used in conjunction. Some such cases are given below.

(1) *Group separations by liquid chromatography*. Though there are gas chromatographic stationary phases which separate hydrocarbon mixtures into aromatics, alkenes, and alkanes, a standard technique using liquid chromatography on silica gel does this efficiently (*24, 25*).

(2) *Use of subtractors*. In a complex mixture containing peaks caused by substances of unknown chemical type, the chromatogram of the mixture can be compared with a chromatogram obtained by removing a specific chemical type with a selective reagent. Thus, olefins may be removed with a pre-column containing sulphuric acid (*26*). A useful subtractor for alkane analysis is molecular sieve 5A, which retains straight chain hydrocarbons almost irreversibly, but allows free passage to any hydrocarbon containing a branch (*27*).

(3) *Use of reactors*. Hydrocarbon analysis may be aided by carrying out preliminary chemical operations on the mixture; these operations may be separate from the gas chromatography or may take place in a column placed in the gas stream between the introducer and the analysing column. For example, the analysis of complicated mixtures of olefins is eased, though made less precise, by saturating them to the corresponding alkanes before analysis, so that the olefins are separated according to their skeletal structure but not according to the positions of their double bonds (*28, 29*). In a similar manner oxidative degradation, followed by gas chromatographic analysis of fragments, can be used for determining the positions of branches in alkane chains (*30, 31*).

(4) *Use of other physical analytical techniques*. Unknown hydrocarbons separated by gas chromatography have frequently been identified by other physical methods of analysis, e.g., mass spectrometry or infrared spectrophotometry; see Chapter 11.

TABLE 12.11

Retentions of Aromatic Hydrocarbons Relative to Benzene

	Boiling point	Apiezon A oil	Liquid paraffin	Apiezon L grease	Benzyl-diphenyl	Benzyl-diphenyl	Dinonyl phthalate	Tricresyl phosphate	Trixylenyl phosphate	Dimethyl sulfolane	1-Chloro-naphtha-lene	Poly-ethylene glycol 1000	Poly-ethylene glycol 400
Temperature (°C):	—	101	120	147	78.5	100	118	78.5	120	50	50	78	100
Reference:	—	1	2	3	4	5	1	4	2	5	5	1	6
Benzene	80.1	1.00	1.00	1.00	1.00	1.00	1.00	1.00	1.00	1.00	1.00	1.00	1.00
Toluene	110.6	2.30	2.06	1.54	2.34	2.05	2.05	2.30	1.87	2.35	3.30	1.89	1.72
Ethylbenzene	136.2	4.58	3.84	2.46	4.92	3.93	3.75	4.65	3.29	5.00	8.96	3.27	—
p-Xylene	138.4	5.10	4.37	2.25	5.24	4.14	4.07	4.93	3.43	5.45	10.30	3.42	—
m-Xylene	139.1	5.15	4.51	2.25	5.48	4.27	4.17	5.06	3.64	5.75	10.92	3.59	2.93
o-Xylene	144.4	6.09	4.93	2.82	6.86	5.25	4.95	6.49	4.31	7.73	14.39	4.71	3.77
Cumene	152.4	7.12	5.63	3.00	—	—	5.47	—	4.53	—	—	4.39	—
n-Propylbenzene	159.2	8.74	7.55	3.50	—	—	6.61	—	5.77	—	—	5.46	—
Mesitylene	164.6	11.21	8.73	4.18	—	—	8.27	—	6.48	—	—	6.65	4.97
Pseudocumene	169.2	13.0	11.20	—	—	—	9.61	—	7.84	—	—	—	—
sec-Butylbenzene	171.0	—	11.31	—	—	—	—	—	7.89	—	—	—	—
p-Cymene	175.0	—	13.45	—	—	—	10.7	—	8.44	—	—	—	—
tert-Amylbenzene	191.0	—	20.60	—	—	—	—	—	13.18	—	—	—	—
Hydrindene	178.0	—	12.60	—	—	—	12.1	—	10.78	—	—	—	—
Styrene	145.2	5.86	4.98	—	—	—	5.33	—	4.89	—	—	7.06	—
α-Methylstyrene	161.5	—	9.18	—	—	—	8.94	—	8.11	—	—	11.0	—
Indene	182.0	—	14.65	—	—	—	14.9	—	15.25	—	—	—	—

12.5. Aromatic Hydrocarbons

(a) Common C_6–C_9 Hydrocarbons

The common C_6–C_9 aromatic hydrocarbons are listed in order of boiling point in Table 12.11. Many workers have determined relative retention volumes on many different stationary phases; Table 12.11 contains a selection of the results. Aromatic hydrocarbons are retained on all stationary phases except those containing a very large proportion of hydroxyl groups, e.g., glycerol. On polyethylene glycols, activity coefficients are rather large, and, though relative retentions are large, values of k are small, with the consequent drawbacks described in Chapters 3, 5, and 6.

On paraffinic stationary phases, there are overlaps between m- and p-xylenes, pseudocumene and sec-butylbenzene, styrene and o-xylene. The last overlap is easily remedied by use of any other type of stationary phase, e.g., dinonyl phthalate; the other two overlaps persist in other stationary phases. The overlap of m- and p-xylene, in particular, has been extensively studied.

(b) Separation of the C_8 Hydrocarbons

Of the four compounds ethylbenzene and the three xylenes, o-xylene is easily separated from the others on any stationary phase. Ethylbenzene is adequately separated from the other two xylenes on paraffinic stationary phases, but the relative retention becomes rather small on more polar phases. The separation of m- and p-xylenes on common stationary phases is relatively difficult, for the relative retention is less than about 1.04. However, such a separation can easily be achieved in a capillary column, as is shown in Fig. 12.8.

Several authors (4, 5, 7) have sought specific stationary phases for the separation of m- and p-xylenes, the analysis of mixtures of which is a

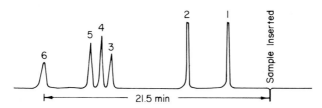

FIG. 12.8. Separation of aromatic hydrocarbons up to C_8 on a capillary column coated with 7,8-benzoquinoline. Desty *et al.* (*8*). 1, Benzene; 2, toluene; 3, ethylbenzene; 4, p-xylene; 5, m-xylene; 6, o-xylene.

common problem. Table 12.12 summarises the results by giving the relative retentions of m-xylene/p-xylene and of p-xylene/ethylbenzene for various stationary phases that have been investigated. It is seen that, in general, the relative retention is greater the lower the temperature, as usual. In addition to this 1-chloronaphthalene and 7,8-benzoquinoline are effective

TABLE 12.12

RELATIVE RETENTIONS OF C$_8$ AROMATIC HYDROCARBONS ON VARIOUS STATIONARY
PHASES ARRANGED IN APPROXIMATE ORDER OF SPECIFICITY

Stationary phase	Temp. (°C)	Relative retentions of:		Ref.
		m-Xylene / p-Xylene	p-Xylene / Ethylbenzene	
Squalane	78.5	1.025	1.120	4
Tricresyl phosphate	78.5	1.026	1.060	4
Benzyldiphenyl	78.5	1.046	1.064	4
Benzyldiphenyl	100	1.031	—	5
Benzyldiphenyl	110.8	1.040	1.061	4
Dimethylsulfolane	50	1.055	—	5
Phenanthrene	110.8	1.053	1.101	4
1-Chloronaphthalene	50	1.060	—	5
7,8-Benzoquinoline	78.5	1.080	1.068	4
7,8-Benzoquinoline	110.8	1.053	1.088	4
Methyl propyl tetrachlorophthalate	110	0.959	—	7
Di-n-propyl tetrachlorophthalate	110	0.959	—	7
Di-n-propyl tetrabromophthalate	110	0.969	—	7

in considerably increasing the natural separation due to the slight difference in volatility, and chlorophthalic esters have a specific effect which reverses the effect of the natural volatility sufficiently to produce an adequate separation in the reverse order. In the case of 7,8-benzoquinoline, the relative retention of p-xylene/ethylbenzene is no greater than that of m-xylene/p-xylene, so that the three peaks are about equally spaced.

An even more specific stationary phase for this separation is alkylammonium montmorillonite used by Hughes *et al.* (*9*). If this material is used by itself, the xylenes are widely separated, with approximate relative retentions being: *p*-xylene, *1.00*; *o*-xylene, 1.28; *m*-xylene, 1.51. With the unmodified adsorbent, the peaks due to aromatics are very diffuse. If, however, it is modified with an oil, e.g. silicone (*10–12*), an efficient column packing can be produced which still exhibits good resolution of the xylenes. Figure 12.9 illustrates the separation achieved.

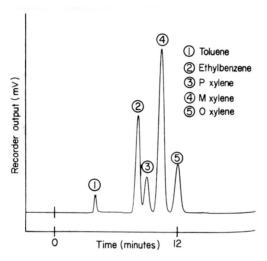

FIG. 12.9. Separation of C_8 aromatic hydrocarbons on a modified Bentonite adsorbent. Spencer (*12*).

(c) *Aromatic Compounds in Quantitative Analysis*

With common detectors including catharometers, argon ionisation detectors, and flame ionisation detectors, the area of a peak is very roughly proportional to the weight per cent of a component consisting of a non-aromatic hydrocarbon (Sections 9.3, 9.8, and 10.8). This rule, which is usually accurate within a few per cent for such compounds, cannot be applied to aromatic hydrocarbons, for which the sensitivities of detectors (Section 8.2) are up to about 50% different. For catharometers, the relative weight sensitivities of a number of compounds [calculated from Rosie and Grob (*13*)] are presented in Table 12.13a, illustrating the difference produced by the presence of an aromatic nucleus. An extreme example of this appears from the results of Hendriks *et al.* (*14*), who find the weight sensitivities given in Table 12.13b for naphthalene, diphenyl, and their hydrogenation products, using nitrogen as carrier gas in a catharometer.

TABLE 12.13

Weight Sensitivities of Vapours in a Catharometer

Compound	Relative weight sensitivity
(a) Vapours in helium relative to n-hexane	
n-Pentane	1.02
n-Hexane	1.00
n-Heptane	0.98
n-Decane	0.97
2,2-Dimethylbutane	0.94
2-Methylpentane	0.97
2-Methylhexane	0.95
Benzene	0.89
Toluene	0.88
Ethylbenzene	0.85
o-Xylene	0.86
sec-Butylbenzene	0.83
(b) Vapours in nitrogen relative to diphenyl	
Diphenyl	1.00
Cyclohexylbenzene	1.20
Dicyclohexyl	1.35
Naphthalene	1.60
Tetralin	2.10
Decalin	2.20

(d) Group Separations of Aromatic Hydrocarbons

The four principal groups of hydrocarbons, i.e., alkanes, alkenes, naphthenes, and aromatics, can frequently be separated one from another by group separations (Section 3.8). The group separation of alkanes from naphthenes is discussed in Section 12.4d, and that of alkanes from alkenes in Section 12.4e. Other group separations involving hydrocarbons are discussed below.

Information on the possibility of group separations in general is easily obtained from graphs of the kind given in either Fig. 3.9 or Fig. 3.12. If, on a particular stationary phase, two lines are spaced by a sufficient boiling point difference (Fig. 3.12) or a sufficient number of carbon atoms (Fig. 3.9), then a group separation covering that range is feasible.

(*1*) *Alkane–Aromatic.* On paraffinic stationary phases, activity coefficients of aromatics are similar to those of alkanes, and they are not selectively retained. Thus, on such phases, benzene appears between n-hexane and n-heptane, as does its boiling point. As the polarity of the stationary phase increases, however, the activity coefficients of the alkanes increase rapidly but those of the aromatics do not, with the result that the aromatics are retained relative to the alkanes. On stationary phases classed as concentrated in Section 3.8, the extra retention of aromatics relative to alkanes is sufficient for these phases to secure complete separation of alkanes from aromatics so long as the least volatile alkane does not boil higher than approximately 150°–170°C. Thus, on polyethylene glycol 400 (*15*) or on oxydipropionitrile (*16*), n-decane (bp 174°C) is eluted before benzene (bp 80.1°C). Concentrated polar stationary phases are thus perfect group separators for alkanes and aromatics for all alkanes up to n-decane, and, if a mixture contains alkanes less volatile than decane, the crudest distillation is adequate to separate them. On dilute polar stationary liquids, the retention of aromatics relative to the alkanes depends on the liquid, becoming greater the larger the polar proportion in it.

Alkylammonium montmorillonite also provides specific retention of aromatics relative to alkanes (*17, 18*). The relative retentions of some alkanes and aromatics are given in Table 4.2, from which it is seen that the relative retentions are probably about the same as those on concentrated polar stationary liquids.

(*2*) *Aromatic–Alkene.* Since polar stationary phases secure a large retention of aromatics relative to alkanes, and a very moderate retention of alkenes relative to alkanes, then they secure a moderate retention of aromatics relative to alkenes. Survey of published data shows that polar stationary phases secure a useful group separation of monoalkenes from aromatics. Thus, on polyethylene glycol 1000, olefins more volatile than nonene-1 (b.p. 146°C) are eluted before benzene (*1*), and Fig. 3.12 shows that on β,β'-oxydipropionitrile, olefins boiling below approximately 160°C are eluted before benzene (*16*). The use of silver nitrate columns makes the separation of alkenes and aromatics worse, since it retards the faster moving alkenes so that they are eluted closer to the aromatics.

(*3*) *Aromatic–Naphthene.* On paraffinic stationary phases, naphthenes have slightly smaller activity coefficients than aromatics. Thus, benzene and cyclohexane, both of which boil at 80°C, separate in the order given with a relative retention of approximately 1.1 on a paraffinic stationary phase. On concentrated polar stationary phases, the aromatics are retarded relative to the naphthenes in much the same way as with alkenes, and thus such stationary phases provide a useful group separation. For example, Fig. 3.12 shows that on β,β'-oxydipropionitrile, any naphthene boiling below approximately 180°C (e.g., n-butylcyclohexane) is eluted in front of benzene. On dilute polar stationary phases, the retention of aromatics is less marked.

12.6. FATTY ACIDS AND ESTERS

There is much literature on the gas chromatography of fatty acids and esters, the analysis of which is required in many branches of technology, e.g., plastics, oil, etc. Most of the work, however, is on the analysis of the higher fatty acids found in animals and plants. The fatty acids can be analysed either as the free acids or as esters. Since the free acids are polar and interact strongly both with themselves and with most support materials, they are very liable to produce peaks which are badly tailed. Thus, in the majority of routine analysis, acids are converted to volatile esters before chromatography.

(a) Chromatography of the Lower Fatty Acids

Acids up to dodecanoic (C_{12}) were analysed by James and Martin in their original work on gas-liquid chromatography (1). On silicone oil on diatomaceous earth, bad tailing was found, but this was considerably reduced by the incorporation of 10% by weight of stearic acid (C_{18}) with the silicone. One possible reason for the advantageous effect of stearic acid is the reduction of adsorption in the support discussed in Section 7.2. Another possibility considered by Beerthuis et al. (2) is that there is a certain amount of specific chemical combination between the solute acids and the stearic acid similar in kind to the familiar dimers formed by acetic acid and other lower fatty acids.

Several authors have described the analysis of free fatty acids up to C_{22} or thereabouts. Most have used stationary liquids in which an acid has been incorporated, e.g. terephthalic acid (3–5) or phosphoric acid (6). Such separations can be done on capillary columns. Some other workers have also succeeded in obtaining satisfactory analyses of free acids on stationary phases not containing an acid (2, 7), but elaborate attention must be paid to deactivating the support and very small samples must be used.

(b) *Preparation of Methyl Esters of Higher Fatty Acids*

In most applications, biological material containing fatty acids must be broken down, e.g., from a glyceride to the free acids, which must then be converted to the methyl ester. There are several methods.

(1) *By Diazomethane.* A convenient method of methylating free acids is for them to be dissolved in a mixture of methanol and ether, and the solution to be treated with sufficient of a methanolic solution of diazomethane. After reaction, excess diazomethane may be stripped, leaving a solution of the esters (8).

The diazomethane technique has been criticised by Stoffel *et al.* (9), since the diazomethane may add to double bonds forming pyrazolines, and also structural changes may occur during the saponification of the original organic material (see Subsection d).

(2) *By Methanol and HCl.* The dangers of spurious chemical reaction occurring during saponification and diazomethane esterification can both be avoided in a transesterification reaction, in which the methoxy group directly replaces the glyceryl or other such group in the starting material. Methanol in the presence of hydrogen chloride achieves this reaction. The following recipe is taken from Stoffel *et al.* (9):

The esters or acids to be methylated (1 to 10 mg) are dissolved in 4 ml of 5% hydrochloric acid in superdry methanol and 0.5 ml of dry benzene in a 15 ml microsublimation tube to which a condenser with a calcium chloride moisture trap is connected. The mixture is refluxed in a silicone bath at 80°C to 100°C for two hours, with frequent shaking at the start to dissolve the mixture. After cooling to room temperature, two volumes of water are added, and the methyl esters are extracted three times with 3 ml of petroleum ether. The pooled extracts are simultaneously neutralised and dried over sodium sulphate-sodium bicarbonate mixture for 1 hour. The esters are then quantitatively transferred with petroleum ether to a second microsublimation tube and the solvent is evaporated to dryness at reduced pressure in a 40°C water bath.

In the technique of Luddy *et al.* (10), the transesterification is performed by potassium methylate in methanol, and the resulting fatty acid esters are removed from unsaponifiable material by silicic acid chromatography.

(3) *With Boron Halides.* If boron trifluoride or trichloride are used in place of HCl as the catalyst for transesterification, the reaction is completed very much more rapidly. Thus, Metcalfe *et al.* describe a technique in which

acids are esterified in ten minutes, using BF_3 (*11*), and Peterson *et al.* describe a rapid transesterification technique using BCl_3 (*12*).

Craig *et al.* (*13*) have found that, with the more volatile fatty acids, it is convenient to prepare esters less volatile than methyl. In their procedure, the acids are converted to their sodium salts, which are reacted with α-bromacetophenone to yield phenacyl esters, which may then be chromatographed at 200°C.

It is possible to chromatograph glyceryl esters at very high temperatures. Huebner (*14*) has partially hydrolysed glycerides derived from coconuts, acetylated the product, and chromatographed the resulting partially acetylated fat at temperatures from 240° to 360°C.

(c) *Methyl Esters on Non-Polar Stationary Phases*

The chromatography of the methyl esters of the higher fatty acids was first reported by Cropper and Heywood (*15–17*), who used silicone grease as the stationary phase, and found that sodium chloride crystals were most satisfactory as a support, since these had a small resistance to flow at the high temperatures used. Most other workers, however, have used diatomaceous earth as support. Many authors give details of separations performed on silicone grease (*2, 18–21*), Apiezon L (*2, 20–22*), or Apiezon M (*21, 23, 24*) grease. Using one or other of these, fatty acid esters up to at least C_{34} (*18*) may be analysed. For this, a temperature of 295°C was used, but for most biochemical applications, which do not involve many acids above about C_{22}, a temperature of approximately 200°C is suitable, and has been used by the majority of workers.

Many authors have given relative retention data for common fatty acid esters on the above stationary phases; a selection of this is included in Table 12.14.

As is general (Section 3.7), retention times of successive normal saturated esters differ by a constant factor, so that a plot of the logarithm of the retention time against carbon number is an accurate straight line. At temperatures of approximately 200°C, the factor is approximately 1.5, as may be seen from Table 12.14.

The retention volumes of unsaturated fatty acid esters are slightly smaller than those of their saturated analogs, and to a rough approximation, the relative retention of an unsaturated ester and its saturated analog is multiplied by a constant factor for every additional unsaturated group, though deviations from this rule can lead to accidental overlaps. This is illustrated from the figures of Table 12.14, but is seen to best advantage

RETENTIONS RELATIVE TO METHYL STEARATE OF METHYL ESTERS OF HIGHER FATTY ACIDS[a]

		Stationary phase								
	Apiezon M	Apiezon M	Apiezon M	Silicone grease	Apiezon L	Reoplex 400	Reoplex 400	Poly(diethylene glycol succinate)	Poly(diethylene glycol succinate)	Poly(vinyl acetate)
Temperature (°C):	197	197	200	200	240	197	240	200	203	210
Reference:	24	23	21	21	27	23	25	21	28	26
Caprylate (C$_8$)	0.013	—	0.012	0.026	—	—	0.07	0.055	—	—
Nonanoate (C$_9$)	0.02	—	0.018	0.038	—	—	—	0.078	—	—
Caprate (C$_{10}$)	0.03	0.029	0.031	0.057	0.047	0.10	0.123	0.108	—	—
Undecanoate (C$_{11}$)	—	0.047	0.049	0.078	0.07	0.13	—	0.136	—	—
Laurate (C$_{12}$)	0.076	0.075	0.077	0.116	0.099	0.16	0.21	0.185	0.22	—
Tridecanoate (C$_{13}$)	—	0.112	0.117	0.166	0.145	0.22	—	0.236	—	—
Myristate (C$_{14}$)	0.179	0.174	0.182	0.237	0.22	0.31	0.355	0.324	0.36	—
Myristolenate (C$_{14}^{1}$)	—	0.159	—	—	—	0.36	—	—	—	—
Pentadecanoate (C$_{15}$)	—	0.270	0.279	0.342	0.32	0.41	—	0.424	—	—
Palmitate (C$_{16}$)	0.43	0.414	0.435	0.488	0.47	0.56	0.61	0.573	0.60	0.58
Palmitolenate (C$_{16}^{1}$)	3.73	0.366	—	—	—	—	0.67	—	0.70	—
Palmitolenate(trs) (C$_{16}^{1}$)	0.386	—	—	—	—	—	—	—	—	—
Heptadecanoate (C$_{17}$)	—	0.649	0.632	0.690	—	0.74	—	0.742	—	—
Stearate (C$_{18}$)	1.00	1.00	1.00	1.00	1.00	1.00	1.00	1.00	1.00	1.00
Eleiadate (C$_{18}^{1}$)	0.88	0.896	—	—	0.90	1.12	—	1.15	1.16	—
Oleate (C$_{18}^{1}$)	0.85	0.860	0.880	—	0.89	1.12	1.09	1.12	1.44	1.13
Linoleate (C$_{18}^{2}$)	0.81	0.801	0.857	—	—	1.33	1.26	1.41	1.68	1.26
Linolenate (C$_{18}^{3}$)	—	0.801	0.805	—	0.85	1.68	1.52	1.81	1.84	1.48
Arachidate (C$_{20}$)	—	2.38	—	2.01	2.13	1.77	1.70	1.78	—	—
(C$_{20}^{1}$)	—	1.99	—	—	—	1.98	—	—	—	—
Arachinodate (C$_{20}^{4}$)	—	1.46	—	—	1.47	2.96	—	3.11	—	2.81

[a] The superscript to the symbol for the fatty acid groups stands for the number of ethylenic bonds.

in Fig. 12.10, which shows the chromatogram of a mixture of fatty acid esters taken on a 200-ft capillary column (*29*), and shows the way in which unsaturated esters precede the saturated esters in order of unsaturation. The difference in retention between saturated and unsaturated esters of the same carbon number is small, and columns of considerable efficiency are required to secure good resolution. In particular, columns of non-polar stationary phases cannot separate the important pair linoleic-linolenic acids, which occur in many fats and oils.

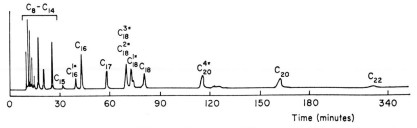

FIG. 12.10. Separation of fatty acid esters at 240°C on a 200-foot capillary column coated with Apiezon L grease. Lipsky *et al.* (*29*).

(d) *Methyl Esters on Polar Stationary Phases*

The overlaps involving unsaturated esters on non-polar stationary phases have led many workers to use polar stationary phases; many of the common polar stationary phases, however, may not be used on account of the high temperatures necessary for the analysis. By far the commonest stationary liquids used for fatty acid ester analysis are polyesters made by the esterification of dibasic acids with alcohols containing more than one hydroxyl group, for example adipic acid and ethylene glycol. In particular, the polyester of succinic acid and diethylene glycol has been extensively used (*28, 31*).

The principal characteristic of the polar stationary phases is that, in contrast to the paraffinic stationary phases, olefinic esters are selectively retained so that they are eluted after the corresponding saturated esters. This is illustrated in Fig. 12.11 from Orr and Callen (*30*), which compares chromatograms of a mixture of saturated and unsaturated esters from C_{16} to C_{20} on a polar and on a non-polar stationary phase. Relative retention data for common fatty acid esters on a variety of polar stationary phases is included in Table 12.14.

The relative positions of a saturated ester and its corresponding unsaturated analogs depend on the exact nature of the stationary phase, and, by making polyesters from different acids and alcohols, the relative reten-

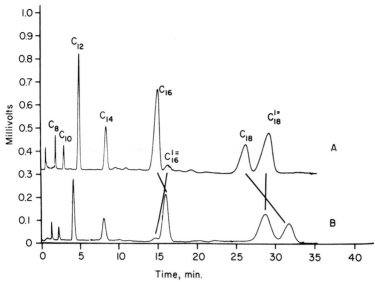

FIG. 12.11. Chromatograms of fatty acid esters on Reoplex 400 polyester and on Apiezon L grease compared. Orr and Callen (*30*).

	A	**B**
Column packing:	20.0 g 40% Reoplex 400 on 60– 80 mesh Celite	23.8 g 20% Apiezon L on 60–80 mesh Celite
Column:	275 × 0.5 cm	275 × 0.5 cm
Flow rate:	117 ml/minute at STP	139 ml/minute at STP
Temperature:	244°C	240°C
Sample volume:	5 μl	4 μl

tions can be varied almost at will. This is illustrated in Table 12.15 (after the similar table given by Orr and Callen (*30*), with additions), which shows the relative retention of methyl stearate/methyl linoleate on a number of different polyester stationary phases. According to the principles given in Section 3.8 and the details of the chromatography of alkenes in comparison with alkanes given in Section 12.4e, it is to be expected that the smaller the proportion of methylene or methyl groups in the stationary phase, the larger the relative retention, and study of the table appears to confirm this. Thus, the relative retention on polyethylene sebacate is greater than that on polypropylene sebacate; similarly for polydiethylene glycol succinate in comparison with polydiethylene glycol adipate.

On nearly all the polyester stationary phases, the polyunsaturated esters are retained longer than the saturated ester with one more carbon atom. Since, however, in very many natural mixtures, the acids with odd number of carbon atoms are virtually absent, this causes no overlaps.

TABLE 12.15

RELATIVE RETENTION OF METHYL STEARATE/METHYL LINOLEATE ON VARIOUS
POLYESTER STATIONARY PHASES

Stationary phase	Relative retention	Temp. (°C)	Ref.
Non-polar	≈0.85	200	—
Polypropylene sebacate/laurate	1.00	240	30
Butyl glyceryl sebacate	1.05	240	30
Polypropylene sebacate/phthalate	1.06	240	30
Polypropylene sebacate	1.06	240	30
Polydiethylene glycol adipate	1.10	240	30
Polyvinyl acetate	1.26	210	30
Polyethylene sebacate	1.28	240	30
Polyoxyalkylene adipate (Reoplex 400)	1.29	240	30
Polyoxyalkylene adipate (Reoplex 400)	1.33	197	23
Polydiethylene glycol/pentaerithritol adipate	1.32	240	30
Polydiethylene glycol succinate	1.41	200	21
Polydiethylene glycol succinate	1.44	203	28

With some of the more polar polyester stationary phases, the polyunsaturated esters are retained beyond the saturated ester with two more carbon atoms, and this may well cause undesirable overlaps. With Reoplex 400 at least, which is a moderately polar stationary phase, monounsaturated esters appear before the saturated ester with one more carbon atom, so that mixtures containing acids with even and odd carbon numbers may be satisfactorily analysed on this so long as polyunsaturated esters are not present which might cause overlaps.

There are two drawbacks to the use of polyesters as stationary phases. The preparation of the materials leads to a product which contains material spanning a large range of molecular weight, and some of it is appreciably volatile. This leads to a slow volatilisation of the column material, causing noise in the detector and eventual deterioration in the efficiency of the column. This effect can be reduced to some extent by pre-treatment of the column at the temperature to be used for the analysis (*30*). The other drawback is the possibility of a transesterification reaction in the column not unlike the reaction described in Section 12.6b for the preparation of methyl esters. This leads to an exchange between the volatile methyl esters and the non-volatile polyesters the extent of which is proportional to the residence time of the volatile ester in the column, with the result that, in quantitative analyses, esters eluted quickly appear in too large a proportion, and esters eluted slowly appear in too small a proportion. Orr and Callen have found that this effect is serious at 240°C, and may lead to as much as 30% error in analysis, but it can be considerably reduced by reducing the temperature of the column. Thus, at 200°C, the error is no greater than 8%. Such an error is still large, however, and further reduction in temperature lengthens analysis times unduly.

It has been suggested that both the above effects may be caused by the acidic activity of the support. Thus, several authors have recommended that if diatomaceous earth material is used as support, it should be carefully treated with both acid and alkali before impregnation, in order to try to produce as inert a surface as possible.

Hornstein *et al.* (*26*) have suggested the use of commercial polyvinyl acetates in place of the polyesters described above. These decompose slowly at about 220°C, but the only product is acetic acid, which does not interfere with the operation of the detector. Such a stationary phase secures a good separation of the C_{18} esters, as may be seen from the appropriate column of Table 12.14.

(e) Effect of Ester Structure on Retention

On all kinds of stationary phase, the linear relation between carbon number and the logarithm of the retention volume holds with great accuracy for the higher fatty acid esters, as is seen from Fig. 3.9 (*21*) and similar figures given by many authors.

The effect of unsaturated links in a linear methylene chain on the retention has been discussed in the previous two sections, most of the results being for the C_{18} acids. In general, it is found, in accord with the principles of Chapter 3, that substitution of a double bond for a single bond in a particular position multiplies the retention by a constant factor whatever the carbon number of the acid, with the result that, on plots of $\log V_R'$ or $\log r$ against carbon number, monounsaturated, diunsaturated, etc., acids give lines parallel to the line for saturated esters, and, to a first approximation, successive lines for successively more unsaturated esters are equally spaced. This is shown in Fig. 12.12 for esters chromatographed on a polyester stationary phase (*32*), and also in Fig. 3.9. Similar plots may be obtained for any stationary phase. In non-polar stationary phases the lines are less well spaced and lie in the reverse order, but are slightly steeper (*32*); see Section 3.6d.

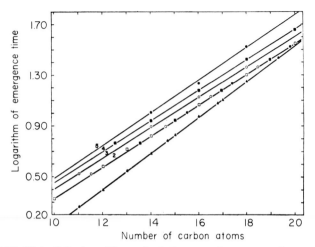

Fig. 12.12. Plot of the logarithms of relative retentions on a polyester stationary phase of variously unsaturated fatty acid esters against carbon number; also, a similar plot for saturated esters on silicone oil. Craig and Murty (*32*). 1, Saturated esters on silicone oil; 2, saturated esters; 3, monoethenoid; 4, diethenoid; 5, triethenoid esters on plasticiser.

Though the retention of an unsaturated ester of a given carbon number is governed largely by the number of double bonds, there is ample evidence that it is also governed to a lesser extent by the positions of the double bonds. Thus, Janak *et al.* (*33*) have shown that isomers such as 3-hexene-1-carboxylic ester and 2-hexene-1-carboxylic ester may be resolved on polyester stationary phases. Daniels and Richmond (*34*) have shown that polyunsaturated fatty acid esters containing conjugated double bonds have considerably greater retentions on polar stationary phases than their unconjugated isomers such as are found in fats. Since double bond migration with the formation of conjugated chains occurs if fatty acids are treated with strong alkali, care should be taken to avoid strong alkali in the preparation of samples for fatty acid analysis. It is apparent also that geometrical isomers have different retentions, for oleic and eliadic acids may be resolved.

The effect of chain branching on the retentions of fatty acid esters is very much as would be anticipated by analogy with alkanes. On both polar and non-polar stationary phases, shifting a carbon atom from the chain into a branch causes a reduction in the retention. This has been studied for acids of the type:

$$\begin{array}{c} CH_3 \\ \\ CH_3 \end{array} \!\!\!\!\! CH-(CH_2)_{n-4}-COOH \quad \text{(iso-acids)}$$

and of the type:

$$CH_3\!\!\diagdown$$
$$CH\!-\!(CH_2)_{n-5}\!-\!COOH \quad \text{(anteiso-acids)}$$
$$CH_3\!-\!CH_2\!\!\diagup$$

the retention of which may be compared with that for the straight chain acid $C_nH_{2n}O_2$. At or near 200°C on either polar or non-polar stationary phases, the relative retention of an iso-acid or an anteiso-acid and its n-acid of the same carbon number is approximately 1.20, and a short column cannot resolve an iso- and an anteiso-acid of the same carbon number (24). On a polar stationary phase, however, Hawke et al. (21) give results which show that the relative retention of iso- and n-acids is slightly greater than that of anteiso- and n-acids. The magnitude of the effect is shown in Fig. 3.9, which shows plots of $\log r$ against carbon number for all three series of saturated acids.

(f) Methods of Qualitative Identification

Many fats and natural products give a large number of peaks the qualitative identification of which may be difficult. In many applications, there are only two unknown parameters for each component of the mixture, carbon number and degree of unsaturation, and, for determining these, the techniques in which the retention is determined on each of two different stationary phases are particularly useful (22). Details of the graphical ways of using retention data on two stationary phases are described in Section 3.9.

Miwa et al. (35) and Woodford and van Gent (36) have introduced a modification of the idea of relative retention for the description of the retention of fatty acid esters. In this, the line for saturated normal esters on a plot of $\log r$ against carbon number is taken as the reference line, and the retention of a substance of relative retention r is described by the abscissa of the point on the line for saturated normal esters the ordinate of which is $\log r$. The retention is thus described by its "Equivalent Carbon Number," i.e., what the carbon number would be of a saturated normal ester having a relative retention r. Equivalent carbon numbers of saturated normal esters are integers equal to their actual carbon number. Equivalent carbon numbers of unsaturated or branched esters are generally non-integral. On polar stationary phases, equivalent carbon numbers of unsaturated esters are greater than their actual carbon number; on non-polar stationary phases, they are less. The advantage of this scheme is that the equivalent carbon number of an ester is independent of most column conditions, and only very slightly dependent on temperature. For practical purposes, equivalent carbon number is a function of the stationary phase only. Table 12.16 exemplifies equivalent carbon numbers of some fatty acid esters on a polar and on a non-polar stationary phase. Unknown esters can be identified from their equivalent carbon numbers on each of two stationary phases in the same way that they can be identified from their position on graphs of the kind described in Section 3.9. The carbon number is very closely related to the Retention Index (Section 3.6f); it is in fact a retention index using the *n*-fatty acid esters as standards and divided by 100.

TABLE 12.16

EQUIVALENT CARBON NUMBERS OF METHYL ESTERS OF HIGHER FATTY ACIDS[a]

	Equivalent carbon number	
Acid	Apiezon L	Diethylene glycol/ Pentaerithritol adipate
Stearic	18.0	18.0
Palmitoleic (*cis*-Δ^9-C_{16})	15.7	16.4
Oleic (*cis*-Δ^9-C_{18})	17.7	18.4
Petroselenic (*cis*-Δ^6-C_{18})	17.7	18.4
Erucic (*cis*-Δ^{13}-C_{22})	21.7	22.4
Linoleic	17.6	19.0
Linolenic	17.6	19.8
Arachidonic	19.2	21.6

[a] See Orr and Callen (*30*).

(g) Use of Capillary Columns

Lipsky *et al.* (*27–29*) have used capillary columns for the analysis of fatty acid esters. Using a 200-ft stainless steel capillary of 0.01 inch diameter coated with Apiezon L grease, an extremely efficient column capable of up to 200,000 plates is obtained. This efficiency is such as to overcome the drawback provided by the small relative retentions between saturates and ethylenics provided by Apiezon L, except in the case of linoleic and linolenic acids, which separate poorly. A chromatogram is shown in Fig. 12.10.

It is possible to prepare capillary columns coated with polyester liquids, and these can be used very effectively for fatty acid ester analysis. The preparation of such columns, however, is apparently more troublesome than for capillary columns coated with liquids of smaller polar component.

(h) Quantitative Analysis

The simple lower fatty acids give anomalous responses in catharometers, since the hot element supplies heat in partly dissociating the dimerised molecules. With acetic acid, this may result in the hot element becoming cooler rather than warmer, thus producing a reversed peak.

The simple lower fatty acids can also give anomalous responses in ionisation detectors (37); no simple reason can be given.

The methyl esters of the higher fatty acids consist principally of a hydrocarbon chain, with the result that weight sensitivities are virtually constant, and that weights are proportional to peak areas independently of the compound. This has been assumed by many workers, including many of those quoted above, and both in catharometers and in ionisation detectors has been found to lead to accurate quantitative analyses. It has been specifically checked by Killheffer and Jungermann (39). In calculating percentages of various fatty acids in a natural product, care must be taken to allow for the weight of the esterifying group, which is included in the gas chromatographic analysis but which must be subtracted out before giving the proportions of fatty acids. With methyl esters of higher fatty acids, the correction is small, but if, for example, phenacyl esters are used, it may be large.

Quantitative accuracy of fatty acid analysis requires careful experimental technique, since there are several possible sources of error in the manipulation (39, 40). In particular, the processes of saponification and esterification or transesterification of the source material may not give 100% yields, and also, they may give different yields for different components. Furthermore, any transesterification or other such reaction occurring during the chromatography may well be selective.

(i) Reviews

Reviews of the applications of gas chromatography to biochemistry, including large sections on fatty acid analysis, have been written by Lipsky and Landowne (41) and by James (42). Burchfield and Storrs have written a book on biochemical applications (43). Quantitative aspects in particular are reviewed by Kuksis (40).

12.7. OXYGENATED COMPOUNDS

Oxygenated aliphatic compounds are polar, and many of them tend to associate into weakly bound dimers. This has two consequences when they are chromatographed on non-polar stationary phases:

(1) They are not very soluble in the non-polar stationary phase, and their activity coefficients (Section 3.4) change rapidly with concentration; the normal effect of this is to produce a diffuse front profile to the peak, which is thus broadened, and to retain the peak maximum so that retention volumes appear too great.

(2) Polar compounds, especially those with OH groups, are easily adsorbed by the support, and, since the solution in the stationary phase is small, the effect of the support is comparatively important; the normal effect of this is to produce a diffuse rear profile to the peak, which is thus broadened. This is further discussed in Section 7.2.

As a general rule, therefore, the chromatography of oxygenated compounds is easier on polar stationary liquids than on non-polar ones. Not only does the polar liquid provide better solubility for the solutes, but also the polar groups of the solvent tend to saturate the adsorption of the support as described in Section 7.2. In spite of this, nearly all classes of oxygenated compounds can be chromatographed on non-polar solvents if carefully deactivated supports are used, and sample sizes are kept sufficiently small.

(a) Alcohols

The lower alkanols up to and including 4-methylbutanol-1 (isoamyl alcohol) and n-pentanol-1, but not including the other six less common pentanols, may all be easily separated on any of several stationary phases, subject to the restrictions given above. Table 12.17 gives specific and relative retention data for these compounds. The lower alkanols can be analysed efficiently on capillary columns using a polar stationary liquid if stabilised with a surfactant agent. Thus, Schwartz and Mathews describe the use of capillaries coated with nonyl phenol plus ethylene oxide for separation of all alkanols up to 1-pentanol (5). Porous polymers used at about 170–200°C will produce good separation of lower alkanols very rapidly. For example, Dave (6) shows separations of C_1 to C_4 alkanols in only one minute. The separation of the eight pentanols has been studied by several authors (7–9). For efficiency, a polar stationary liquid should be used. On polyethylene glycols, on hexadecanol or dodecanol, the only serious overlap

TABLE 12.17

Specific and Relative Retention Volumes of Lower Alkanols

	Squalane	Squalane	1-Dodecanol	1-Dodecanol	Poly-ethylene glycol 400	Silicone oil	Dioctyl sebacate	Dioctyl sebacate	Dioctyl phthalate	Didecyl phthalate	Hexam-ethylene glycol Dimethyl Ether	Poly-ethylene glycol	β,β'-Oxydi-propio-nitrile
Specific or relative:	S	S	S	S	S	R	R	R	R	R	R	R	R
Temperature:	56.0	80.0	56.0	80.0	100	100	50	100	50	100	70	100	70
Reference:	1	1	1	1	2	3	3	3	3	3	4	3	4
Methanol	17.3	11.4	113	47.1	38.5	0.34	1.26	0.71	1.19	0.94	0.53	23.4	0.91
Ethanol	25.3	13.7	218	81.8	46.1	0.69	2.47	1.49	2.22	1.68	0.73	31.5	1.1
iso-Propanol	30.0	16.9	298	112	—	1.03	3.46	2.13	2.96	2.16	0.78	28.8	1.0
n-Propanol	59.6	27.8	528	196	80.0	1.51	5.38	3.75	6.79	3.91	1.6	59.3	1.2
tert-Butanol	37.7	19.9	403	136	—	—	—	—	—	—	—	—	0.9
sec-Butanol	75.6	36.2	770	261	—	—	—	—	—	—	1.7	—	1.8
iso-Butanol	88.9	46.9	1045	320	—	—	—	—	—	—	2.4	—	2.6
n-Butanol	162.7	67.3	1460	470	146	3.57	—	8.72	20.0	9.11	3.6	111	3.5
iso-Pentanol	258.7	117.7	3064	847	—	—	—	—	—	—	—	—	—
n-Pentanol	361.3	155.9	4348	1146	239	—	—	—	—	—	—	—	—
n-Pentane	—	—	—	—	—	—	—	—	—	—	1.00	—	—
Benzene	—	—	—	—	—	1.00	1.00	1.00	1.00	1.00	—	1.00	1.00

Stationary phase

is between 2-methyl-butanol-1 (iso-amyl alcohol) and 3-methyl-butanol-1, for which the relative retention is about 1.05. Any column which can resolve this can resolve all eight isomers.

A plot of the logarithm of the retention volumes of the n-alkanol-1's against carbon number gives a good straight line with all members of the series other than methanol, both on dinonyl phthalate (*10*) and on polyethylene glycol (*2*). As is usual, branching produces a reduction in retention volume, and, to a good approximation, the same kind of branching produces the same change in log V_R'. Thus, the line for "iso"-alcohols lies parallel to and below the plot of n-alcohols.

The gas chromatography of tertiary alcohols is often accompanied by dehydration, leading to smeared peaks and poor quantitative analysis, possibly because of the catalytic effect of the support (Section 7.2).

The chromatography of the higher alcohols resembles closely the chromatography of the fatty acid esters described in Section 12.6 (*11–14*). Thus, the alcohols may be analysed either free or esterified as their carbomethoxy derivatives; i.e., as their acetates. Suitable separations of those mostly of biochemical interest (C_{16}–C_{22}) occur at about 200°C. On non-polar stationary liquids, iso- and unsaturated alcohols are eluted in front of the n-alcohols or esters. On polar stationary liquids, e.g., polyesters, the unsaturated esters are eluted after the saturated ones, as with the fatty acid esters.

A particularly important application of gas chromatography is the analysis of sterols and their derivatives. This application has grown extensively since its beginning in about 1960 (*15–18*) and has recently been extensively reviewed (*19*). Sterols and their derivatives can be chromatographed at temperatures in the range of 250–300°C, various grades of silicone oil being the most commonly used stationary liquids. Polyesters can be used where a polar liquid is required. Polar compounds, e. g., the alcohols, are generally either esterified or converted to ethers such as the trimethylsilyl ether before chromatography. Because of the high temperatures, there is always the risk of decomposition or rearrangement of the more labile compounds. Thus, care must be taken to avoid possible sites for catalytic reaction, and to ensure that the chromatography is as efficient as possible, so that the residence time of compounds on the column is as short as possible.

(b) Esters

Esters as usually encountered in biological applications are discussed in Section 12.6. This section deals with other esters, e.g., as found in commercial solvents, etc.

SPECIFIC AND RELATIVE RETENTION VOLUMES OF LOWER ESTERS

Stationary phase

	Boiling point	Silicone	Silicone fluid DC 702	Didecyl phthalate	Didecyl phthalate	Dinonyl phthalate	Hexamethylene glycol dimethyl ether	Tricresyl phosphate	Polyethylene glycol	Polyethylene glycol	Polyethylene glycol 400	β,β'-Oxydipropionitrile
Specific or relative:		R	S	R	R	S	R	S	R	R	S	R
Temperature (°C):		100	97	50	100	97.5	70	97	50	100	100	70
Reference:		3	20	3	3	20	4	20	3	3	2	4
Methyl formate	31.5	0.53	—	0.85	0.91	—	0.24	—	15.2	6.95	—	0.50
Ethyl formate	54.1	1.23	20	2.16	1.91	—	0.43	—	23.6	11.7	—	0.75
(Acetone)	56.5	0.96	—	2.14	1.92	—	0.41	—	24.2	13.7	—	1.1
Methyl acetate	57.1	1.26	21	2.38	2.12	—	0.43	19.0	23.6	14.1	—	0.82
Vinyl acetate	72.5	—	—	—	—	—	0.73	—	—	—	28.1	0.97
Ethyl acetate	77.1	2.36	38.2	5.33	3.70	42.5	0.73	33.1	38.4	19.3	—	1.1
Methyl propionate	79.7	2.40	43.1	6.27	4.32	—	0.82	—	44.9	22.6	—	1.24
Methyl acrylate	80.5	—	—	—	—	—	0.96	—	—	—	—	1.41
Isopropyl acetate	89.0	3.04	—	7.44	4.95	—	0.88	41.7	42.5	20.9	—	1.0
Methyl isobutyrate	92.3	3.73	—	8.90	6.16	—	1.0	—	53.3	26.3	—	—
Ethyl propionate	99.1	4.60	—	11.8	7.43	—	—	—	69.2	31.7	—	—
n-Propyl acetate	101.6	4.63	77	12.8	7.81	88.7	1.5	66.0	71.8	34.9	46.5	1.8
Methyl n-butyrate	102.3	5.20	—	13.5	8.63	—	1.5	—	84.7	39.4	—	—
Ethyl isobutyrate	110.1	6.89	—	—	10.0	—	—	—	71.8	32.7	—	—
Isobutyl acetate	116.5	7.09	—	—	13.2	—	—	91.2	105	48.6	—	—
Ethyl n-butyrate	120.0	8.60	—	—	14.5	—	2.5	—	—	48.5	—	2.3
n-Butyl acetate	126.5	8.89	—	—	16.8	188	3.1	—	—	63.9	79.4	3.0
n-Pentane	—	1.00	—	1.00	1.00	—	—	—	1.00	1.00	—	—
Benzene	—	—	—	—	—	—	1.00	—	—	—	—	1.00

Table 12.18 contains retention data for a number of common solvent esters arranged in order of boiling point, including relative retention data and specific retention volumes. In particular it should be noticed that mixtures of isomers such as ethyl acetate, methyl propionate, and n-propyl formate can be satisfactorily resolved even though their boiling points are comparatively close.

Less volatile esters, esters of dibasic acids, etc., can be chromatographed by the same techniques as are described for esters of biochemical interest in the previous section, as has been illustrated for various sebacates, adipates, etc., by Bartsch et al. (21).

(c) Ethers

Diethyl ether is frequently used as a solvent for less volatile samples of interest; the ether gives a large peak before any of the peaks caused by the mixture. Diethyl ether is commonly contaminated with ethanol; on any but a paraffinic stationary phase, the activity coefficients of both ether and alcohol are of the order of unity, and the two separate widely. On a paraffinic stationary phase, however, the activity coefficient of the alcohol is large, and diethyl ether and ethanol may overlap.

Mixtures for anaesthesia containing ether, ethanol, and other substances have been considered by Adlard and Hill (22) and by Hill (23); see also Section 12.9a.

Many sugars and sugar derivatives which are themselves non-volatile have been analysed by gas chromatography by converting them to methyl ethers, which are sufficiently volatile. Apiezon M at 170°C (24), Apiezon M grease at 150°C, poly(butanediol succinate) at 150°C (25), and methylated hydroxyethylcellulose at approximately 200°C (26) have been used as stationary phases. The combination of one polar and one non-polar column enables a large range of such sugar derivatives to be analysed.

Gas chromatography has been used in connection with the Zeisel method for the determination of alkoxy groups, e.g., by Vertalier and Martin (27, 28), Kratzl and Gruber (29), and Haslam et al. (30). The alkyl iodides corresponding to the alkyl groups from the alkoxy compounds are analysed and identified chromatographically, e.g., on dinonyl sebacate at 75°C (30).

(d) Aldehydes and Ketones

The chromatography of the lower aliphatic aldehydes other than formaldehyde is straightforward. Relative retentions of the common aldehydes are listed in Table 12.19.

TABLE 12.19

RELATIVE RETENTIONS OF LOWER ALDEHYDES AND KETONES

	Boiling point	Stationary phase					
		Silicone	Dioctyl sebacate	Didecyl phthalate	Hexamethylene glycol dimethyl ether	Polyethylene glycol	β,β'-Oxydi-propionitrile
Temperature (°C):	—	100	100	100	70	100	70
Reference:	—	3	3	3	4	3	4
Acetaldehyde	21	—	—	—	0.16	—	0.43
Propional dehyde	48.8	0.80	1.36	1.70	0.34	10.5	0.72
Acraldehyde	52.2	0.74	1.49	1.96	0.46	13.9	0.96
Isobutyraldehyde	61.5	1.48	2.26	2.82	0.46	12.2	0.78
n-Butyraldehyde	75.7	1.97	3.12	4.06	0.69	19.3	1.2
Crotonaldehyde	104.0	3.22	6.00	8.43	1.9	58.4	4.0
Paraldehyde	124.4	12.8	26.8	13.2	—	61.7	—
Acetone	56.5	0.96	1.34	1.92	0.41	13.7	1.1
Methyl ethyl ketone	79.6	2.07	3.21	4.44	0.79	22.7	1.7
Diethyl ketone	102.7	4.29	6.68	9.01	1.5	37.9	2.4
Acetylacetone	139.0	8.10	17.5	22.9	—	159	—
Ethanol	78.3	0.69	1.49	1.68	0.73	31.5	1.1
n-Pentane	—	1.00	1.00	1.00	—	1.00	—
Benzene	—	—	—	—	1.00	—	1.00

On many stationary phases, formaldehyde is polymerised before being eluted; this is common experience, and is reported specifically for ethylene carbonate and propylene carbonate by Zlatkis and Oro (*31*). It is, however, possible to get peaks for formaldehyde (*32–34*). Schepartz and McDowell (*32*) have used a column of polyethylene glycol 20,000 at 90°C, Kelker (*33*) has used Citroflex A, which is *O*-acetyl triethylhexyl citric ester, at 120°C, and Sandler and Strom (*34*) have used the surfacant agent extracted from commercial detergent at 145°C. In all cases, other conditions are such that formaldehyde is eluted in 1 or 2 minutes. Kelker describes the quantitative estimation of formaldehyde by gas chromatography.

Aldehydes have also been analysed by gas chromatography as their oximes (*35*) and as their dimethyl acetals (*36*). Gray (*36*) uses acetals for the gas chromatography of long chain fatty aldehydes, using techniques similar to those for long chain fatty acid esters, and finds that their chromatography resembles that of the fatty acid esters. Retention data for some acetals of lower aldehydes is given by Kelker (*4*).

Aldehydes, and also several other classes of carbonyl compound, can be analysed by "Flash Exchange Gas Chromatography," discussed in detail in Section 11.6.

The chromatography of the lower ketones is straightforward. Retention data for the commonest is included in Table 12.19.

(e) *Phenols*

The gas chromatography of phenols has been studied extensively (*37–47*). A selection of retention data is given in Table 12.20.

The separation of phenol, the cresols, and the xylenols is commonly required. The complete separation requires a capillary column to give sufficient column performance. This is illustrated by Fig. 12.13 (*47*), which shows the separation of the compounds most commonly encountered.

On non-polar stationary phases, lower phenols separate in almost perfect order of boiling points, and there is little or no selection according to chemical type. Since there are no cases in which a phenol boils at a lower temperature than a phenol with one carbon atom fewer, phenols on non–polar stationary phases are collected into groups according to carbon number. This may be seen from the observation from Table 12.20 that the relative retentions of phenol, the cresols, and the xylenols at temperatures at or near 175°C are very roughly 1 : 2 : 3. In contrast, on hydroxylic stationary phases there is considerable specificity among different isomers, but very much less separation according to carbon number (*40*). The phenols can therefore also be resolved by initial separation into carbon numbers,

TABLE 12.20

RETENTION DATA FOR PHENOLS

	Boiling point	Stationary phase												
		Silicone (dimethyl polysiloxane)	Apiezon L grease	Apiezon M grease	Apiezon L grease	Apiezon L grease	Silicone grease	Didecyl phthalate	Dinonyl phthalate	Benzyl arabino-side	Galac-tonic acid γ-lactone	Glycerol	Dulcitol	Erithritol
Temperature (°C):	—	170	170	170	155	165	165	150	170	176	150	160	170	150
Reference:	—	40	40	40	37	46	46	43	40	40	40	40	40	40
Phenol	182	1.00	1.00	1.00	1.00	1.00	1.00	1.00	1.00	1.00	1.00	1.00	1.00	1.00
o-Cresol	191	1.93	1.65	1.67	1.52	1.68	1.46	1.39	1.38	1.03	0.61	0.60	0.50	0.52
m-Cresol	202	2.15	1.79	1.80	1.83	1.77	1.57	1.77	1.73	1.39	0.98	0.97	0.84	0.94
p-Cresol	201	2.15	1.75	1.79	1.83	1.77	1.57	1.77	1.71	1.36	0.97	0.97	0.83	0.88
o-Ethylphenol	207	2.52	2.54	—	—	2.77	2.14	2.15	—	1.25	—	0.50	—	0.40
m-Ethylphenol	217	2.75	2.88	—	3.14	3.12	2.44	2.89	—	1.99	—	0.90	—	0.83
p-Ethylphenol	218	2.75	2.83	—	—	—	2.44	2.89	—	1.97	—	0.92	—	0.84
2,3-Dimethylphenol	218	3.07	3.44	3.38	3.24	3.38	2.62	2.66	2.69	1.72	0.75	0.76	0.54	0.67
2,4-Dimethylphenol	211	2.70	2.90	2.93	2.76	2.93	2.28	2.55	2.21	1.34	0.56	0.62	0.46	0.47
2,5-Dimethylphenol	211	2.72	2.90	2.92	2.79	2.93	2.28	2.24	2.27	1.37	0.50	0.53	0.38	0.45
2,6-Dimethylphenol	212	2.63	2.75	—	2.38	2.77	2.01	1.52	—	0.78	0.35	0.33	0.30	0.23
3,4-Dimethylphenol	226	3.34	3.64	3.50	3.69	3.56	2.77	3.26	3.19	2.32	1.28	1.26	0.89	1.17
3,5-Dimethylphenol	220	3.27	3.16	2.97	3.24	3.12	2.44	2.94	2.90	1.92	0.94	0.96	0.81	0.86
m-n-Propylphenol	231	—	4.45	—	4.76	—	—	—	—	—	—	—	—	0.66
2-Methyl-4-ethylphenol	—	—	4.42	—	4.72	—	—	—	—	—	—	—	—	0.40
3-Methyl-5-ethylphenol	235	—	4.90	—	5.07	—	—	—	—	—	—	—	—	0.82
4-Methyl-2-ethylphenol	—	—	4.10	—	—	—	—	—	—	—	—	—	—	0.33
3-n-Butylphenol	—	—	7.7	—	—	—	—	—	—	—	—	—	—	0.64
V_g for phenol	—	18.8	32.6	35.2	29	—	—	—	—	294	59.6	—	16.9	132

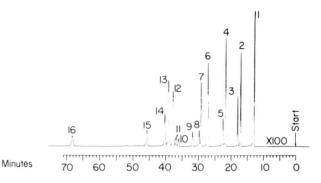

FIG. 12.13. Chromatogram of phenols on a 150-foot open-tube capillary column coated with di-*n*-decyl phthalate + detergent operated at 120°C. Ettre and Averill (*47*). 1, phenol; 2, *o*-cresol; 3, 2,6-xylenol; 4, *p*-cresol; 5, *m*-cresol; 6, *o*-ethylphenol; 7, 2,4-xylenol; 8, 2,5-xylenol; 9, 2,4,6-trimethylphenol; 10, 2,3-xylenol; 11, 2,3,6-trimethylphenol; 12, *p*-ethylphenol; 13, *m*-ethylphenol; 14, 3,5-xylenol; 15, 3,4-xylenol; 16, 3-methyl-5-ethylphenol.

followed by individual analyses of the separate carbon number fractions on a hydroxylated stationary liquid.

The most notable feature of the specificity shown on hydroxylic stationary phases is the specific acceleration of *o*-substituted phenols relative to others. Thus, on silicone or Apiezon grease, *o*-cresol appears only just before *m*- and *p*-cresols, but on erithritol its retention volume is only just over half that of the other two. The same applies with *o*-ethylphenol, and with all the 2-substituted dimethylphenols. In particular, the diortho compound 2,6-dimethylphenol is enormously accelerated in hydroxylic stationary phases. The other notable feature is that in the hydroxylic stationary phases the methyl groups tend to accelerate rather than retard. Thus, in erithritol, all the cresols and all the dimethylphenols except one appear before phenol. It was pointed out in Section 3.8 that polar phases tended to crowd successive homologs. The phenols (and also the pyridines, see Section 12.8) demonstrate this particularly well, since they are soluble in very polar hydroxylated stationary phases. Most other series of compounds with which the effect might be demonstrated in such stationary phases are virtually insoluble, so that all retentions are virtually nil, and no such demonstration is possible. Stationary phases of the ester type give intermediate behaviour in which there is a moderate separation according to carbon number and a moderate specificity for isomers. Thus, with dinonyl or didecyl phthalate, 2,6-dimethylphenol appears in the middle of the cresols (*44*).

It will be observed from Table 12.20 that no stationary phase, polar, hydroxylic, or non-polar, can easily separate certain pairs, e.g., m- and p-cresols, m- and p-ethylphenols, and in no case is there any large relative retention of 2,4- and 2,5-dimethylphenols. Brooks (45) has sought stationary phases to resolve such pairs, and has tried a number of phosphate esters of various phenols. He finds that tri(2,4-xylenyl) phosphate gave the best separation of m- and p-cresols and 2,4- and 2,5-xylenols, but that it also causes overlaps not found on many other stationary phases, e.g., p-ethylphenol and 3,5-xylenol. The conclusion is that there is not yet a single stationary phase which can produce an easy separation of all thirteen C_6–C_8 phenols. Some such overlaps may be cured by chromatographing phenyl ethers as described below rather than the phenols themselves.

TABLE 12.21

RELATIVE RETENTIONS OF PHENYL ETHERS

Aryl part	Stationary phase				
	Apiezon M grease	Didecyl phthalate	Didecyl phthalate	Silicone	Di-n-butyl tetrachloro-phthalate
Temperature (°C):	145	150	150	125	125
Reference:	48	43	43	49	49
Other part:	Methyl	Methyl	Ethyl	Tri-methylsilyl	Tri-methylsilyl
Phenyl	1.00	1.00	1.00	1.00	1.00
o-Cresyl	1.56	1.54	1.47	1.59	1.68
m-Cresyl	1.67	1.73	1.72	1.71	1.75
p-Cresyl	1.67	1.73	1.75	1.84	1.89
o-Ethylphenyl	—	2.26	1.60	2.36	2.34
m-Ethylphenyl	—	2.80	2.80	2.80	2.81
p-Ethylphenyl	—	2.89	2.90	3.05	3.10
2,3-Xylenyl	2.96	3.03	3.13	3.3	3.75
2,4-Xylenyl	2.42	—	—	2.77	3.01
2,5-Xylenyl	2.50	2.57	2.43	2.48	2.69
2,6-Xylenyl	2.05	2.00	1.54	3.06	3.55
3,4-Xylenyl	3.16	3.42	3.82	3.61	3.89
3,5-Xylenyl	2.50	3.03	3.11	2.86	2.85
o-Methoxyphenyl	2.51	—	—	3.23	3.48
m-Methoxyphenyl	3.11	—	—	—	—
2,4,6-Trimethylphenyl	—	—	—	5.33	6.07
V_g for phenyl	—	—	—	330	477

(f) *Phenyl Ethers*

The methyl ethers of phenols have been chromatographed in Apiezon M grease by Carruthers *et al.* (*48*) and on didecyl phthalate and on silicone oil by Bergmann and Jentzsch (*43*). Relative retention data is given in Table 12.21. It is seen that the order of elution on non-polar stationary phases resembles that for the parent phenols, and that there are overlaps between the ethers of *m*- and *p*-cresols, etc., as with the parent phenols. On didecyl phthalate, the results of Bergmann and Jentzsch show that there is a slight relative acceleration of *o*-substituted ethers, especially noticeable in the case of 2,6-dimethyl phenyl ethers.

Langer *et al.* (*49*) have studied the chromatography of phenols by first converting them to their trimethylsilyl ethers by reaction with either trimethylchlorosilane, or preferably with hexamethylsilazane (see Section 7.2). Retention volumes of the trimethylsilyl ethers relative to the phenyl ether on silicone and on di-*n*-butyl tetrachlorophthalate are given in Table 12.21. It is seen that on either stationary phase all three cresols are easily resolved, and that all the xylenols may be separated, though there are overlaps between xylenols and ethylphenols. The trimethylsilyl ethers do not show the specificity characteristic of *o*-phenols, even on the polar stationary phase; neither is the relative retention of the *m*- and *p*-cresyl ethers changed by use of a tetrachlorophthalate ester as stationary phase as was reported by Langer *et al.* in connection with the separation of *m*- and *p*-xylenes (Section 12.5).

12.8. Nitrogen Compounds

(a) *Ammonia and Methylamines*

The separation of these was one of the first applications of partition chromatography by James *et al.* (*1*), and is also described by James and Martin (*2, 3*). The comparison of their retentions on polar and on non-polar stationary liquids provided one of the first examples of the shifts in retention which could be produced by changing from one stationary liquid to another.

Relative retention data for ammonia and the methylamines are given in Table 12.22. On stationary phases of polarity comparable with that of the amines, separation is in order of boiling points; this is the case on hendecanol. On non-polar stationary phases, dimethylamine, which would otherwise be selectively retained because of hydrogen bonding, is

TABLE 12.22

Retention Data for the Methylamines Relative to Ammonia at 20°C[a]

	Boiling point	Hendecanol	Hendecanol + 15% paraffin	Hendecanol + 50% paraffin	Paraffin + 33% hendecanol	Paraffin	Polyethylene glycol	Glycerol
					Stationary phase			
Ammonia	−33.4	1.00	1.00	1.00	1.00	1.00	1.00	1.00
Methylamine	−6.5	3.4	3.6	4.2	3.8	1.65	3.16	2.5
Dimethylamine	7.4	5.2	5.8	7.5	6.8	2.7	2.80	1
Trimethylamine	3.5	4.2	4.6	7.5	6.8	2.7	1.67	0.47

[a] See James et al. (1), and O'Donnell and Mann (4).

not so retained, and appears together with the trimethylamine; this is the case on liquid paraffin. James *et al.* also tried several mixtures of hendecanol and paraffin, from which they found that the greatest relative retention of di- and trimethylamine was given on a mixture containing 15% paraffin. On very hydroxylated stationary phases, the retention is largely determined by hydrogen bonding. Monomethylamine, and dimethylamine are all retained longer than trimethylamine which possesses no labile hydrogens. On these stationary phases, activity coefficients increase in the same order as boiling points, and this has the result that, on glycerol at least, ammonia and dimethylamine are eluted together.

(b) *Higher Aliphatic Amines*

The amines, being basic, interact with acidic sites on any form of silica used as a support. Thus, they have a tendency to produce tailed peaks on all diatomaceous packings. For this reason, it has become common practice either to treat the support with an alkali before impregnating it with stationary liquid, or to dissolve an alkali in the stationary liquid. Commonly, sodium or potassium hydroxide are used so as to make up between 0.1 and 2% of the total packing weight (*4–7*).

James (*8*) gives the relative retention data for common aliphatic amines from methyl to butyl including benzyl on silicone oil DC 550, liquid paraffin, oil, and "Lubrol MO," a polyethylene oxide oil of moderate polar content (Table 12.23).

The chromatography of higher fatty amines has been described by several authors (*9–11*). The chromatography of these compounds resembles that of the higher fatty acids and higher fatty alcohols described in previous sections.

Amines are often advantageously analysed in the form of derivatives. With the more volatile amines, this has the advantage that the derivatives are more easily handled, and also, the derivatives do not give such bad tailing. For example, 2,4-dinitrofluorobenzene gives the 2,4-dinitrophenyl derivative of primary and secondary amines (*12*), and the trimethylsilyl derivatives may be used (*13*). Vandenheuvel *et al.* (*14*) have surveyed the many possible volatile derivatives.

(c) *Aromatic Amines*

James (*15*) has given retentions relative to aniline of a large number of N- and C-substituted anilines. A small selection of the data is given in Table 12.24. Many separations involving specific activity effects are

TABLE 12.23

RETENTION DATA FOR ALIPHATIC AMINES RELATIVE TO ETHYLAMINE AT 100°C[a]

Amine	bp (°C)	Stationary liquid	
		Paraffin	Lubrol MO
Methyl	—6.5	0.61	0.68
Dimethyl	7.4	0.93	0.81
Ethyl	16.6	*1.00*	*1.00*
Trimethyl	3.5	1.17	0.67
i-Propyl	34	1.49	1.42
n-Propyl	48.7	2.20	2.10
Diethyl	55.5	3.25	2.10
sec-Butyl	63	3.57	2.8
i-Butyl	68	3.70	3.1
Ethylenediamine	118	4.65	15.5
n-Butyl	77.8	4.7	4.4
Ethanolamine	172.2	5.25	25.8
Di-i-propyl	83	6.8	3.00
Triethyl	89.5	8.6	3.1
i-Pentyl	95	8.8	7.3
n-Pentyl	104	10.5	9.7
Di-n-propyl	110.7	13.2	7.2
4-Methylpentyl-1-	123.9	17.8	13.8
n-hexyl	132.7	22.6	19.6
Di-sec-butyl	132.0	27.6	9.74
Cyclohexyl	134	28.4	25.9
Di-i-butyl	139	30.4	10.9
n-Heptyl	158.3	49.5	40.05
Tri-n-propyl	156	49.6	15.1
Di-n-butyl	159	62.1	27.6
Tri-n-butyl	214	—	85.5
Benzyl	185	81.0	91.5

[a] See James (8).

possible on both polar and non-polar stationary phases. In general, polar stationary phases accelerate N-substituted amines relative to those possessing free N—H bonds; non-polar stationary phases accelerate amines possessing free N—H bonds relative to N-substituted amines. This may be seen from the figures given in Table 12.24 for methylaniline and dimethylaniline, which boil within one degree. On paraffin wax, dimethylaniline is eluted first, but on the polar stationary phase Lubrol MO methylaniline is eluted first. In either case, the pair is well resolved.

TABLE 12.24

RETENTIONS AT 137°C RELATIVE TO ANILINE OF SOME AROMATIC AMINES[a]

	Paraffin wax	Lubrol MO (polyethylene oxide condensate)	Benzyldiphenyl
Aniline	*1.00*	*1.00*	*1.00*
p-Toluidine	1.95	1.63	1.75
m-Toluidine	2.0	1.56	1.86
o-Toluidine	2.05	1.53	1.8
N-Methylaniline	2.05	1.28	1.73
N-Dimethylaniline	2.60	1.05	1.68
N-Ethylaniline	3.18	1.66	2.33

[a] See James (15).

Jones et al. (16) have chromatographed a number of alkylaminobenzenes from toluidine onwards on silicone fluid at 200°C. They point out that the relative positions and the number of alkyl groups on the benzene nucleus appear to be more significant in determining the retention than the position of the amino group. Thus, two aminoethyl benzenes are eluted together, as are the three possible amino-m-xylenes and the two amino-o-xylenes. Furthermore, the relative retentions of these three groups of peaks are close to those of ethylbenzene, o-xylene, and p-xylene. The authors show that this behaviour applies with all alkylaminobenzenes up to at least four alkyl carbon atoms. The retention data of James, however, shows that isomers differing only in the position of the amino group may be resolved with a sufficiently efficient column.

(d) Pyridine and Its Homologs

Table 12.25 gives relative retention data on various stationary phases for pyridine, the picolines (methylpyridines), the lutidines (dimethylpyridines), and the collidines (trimethylpyridines), selected from tables of Brooks and Collins (17), and Decora and Dineen (18). Data on other stationary phases are also given by Brooks and Collins, and Decora and Dineen; where comparable, James (8) gives results which agree well with those of Brooks and Collins. The results of Brooks and Collins on glycerol are confirmed by Murray and Williams (19). The apparently large discrepancy between the columns of results on paraffin oil and on squalane is in fact caused solely by a discrepancy in the retentions of pyridine.

TABLE 12.25

RETENTIONS OF PYRIDINE HOMOLOGS RELATIVE TO PYRIDINE

	Boiling point	Liquid paraffin	Squalane	Silicone oil M430	Trixylenyl phosphate	Tricresyl phosphate	Polyethylene glycol 1000	Glycerol
Stationary phase								
Temperature (°C):	—	120	130	140	120	130	120	90
Reference:	—	17	18	17	17	18	17	17
Pyridine	115.3	1.00	1.00	1.00	1.00	1.00	1.00	1.00
2-Picoline	129.4	1.80	1.53	1.60	1.72	1.33	1.22	0.82
3-Picoline	144.1	2.55	2.13	2.10	3.12	2.02	1.98	1.54
4-Picoline	145.4	2.55	2.13	2.10	3.12	2.08	2.07	1.86
2,6-Lutidine	144.0	2.90	2.43	2.31	2.64	1.70	1.43	0.53
2,5-Lutidine	157.0	4.34	3.34	3.06	4.40	2.50	2.25	1.22
2,4-Lutidine	157.9	4.42	3.34	3.06	4.47	2.68	2.43	1.55
2,3-Lutidine	160.8	4.95	3.64	3.45	4.85	3.02	2.79	1.51
3,5-Lutidine	172.2	6.10	—	4.07	6.85	—	3.68	2.30
2-Ethylpyridine	148.7	3.25	2.70	2.72	3.24	1.95	1.74	0.62
3-Ethylpyridine	165.0	5.25	—	3.44	5.73	—	2.99	1.65
4-Ethylpyridine	167.7	5.20	3.97	3.84	6.25	3.58	3.60	2.11
2,4,6-Collidine	170.3	6.95	5.00	4.27	6.20	3.55	2.83	1.00
2,3,5-Collidine	186.8	11.17	—	6.29	11.08	—	4.74	2.46
2,3,4-Collidine	192.7	13.75	—	7.33	13.15	—	6.80	4.03
2-Methyl-6-ethyl-pyridine	160.1	5.00	—	3.84	4.40	—	1.83	0.30

The chromatography of the pyridines is very similar to that of the phenols. It is seen from Table 12.25 that liquid paraffin or silicone oil are effective in separating the compounds listed into groups according to carbon at least up to $C_8H_{11}N$. On paraffinic stationary phases, isomers other than those with substituents in the ortho position are not well separated. Thus, 3- and 4-picolines fail to separate, as do 2,4- and 2,5-lutidines. On ester type phases, e.g., trixylenyl phosphate, the separation according to carbon number still predominates, but there is a slightly greater spread, so that 2,6-lutidine spreads out into the picolines, and 2,4,6-collidine into the lutidines. On glycerol, the separation according to carbon number is completely absent, and a good separation is obtained within each carbon number, with 3- and 4-picolines clearly resolved. The separation of 2,4- and 2,5-lutidines is satisfactory, but there is a new overlap of 2,4- and 2,3-lutidines. Polyethylene glycol 1000, which is not so polar as glycerol, provides a compromise by which it is possible to resolve all the picolines and lutidines on a single column, so long as the efficiency is great enough to resolve the 3- and 4-picolines the relative retention of which is approximately 1.15. It is apparent, however, that the easiest route to complete separation of all components involves the consecutive use of a non-polar and a polar column.

The pyridine homologs provide a very clear example of the operation of the effect in which ortho-substituted components are accelerated on polar columns. Thus, on glycerol, 2,4,6-collidine overlaps with pyridine boiling 55°C lower, and the 2-methyl-o-ethylpyridine gives the first peak to appear.

The chromatography of quinolines, isoquinolines, and indoles is described by Janak and Hrivnac (20), who give extensive relative retention data for several common stationary phases.

(e) Amino Acids

Amino acids themselves are involatile; they must therefore be converted to characteristic volatile derivatives before they can be analysed by gas chromatography. The two principal derivatives are (1) esters and (2) aldehydes formed by reaction with ninhydrin. Gas chromatographic determination of aminoacids is more rapid and more sensitive than standard methods using ion exchange or liquid-liquid partition chromatography. The gas chromatography of amino acids has been reviewed (21).

(1) Esterification Method. Both the COOH group and the NH_2 group of the amino acid may be esterified, and the principal difference between the techniques of different workers is in the choice of esterifying groups.

The most common choice is to esterify the carboxyl group with an alkyl group, for example methyl (*22–28*), *n*-butyl (*29–33*), or pentyl (*30, 34, 35*), and to esterify the amine with the trifluoracetyl group. A general technique for treating aminoacids according to this scheme is given by Halasz and Bunnig (*36*). Alternatively, the trimethylsilyl derivative may be used (*37, 38*). Another possibility is to react the mixed amino acids with a mixture of hydrochloric and nitric acids, thus converting the NH_2 group into a Cl atom. The methyl ester of the corresponding chloro acid is then chromatographed (*39*). Most of the workers listed above use polar columns, e.g. polyesters of polyethylene glycols at between 130 and 200°C. However, it is also possible to use non-polar stationary liquids, e.g. silicones. The esters of the common amino acids can all be caused to resolve on a suitable column.

(2) *Aldehyde method*. In this, the mixture of amino acids is converted to aldehydes by the quantitative reaction:

$$
\begin{array}{c}
\text{CO} \\
\backslash \\
\text{C(OH)}_2 + \text{R—CH—COOH} \rightarrow \\
/ \\
\text{CO} \\
\qquad | \\
\qquad NH_2
\end{array}
$$

$$
\begin{array}{c}
\text{CO} \\
\backslash \\
\text{CHOH} + \text{RCHO} + NH_3 + CO_2. \\
/ \\
\text{CO}
\end{array}
$$

The aldehydes may then be chromatographed (*40–44*). Table 12.26 shows the aldehydes obtained from some of the common amino acids. The pair

TABLE 12.26

Aldehydes Obtained by Ninhydrin Oxidation of Amino Acids[a]

Acid	Aldehyde	Aldehyde bp (°C)
Glycine	Formaldehyde	−21
Alanine	Acetaldehyde	21
2-Aminobutyric acid	Propionaldehyde	48
Valine	2-Methylpropanal-1	63
Leucine	3-Methylbutanal-1	92.5
Isoleucine	2-Methylbutanal-1	93
Norleucine	Pentanal-1	103
Methionine	Methylmercaptopropanal	60/12 mm
Phenylalanine	Phenylacetaldehyde	194

[a] See Bier and Teitelbaum (*42*).

3-methylbutanal and 2-methylbutanal arising from leucine and isoleucine are rather hard to separate (*45*), but Hunter *et al.* (*40*) show that they may be resolved on a column of silicone oils with a retention of approximately 1.1. Apart from the problem of resolving leucine and isoleucine, the stationary phase used for this analysis is probably not very critical; silicone oil (*40*), dimethylsulfoxide (*42*), and a mixture of ethylene and propylene carbonates (*43*) have all been used satisfactorily. In the technique of Zlatkis *et al.*, 1 part of 0.28 *M* amino acid solution is mixed with 1 part of saturated aqueous ninhydrin solution, and the mixture is introduced into a gas-chromatographic apparatus containing a preliminary reaction tube filled with 30% ninhydrin supported on firebrick held at 140°C. A chromatogram obtained from a mixture of aminoacids in this way is shown in Fig. 12.14.

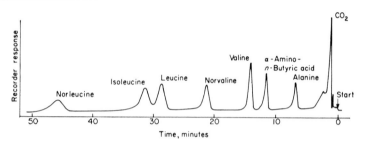

Fɪɢ. 12.14. Chromatogram of aldehydes derived from the amino acids indicated. Zlatkis *et al.* (*43*).

Amino acids may also be converted into aldehydes by reaction with alkaline hypochlorite. This reaction has been used by Bayer (*22*) prior to chromatography of the aldehydes, but the method is restricted by the fact that different amino acids may give the same products, and that amino acids containing sulphur or acid groups give complex products.

12.9. Hᴀʟᴏɢᴇɴᴀᴛᴇᴅ Cᴏᴍᴘᴏᴜɴᴅs

(a) *Halogenated Methanes*

Retention data for the chlorinated methanes have been studied by many authors, and a selection of the results is given in Table 12.27. The chlorinated methanes provided one of the earliest illustrations of a change in the order of elution being produced by a change in stationary phase. On non-polar stationary phases, the compounds are eluted in order of

TABLE 12.27

SPECIFIC AND RELATIVE RETENTION VOLUMES OF CHLORINATED METHANES

	Boiling point	Liquid paraffin	Silicone oil DC 702	Silicone oil DC 702	Silicone oil MS 710	Dinonyl phthalate	Dinonyl phthalate	Dibutyl phthalate	Tricresyl phosphate	Hexamethylene glycol dimethyl ether	β,β'-Oxydipropionitrile	Glycerol	Silicone oil DC 702	Dinonyl phthalate	Glycerol
Specific, relative, or activity coefficient:	—	R	S	S	R	S	R	S	R	R	R	S	γ	γ	γ
Temperature(°C):	—	35	20.2	56.7	35	57.2	35	57.0	35	70	70	24.4	77.0	76.8	40.1
Reference:	—	1	2	2	1	2	1	2	1	3	3	2	4	4	4
Methyl chloride	−23.7	—	25.1	10.0	—	—	—	—	—	0.06	0.08	2.16	0.37	0.45	14.8
Methyl dichloride	40.1	196	232	60.5	332	82.8	595	108	530	0.76	0.64	12.9	0.44	0.46	25.7
Chloroform	61	580	595	136	775	210	1620	254	1520	1.6	0.91	16.75	0.40	0.38	39.2
Carbon tetrachloride	76.5	960	746	180	940	173	1180	182	980	0.70	0.36	3.85	0.50	0.71	226

boiling point, which is also the order of increasing chlorination. On dilute polar stationary phases, carbon tetrachloride, which alone of the four compounds is non-polar, is accelerated relative to the others so that it is eluted before chloroform. On concentrated polar stationary phases, carbon tetrachloride is further accelerated so that it appears before methylene dichloride. The columns of Table 12.27 are arranged in approximate order of polarity of the stationary phase, so that the progress of carbon tetrachloride from the end of the chromatogram to close to the beginning as the polar concentration in the stationary phase increases may be clearly seen.

The activity coefficients of the chlorinated methanes on various stationary phases have been calculated by Hardy (4) from the results of Pollard and Hardy (2, 5); these are contained in the last three columns of Table 12.27. It is apparent that on the non-polar or the dilute polar stationary phases, activity coefficients are small, but on the concentrated polar stationary phase, they are of the order of 10, and of the order of 100 for carbon tetrachloride, with the consequent tendency to cause peak broadening, as described in Chapters 3 and 6.

The chlorinated ethanes and ethylenes commonly used as solvents have been chromatographed by many workers (1, 3, 6). Table 12.28 gives retention data relative to chloroform for the commonest of these compounds.

The chromatography of methanes, etc., halogenated with bromine or iodine appears to be similar to that of the chlorinated compounds; thus, Hardy (4) shows that activity coefficients of bromomethanes and bromochloromethanes in silicone or dinonyl phthalate are of the order of unity, whereas activity coefficients in glycerol are of the order of 10. The special features of fluorinated compounds are discussed in Subsection d.

Anaesthetic gases, e.g. "Schleich's Mixture," (chloroform, ether, and ethyl chloride), have been extensively studied, with the emphasis on obtaining rapid analysis during their application (7–11). Separations are generally very easy, e.g., on silicone (8) at 35°C, on which components appear in order of boiling point. On silicone or other non-polar stationary liquid, ethanol, if present, may overlap with ether. In this case, a dilute polar stationary liquid such as dinonyl phthalate should prove satisfactory.

(b) Higher Alkyl Halides

The chromatography of the homologous series of alkyl chlorides has no special features of interest. James and Martin (12) have shown that the n-alkyl chlorides give a linear plot of log V_R' versus carbon number; the

TABLE 12.28

RELATIVE RETENTION DATA FOR CHLORINATED ETHANES AND ETHYLENES[a]

		Stationary phase			
	Boiling point	Paraffin oil	Dinonyl phthalate	Tricresyl phosphate	β,β'-Oxy-dipropio-nitrile
Temperature		77°C	77°C	77°C	70°C
Solute					
Ethyl Chloride	12.2	—	—	—	0.15
1,2-Dichlorethylene	37	0.39	0.26	0.21	0.18
trans-1,2-Dichloroethylene	48.4	0.67	0.42	0.38	0.38
1,1-Dichloroethane	57.3	0.67	0.59	0.52	0.64
cis-1,2-Dichloroethylene	60.1	0.86	0.84	0.86	0.96
Chloroform	61	1.00	1.00	1.00	1.00
1,1,1-Trichloroethane	74.1	1.42	0.84	0.69	0.54
1,2-Dichloroethane	83.5	1.25	1.28	1.41	2.3
Trichloroethane	87	2.44	1.59	1.35	0.85
1,1,2-Trichloroethane	113.5	2.58	4.12	4.66	6.4
Tetrachloroethylene	121.2	—	—	—	1.08

[a] See Harrison and Kelker (1) and (3).

same conclusion is derived from results given by Kovats (13) and by Harrison (1).

A number of alkyl bromides has been studied by McFadden (14), using temperature programmed columns of mixed silicone and "Tween 60". No difficulties are encountered in the separation of monobromoalkanes, but a number of dibromoalkanes overlap on either pure stationary phase. Dibromo-substituted alkanes have smaller activity coefficients on the more polar Tween 60, and by correct choice of proportions in a mixture of both stationary liquids good separation may be obtained. In another paper, Harris and McFadden (15) find that the secondary halide 2-bromobutane overlaps with primary halide 1-bromo-2-methylpropane on all stationary phases. The authors make use of the fact that silver nitrate will react completely with secondary or tertiary bromides, but not with primary. Two runs are performed on the mixture, one with a silver nitrate pre-column, and one without, so that the proportion of 2-bromobutane may be determined by difference. The secondary butyl nitrate formed in the reaction may be removed by acidifying the silver nitrate with sulphuric acid. This method can be used for distinguishing other secondary and tertiary bromides from primary.

Alkyl iodides have been chromatographed in connection with alkoxy-determinations; see Section 12.7c. Moussebois and Duyckaerts (*16*) have chromatographed *n*-alkyl and isoalkyl iodides on dinonyl phthalate at 100°C, obtaining satisfactory separations of all species up to C_5, with a good linear relation between log V_R' and carbon number for both *n*- and iso-iodides.

(c) *Aromatic Halides*

Chlorobenzene, *o*- and *p*-chlorotoluenes, and *o*- and *p*-dichlorobenzenes may be separated easily on columns of silicone DC 702 or dinonyl phthalate (*17*) at temperatures in the region of 150°C. Freeman (*18*) describes the separation of various monochloro- and dichlorotoluenes.

(d) *Fluorocarbons*

Methanes and ethanes variously substituted with fluorine and chlorine are used extensively, e.g., as refrigerants and as components of aerosol products. Specific retention volumes (*2*) and activity coefficients (*4*) for some of these compounds are listed in Table 12.29. It is seen that on silicone oil or charcoal, the substances separate in order of boiling point, and that activity coefficients, though by no means constant, are of the order of unity and exhibit no large irregularities. Separations of incompletely fluorinated methanes and chlorofluoromethanes in order of boiling point on non-polar stationary phases are also shown by Root (*19*). On dilute polar stationary phases, the order of elution is not necessarily that of boiling point, as the results of Table 12.29 show, but Green shows that the series of CCl_nF_{4-n} separate on dibutyl phthalate in serial order of *n* which is also the order of boiling point (*20*).

The chromatography of perfluorinated compounds appears to be distinct from that of compounds also containing any kind of bond other than C—C and C—F. Reed (*21*) has studied the chromatography of perfluoro-alkanes, C_5F_{12}, C_6F_{14}, and C_7F_{16} (*n*-compounds, together with unidentified isomers), on a range of stationary phases. On stationary phases that are themselves perfluorinated, e.g., perfluorokerosine, or perfluorotributyl-amine, activity coefficients are of the order of unity, and the chromatography is normal. Such stationary phases are suitable for the chromatography. On ordinary paraffinic stationary phases, however, activity coeffi-

TABLE 12.29

SPECIFIC RETENTION VOLUMES AND ACTIVITY COEFFICIENTS
OF SOME FLUOROMETHANES[a]

		Stationary phase					
	Boiling point	Silicone DC 702 fluid	Dinonyl phthalate	Dibutyl phthalate	Charcoal	Silicone	Dinonyl phthalate
Temperature (°C):	—	40.1	24.5	20	137	40	24.5
Coefficient:	—	V_g	V_g	V_g	V_g	γ	γ
CF_3H	—82.2	0.45	1.8	2.5	7.6	1.61	0.82
CF_3Cl	—80	0.54	0.6	0.6	17.3	1.80	3.4
CF_2ClH	—40.8	5.57	17.3	21.6	53.0	—	0.57
CF_2Cl_2	—28	6.10	9.5	8.3	152	0.76	0.91
$CFCl_2H$	8.9	41.0	131.5	88.0	453	0.37	0.29
$CFCl_3$	24.1	47.0	80.5	171	1160	0.53	0.80
CH_3Cl	—23.7	22.0	27.3	—	57.5	—	—

[a] See Pollard and Hardy (2) and (4).

cients of perfluoroalkanes are very large indeed; Reed quotes activity coefficients of 16.6, 53, and 75 for C_5F_{12}, C_6F_{14}, and C_7F_{16} on n-hexadecane at 30°C. The result is that the perfluoroalkanes are scarcely retained at all. If, however, the compound possesses at least one hydrogen atom or atom of another halogen, the chromatography on paraffinic stationary phases is normal, with activity coefficients of the order of unity; this is shown by the figures of Table 12.29. Perfluoronaphthenes on paraffinic stationary phases appear to resemble perfluoroalkanes in that they are scarcely retained at all, but the substitution of one of the fluorines by any other atom produces a significant retention. Serpinet (22) describes the chromatography of a number of fluoro- and fluorochlorocarbons on dibutyl phthalate at 20°C. As in other cases, perfluorinated compounds are eluted almost at once, followed by compounds containing at least one other atom, which are retained and resolved. Among the compounds retained are perfluoroalkenes; thus, perfluorocyclobutane is eluted immediately, but perfluorocyclobutene is retained.

(e) *Pesticides*

The analysis of halogenated pesticides such as "Aldrin," "Dieldrin," "Gammexane," etc., is conveniently done by gas chromatography (*23–31*); the use of GC for this purpose has been reviewed (*32*). The main application is in the analysis of trace quantities of pesticides in materials such as fruit, water, oils, blood, etc. For this purpose, the electron capture detector (Section 9.6) is almost invariably used, since it is particularly sensitive to compounds containing halogens. By comparing the chromatogram of a mixture as measured by the flame ionisation detector with that given by the electron capture detector, the halogenated compounds are easily distinguished. The flame ionisation detector may also be used in conjunction with a sodium thermionic detector (Section 9.3f) in the same way. Figure 12.15 shows an example of a chromatogram of some common pesticides (*28*).

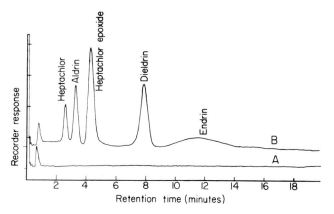

Fig. 12.15. Chromatogram of an extract from wheat containing 0.01 p.p.m. of each of the pesticides indicated; B, electron capture detector, column of SE30 silicone at 175°C. A, same on FID. Saha (*28*).

12.10. Sulphur Compounds

The lower thiols have been chromatographed by Spencer *et al.* (*1*), Amberg (*2*), Ryce and Bryce (*5*), Sunner *et al.* (*4*), Karchmer (*5*), and others. Temperature-programmed analyses of thiols are described by Sullivan *et al.* (*6*). Carson *et al.* (*7*) describe a flash-exchange technique (Section 11.6c) suitable for use with thiols. Relative and specific retention data for these compounds is given in Table 12.30. Thiols are compounds with a slightly polar group, and they may be chromatographed satisfactorily in either polar or non-polar stationary phases.

TABLE 12.30

RETENTION DATA FOR THIOLS

	Boiling point	Stationary phase			
		Mineral oil	Dinonyl phthalate	Tricresyl phosphate	β,β'-Iminodi-propionitrile
Relative or specific:	—	R	S	R	R
Temperature (°C):	—	84	50	85	84
Reference:	—	5	1	2	5
Methanethiol	6.0	—	19.6	—	—
Ethanethiol	35.0	—	53.3	—	—
2-Propanethiol	53.6	0.45	82.1	0.36	0.29
2-Methyl-2-propanethiol	64.2	—	109	0.41	—
1-Propanethiol	67.6	0.67	143	0.58	0.50
2-Butanethiol	85.0	—	238	—	—
2-Methyl-1-propanethiol	88.7	1.19	271	0.92	0.66
1-Butanethiol	98.5	1.59	389	—	0.88
1-Pentanethiol	126.6	3.74	1070	—	1.50
Benzene	—	1.00	—	1.00	1.00

The lower sulphides have been chromatographed by Spencer et al. (1), Amberg (2), Karchmer (5), Desty and Whyman (8), and Petranek (9). Retention data for sulphides are given in Table 12.31. The characteristics of the chromatography are similar to those for thiols. On non-polar stationary phases, separations are in order of boiling point. On polar stationary phases, there is no gross difference in retention, but there are significant differences which enable close boiling isomers to be resolved. Retention data for disulphides and trisulphides is given by Carson and Wong (10).

The separation of benzene (boiling point, 80.2) and thiophene (boiling point, 84.1), which commonly occur together and which are not easily separated by distillation, is easily performed by gas chromatography on any but paraffinic stationary phases. Table 12.32 gives the relative retentions of the two compounds on a variety of stationary phases.

Gas chromatography enables many sulphur compounds which have not hitherto been characterised chemically to be isolated and identified. Thomp-

TABLE 12.31

RETENTION DATA FOR SULPHIDES

Alkyl groups of sulphides		Stationary phase			
	Boiling point	Silicone oil	Dinonyl phthalate	Tricresyl phosphate	7,8-Benzo-quinoline
Relative or specific:	—	R	S	R	R
Temperature (°C):	—	100	50	85	100
Reference:	—	*9*	*1*	*2*	*9*
Dimethyl	38	0.34	63.2	0.137	—
Methyl ethyl	67	0.66	122	0.272	—
Diethyl	92	1.17	311	0.49	—
Ethyl isopropyl	107	1.62	494	—	1.74
Methyl isobutyl	113	1.96	—	—	2.05
Methyl *sec*butyl	113	1.96	—	—	2.19
Ethyl *n*-propyl	118	—	772	—	—
Di-isopropyl	120	1.96	—	—	2.19
n-Propyl isopropyl	132	3.08	—	—	3.12
Ethyl isobutyl	133	3.08	1260	—	3.45
Ethyl *sec*butyl	133	3.08	—	—	3.45
Di-*n*-propyl	143	4.35	—	—	4.98
Ethyl *n*-butyl	143	4.35	2000	—	4.98
*iso*Propyl isobutyl	143	4.35	—	—	4.01
*iso*Butyl *sec*butyl	166	8.25	—	—	7.75
n-Propyl *n*-butyl	167	8.25	—	—	9.19
Di-*n*-butyl	182	15.2	—	—	—
Benzene	80	*1.00*	—	—	*1.00*
Thiophene	84	—	—	*1.00*	—
V_g for benzene	—	37	—	—	46

son *et al.* (*12*), therefore, desulphurise complex mixtures of sulphur compounds catalytically, and obtain partial knowledge of the mixture by identifying the hydrocarbon so produced. This procedure is comparable with that in which the skeletal structure of olefins is determined by hydrogenation followed by identification of the alkanes described in Section 12.3f.

TABLE 12.32

Relative Retention of Benzene and Thiophene (Thiophene/Benzene) on
Various Stationary Phases

Stationary phase	Temp. (°C)	Relative retention	Ref.
Hexatriacontane	78.5	1.09	8
Paraffin oil	84	1.11	5
Tricresyl phosphate	65	1.38	2
Benzyldiphenyl	78.5	1.40	8
Polypropylene glycol adipate	85	1.62	11
β,β'-Iminodipropionitrile	84	1.63	5

12.11. Polymers and Other Non-Volatiles

Polymers and other non-volatile organic compounds can frequently be identified and analysed by a technique in which the polymer, etc., is pyrolysed, and the volatile products of pyrolysis are gas chromatographed. The pyrolysis may be performed in a separate apparatus, the pyrolysis products being condensed and subsequently transferred to gas chromatography apparatus, or the pyrolysis may be conducted on a micro scale in the introducer of a gas chromatography apparatus. The latter technique has become very common in recent years, and is called "Pyrolysis Gas Chromatography." Most of its applications are to polymers; particularly to those polymers which can be pyrolysed to give good yields of their monomers. It can, however, be applied to many other compounds, and is useful even if the fragments produced by pyrolysis are only distantly related with the structure of the starting material. Examples of its use are to alkaloids, barbiturates, proteins, etc. Pyrolysis GC has been reviewed by several authors (1–4). Papers presented at a symposium on the subject have been published (5).

(a) Apparatus and Technique

When the pyrolysis is performed separately from the chromatography (static technique), a sample of the polymer is placed in a small glass pyrolysis vessel and heated. A small condenser is attached, and volatile products are condensed. Different authors use slightly different pyrolysis temperatures and different conditions. Davison et al. (6) pyrolyse rubber, artificial rubbers, and acrylate polymers at 650°C in a stream of nitrogen, following which they chromatogram that part of the pyrolysate boiling below 100°C. Strassburger *et al.* (7) pyrolyse methacrylate polymers and copolymers at 350°C in a glass tube enclosed in a furnace, and condense all but the gaseous part of the pyrolysate. Radell and Strultz (8) attach to the gas-handling section of a commercial gas chromatograph a small metal pyrolysis tube in which methacrylate polymers are pyrolysed by surrounding the tube with a bath of Wood's metal at 500°C.

When the pyrolysis is performed in the introducer of the gas chromatograph, there are essentially two techniques. In one, the "flash" technique, the introducer contains an element which can suddenly be heated up to the pyrolysis temperature for a short period during which pyrolysis occurs. In the other, there is a hot element continuously heated, and it is the sample that is suddenly applied to it.

The flash technique is commonest. Most authors use a technique in which a small sample of polymer is placed on a helix or other such shape of wire, which may then be heated electrically to the required pyrolysis temperature; the general features of the apparatus are shown in Fig. 12.16.

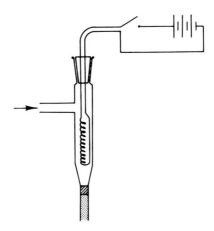

Fig. 12.16. Schematic diagram of apparatus for pyrolysis at the column inlet.

In the technique, the coil is generally of nichrome or other such heat resistant wire of large specific electrical resistance; the polymer is dissolved in or made into a fine suspension in a suitable solvent; a sample of the solution or suspension is painted or otherwise deposited on the wire, after which the solvent dries off. The wire is then inserted in the introducer and carrier gas is set flowing. The chromatogram is then started by passing a predetermined current through the wire. The heat capacity of the wire is small, so that it may be heated very rapidly to the required pyrolysis temperature, and the quantity of polymer is sufficiently small that the pyrolysis is complete within seconds. Thus the introduction of the pyrolysate to the column is sufficiently fast that band spreading at introduction is negligible. A modification of the above technique is to form the heating wire into a basket which contains a small Vycor crucible in which the sample is placed (9, 10).

It is important that the pyrolyser should heat evenly. Thus, Barlow *et al.* (11) use a helical wire slightly spiralled outwards towards each end from the middle, thus giving a shape like an upholstery spring; such a shape can be made so as to have small temperature differential along its length.

Lehrle and Robb (12) have described a related technique in which a polymer is formed into a dielectric in the introducer of a gas chromatograph, and the dielectric is broken down by applying a powerful spark discharge. They found that the degradation produced by this was very profound. The principal products are very simple molecules, e.g., acetylene, ethylene, and these have insufficient structure characteristic of the original polymer to be used for identification.

Giacobbo and Simon (13, 14) have introduced a pyrolysis chamber making use of the "Curie Point" of ferromagnetic material, i.e., that temperature above which the material ceases to be ferromagnetic. In their design (Fig. 12.17), the gas path leading to the column is of glass and contains a small wire of ferromagnetic material. The glass tube is surrounded by a coil of wire passing a high-frequency current. A current is thereby induced in the wire, and its temperature rises till it reaches the Curie point, at which temperature no further energy can be transferred to it since the induction fails. Thus, the wire remains at the Curie temperature. With a sufficient inducing current and a small enough wire, the Curie point can be reached in a matter of milliseconds. Since the pyrolysis temperature

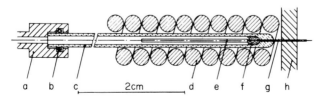

FIG. 12.17. Design for a Curie-Point pyrolyser. Simon and Giacobbo (14). (a) Introducer; (b) 0-ring; (c) glass tube; (d) induction coil; (e) ferromagnetic wire; (f) porous pad at entrance to capillary (g) leading to column through rubber cap (h).

is reproducible, this type of pyrolyser enables the conditions of pyrolysis GC to be reproduced much more precisely, and thus improves the reproducibility of the technique. Different metals have different Curie points, and, by a suitable choice, temperatures in the range 400 to 800°C are accessible.

In addition to the "flash" technique, pyrolysers either of the filament design or the Curie point design can be operated continuously at their operating temperature, so that pyrolysis occurs whenever a vapour arrives at them. Some authors have described micro-furnaces filled with catalytic packing at which pyrolysis can occur (15, 16). Such units are particularly suitable for pyrolysis of gaseous samples, using a technique in which the structure of complex volatile material of unknown composition can be diagnosed by partial pyrolysis (17, 18).

(b) Products and Conditions

One may classify pyrolysis GC into three classes according to the pyrolysis temperatures employed.

(1) *Mild Degradation*, usually at temperatures between 100°C and 400°C. There are many labile organic substances which yield characteristic volatile products at these comparatively low temperatures, e.g., quaternary ammonium compounds (19), salts of aliphatic amines (20), oxalates and formates (21), etc. The literature contains several examples of the use of pyrolysis GC for their identification.

(2) *Medium Pyrolysis* at between 500°C and 800°C. In this range, nearly all of the polymers which commonly go to make plastics will pyrolyse to give volatile products. Thus, this is the range of temperature in which most pyrolysis GC is performed.

In the pyrolytic identification of linear polymers, the ideal sole product is monomer, or, in the case of copolymers, a mixture of monomers. In practice, there is very often a large proportion of monomer and conditions can be adjusted to maximise this, but there are also secondary products. This is firstly because the bond linking the monomer units in a polymer may not be the weakest bond, and therefore pyrolysis does not necessarily yield monomer alone, and secondly, because primary products of pyrolysis may undergo further reaction before they leave the hot region of the pyrolyser.

In general, low pyrolysis temperatures favour monomer formation. Thus, in their static technique described above, Radell and Strultz (8) find that above 500°C, the pyrolysis yields secondary products and analyses are irreproducible, that below 500°C, the pyrolysis is incomplete, and that only at 500°C are conditions satisfactory. Using the micro-technique, lower pyrolysis temperatures seem to be more satisfactory with acrylate polymers. Thus, Strassburger *et al.* (7) and also Lehmann and Brauer (10) find that pure yields of monomer are obtained by pyrolysis at 450°C; Lehmann and Brauer have studied the increase in the proportion of secondary products with increase in the pyrolysis temperature; Fig. 12.18 shows chromatograms of pyrolysis products with successively higher pyrolysis temperatures (10). Barlow *et al.* (11) have used their spiral helical pyrolyser coil at successively greater temperatures, and from the pyrolysis products obtained have been able to arrange the bonds in a polymer in order of their stability to heat.

Apart from the correct choice of temperature, there are other necessary conditions for formation of useful chromatograms of pyrolysis products.

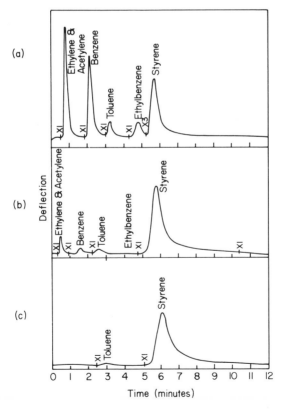

FIG. 12.18. Chromatograms of pyrolysis products from polystyrene. Lehmann and Brauer (10). Pyrolysis at (a) 1025°C, (b) 825°C, (c) 425°C.

The pyrolysis must be rapid; this may be achieved by spreading the minimum sample of polymer over a large heating area, and this is facilitated by the use of sensitive detectors. Gas diffusion of the pyrolysis products must be minimised in order to prevent secondary reactions; this may be achieved by ensuring a fast flow of carrier gas over the pyrolyser. Also, risk of condensation of the pyrolysate should be avoided by containing the pyrolysis unit in a region at the column temperature. With conditions such as these, pyrolysis analyses are reproducible, but it is apparent by comparing papers in which the same polymers are pyrolysed by different techniques, that it is very easy to get irreproducible, or at least non-transferable, results.

(3) *High Temperature Pyrolysis.* In this, the pyrolysis temperature may be up to 1200°C, which causes organic compounds to degrade to comparatively simple fractions. Often, a particular compound may pyrolyse in these conditions to give products which yield a chromatogram with a characteristic pattern which is reproducible at least in a given apparatus, and can thus be used for qualitative identification, even though the nature of the reactions and the nature of the products forming the pattern may be unknown. This technique, in which compounds are "fingerprinted," has been used extensively, e.g. for identification of drugs, amino acids, proteins, etc. (*17, 18, 22–24*).

(c) *Analysis of Copolymers and Mixed Polymers*

Copolymers and mixed polymers pyrolyse in suitable conditions to give mixtures of the monomers from which they are composed. Ideally, a copolymer or mixed polymer should pyrolyse to give a mixture of monomers in the same proportions as present in the polymer; this would provide a very simple means of determining the constitution of the polymer. Most authors, however, find that the composition of the mixture of monomers is significantly different from the composition of the polymer. However, there appears to be a reproducible relation between monomer composition and pyrolysate composition, so that if one is plotted against the other, a smooth curve is obtained which serves as a calibration for the analysis of unknown mixtures (*7, 11*). Strassburger *et al.* (*7*) have shown that the chromatogram of the products of pyrolysis of a mixture of two polymers differs from that of a copolymer of the two in the same proportions (using methyl methacrylate and ethylene dimethacrylate); from this it is apparent that the ideal behaviour postulated above cannot be general, even though it may sometimes be approximately true in specific cases.

12.12. Inorganic Substances

Volatile inorganic substances, like organic substances, can be analysed by gas chromatography. In the case of covalent volatile inorganic substances which are stable to air and to heat, the chromatography is usually normal both in theory and in practice. Many inorganic volatile substances, particularly many of fairly recent discovery, are reactive, and may be sensitive to heat or components of the atmosphere. The use of gas chromatography for analysis of such substances is growing. Most of the workers referred to below who use reactive substances also describe the technology of handling them.

(a) Separation of Metals

Nearly all metals form some kind of volatile compound, and these may be chromatographed, thus enabling mixtures of metals to be separated. Several different classes of volatile metal compounds have been studied.

(1) *Halides*. All but the most electropositive metals form appreciably volatile halides. Table 12.33 gives the boiling points of some of the more familiar metal halides.

The gas chromatography of metal halides has been studied by many authors (1–15). Metal halides may be chromatographed on packed columns of ordinary design using various hydrocarbons as stationary phases. Keller (4), however, finds that not all paraffinic stationary phases are satisfactory. Of octadecane, squalane, Apiezon L grease, silicone oil, and paraffin wax, the first two were satisfactory, but the others were less satisfactory, and with silicone grease and Apiezon L grease, peaks sometimes failed to be eluted. Similar results were obtained by Wachi (2). It is clear from these results, and also from the fact that pure substances sometimes produce spurious peaks, that the halides react with certain paraffinic stationary phases. On octadecane and squalane, the chromatography of metal halides is normal. Keller (4) and Keller and Freiser (1) list specific retention volumes of the halides $SnCl_4$, $TiCl_4$, $NbCl_5$, and $TaCl_5$, which are eluted in the order given. Keller (4) has determined specific retention volumes at different temperatures, and finds that plots of $\log V_g$ against $1/T$ are reasonably linear, and that the heats of solution obtained from them are not very different from differential heats of volatilisation obtained from vapour pressure data.

The halides $NbCl_5$ and $TaCl_5$ separate with a relative retention of approximately 2. Gas chromatography is thus shown to secure an easy separa-

TABLE 12.33

BOILING POINTS OF VOLATILE METAL HALIDES[a]

	Boiling point (°C)		
	Chloride	Bromide	Iodide
Boron	13	91	210
Silicon	58	153	290
Germanium	86	186	375
Tin (IV)	114	202	340
Arsenic (III)	130	221	403
Titanium (IV)	136	230	360
Vanadium (IV)	149	—	—
Antimony (V)	172	—	400
Aluminium	178	268	382
Gallium	215	—	—
Antimony (III)	220	280	401
Niobium (V)	240.5	270	—
Tantalum (V)	242	320	—
Gold (III)	265	—	—
Molybdenum (V)	268	—	—
Tungsten (V)	275	333	—
Mercury (II)	304	322	354
Hafnium (IV)	317	—	—
Iron (III)	319	—	—
Zirconium (IV)	331	—	—
Tungsten (VI)	337	—	—

[a] See Keller and Freiser (1).

tion of two elements the separation of which by chemical methods is rather difficult.

Many of the common stationary liquids are too volatile for effective chromatography of the less volatile metal halides. For these, therefore, Juvet et al. (2, 3, 15) have used stationary phases consisting of eutectic mixtures of ionic inorganic halides at temperatures above their melting points. Suitable mixtures are $BiCl_3/PbCl_2$ (mp 217°C), $KCl/CdCl_2$ (mp 383°C), etc. The volatile covalent halides used as solutes interact with such solvents at least partially through the formation of halo-anion complexes. Thus, solvent halides which do not form halo-anions, for example, eutectics composed from the alkali metal halides, give small retentions, while solvents at least one component of which is the halide of a metal which readily forms halo-anions give large retentions. Since the elements which tend to form halo-anions are often also those which have volatile halides, the ideal solvent is a compromise between complexing power and volatility. Juvet *et al.* find that the halides of the non-transition elements of the middle of the periodic table, e.g., indium, thallium, lead, are the most generally satisfactory.

The gas chromatography of metal halides is complicated in practice by the fact that the halides react with water. Care must be taken not to allow either the samples or the column to come into contact with moist air.

(2) Chelate complexes. Nearly all metals form complexes with chelating ligands; by choice of ligand and the conditions, neutral (i.e., non-ionic) complexes may be prepared, and these are appreciably volatile. Many workers have studied the separation of these volatile compounds. In early work (*16–18*), acetylacetone was generally used as the chelating agent. In more recent work, the tendency has been to use fluorinated derivatives of this, particularly trifluoroacetylacetone and hexafluoroacetylacetone, since the more fluorine in the molecule, the more volatile the resulting chelate complex (*18–20*). The field has been reviewed comprehensively by

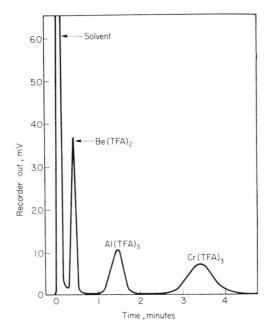

FIG. 12.19. Chromatogram of the trifluoroacetylacetonates of beryllium, aluminum, and chromium III. Hill and Gesser (*18*). Column of 7.5% SE30 silicone on firebrick, 1 foot long, operated at 106°C.

Moshier and Sievers (*21*). Fig. 12.19 (*18*) illustrates how the technique can be used to provide very easy separation of elements (Be and Al) which are chemically very similar.

(*3*) *Metal-organic compounds.* Most metals form covalent compounds with organic groups, e.g., alkyl groups or alkoxy groups. Many such compounds, especially the metal alkyls, are volatile. Their chromatography has been reported occasionally (e.g., *22, 23*), especially in the case of the lead alkyls (e.g., *24*). However, since the metal alkyls are often difficult to handle, they are less suitable for metal analysis than chelate compounds.

(*4*) *Elements.* Some elementary metals are sufficiently volatile for gas chromatography at high temperatures. The possibility of chromatographing metals has been demonstrated by DeBoer (*25*), who used a column consisting of lithium chloride (20%) on sea sand (80%) heated above the melting point of the salt. Using a sample consisting of an alloy of zinc and cadmium, he showed that the vapour appearing at the end of the column consisted of pure cadmium with less than 0.5% zinc, and, by omitting the column, showed that the process was one of chromatography and not of simple distillation.

In the GC of metals, a useful detector is provided by a flame photometer, since by examining the spectrum given by a flame coloured by a metal, the metal can be identified. Techniques for coupling a flame photometer to the outlet of a GC columns are described by Juvet and Durbin (*26, 27*). If fluorinated chelating agents are used for metals, the fluorine is conveniently detected in an electron capture detector (*21*).

(b) Covalent Inorganic Compounds

The numerous volatile compounds of boron, silicon, phosphorus, germanium, tin, etc. are generally capable of analysis by GC, and this method has been extensively used. In many cases, the inorganic compounds are reactive and are handled by standard vacuum techniques. Samples are therefore transferred to the column through a trap which can be connected by suitable stopcocks alternately to the vacuum system and to the system carrying the carrier gas. Most published applications describe the simple apparatus for this transfer.

The GC of inorganic and mixed organic-inorganic compounds follows the same general principles as those described in Chapter 3 for organic compounds. Thus, in general, each structural unit in the molecule produces a constant characteristic increment to the logarithm of the retention. This has been illustrated for alkyl borons by Schomburg *et al.* (*28*), by Koster and Bruno (*29*), and by Seely *et al.* (*30*); for substituted boron hydrides by Blay *et al.* (*31, 32*); for the silanes and germanes by Borer and Phillips (*33*), and similarly by many other workers.

The more reactive inorganic substances are usually chromatographed on non-polar stationary phases, since many would react with any polar groups. In non-polar liquids, the general relations between retention and structure described in Sections 3.5–3.7 hold. Thus, non-polar or weakly polar substances separate roughly in order of boiling point. For example, phosphorus trichloride (bp 76°C) is eluted before phosphorus oxychloride (bp 105°C) on silicone (*34, 35*); similarly B_5H_9 is eluted before B_5H_{11}, which has the larger molecule (*36, 37*). Polar stationary liquids, if usable, cause extra retention of polar solutes, as with organic compounds. For example, in the important and common analysis of the series of chloromethylsilanes, the use of a polar stationary liquid enables the polar $SiMe_3Cl$ to be eluted after the non-polar $SiCl_4$, even though these two compounds boil at the same temperature (58°C) and are eluted together on a non-polar substrate (*38, 39*).

(c) Halogens and Their Inorganic Derivatives

The use of GC for the analysis of corrosive material is probably best exemplified by the work done on the analysis of such compounds as the halogen elements and interhalogen compounds such as chlorine trifluoride (*40–47*). The chromatography of these compounds is regular, but apparatus for handling them must be specially constructed. Ellis *et al.* (*40–42*) consider that the only substances which may be allowed to come into contact with fluorinated gases are nickel, monel metal, polytetrafluoroethylene, or polytrifluoromonochloroethylene. In particular, it should be noted that stainless steel should be avoided, since the iron and chromium in it form volatile halides. Granulated polytetrafluoroethylene forms a suitable support, and the most commonly used stationary liquid for halogens, etc., is polytrifluoromonochloroethylene oil. It should be noted that unfluorinated polythene exchanges with fluorine and halogen fluorides.

The corrosive nature of fluorinated compounds puts some restriction on the choice and design of detectors. Ellis, Iveson *et al.* (*40–42*) have used a catharometer in which the hot element is a nickel wire, and in which all insulation in contact with the column effluent is of polytetrafluoroethylene. Neely (*44*) has used an ordinary general purpose catharometer in his chlorine analyses, but this would almost certainly fail for fluorinated gases.

Phillips and Owens (43) use a hydrogen flame detector, but find that it is necessary to have a separate hydrogen flame into which the column effluent is injected, instead of either using hydrogen as carrier gas, or pre-mixing the column effluent with hydrogen. The authors use a jet consisting of the ends of two concentric tubes, the inner tube carrying hydrogen which burns, and the outer one carrying the column effluent.

REFERENCES*

Note: References are numbered beginning with (*1*) in each section, and are here grouped together according to section.

Section 12.2

1. Janák, J., *Collection Czechoslov. Chem. Commun.*, **19**, 917 (1954).
2. Greene, S. A., *Anal. Chem.* **31**, 480 (1959).
3. Krejci, M., Tesarik, K., and Janak, J., *in* "Gas Chromatography," I.S.A. Symposium, June, 1959 (H. J. Noebels, R. F. Wall, and N. Brenner, eds.), p. 255. Academic Press, New York, 1961.
4. Gluekauf, E., and Kitt, G. P., *Proc. Roy. Soc.* **A234**, 557 (1956).
5. Koch, R. C., and Grandy, G. L., presented at the Pittsburgh Conference on Analytical Chemistry, March 1960.
6. Koch, R. C. and Grandy, G. L., *Anal. Chem.* **33**, 43 (1961).
7. Gluekauf, E., *in* "Gas Chromatography 1958," Proceedings of the Second Symposium, Amsterdam, May, 1958 (D. H. Desty, ed.), p. 69. Academic Press, New York, 1958.
8. Gluekauf, E., *Ann. N.Y. Acad. Sci.* **72**, 562 (1959).
9. Bethune, J. L., and Rigby, F. L., *J. Inst. Brewing* **64**, 170 (1958).
10. Kyryacos, G., and Boord, C. E., *Anal. Chem.* **29**, 787 (1957).
11. Greene, S. A., and Pust, H., *Anal. Chem.* **29**, 1055 (1957).
12. Madison, J. J., *Anal. Chem.* **30**, 1859 (1958).
13. Heylmun, G. W., *J. Gas Chromatog.* **3**, 82 (1965).
14. Vizard, G. S., and Wynne, A., *Chem. Ind. (London)*, p. 196 (1960).
15. Karlsson, B.M., *Anal. Chem.* **38**, 668 (1966).
16. Lord, E. W., and Horn, R. C., *Anal. Chem.* **32**, 878 (1960).
17. Pietsch, H., *Erdöl u. Kohle* **11**, 157 (1958).
18. Fukuda, T., Omori, H., and Kusama, T., *Bunseki Kagaku* **6**, 647 (1957).
19. Wencke, K., *Chem. Tech. (Berlin)* **8**, 728 (1956).
20. Wencke, K., *Chem. Tech. (Berlin)* **9**, 404 (1957).
21. Graven, W. M., *Anal. Chem.* **31**, 1197 (1959).
22. Falconer, J. W., and Knox, J. H., *Proc. Roy. Soc.* **A250**, 493 (1959).
23. Hollis, O. L., and Hayes, W. V., "Gas Chromatography 1966," Proceedings of the Sixth International Symposium (A. B. Littlewood, ed.), p. 57. Institute of Petroleum, London, 1967.
24. Szulczewski, D. H., and Higuchi, T., *Anal. Chem.* **29**, 1541 (1957).
25. Marvillet, L., and Tranchant, J., "Gas Chromatography 1960," Proceedings of the Third International Symposium (R. P. W. Scott, ed.), p. 321. Academic Press, New York, 1961.

26. Adlard, E. R., and Hill, D. W., *Nature* **186**, 1045 (1960).

27. Horton, A. D., from Office of Technical Services, Dept. of Commerce, Washington D.C., ORNL-2866, U.C.-4 Chemistry-General, TID 4500 (15th ed.).

28. Greene, S. A. and Pust, H., Advances in Gas Chromatography, *Am. Chem. Soc. Symposium, New York, Sept. 1957*, p. D 107; *Anal. Chem.* **50**, 1039 (1958).

29. Smith, D. H., Nakayama, F. S., and Clark, F. E., *Soil Sci. Am. Proc.* **24**, 145 (1960).

30. Ohkoshi, S., Fujita, Y. and Kwan, T., *Bull. Chem. Soc. Japan* **31**, 770 (1958).

31. Ohkoshi, S., Tenma, S., Fujita, Y., and Kwan, T., *Bull. Chem. Soc. Japan* **51**, 772 (1958).

32. Ohkoshi, S., Tenma, S., Fujita, Y., and Kwan, T., *Bull. Chem. Soc. Japan* **31**, 773 (1958).

33. Smith, H. A., and Hunt, P. P., *J. Phys. Chem.* **64**, 383 (1960).

34. Gant, P. L., and Yang, K., *Science* **129**, 1548 (1959).

35. Riedel, O., and Uhlmann, E., *Z. Anal. Chem.* **166**, 433 (1959).

36. Arnett, E. M., Presented at the Pittsburgh Conference on Analytical Chemistry, March, 1960.

37. Gluekauf, E., and Kitt, G. P., *in* "Vapour Phase Chromatography," Proceedings of the First Simposium, London, June, 1956 (D. H. Desty, ed.), p. 422. Academic Press, New York, 1957.

38. Thomas, C. O., and Smith, H. A., *J. Phys. Chem.* **63**, 427 (1959).

39. Moore, W. R., and Ward, H. R., *J. Am. Chem. Soc.* **80**, 2909 (1958).

40. van Hook, W. A., and Emmett, P. H., *J. Phys. Chem.* **64**, 673 (1960).

41. Erb, E., *in* "Gas Chromatography," I.S.A. Symposium, June, 1959 (H. J. Noebels, R. F. Wall, and N. Brenner, eds.), p. 357. Academic Press, New York, 1961.

42. Mohnke, M., and Saffert, W., "Gas Chromatography 1962," Proceedings of the Fourth International Symposium, (van M. Swaay, ed.), p. 216. Academic Press, New York, 1962.

Section 12.3

1. Turkeltaub, N. M., *Zhur. Anal. Khim.* **5**, 200 (1950); *Chem. Abstr.* **50**, 7663 (1956); Turkeltaub, N. M., and Zhukhovitskii, A. A., *Zavodskaya Lab.* **22**, 1032 (1956) (review); Turkeltaub, N. M., Kolyubyakina, A. I., and Selenkina, N. S., *Zhur. Anal. Khim.* **12**, 302 (1957); Turkeltaub, N. M., Porshneva, N. V., and Kancheeva, O. A., *Zavodskaya Lab.* **22**, 735 (1956); Vyakhirev, D. A., and Bruk, A. I., *Zhur. Fiz. Khim.* **31**, 1713 (1957); Vyakhirev, D. A., Bruk, A. I., and Guglina, S. A., *Doklady Akad. Nauk S.S.S.R.* **90**, 577 (1953); Zhukhovitskii, A. A., Kasansky, B. A., Sterligov, O. D., and Turkeltaub, N. M., *ibid.* **94**, 77 (1954).

2. Condon, R. D., *Anal. Chem.* **31**, 1717 (1959).

3. Desty, D. H., Goldup, A., and Whyman, B. H. F., *J. Inst. Petrol.* **45**, 287 (1959).

4. Heine, E., Thesis, Frankfurt/Main, 1963.

5. Hollis, O. L., and Hayes, W. V., "Gas Chromatography 1966," Proceedings of the Sixth International Symposium (A. B. Littlewood, ed.), p. 57. Institute of Petroleum, London, 1967.

6. Hollis, O. L., *Anal. Chem.* **38**, 309 (1966).

7. Hollis, O. L., and Hayes, W. V., *J. Gas Chromatog.* **4**, 235 (1966).

8. Patton, H. W., Lewis, J. S., and Kaye, W. I., *Anal. Chem.* **27**, 170 (1955).

9. Ohkoshi, S., Fujita, Y., and Kwan, T., *Shokubai* **15**, 1 (1958).

10. Ray, N. H., *J. Appl. Chem.* **4**, 21 (1954).
11. Greene, S. A., Moberg, M. L., and Wilson, E. M., *Anal. Chem.* **28**, 1369 (1956).
12. Greene, S. A., and Pust, H., *Anal. Chem.* **29**, 1055 (1957).
13. Morrow, H. N., and Buckley, K. B., *Petrol. Refiner* **36**, 157 (1957).
14. Taylor, G. W., and Dunlop, A. S., *in* "Gas Chromatography," I.S.A. Symposium, August, 1957 (V. J. Coates, H. J. Noebels, and I. S. Fagerson, eds.), p. 73. Academic Press, New York, 1958.
15. Fredericks, E. M., and Brooks, F. R., *Anal. Chem.* **28**, 297 (1956).
16. Bradford, B. W., Harvey, D., and Chalkley, D. E., *J. Inst. Petrol.* **41**, 80 (1955).
17. Primavesi, G. R., *Nature* **184**, 2010 (1959).
18. Barnard, J. A., and Hughes, H. W. D., *Nature* **183**, 250 (1959).
19. Dietz, W. A., and Dudenbostel, B. F., Advances in Gas Chromatography, *Am. Chem. Soc. Symposium, New York, Sept. 1957*, p. D 171.
20. van der Craats, F., *Anal. Chim. Acta* **14**, 136 (1956).
21. Wirth, M. M., *in* "Vapour Phase Chromatography," Proceedings of the First Symposium, London, June, 1956 (D. H. Desty, ed.), p. 154. Academic Press, New York, 1957.
22. I. P. Methods 169 (A, B, and C)/59 (tentative), Institute of Petroleum Standard Methods for Testing Petroleum and Its Products, 19th ed., 1960.
23. Hively, R. A., *J. Chem. Eng. Data* **5**, 237 (1960).
24. Keulemans, A. I. M., Kwantes, A., and Zaal, P., *Anal. Chim. Acta* **13**, 357 (1955).
25. McKenna, T. A., and Idleman, J. A., *Anal. Chem.* **31**, 2000 (1959).
26. McKenna, T. A., and Idleman, J. A., *Anal. Chem.* **31**, 1021 (1959).
27. Scott, C. G., *J. Inst. Petrol.* **45**, 118 (1959).
28. Favre, J. A., Hines, W. J., and Smith, D. E., *Proc. 37th Ann. Conv, Nat. Gasoline Assoc. Am.*, p. 27 (1958); see *J. Inst. Petrol.* **45**, 29A (1959).
29. Knight, H. S., *Anal. Chem.* **30**, 9 (1958).

Section 12.4

1. Hively, R. A., *J. Chem. Eng. Data* **5**, 237 (1960).
2. Merchant, P., Jr., *Anal. Chem.* **40**, 2153 (1968).
3. Brunnock, J. V., and Luke, L. A., *Anal. Chem.* **40**, 2158 (1968).
4. Schwartz, R. D., and Brasseaux, D. J., *Anal. Chem.* **35**, 1374 (1963).
5. Durrett, L. R., Taylor, L. M., Wantland, C. T., and Dvoretzki, I., *Anal. Chem.* **35**, 637 (1963).
6. Huyten, F. H., *Chem. Weekblad.* **59**, 457 (1963).
7. Desty, D. H., and Whyman, B. H. F., *Anal. Chem.* **29**, 320 (1957).
8. Scott, R. P. W., Benzol Producers Ltd., Watford, England, Research Paper 8-1957.
9. Kwantes, A., and Rijnders, G. W. A., *in* "Gas Chromatography 1958," Proceedings of the Second Symposium, Amsterdam May, 1958 (D. H. Desty, ed.), p. 125. Academic Press, New York, 1958.
10. James, A. T., and Martin, A. J. P., *J. Appl. Chem.* **6**, 105 (1956).
11. Sullivan, L. J., Lotz, J. R., and Willingham, C. B., *Anal. Chem.* **28**, 495 (1956).
12. Dietz, W. A., and Dudenbostel, B. F., *Advan. Gas Chromatog.* (*ACS Symp., New York, Sept. 1957*), p. D 171.
13. Hively, R. A., *J. Chem. Eng. Data* **5**, 237 (1960).
14. Desty, D. H., Goldup, A., and Whyman, B. H. F., *J. Inst. Petrol.* **45**, 287 (1959).
15. Eggertsen, F. T., and Groennings, S., *Anal. Chem.* **30**, 20 (1958).

16. Zlatkis, A., *Anal. Chem.* **30**, 332 (1958).
17. Eggertsen, F. T., Knight, H. S., and Groennings, S., *Anal. Chem.* **28**, 303 (1956).
18. Data Subcommittee of the Gas Chromatography Discussion Group, *in* "Gas Chromatography Abstracts 1966," p. 233. Institute of Petroleum, London, 1967.
19. Eggertsen, F. T., and Knight, H. S., *Anal. Chem.* **30**, 15 (1958).
20. Knight, H. S., *Anal. Chem.* **30**, 9 (1958).
21. Armitage, F., *J. Chromatog.* **2**, 655 (1959).
22. Bradford, B. W., Harvey, D., and Chalkley, D. E., *J. Inst. Petrol.* **41**, 80 (1955).
23. Bednas, M. E. and Russell, D. S., *Can. J. Chem.* **36**, 1272 (1958).
24. I. P. Method 156/58, Institute of Petroleum Standard Methods for Testing Petroleum and Its Products, 19th ed., 1960.
25. Blundell, R. V., Griffiths, S. T., and Wilson, R. R., "Gas Chromatography 1960," Proceedings of the Third International Symposium (R. P. W. Scott, ed.) p. 360. Academic Press, New York, 1961.
26. Martin, R. L., *Anal. Chem.* **32**, 336 (1960).
27. Whitham, B. T., *Nature* **182**, 391 (1958).
28. Smith, B., and Ohlson, R., *Acta Chem. Scand.* **14**, 1317 (1960).
29. Nelson, K. H., Hines, W. J., Grimes, M. D., and Smith, D. E., *Anal. Chem.* **32**, 1110 (1960).
30. Murray, K. E., *Australian J. Chem.* **12**, 657 (1959).
31. Cason, J., Fessenden, J. S., and Agre, C. L., *Tetrahedron* **7**, 289 (1959).

Section 12.5

1. Scott, R. P. W., Benzol Producers Ltd. Watford, England, Research Paper 8-1957.
2. Brooks, V. T., and Collins, G. A., *Chem. Ind.* (*London*) p. 921 (1956).
3. Jones, W. C., *Advanc. Gas Chromatog.* (ACS Symp., New York, Sept. 1957), p. D 117.
4. Desty, D. H., Goldup, A., and Swanton, W. T., *Nature* **183**, 107 (1959).
5. Zlatkis, A., Ling, S., and Kaufman, H. R., *Anal. Chem.* **31**, 945 (1959).
6. Adlard, E. R., *in* "Vapour Phase Chromatography," Proceedings of the First Simposium, 1956 (D. H. Desty. ed.), p. 98. Academic Press, New York, 1957.
7. Langer, S. H., Zahn, C., and Pantazoplos, G. *Chem. & Ind.* (*London*), p. 1145 (1958).
8. Desty, D. H., Goldup, A., and Whyman, B. H. F., *J. Inst. Petrol.* **45**, 287 (1959).
9. Hughes, M. A., White, D., and Roberts, A. L., *Nature* **184**, 1796 (1959).
10. van Rysselberghe, J., and van der Stricht, M., *Nature* **193**, 1281 (1962).
11. Mortimer, J. V., and Gent, P. L., *Nature* **197**, 789 (1963).
12. Spencer, S. F., *Anal. Chem.* **35**, 592 (1963).
13. Rosie, D. M., and Grob, R. L., *Anal. Chem.* **29**, 1263 (1957).
14. Hendriks, W. J., Soemantri, R. M., and Waterman, H. I., *J. Inst. Petrol.* **43**, 94 (1957).
15. Anderson, J. R. A. and Napier, K. H., *Australian J. Chem.* **9**, 541 (1956).
16. Tenney, H. M., *Anal. Chem.* **30**, 2 (1958).
17. White, D., *Nature* **179**, 1075 (1957).
18. White, D. and Cowan, C. T., *Trans. Faraday Soc.* **54**, 557 (1958).

Section 12.6

1. James, A. T., and Martin, A. J. P., *Biochem. J.* **50**, 679 (1952).
2. Beerthuis, R. K., Dijkstra, G., Keppler, J. G., and Recourt, J. H., *Ann. N.Y. Acad. Sci.* **72**, 616 (1959).

3. Byars, B., and Jordan, G., *J. Gas Chromatog.* **2**, 304 (1964).
4. Kabot, F. J., and Ettre, L. S., *J. Gas Chromatog.* **1**, 17 (1963).
5. Kabot, F. J., and Ettre, L. S., *J. Gas Chromatog.* **1**, 7 (1963).
6. Metcalfe, L. D., *Nature* **188**, 142 (1960).
7. Maruyama, M., and Sakaguchi, H., *Bunseki Kagaku* **15**, 56 (1966).
8. Quin, L. D., and Hobbs, M. E., *Anal. Chem.* **30**, 1400 (1958).
9. Stoffel, W., Chu, F., and Ahrens, E. H., *Anal. Chem.* **31**, 307 (1959).
10. Luddy, F. E., Barford, R. A., and Riemenschneider, R. W., Am. Oil Chemists' Soc. Meeting, April, 1959.
11. Metcalfe, L. D., Schmitz, A. A., and Pelka, J. R., *Anal. Chem.* **38**, 514 (1966).
12. Peterson, J. I., de Schmertzing, H., and Abel, K., *J. Gas Chromatog.* **3**, 126 (1965).
13. Craig, B. M., Tulloch, A. P., and Murty, N. L., 33rd Fall Meeting, Am. Oil Chemists' Soc., Sept. 1959.
14. Huebner, V. R., 33rd Fall Meeting, Am. Oil Chemists' Soc., Sept. 1959.
15. Cropper, F. R., and Heywood, A., *Nature* **174**, 1063 (1954).
16. Cropper, F. R., and Heywood, A., *Nature* **172**, 1101 (1953).
17. Cropper, F. R., and Heywood, A., *in* "Vapour Phase Chromatography," Proceedings of the First Symposium, London, June, 1956 (D. H. Desty, ed.), p. 316. Academic Press, New York, 1957.
18. Khan, M. A., and Whitham, B. T., *J. Appl. Chem.* **8**, 549 (1958).
19. Adlard, E. R., and Whitham, B. T., *in* "Gas Chromatography 1958," Proceedings of the Second Symposium, Amsterdam, May, 1958 (D. H. Desty, ed.), p. 351. Academic Press, New York, 1958.
20. Beerthuis, R. K., and Keppler, J. G., *Nature* **179**, 731 (1957).
21. Hawke, J. C., Hansen, R. P., and Shorland, F. B., *J. Chromatog.* **2**, 547 (1959).
22. James, A. T., *J. Chromatog.* **2**, 552 (1959).
23. Insull, W., and Ahrens, E. H., *Biochem. J.* **72**, 27 (1959).
24. James, A. T., and Martin, A. J. P., *Biochem. J.* **63**, 144 (1956).
25. Orr, C. H., and Callen, J. E., *J. Am. Chem. Soc.* **80**, 249 (1958).
26. Hornstein, I., Elliott, L. E., and Crowe, P. F., *Nature* **184**, 1710 (1959).
27. Lipsky, S. R., Lovelock, J. E., and Landowne, R. A., *J. Am. Chem. Soc.* **81**, 1010 (1959).
28. Lipsky, S. R., and Landowne, R. A., *Ann. N.Y. Acad. Sci.* **72**, 666 (1959).
29. Lipsky, S. R., Landowne, R. A., and Lovelock, J. E., *Anal. Chem.* **31**, 852 (1959).
30. Orr, C. H., and Callen, J. E., *Ann. N.Y. Acad. Sci.* **72**, 649 (1959).
31. Lipsky, S. R., Landowne, R. A., and Godet, M. R., *Biochim. et Biophys. Acta* **31**, 336 (1959).
32. Craig, B. M., and Murty, N. L., *Can. J. Chem.* **36**, 1297 (1958).
33. Janak, J., Dobiasova, M., and Veres, K., *Collection Czech. Chem. Commun.* **25**, 1566 (1960).
34. Daniels, N. W. R., and Richmond, J. W., *Nature* **187**, 55 (1960).
35. Miwa, T. K., Mikolajczak, K. L., Earle, F. R., and Wolff, I. A., *Anal. Chem.* **32**, 1739 (1960).
36. Woodford, F. P., and van Gent, C. M., *J. Lipid Research* **1**, 188 (1960).
37. Bottcher, C. J. E., Clemens, C. F. G., and van Gent, C. M., *J. Chromatog.* **3**, 582 (1960).
38. Killheffer, J. V., and Jungermann, E., *J. Am. Oil Chemists' Soc.* **37**, 456 (1960).
39. Horning, E. C. *et al.*, *J. Lipid Res.* **5**, 20 (1964).

40. Kuksis, A., *Chromatog. Rev.* **8**, 172 (1966).
41. Lipsky, S. R., and Landowne, R. A., *Ann. Rev. Biochem.* (1960).
42. James, A. T., *in* "Methods of Biochemical Analysis" (D. Glick, ed.). Wiley (Interscience), New York, 1960.
43. Burchfield, H. P., and Storrs, E. E. (eds.), "Biochemical Applications of Gas Chromatography." Academic Press, New York, 1962.

Section 12.7

1. Littlewood, A. B., and Willmott, F. W., *Anal. Chem.* **38**, 1031 (1966).
2. Adlard, E. R., *in* "Vapour Phase Chromatography," Proceedings of the First Symposium, London, June, 1956 (D. H. Desty, ed.), p. 98. Academic Press, New York, 1957.
3. Raupp, G., *Z. Anal. Chem.* **164**, 135 (1958).
4. Kelker, H., *Angew. Chem.* **71**, 218 (1959).
5. Schwartz, R. D., and Mathews, R. G., "Advances in Chromatography 1969," A. Zlatkis, ed., p. 36. Preston Technical Abstracts, Evanston, Illinois, 1969.
6. Dave, S. B., *J. Chromatog. Sci.* **7**, 389 (1969).
7. Kuffner, F., and Kallina, D., *Monatsh. Chem.* **91**, 289 (1960).
8. Warren, G. W., Haskin, J. F., Kourey, R. E., and Yarborough, V. A., *Anal. Chem.* **31**, 1624 (1959).
9. Littlewood, A. B., and Willmott, F. W., *Anal. Chem.* **38**, 1076 (1966).
10. Ray, N. H., *J. Appl. Chem.* **4**, 21 (1954).
11. Broughton, B., and Wheatley, V. R., *Biochem. J.* **73**, 144 (1959).
12. Link, W. E., Hickman, H. M., and Morrissette, R. A., *J. Am. Oil Chemists' Soc.* **36**, 20 (1959).
13. Link, W. E., Hickman, H. M., and Morrissette, R. A., *J. Am. Oil Chemists' Soc.* **36**, 300 (1959).
14. Cropper, F. R., and Heywood, A., *in* "Vapour Phase Chromatography," Proceedings of the First Symposium, London, June, 1956 (D. H. Desty, ed.), p. 316. Academic Press, New York, 1957.
15. Beerthuis, R. K., and Recourt, J. H., *Nature* **186**, 372 (1960).
16. Vandenheuvel, W. J. A., Sweeley, C. C., and Horning, E. C., *Biochem. Biophys. Research Communs.* **3**, 33 (1960).
17. Vandenheuvel, W. J. A., Sweeley, C. C., and Horning, E. C., *J. Am. Chem. Soc.* **82**, 3481 (1960).
18. Sweeley, C. C., and Horning, E. C., *Nature* **187**, 144 (1960).
19. Lipsett. M. B. (ed.), "Gas Chromatography of Steroids in Biological Fluids," Plenum Press, New York, 1965; Wotiz, H. H., and Clark, S. J., "Gas Chromatography in the Analysis of Steroid Hormones," Plenum Press, New York, 1966.
20. Littlewood, A. B., Unpublished Results.
21. Bartsch, R. C., Miller, F. D., and Trent, F. M., *Anal. Chem.* **32**, 1101 (1960).
22. Adlard, E. R., and Hill, D. W., *Nature* **186**, 1045 (1960).
23. Hill, D. W., "Gas Chromatography 1960," Proceedings of the Third International Symposium (R. P. W. Scott, ed.), p. 344. Academic Press, New York, 1961.
24. McInnes, A. G., Ball, D. H., Cooper, and Bishop, C. T., *J. Chromatog.* **1**, 556 (1958).
25. Bishop, C. T., and Cooper, F. P., *Can. J. Chem.* **38**, 388 (1960).
26. Kircher, H. W., *Anal. Chem.* **32**, 1103 (1960).

27. Martin, F., and Vertalier, S., Presented at 15th Congress of Pure and Applied Chemistry, Lisbon, Sept. 1956.
28. Vertalier, S., and Martin, F., *Chim. Anal.* **40**, 80 (1958).
29. Kratzl, K. and Gruber, K., *Monatsh. Chem.* **89**, 618 (1958).
30. Haslam, J., Hamilton, J. B., and Jeffs, A. R., *Analyst* **83**, 66 (1958).
31. Zlatkis, A., and Oro, J. F., *Anal. Chem.* **30**, 1156 (1958).
32. Schepartz, A. I., and McDowell, P. E., *Anal. Chem.* **32**, 723 (1960).
33. Kelker, H., *Z. Anal. Chem.* **176**, 3 (1960).
34. Sandler, S., and Strom, R., *Anal. Chem.* **32**, 1890 (1960).
35. Cason, J., and Harris, E. R., *J. Org. Chem.* **24**, 676 (1959).
36. Gray, G. M., *J. Chromatog.* **4**, 52 (1960).
37. Irvine, L., and Mitchell, T. J., *J. Appl. Chem.* **8**, 3 (1958).
38. Irvine, L., and Mitchell, T. J., *J. Appl. Chem.* **8**, 425 (1958).
39. Janak, J., and Komers, R., *Z. Anal. Chem.* **164**, 69 (1958).
40. Janak, J., and Komers, R., *in* "Gas Chromatography 1958," Proceedings of the Second Symposium, Amsterdam, May, 1958 (D. H. Desty, ed.), p. 343. Academic Press, New York, 1958.
41. Janak, J., and Komers, R., *Collection Czech. Chem. Commun.* **24**, 1960 (1959).
42. Janak, J., Komers, R., and Sima, J., *Chem. Listy* **52**, 2296 (1958).
43. Bergmann, G., and Jentzsch, D., *Z. Anal. Chem.* **164**, 10 (1958).
44. Karr, C., Brown, P. M., Estep, P. A., and Humphrey, G. L., *Anal. Chem.* **30**, 1413 (1958).
45. Brooks, V. T., *Chem. Ind.* (*London*), p. 1317 (1959).
46. Kreyenbuhl, A., and Weiss, H., *Bull. Soc. Chim. France*, p. 1880 (1959).
47. Ettre, L. S., "Open Tube Columns in Gas Chromatography," Plenum Press, New York, 1965.
48. Carruthers, W., Johnstone, R. A. W., and Plimmer, J. R., *Chem. Ind.* (*London*), p. 331 (1958).
49. Langer, S. H., Pantages, P., and Wender, I., *Chem. Ind.* (*London*), p. 1664 (1958).

Section 12.8

1. James, A. T., Martin, A. J. P., and Smith, G. H., *Biochem. J.* **52**, 238 (1952).
2. James, A. T., and Martin, A. J. P., *Analyst* **77**, 915 (1952).
3. James, A. T., and Martin, A. J. P., *Brit. Med. Bull.* **10**, 170 (1954).
4. O'Donnell, J. F., and Mann, C. K., *Anal. Chem.* **36**, 2097 (1964).
5. Ciepelinski, E. W., *Anal. Chem.* **38**, 928 (1966).
6. Thompson, G. F., and Smith, K., *Anal. Chem.* **37**, 1591 (1965).
7. Kerr, J. A., Sekhar, R. C., and Trotman-Dickinson, A. F., *J. Chem. Soc.* (*London*) **1963**, 3217.
8. James, A. T., *Biochem. J.* **52**, 242 (1952).
9. Link, W. E., Morrissette, R. A., Cooper, A. D., and Smullin, C. F., *J. Am. Oil Chemists' Soc.* **37**, 364 (1960).
10. Nelson, J., and Milun, A., *Chem. Ind.* (*London*) p. 663 (1960).
11. Grossi, G., and Vece, R., *J. Gas Chromatog.* **3**, 170 (1965).
12. Day, E. W., Golab, T., and Koons, J. R., *Anal. Chem.* **38**, 1053 (1966).
13. Capella, P., and Horning, E. C., *Anal. Chem.* **38**, 316 (1966).
14. Vandenheuvel, W. J. A., Gardiner, W. L., and Horning, E. C., *Anal. Chem.* **36**, 1550 (1964).

15. James, A. T., *Anal. Chem.* **28**, 1564 (1956).
16. Jones, J. H., Ritchie, C. D., and Heine, K. S., *J. Assoc. Offic. Agr. Chemists* **41**, 749 (1958).
17. Brooks, V. T., and Collins, G. A., *Chem. Ind. (London)* p. 1021 (1956).
18. Decora, A. W., and Dineen, G. U., *Anal. Chem.* **32**, 164 (1960).
19. Murray, W. J., and Williams, A. F., *Chem. Ind. (London)* p. 1020 (1956).
20. Janak, J., and Hrivnac, M., *Collection Czech. Chem. Commun.* **25**, 1557 (1960).
21. Potteau, B., *Bull. Soc. Chim. France* **1965**, 3747.
22. Bayer, E., *in* "Gas Chromatography 1958," Proceedings of the Second International Symposium (D. H. Desty, ed.), p. 333. Academic Press, New York, 1958.
23. Bayer, E., Reuther, K. H., and Born, F., *Angew. Chem.* **69**, 640 (1957).
24. Saroff, H. A., and Karmen, A., *Anal. Biochem.* **1**, 344 (1960).
25. Melamed, M., and Renard, M., *J. Chromatog.* **4**, 339 (1960).
26. Gee, M., Graham, R. P., and Morgan, A. I., *J. Food Sci.* **32**, 78 (1967).
27. Makisumi, S., and Saroff, H. A., *J. Gas Chromatog.* **3**, 21 (1965).
28. Crichton, R. R., and Leaf, G., *Biochem. J.* **99**, 47P, (1966).
29. Youngs, C. G., *Anal. Chem.* **31**, 1019 (1959).
30. Johnson, D. E., Scott, S. J., and Meister, A., *Anal. Chem.* **33**, 669 (1961).
31. Stefanovic, M., and Walker, B. L., *Anal. Chem.* **37**, 383 (1965).
32. Gehrke, C. W., Lamkin, W. M., Stalling, D. L., and Shahrokhi, F., *Biochem. Biophys. Res. Commun.* **19**, 328 (1965).
33. Lamkin, W. M., and Gehrke, C. W., *Anal. Chem.* **37**, 383 (1965).
34. Darbre, A., and Blau, K.. *Biochem. J.* **88**, 9P (1963).
35. Darbre, A., and Blau, K., *J. Chromatog.* **29**, 58 (1967).
36. Halasz, I., and Bunnig, K., *Z. Anal. Chem.* **211**, 1 (1965).
37. Smith, E. D., and Sheppard, H., *Nature* **208**, 878 (1965).
38. Ruhlmann, K., and Michael, G., *Bull. Soc. Chim. Biol.* **47**, 1467 (1965).
39. Melamed, M., and Renard, M., *J. Chromatog.* **4**, 339 (1960).
40. Hunter, I. R., Dimick, K. P., and Corse, J. W., *Chem. Ind. (London)* p. 294 (1956).
41. Zlatkis, A., and Oro, J. F., *Anal. Chem.* **30**, 1156 (1958).
42. Bier, M., and Teitelbaum, P., *Ann. N.Y. Acad. Sci.* **72**, 641 (1959).
43. Zlatkis, A., Oro, J. F., and Kimball, A. P., *Anal. Chem.* **32**, 162 (1960).
44. Baraud, J., *Bull. Soc. Chim. France* p. 785 (1960).
45. Warren, G. W., Haskin, J. F., Kourey, R. E., and Yarborough, V. A., *Anal. Chem.* **31**, 1624 (1959).

Section 12.9

1. Harrison, G. F., *in* "Vapour Phase Chromatography," Proceedings of the First Symposium, London, June, 1956 (D. H. Desty, ed.), p. 332. Academic Press, New York, 1957.
2. Pollard, F. H., and Hardy, C. J., *in* "Vapour Phase Chromatography," Proceedings of the First Symposium, London, June, 1956 (D. H. Desty, ed.), p. 115. Academic Press, New York, 1958.
3. Kelker, H., *Angew. Chem.* **71**, 218 (1959).
4. Hardy, C. J., *J. Chromatog.* **2**, 490 (1959).
5. Pollard, F. H., and Hardy, C. J., *Anal. Chim. Acta* **16**, 135 (1957).

6. Harrison, G. F., Knight, P., Kelly, R. P., and Heath, M. T., "Gas Chromatography 1958," Proceedings of the Second Symposium, Amsterdam, May, 1958 (D. H. Desty, ed.), p. 216. Academic Press, New York, 1958.

7. Gloesener, E., Lapiere, C. L., and Versie, J., *J. Pharm. Belg.* **13**, 389 (1958).

8. Domange. L., and Longuevalle, S., *Ann. Pharm. Franc.* **15**, 448 (1957).

9. Adlard, E. R., and Hill, D. W., *Nature* **186**, 1045 (1960).

10. Hill, D. W., Hook, J. R., and Mable, S. E. R., *J. Sci. Inst.* **39**, 214 (1962).

11. Chapman, J., Hill, R., Muir, J., Suckling, C. W., and Viney, D. J., *J. Pharm. Pharmacol.* **19**, 231 (1967).

12. James, A. T., and Martin, A. J. P., *Brit. Med. Bull.* **10**, 170 (1954).

13. Kovats, E., *Helv. Chim. Acta* **41**, 1915 (1958).

14. McFadden, W. H., *Anal. Chem.* **30**, 479 (1958).

15. Harris, W. E., and McFadden, W. H., *Anal. Chem.* **31**, 114 (1959).

16. Moussebois, C., and Duyckaerts, G., *J. Chromatog.* **1**, 200 (1958).

17. Troupe. R. A., and Golner, J. J., *Anal. Chem.* **30**, 129 (1958).

18. Freeman, S. K., *Anal. Chem.* **32**, 1304 (1960).

19. Root, M. J., *in* "Gas Chromatography," I.S.A. Symposium, August, 1957 (V. J. Coates, H. J. Noebels, and I. S. Fagerson, eds.), p. 99. Academic Press, New York, 1958.

20. Green, S. W., *in* "Vapour Phase Chromatography," Proceedings of the First Symposium, London, June, 1956 (D. H. Desty, ed.), p. 388. Academic Press, New York, 1957.

21. Reed, T. M., *Anal. Chem.* **30**, 221 (1958).

22. Serpinet, J., *Chim. Anal.* **41**, 146 (1959).

23. Noren, K., *Analyst* **93**, 39 (1968).

24. Sissons, D. J., Telling, G. M., and Usher, C. D., *J. Chromatog.* **33**, 435 (1968).

25. Simmons, J. H., and Tatton, J. O'G., *J. Chromatog.* **27**, 253 (1967).

26. Kanazawa, J., *Bunseki Kagaku* **15**, 934 (1966).

27. Buescher, C. A., Dougherty, J. H., and Skrinde, T. R., *J. Water Pollution Control Federation* **36**, 1005 (1964).

28. Saha, J. G., *J. Assoc. Offic. Agr. Chemists* **49**, 768 (1966).

29. Jain, N. C., Fontan, C. R., and Kirk, P. L., *J. Pharm. Pharmacol.* **17**, 362 (1965),

30. Pennington, S., and Meloan, C. E., *J. Chromatog.* **27**, 250 (1967).

31. Koon, J. R., and Wesselman, H. J., *J. Agr. Food Chem.* **12**, 550 (1964).

32. Firestone, D., *J. Am. Oil Chemists' Assoc.* **45**, 210A (1968).

Section 12.10

1. Spencer, C. F., Baumann, F., and Johnson, J. F., *Anal. Chem.* **30**, 1473 (1958).

2. Amberg, C. H., *Can. J. Chem.* **36**, 590 (1958).

3. Ryce, S. A., and Bryce, W. A., *Anal. Chem.* **29**, 925 (1957).

4. Sunner, S., Karrman, K. J., and Sunden, V., *Mikrochim. Acta* p. 1144 (1956).

5. Karchmer, J. H., *Anal. Chem.* **31**, 1377 (1959).

6. Sullivan, J. H., Walsh, J. T., and Merritt, C., *Anal. Chem.* **31**, 1826 (1959).

7. Carson, J. F., Weston, W. J., and Ralls, J. W., *Nature* **186**, 801 (1960).

8. Desty, D. H., and Whyman, B. H. F., *Anal. Chem.* **29**, 320 (1959).

9. Petranek, J., *J. Chromatog.* **5**, 254 (1961).

10. Carson, J. F., and Wong, F. F., *J. Org. Chem.* **24**, 175 (1959).

11. Hrivnac, M., and Janak, J., *Chem. Ind. (London)* p. 930 (1960).

12. Thompson, C. J., Coleman, H. H., Ward, C. C. and Rall, H. T., *Anal. Chem.* **32**, 424 (1960).

Section 12.11

1. Levy, R. L., *Chromatographic Reviews* **8**, 49 (1966).
2. Perry, S. G., *J. Gas Chromatog.* **2**, 54 (1964).
3. Barbour, W. M., *J. Gas Chromatog.* **3**, 228 (1965).
4. Brauer, G. M., *J. Polymer Sci.* **8**, 3 (1965).
5. *J. Gas Chromatog.* **5**, pp. 1–157 (1967).
6. Davison, W. H. T., Slaney, S., and Wragg, A. L., *Chem. Ind.* (*London*) p. 1356 (1954).
7. Strassburger, J., Brauer, G. M., Tryon, M., and Forziati, A. F., *Anal. Chem.* **32**, 454 (1960).
8. Radell, E. A., and Strultz, H. C., *Anal. Chem.* **31**, 1890 (1959).
9. Miller, D. L., Samsel, E. P., and Cobler, J. G., *Anal. Chem.* **33**, 677 (1961).
10. Lehmann, F. A., and Brauer, G. M., *Anal. Chem.* **33**, 673 (1961).
11. Barlow, A., Lehrle, R. A., and Robb, J. C., *Polymer* **2**, 27 (1961).
12. Lehrle, R. S., and Robb, J. C., *Nature* **183**, 1671 (1959).
13. Giacobbo, H., and Simon, W., *Pharm. Acta Helv.* **39**, 162 (1964).
14. Simon, W., and Giacobbo, H., *Chem. Ing.-Tech.* **37**, 709 (1965).
15. Ettre, K., and Varadi, P. F., *Anal. Chem.* **35**, 69 (1963).
16. Cox, B. C., and Ellis, B., *Anal. Chem.* **36**, 90 (1964).
17. Levy, R. L. *et al.*, *J. Gas Chromatog.* **2**, 254 (1964).
18. Jennings, E. C., Jr., and Dimick, K. P., *Anal. Chem.* **34**, 1543 (1962).
19. Hetman, N. E., Arlt, H. G., Jr., Paylor, R., and Feinland, R., *J. Am. Oil Chemists' Soc.* **42**, 255 (1965).
20. Ainsworth, C., and Easton, N. R., *J. Org. Chem.* **27**, 4118 (1962).
21. Langenbeck, W., and Dreyer, H., *Z. Anorg. Allgem. Chem.* **329**, 179 (1964).
22. Janak, J., "Gas Chromatography 1960," Proceedings of the Third International Symposium (R. P. W. Scott, ed.), p. 387. Academic Press, New York, 1961.
23. Janak, J., *Nature* **185**, 684 (1960).
24. Wist, A. O., *J. Gas Chromatog.* **5**, 157 (1967).

Section 12.12

1. Keller, R. A., and Freiser, H., "Gas Chromatography 1960," Proceedings of the Third International Symposium (R. P. W. Scott, ed.), p. 301. Academic Press, New York, 1961.
2. Wachi, F. M., *Dissertation Abstr.* **20**, 53 (1959).
3. Juvet, R. S., and Wachi, F. M., *Anal. Chem.* **32**, 290 (1960).
4. Keller, R. A., *J. Chromatog.* **5**, 225 (1961).
5. Freiser, H., *Anal. Chem.* **31**, 1440 (1959).
6. Juvet, R. S., and Fisher, R. L., *Anal. Chem.* **38**, 1860 (1966).
7. Soulages, N. L., *Anal. Chem.* **38**, 28 (1966).
8. Juvet, R. S., and Zado, F. M., "Advances in Chromatography" (J. C. Giddings, and R. A. Keller, ed.), p. 249. Dekker, New York, 1965.
9. Juvet, R. S., and Fisher, R. L., *Anal. Chem.* **37**, 1752 (1965).
10. Tadmor, J., *Anal. Chem.* **36**, 1565 (1964).
11. Tadmor, J., *J. Gas Chromatog.* **2**, 385 (1964).
12. Dennison, J. E., and Freund, H., *Anal. Chem.* **37**, 1766 (1965).

13. Wilke, J., Losse, A., and Sackman, H., *J. Chromatog.* **18**, 482 (1965).
14. Sievers, R. E., Wheeler, G., and Ross, W. D., *Anal. Chem.* **38**, 306 (1966).
15. Zado, F. M., and Juvet, R. S., "Gas Chromatography 1966," Proceedings of the Sixth International Symposium (A. B. Littlewood, ed.), p. 283. Institute of Petroleum, London, 1967.
16. Duswalt, A. A., *Dissertation Abstr.* **20**, 52 (1959).
17. Bierman, W. J., and Gesser, H., *Anal. Chem.* **32**, 1525 (1960).
18. Hill, R. D., and Gesser, H., *J. Gas Chromatog.* **1**, (10) 11 (1963).
19. Sievers, R. E., Ponder, B. W., Morris, M. L., and Moshier, R. W., *Inorg. Chem.* **2**, 693 (1963).
20. Ross, W. D., and Sievers, R. E., "Gas Chromatography 1966," Proceedings of the Sixth International Symposium (A. B. Littlewood, ed.), p. 272. Institute of Petroleum, London, 1967.
21. Moshier, R. W., and Sievers, R. E., "Gas Chromatography of Metal Chelates." Pergamon Press, Oxford, 1965.
22. Abel, E. W., Nickless, G., and Pollard, F. H., *Proc. Chem. Soc. (London)* **1960**, 288.
23. Longi, P., and Mazzocchi, R., *Chim. Ind. (Milan)* **48**, 718 (1966).
24. Soulages, N. L., *Anal. Chem.* **38**, 28 (1966).
25. DeBoer, F. E., *Nature* **185**, 915 (1960).
26. Juvet, R. S., and Durbin, R. P., *J. Gas Chromatog.* **1**, 14 (1963).
27. Juvet, R. S., and Durbin, R. P., *Anal. Chem.* **38**, 565 (1966).
28. Schomburg, G., Koster, R., and Henneberg, D., *Z. Anal. Chem.* **170**, 285 (1959).
29. Koster, R., and Bruno, G., *Ann.* **629**, 89 (1960).
30. Seely, G. R., Oliver, J. P., and Ritter, D. M., *Anal. Chem.* **31**, 2000 (1959).
31. Blay, N. J., Dunstan, I., and Williams, R. L., *J. Chem. Soc.* p. 430 (1960).
32. Blay, N. J., Williams, J., and Williams, R. L., *J. Chem. Soc.* p. 424 (1960).
33. Borer, K., and Phillips, C. S. G., *Proc. Chem. Soc. (London)* p. 189 (1959).
34. Stanford, F. G., *J. Chromatog.* **4**, 419 (1960).
35. Shipotofsky, S. F., and Moser, H. C., *Anal. Chem.* **33**, 521 (1961).
36. Kaufman, J. J., Todd J. E., and Koski, W. S., *Anal. Chem.* **29**, 1032 (1957).
37. Borer, K., Littlewood, A. B., and Phillips, C. S. G., *J. Inorg. & Nuclear Chem.* **15**, 316 (1960).
38. Fritz, G. and Ksinsik, D., *Z. Anorg. Allgem. Chem.* **304**, 241 (1960).
39. Friedrich, K., *Chem. Ind. (London)* p. 47 (1957).
40. Ellis, J. F., and Iveson, G., *in* "Gas Chromatography 1958," Proceedings of the Second Symposium, Amsterdam, May, 1958 (D. H. Desty, ed.), Academic Press, New York, 1958, p. 300.
41. Ellis, J. F., Forrest, C. W., and Allen, P. L., *Anal. Chim. Acta* **22**, 27 (1960).
42. Iveson, G., and Hamlin, A. G., "Gas Chromatography 1960," Proceedings of the Third International Symposium (R. P. W. Scott, ed.), p. 333. Academic Press, New York, 1961.
43. Phillips, T. R., and Owens, D. R., "Gas Chromatography 1960," Proceedings of the Third International Symposium (R. P. W. Scott, ed.), p. 308. Academic Press, New York, 1961.
44. Neely, E. E., *Anal. Chem.* **32**, 1382 (1960).
45. Janak, J., Nederost, M., and Bubenikova, V., *Chem. Listy* **51**, 890 (1957).
46. Dayan, V. H., and Neale, B. C., *Advan. Chem. Ser.* **54**, 223 (1965).
47. Hamlin, A. G., Iveson, G., and Phillips, T. R., *Anal. Chem.* **35**, 2037 (1963).

List of Symbols

The number in the right-hand margin indicates the section in which the symbol is first mentioned or defined. Symbols conform where possible to standard usage. Some symbols used only in one subsection of the text are not included.

A	constant of integration in Young's or Antoine's equation	3.3
	area of peak	5.5
	surface area of solvent phase	6.3
	constant in simplified form of van Deemter's equation	6.9
B	constant in Antoine's equation	3.3
	constant in simplified form of van Deemter's equation	6.11
B_{22}	second virial coefficient of solute	3.2
B_{32}	mixed second virial coefficient of solute and carrier gas	3.2
C	constant in Antoine's equation	3.3
	constant in simplified form of van Deemter's equation	6.11
C_l	van Deemter constant C attributable to liquid phase	6.11
C_g	van Deemter constant C attributable to gas phase	6.11
C_p	molar specific heat of carrier gas at constant pressure	10.2
D_g	diffusion coefficient of a solute in the gas phase	6.2
D_l	diffusion coefficient of a solute in the solvent phase	6.3
E	EMF across the Wheatstone's bridge of a catharometer	10.2
E_g	voltage output of a detector	8.1
E_n	EMF across the arm of a Wheatstone's bridge, R_n	10.2
G	Gibbs free energy	3.3
	geometrical catharometer constant	10.2
G^M	Gibbs free energy of mixing	3.4
H	height equivalent to a theoretical plate	5.2
H^M	heat of mixing	3.4
ΔH_s	molar heat of evaporation of solute from solution	3.10
ΔH_v	molar heat of vaporisation of pure liquid solute	3.3
I	retention index	3.6
	electrical current	9.5, 10.2
I_n	current in arm of Wheatstone's bridge, R_n	10.2
J	Joule's constant	10.2

K	rate constant	6.3
K, K'	used as local constants in a particular discussion	
L	peak retention measured as a distance on the chart paper	2.6
M	molecular weight	3.2
	distance apart at the base line of tangents drawn at the points of inflection of a peak	5.5
N_1	inverse molar volume of the solvent	3.2
P	hydrostatic pressure	2.4
P_o	pressure at column outlet	2.4
P_i	pressure at column inlet	2.4
Q	molecular ionisation cross-section	9.5
R	gas constant	3.2
	column resolution	5.6
	resistance of the hot element of a catharometer	10.2
R_F	retardation factor	2.3
R_n	resistance of arm of a Wheatstone's bridge R_n	10.2
S_c	sensitivity of a concentration dependent detector	8.1
S_w	sensitivity of a mass-flow sensitive detector	8.1
T	temperature ($^\circ$K)	2.5
T_c	temperature of column	2.5
T_B	boiling point of a pure liquid solute	3.3
T_o	starting temperature in programmed temperature operation	7.5
T_R	emergence temperature of a peak in programmed temperature operation	7.5
T_1	temperature of catharometer walls	10.2
T_2	temperature of catharometer hot element	10.2
T'	average temperature difference between gas entering and leaving a catharometer	10.2
V	volume of gas passed through a column	1.2
$V_R{}^0$	corrected retention volume	2.3
V_M	gas hold-up of the column	2.3
V_R	measured retention volume	2.4
V_R'	adjusted retention volume	2.4
V_N	net retention volume	2.4
V_g	specific retention volume	2.5
V_i	volume of sample injector cavity	2.7
V_I	volume occupied by the input distribution	6.7
$\dot{V}$	volume flow rate of carrier gas	2.3

$\dot{V}'$	molar flow rate of carrier gas	10.2
$\dot{V}_o$	volume flow rate of carrier gas at column outlet	2.4
V_s	specific retention volume for adsorbents	4.1
W	weight of stationary phase in column	2.3
	power dissipated by the hot element of a catharometer	10.10
a	constant in the Langmuir isotherm	1.4
	volume of gas phase per unit length of column, i.e., cross-sectional area of column occupied by gas phase	2.2 5.2
b	constant in the Langmuir isotherm	1.4
	cross-sectional area of column occupied by the solvent phase	5.2
c	concentration of vapour in the gas phase	1.1
d_p	average particle diameter of column packing	6.5
d_f	equivalent thickness of liquid film in a packed column	6.3
g	pressure correction factor for A and B terms of the van Deemter equation	6.18
h	peak height	5.5
j	pressure correction factor	2.4
k	partition ratio, $=m\beta/a$	2.1
l	length of column	2.2
	length of catharometer filament	10.2
m	mass of stationary phase per unit length of column	2.2
n	number of incremental volumes in plate theory	5.2
	carbon number	3.3
	height equivalent to an effective theoretical plate	6.14
n_1	number of moles of solvent in a solution	3.2
n_2	number of moles of solute in a solution	3.2
p	quantity used in discussion of plate theory	5.2
p_2	vapour pressure of solute above its solution	3.2
p_2^0	vapour pressure of pure liquid solute	3.2
q	concentration of solute in the stationary phase	1.1
	quantity used in discussion of the plate theory	5.2
r	relative retention	2.6
	ratio of lattice site occupation of solvent and solute	3.5
	serial number of a theoretical plate	5.2
	column radius	6.3
	heating rate in programmed temperature operation	7.5
r_{nm}	relative retention of components n and m	2.6
r_1	radius of catharometer cavity	10.2
r_2	radius of catharometer hot element	10.2

s_i	lateral flux of solute in phase i due to non-equilibrium	6.4
t	time	2.4
	temperature (°C)	3.3
t_R	retention time	2.1
t_M	gas hold-up time	2.1
t_B	boiling point of solute (°C)	3.3
u	linear flow rate of carrier gas	2.3
v_2	molar volume of solute	3.2
w	mass of solute	1.2
	coordinate of length along the column moving with the peak maximum	6.2
w_1	weight of solvent in a solution	3.2
w_2	weight of solute in a solution	3.2
x	distance from inlet end of the column	2.2
x_i	mole fraction of species i	3.4
x_2	solute mole fraction	3.2
z	argument of a function coordination number (in general)	3.5
	smaller dimension of the cross section of a flat rectangular column	6.3
$z(t)$	chromatogram as plotted by a recorder	6.8
α	dimensionless partition coefficient	3.1
	temperature coefficient of resistance of the hot element of a catharometer	10.2
β	partition coefficient with dimensions ml^{-3}	1.1
γ	activity coefficient	3.2
ε	non-equilibrium	6.4
η	gas viscosity	2.4
	coefficient of thermal expansion of solvent	3.10
$\eta_{m_2:m_3}$	impurity fraction of solute 2 in solute 3 and vice versa, for components divided by a single cut	5.6
θ	$T_2 - T_1$ for catharometers	10.10
λ	thermal conductivity	10.2
λ_1	thermal conductivity of carrier gas	10.2
λ_2	thermal conductivity of vapour	10.2
λ_{12}	thermal conductivity of mixed vapour and carrier gas	10.2
μ	chemical potential	3.2
ϱ	density of stationary phase	3.1
σ	standard deviation of a peak	5.2
	collision diameter of a molecule	10.2

$\sigma_{(v)}$	standard deviation of a peak measured as a volume of carrier gas	5.2
$\sigma_{(r)}$	standard deviation of a peak measured as a number of plates	5.2
$\sigma_{(x)}$	standard deviation of a peak measured as a length along the column	5.3
$\sigma_{(L)}$	standard deviation of a peak measured as a distance on chart paper	5.5
$\sigma_{(t)}$	standard deviation of a peak measured in time units	6.2
σ_g	standard deviation as a result of lateral diffusion of solute in the gas phase	6.3
σ_l	standard deviation as a result of lateral diffusion of solute in the liquid phase	6.3
σ_C	standard deviation as a result of the column	6.7
σ_I	standard deviation as a result of the sample injector	6.7
φ	arbitrary function	2.3
	function of temperature	10.2
χ	interaction energy	3.5
$\omega_{1/2}$	peak-width halfway up the peak	5.5
$\mathscr{D}$	equivalent coefficient of longitudinal diffusion to account for lateral non-equilibrium	6.4
$\mathscr{H}$	phenomenological plate-height	6.18
$\mathscr{N}$	number of theoretical plates in a column	5.2
$\mathscr{N}'$	number of theoretical plates as measured from a chromatogram	6.7

Subscripts

1	pertaining to solvent
2	pertaining to solute
23	pertaining to two solutes

Author Index

Numbers in parentheses are reference numbers and indicate that an author's work is referred to although his name is not cited in the text. Numbers in italics show the page on which the complete reference is listed.

A

Abel, E. W., 502 (22), *514*
Abel, K., 456 (12), *508*
Ackman, R. G., 244 (52), *276*, 306 (25, 26, 27), *337*
Adlard, E. R., 448 (6), 456 (19), 467 (2), 468 (2), 469 (2), 470 (22), 486 (9), *507*, *508*, *509*, *512*
Agre, C. L., 447 (31), *507*
Ahrens, E. H., 455 (9), 456 (23), 457 (23), 460 (23), *508*
Ainsworth, C., 496 (20), *513*
Allen, P. L., 503 (41), *514*
Allen, R. R., 402 (102), *417*
Altshuller, A. P., 320 (54), *338*
Amberg, C. H., 490 (2), 491 (2), 492 (2), 493 (2), *512*
Ambrose D., 33 (10), *43*, 266 (107), *278*, 372 (60), *381*
Amundsen, N. R., 171 (7), *229*
Anderson, A. H., 413 (169), 414 (169), *419*
Anderson, J. R. A., 105 (56), 453 (15), *507*
Andreatch, A. G., 301 (9), *336*
Annis, J. L., 397 (93), *417*
Aoyagi, M., 370 (47), *381*
Argabright, P. A., 368 (45), 369 (45), *381*
Aris, R., 175 (18), *230*
Arlt, H. G., Jr., 496 (19), *513*
Armitage, F., 445 (21), 446 (21), *507*
Armstrong, W. H., 367 (40), *380*
Arndt, R. R., 301 (10), *336*
Arnett, E. M., 428 (36), *505*
Ash, S. G., 124 (2), 126 (2), *141*
Ashbury, G. K., 372 (51), 376 (51), *381*

Atkinson, E. P., 264 (103), 265 (103), 266 (103), *278*
Aul, F., 255 (90), *278*, 366 (35), *380*
Aunstrup, K., 391 (52), *416*
Averill, W., 247 (68), 248 (71), *277*, 301 (3), 302 (3), 307 (3), 331 (3), *336*, 386 (22), *415*
Ayers, B. O., 163 (16), *163*, 204 (57), 205 (57), 213 (68), *231*

B

Baker, W. J., 219 (73), *231*, 237 (32), 240 (32), *276*, 372 (59), 373 (59), *381*
Ball, D. H., 470 (24), *509*
Banner, A. E., 397 (92), *417*
Baraud, J., 483 (44), *511*
Barber, D. W., 104 (57), *120*
Barbour, W. M., 493 (3), *513*
Barford, R. A., 455 (10), *508*
Barker, J. A., 124 (3), 126 (3), *141*
Barker, K. H., 171 (6), *229*
Barker, P. E., 268 (110, 111), *279*
Barlow, A., 495 (11), 497 (11), 498 (11), *513*
Barnard, J. A., 252 (83), *278*, 433 (18), *506*
Barrall, E. M., 132 (32), *142*
Barrer, R. M., 132 (25), *142*
Barsby, M. H., 344 (15), *380*
Bartsch, R. C., 470 (21), *509*
Bartz, A. M., 403 (109), *417*
Basson, R. A., 336 (81), *338*
Batt, L., 303 (21), *337*
Baumann, F., 413 (166), *419*, 49 (1), 491 (1), 492 (2), *512*

521

Subject Index

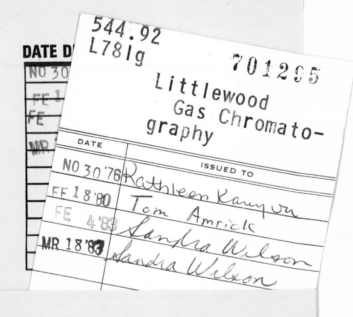

DATE D

NO 30

FE 1

FE

MR